Consulting Editor's Statement

The dilemma confronting contemporary educators in the field of physics is twofold: are we, in a world in which physics plays an increasingly important role, to impart to nonspecialist students a miniaturized version of the education which we have received, or are we to denature and popularize the subject, presenting a panorama of ideas and concepts upon which the study of physics is founded?

Choice of the former method involves diminution of the excitement of discovery which we all feel, and almost invariably treats in a most cursory manner the existing developments about which the student may have heard, thus reducing the effectiveness of an area which can be used to advantage in the motivation of learning. Furthermore, it is possible to question the efficacy of this whole approach in respect to the student who will not make use of physics again. The latter approach does little justice to the intellectual capacity of most students and does not provide sufficient grounding in the fundamentals of the subject to enable the student to appraise and appreciate the more sophisticated recent concepts which will follow.

Professors Harnwell and Legge have most ambitiously attempted to avoid the pitfalls of both approaches. The emphasis here is upon contemporary ideas without sacrificing a sound, albeit abbreviated, introduction to classical concepts. They are not afraid to introduce *physically* motivated mathematics where it is natural and leads to clarification. The presentation is not dependent, however, upon the use of relatively sophisticated mathematics, and most of this is relegated to appendices.

This is a unique text for the nonmajor which gives new direction, and, I believe, much needed new vigor to such courses.

Leon F. Landovitz

REINHOLD PUBLISHING CORPORATION
A subsidiary of Chapman-Reinhold, Inc.
New York   Amsterdam   London

PHYSICS

Matter, Energy and the Universe

GAYLORD P. HARNWELL

President and Professor of Physics
University of Pennsylvania
Philadelphia, Pennsylvania

GEORGE J. F. LEGGE

Senior Lecturer
University of Melbourne
Victoria, Australia

Preface

The chapters of this book were initially prepared as lectures for an introductory physics course designed for students who did not anticipate a career in physics or its technical applications. The purpose was to introduce these students to the quantitative concepts and procedural definitions of this science in order that they might develop both an understanding and an appreciation of the description of physical phenomena in terms of the properties of elementary particles. The objective of this book is the same, and the discussion of classical physics is limited to those aspects that are directly relevant to a comprehension of the modern particle concept of matter.

Mathematics is kept minimal, and a previous knowledge of calculus is not necessary. However, the subject matter cannot be presented satisfactorily without an introduction to the elementary concepts of differentials and integrals. Many high school graduates have enough background in mathematics to follow the introduction in the text, but the first two weeks of the course may be given to an explanation of these concepts.

The ideas of space, time, and motion are introduced, first from an intuitive point of view and then quantitatively. The concepts of mass, force, angular momentum, and energy are developed similarly, and a description of the physical processes in which they are involved is given in terms of simple symmetries and the conservation laws relating to them. The categories of classical physics are outlined briefly as they relate to the attributed origins of the forces observed in connection with them.

Gravitational interaction is the first to be introduced and the planetary system is used as an illustration of its properties. This is followed by a description of the properties of wave motion, and the theory of relativity is developed upon the basis of the observed constancy of the velocity of light.

Next, electrical interactions, the concept of charge, and the properties of charges at rest and in relative motion are discussed and extended to the electrical properties of the elementary particles. The basic properties of such particles are summarized in terms of their moments, both mechanical and electrical.

The evidence for the atomicity of matter, energy, and angular momentum is presented next. This is followed by an account of the nature of atomic structure and the interactions between atomic nuclei and electrons describing atomic aggregates and the exchange of energy between atoms and molecules through the medium of radiation. Since the purpose is to relate the particulate description of physical phenomena to the broadest possible context of experience, it is necessary to explain the statistical method for describing the macroscopic behavior of matter. As this topic tends to be abstruse to students who first encounter it, analogies with more familiar situations such as mortality tables are drawn upon and the simple mathematics required is provided in a supplementary section.

The properties of matter are presented very briefly by categories of gases, liquids and solids in terms of the characteristics of atomic systems; and illustrations are drawn from astronomy, chemistry, aerodynamics and the electronic and magnetic behavior of crystals. In the discussion of these topics, use is made of traditional physics in explaining such topics as viscosity, surface tension, elasticity, etc.

Our knowledge of atomic nuclei is presented in terms of the concepts found successful in the description of atomic systems, and the interaction between the permanent and ephemeral fundamental particles so far identified. Radioactive disintegration and nuclear reactions are described, with emphasis upon the frontier nature of knowledge in this area. Illustrations are drawn from astrophysics and current terrestrial applications.

The senior author is very conscious of the fact that the account of physics given here must bear strong evidence that it was initially drafted by one who has not been a firsthand participant in research for many years, but who has continued to teach a subject that has been a lifelong object of intellectual beauty, fascination, and discipline. He is greatly indebted to the Department of Physics at the University of Pennsylvania for permission to participate in an elementary course and to the many of its younger members who actually conducted it and thus enabled him to turn a vocation into an avocation and, while primarily engaged in administrative responsibilities, to continue to enjoy the experience of teaching and the maintenance of a perspective, if increasingly remote, of the development of physics during its most absorbing era.

Gaylord P. Harnwell
George J. F. Legge

Contents

1 *The nature of physics*   1

    1-1 Introduction *1*
    1-2 Evolution of scientific theory *3*
    1-3 Symmetry and recurring sequences or structures *5*
    1-4 Relation of mathematics to science *7*
    1-5 Elementary mathematical manipulation *10*

2 *Concepts and units of physical measurement*   16

    2-1 Observation and measurement *16*
    2-2 Time and its measurement *17*
    2-3 Measurement of length and specification of relative position *19*
    2-4 Velocity and the concept of time rate of change *27*
    2-5 Mathematical note: relation between a function and its rate of change *32*

3 *The concepts of force and momentum and the relationship*   38
   between them

    3-1 Force and its measurement *38*
    3-2 The concepts of mass and momentum; Galileo and Newton *42*
    3-3 Motion under the force of gravity at the earth's surface *45*
    3-4 Rotational motion *52*
    3-5 The motion of masses that change with time *58*

4 *Work and energy and the conservation laws relating to*   63
   momentum and energy

    4-1 The concept of energy *63*
    4-2 Conservation of energy *66*

4-3   Conservation of momentum and angular momentum *74*

4-4   Impact of one body on another as an illustration of the conservation laws *84*

5   *The universal law of gravitation and the motion of bodies under its influence*   91

5-1   The universal law of gravitation *91*

5-2   Gravitational potential energy and the relation between "G" and "g" *98*

5-3   Gravitational field strength and potential *102*

5-4   Motion of planets and satellites *106*

5-5   Supplementary mathematic section *119*

6   *Simple harmonic motion and waves*   123

6-1   Oscillatory motion *123*

6-2   Simple harmonic motion *126*

6-3   Wave motion *135*

6-4   Simple harmonic waves *137*

6-5   Standing waves *140*

6-6   Superposition of waves and interference *144*

6-7   Supplementary mathematical section *149*

7   *The propagation of light and the special theory of relativity*   153

7-1   Wave nature of light *153*

7-2   Velocity of propagation of light *157*

7-3   The Doppler effect *158*

7-4   The Michelson-Morley experiment *161*

7-5   Einstein's interpretation of the Michelson-Morley results *164*

7-6   The Galilean transformation of coordinates *165*

7-7   The Lorentz transformation of coordinates *168*

7-8   Certain consequences of the Lorentz transformation *171*

7-9   The Doppler effect for light *175*

8   *Implications of the special theory of relativity for mechanics and the more general theory of relativity*   180

8-1   Implications of the Lorentz transformation for mechanics *180*

8-2   The conservation of momentum *181*

8-3   The conservation of energy   *183*

8-4   The general theory of relativity   *188*

9   Electricity

195

9-1   Introduction   *195*

9-2   The electrostatic law of force   *196*

9-3   Electric field and electric potential   *201*

9-4   Conduction of electricity   *204*

10   Moving charges or electric currents

211

10-1   Experimental observation of a velocity-dependent force between moving charges or currents   *211*

10-2   The velocity-dependent force as a consequence of relativistic invariance   *213*

10-3   Analogy between the velocity-dependent law and the static laws; the magnetic potential   *218*

10-4   Forces and torques on complete current-carrying circuits   *222*

10-5   Induction or the change in electric currents with time, under the assumption of constant total available energy   *225*

10-6   Electromagnetic waves   *226*

10-7   Electrical phenomena as described by observers in relative motion   *228*

11   Magnetism; circulating and rotating electric charges

231

11-1   Equivalence between magnetized materials and circulating currents   *231*

11-2   The circuital nature of the electrodynamic potential and the magnetic field   *235*

11-3   Motion and energies of charged particles in magnetic fields   *240*

11-4   Spinning charges and magnetic moments   *245*

11-5   Summary of the concepts and laws of classical physics applicable to the atomic domain   *248*

12   The concept of atomicity and the determination of atomic masses

252

12-1   Evidence for the atomicity of matter   *252*

12-2   Masses and dimensions of atoms   *256*

12-3 Quantitative determination of Avogadro's number and atomic masses *258*

13 *The electrical properties of atoms and their constituents* 265

13-1 Early experiments in the conduction of electricity through gases *265*
13-2 Measurement of atomic charge-to-mass ratio *266*
13-3 The electron, its charge and its charge-to-mass ratio *271*
13-4 Electronic structure of atoms *274*
13-5 Electrical phenomena in gases *277*

14 *The interaction of radiant energy and electrons; the extension of the concept of wave motion to the atomic domain* 282

14-1 The conservation of energy in the emission and absorption of radiation by electrons *282*
14-2 Conservation of momentum and angular momentum in the interaction between electrons and photons *289*
14-3 The spatial location of a photon and the principle of indeterminacy *293*
14-4 The wavelike aspect of material particles, and the defining properties of the electron *295*

15 *Radiation from atomic systems and the one-electron atom* 302

15-1 Electronic structure of atoms *302*
15-2 Radiation from atoms *304*
15-3 The nuclear atomic concept *307*
15-4 The theory of hydrogen as the prototype of the one-electron atom *311*
15-5 The fine structure of the energy levels of the hydrogen atom *314*

16 *Polyelectronic atoms and molecules* 320

16-1 The interaction of electrons in atomic systems *320*
16-2 The effects produced by an external magnetic field *323*
16-3 Enumeration of the electrons in a polyelectronic atom *325*
16-4 Combinations of atoms forming molecules *330*

17 *Equilibrium conditions characterizing large aggregates of atoms and molecules*   335

17-1 Energy exchange and the interaction energy between atoms and molecules *335*

17-2 Elementary statistical considerations bearing on the distribution of energy among a group of interacting particles *337*

17-3 The law for the distribution of a very large number of particles over an extended system of energy levels which in general have different probabilities of occupancy *342*

17-4 Supplementary section: derivation of the inverse exponential distribution law *344*

18 *The relation of the concepts of heat and temperature to the expression for statistical equilibrium*   350

18-1 The determination of the constants introduced in the statistical description of an assembly of molecules in terms of the number of particles concerned and the temperature *350*

18-2 Thermodynamics *354*

18-3 Specific heats *359*

18-4 Other consequences of the distribution law *360*

18-5 Supplementary section on the gas thermometer *364*

18-6 Supplementary mathematical section *365*

19 *The fluid state of matter*   369

19-1 The states of matter *369*

19-2 The gaseous state *371*

19-3 The liquid state *380*

19-4 Supplementary section: propagation of a wave through a compressible fluid, as in the case of a sound wave through a gas *386*

20 *The solid state of matter*   390

20-1 Amorphous solids *390*

20-2 Crystalline solids *393*

20-3 Molecular crystals *395*

20-4 Polar crystals *396*

20-5 Valence crystals *401*

20-6 Metals *405*

21 *Techniques of atomic measurement* 411

21-1 Measurements of atomic parameters *411*

21-2 Measurements in the low-energy range *413*

21-3 Measurement of single high-energy atomic events *417*

22 *Radioactivity* 425

22-1 Introduction *425*

22-2 Early observations of radioactivity *425*

22-3 Radiations from radioactive substances *427*

22-4 Laws of radioactive decay *431*

22-5 The rate of radioactive decay *434*

22-6 Use of radioactive materials in dating; the establishment of calendars *436*

23 *Atomic nuclei and their constituents* 442

23-1 Artificially induced nuclear reactions *442*

23-2 The discovery of the neutron *444*

23-3 Structure of atomic nuclei *449*

24 *The generation and annihilation of particles* 455

24-1 Discovery of the positive electron *455*

24-2 Production and annihilation of electrons and positrons *458*

24-3 Postronium *461*

24-4 Positron beta-emission processes *461*

24-5 Compatible heavy particles—antimatter *463*

25 *Neutrinos and the interactions between leptons and nucleons* 470

25-1 Summary of the interactions between elementary particles that have been discussed in preceding chapters *470*

25-2 The interaction process between leptons and nucleons *473*

25-3 Evidence for the existence of the neutrino *475*

25-4 Asymmetry associated with neutrino processes *480*

26 *The fission of atomic nuclei and nuclear reactors*   486

  26-1   Nuclear fission   *486*
  26-2   Nuclear reactors   *491*
  26-3   Applications of reactor technology in research   *496*
  26-4   Implications of the employment of radioactive materials for human
         health   *499*

27 *Nuclear fusion reactions and cosmic rays*   503

  27-1   Energetics of chemical or nuclear fusion reactions   *503*
  27-2   Nuclear fusion reactions   *504*
  27-3   Fusion as the source of stellar energy   *507*
  27-4   Cosmic rays   *510*

28 *High-energy particle events*   517

  28-1   Particle accelerators   *517*
  28-2   Electrostatic and electromagnetic machines   *518*
  28-3   Linear cyclic accelerators   *518*
  28-4   Circular cyclic accelerators   *521*
  28-5   Known types of elementary particles and their relations to one
         another   *525*

  References   537

  Answers to problems   538

  Appendix   543

  Index   549

The nature of physics

1

Introduction 1-1

A helpful definition of physics is difficult to formulate at the outset of an account such as this, since the body of experience that makes such a definition meaningful is lacking. To a person born into an age of rapidly evolving technology, science tends to be associated with the great array of useful things of man's devising; and, indeed, the close and mutually stimulating relationship between science and technology lends credence to the concept of science as the chief source of technology, though human needs and human industry are contributors as well. But in a more complete sense science is intellectual, rather than material, and physics may be thought of as knowledge that has been accumulated from observation of physical phenomena, systematized, and formulated in reference to general statements in the form of "theories" or "laws" which provide a grasp or a sense of greater understanding of the world in which we live.

First-hand observation and personal experience with phenomena are essential elements in the scientific process, which is why the laboratory plays such an important role in it. The control of conditions and the detailed physical manipulations that are part of this process enter very deeply into the formulation of the concepts in terms of which results are described and generalizations drawn. Indeed the orderliness and regularities that emerge can be stated in terms of procedural definitions —definitions based on procedures that anyone can follow and achieve the same results. This leads to the simple, meaningful statements which in the aggregate constitute the corpus of science.

The totality of physics, summarizing our knowledge of the world and its constituents and providing the basis for all engineering and technology, is enormously ramified and detailed. Our present abilities to describe completely, simply, and precisely the properties of the matter that constitutes our world and universe are severely limited. The nature of the partial successes we have achieved in the formulation of an account of physical phenomena encourages us to seek further along the same or similar lines in the hope of increasingly greater insights, simplifications, unifications, and amplifications in the detailed adequacy of our theories. This search, which is essentially one for greater understanding, constitutes the chief challenge and greatest fascination for the student of science. This quest generates a growing and evolving body of knowledge that is never complete and always subject to modifications, both major and minor, as a result of new experimental evidence, new interpretations of earlier results, or new and deeper insights which bring a greater unity or breadth of comprehension.

The purpose of this account is primarily to follow the broad central core of modern physical scientific thinking. The emphasis is on the methods and results that have come to be of particular practical or ideological interest; rather than on a complete historical development or a comprehensive list of relevant examples. Particular attention is paid to the role of observation and experiment both in the evolution of concepts in terms of which the description of natural phenomena is formulated, and in the procedural definitions whereby these concepts acquire universal acceptability. The objective is to formulate a description of physical phenomena that will be directly and immediately comparable with observation, that is as simple and clear as possible, that is capable of the ultimate in accuracy and precision, that is as general in application as can be achieved, and finally that may be cast in a fruitful and imaginatively suggestive form so it may bear within itself the seeds of its own evolution and extension.

At present, such a description or theory is to be found in terms of elementary particles and the atomic systems that they constitute. Though these are too small for direct sensory perception, they may be described quite simply in terms of precise concepts that have emerged from our observations of large-scale phenomena and then been unambiguously extended in application to the realm of the excessively minute. The raw material of observation comes from all our sensory organs, but two of these make the major contribution. The first is our sense of sight, because of the precision associated with it and the semipictorial nature of the physical description that evolves; and the second is our tactile or kinesthetic sense, which, together with the processes of experimental manipulation, contribute most to the ideas which form the basis of the resulting theoretical structure.

In very general terms, all science is the evolving record of our observation of natural phenomena. Out of this welter of impressions are abstracted the properties of the things observed and generalizations from the phenomena displayed which, successively refined and defined, yield concepts capable of precise measurement and unambiguous specification. The essence of the process is that since every observer has access to the raw material of experience, a common appreciation may be evolved which can be convincingly demonstrated and shared by everyone. The everyday language in terms of which the phenomena, their similarities, differences, and details are phrased tends to take on special significance; definitions are refined so that words can acquire a sharper and more specific meaning and thus be adequate to differentiate clearly between the ideas and concepts that emerge. Terms such as duration, position, length, direction, etc. can be specified in terms of certain manipulative processes that give rise to the basic procedural definitions that lie at the foundation of the concepts involved. The same is true of the mechanical quantities such as mass, momentum, force, and energy and the electrical quantities centering on charges at rest and in motion. With the aid of such concepts, it is possible to describe phenomena in terms of atomic entities too small to be available to any sensory perception.

Evolution of scientific theory 1-2

Physical science then becomes the ordering of the description of natural phenomena in terms of basic concepts. Generalization from the specific instance to the universal statement, in terms of only those features that are relevant and significant, is central to the evolution of the desired physical description or scientific theory of the phenomena. It involves the observation of commonality of aspect; the abstraction of significant features; testing the relevance or irrelevance of detail by careful observation and variation; quantitative measurement with a thorough appreciation of the limits of precision and the sources of error; and a skeptical open-mindedness to the innumerable possibilities of misunderstanding, misinterpretation, confusion, and ambiguity. It is a continuing evolutionary process, and the growth of science is the process of observing, testing, refining, simplifying, and generalizing the description which we call a theory.

The objective of this process is a better understanding of the physical world. There are a number of desiderata for a good theory; in the attainment of each, science is in its infancy. (1) A theory should be clear, definite, simple, and in general as understandable and as intuitively satisfying as possible. (2) A theory should be general and universal; it should be highly regular, with no exceptions, and completely reliable within its recognized limitations. (3) A theory must be susceptible of experimental verification, be directly comparable with observation at as many points as possible, involve only procedurally definable concepts, and be in every way as directly related to the phenomena as it can be. (4) An important objective is that a theory should have the greatest possible quantitative precision, for the extent to which it is numerical is a measure of its significant content. (5) A theory must also be open-ended and capable of growth and evolution as well as interesting and suggestive of its own most promising direction of development. In other words it should be a useful and fruitful guide to research and experiment.

A theory cannot be judged in terms of uniqueness, truth, or reality in the vague and common meaning of these words, as there are no procedural criteria to apply as tests for these qualities. The word "truth" is often used in science; but here it has a rather special meaning in that no absolute and eternal verity is implied, but simply a high degree of confidence in a statement, subject always to the possibility that later observations will find it incomplete, imperfect, or even a quite misleading interpretation of the facts. Similarly, the word "law" is frequently employed, but again in the special sense that it is a statement to which no exceptions are presently known. Such a word in science carries no implication of immutability or of being a competitor for our credence with experimental observation.

The achievements of science and the merits of a theory which epitomizes our description of it may be considered threefold. (1) A scientific theory provides the intellectual satisfaction of our desire to "understand" an important area of experience. By this we mean that we have some familiarity with the matter involved and are able to formulate a reasonably simple and acceptable description of it. (2) A theory brings with it a certain mastery over phenomena, which we call technology. Technology and science in comparatively recent years have become mutually interdependent and stimulating. As a result, science has grown very rapidly in general cultural significance. (3) A theory furnishes a compelling method of orderly intellectual procedure which has already spread far beyond the physical sciences in the academic community, and may possibly offer the promise of extending its beneficent influence to such matters as ethics and general human relations.

The simple and familiar concept of symmetry, which is capable of precise formulation, is becoming increasingly important in the description of the elementary particles of physics and the aggregates that they compose. Symmetry, in the sense of a balance of proportion and regularity of form, is a property of many naturally occurring objects both animate and inanimate and also of man's artifacts, artistic or utilitarian. Our recognition and appreciation of symmetry provide a source of aesthetic appeal and intellectual satisfaction that lend cogency to a description of the ultimate entities composing the universe which we instinctively tend to think of as being well-ordered and regular.

Specifically, there are several more precisely definable varieties of symmetry that are important in the formulation of physical descriptions. One of these is the maintenance or recurrence of identical forms in the course of the rotation of a two-dimensional figure or a three-dimensional body as illustrated in Fig. 1-1. An equilateral triangle con-

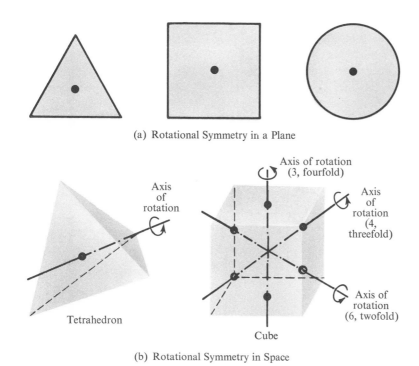

(a) Rotational Symmetry in a Plane

(b) Rotational Symmetry in Space

Figure 1-1 *Rotational symmetry.*

forms to itself three times during a complete rotation about its central point. A square has a fourfold rotational symmetry in this sense, and so on for other regular polygons. A circle, of course, remains continuously the same during such a rotation through any angle. Solid bodies similarly have axes of rotational symmetry. The tetrahedron has four axes of threefold symmetry, each passing through an apex and the center of the opposite side. The cube has three fourfold axes through the midpoints of opposite sides, four threefold axes through opposite apexes, and six twofold axes through the midpoints of opposite edges. The rotational symmetries of the other three regular solids, namely the octahedron, dodecahedron, and icosahedron, can be determined by inspection; of course, the sphere remains the same when rotated about any axis through its center.

Another form of symmetry is reflection, or mirror symmetry, which is equivalent to the reversal of a coordinate axis in a plane or in space, as illustrated in Fig. 1-2. This is the left and right bilateral symmetry of the human form. One's image in a mirror appears to be oneself who has moved behind the mirror and done an about-face, except that when one moves the right hand the image apparently moves the left. A body

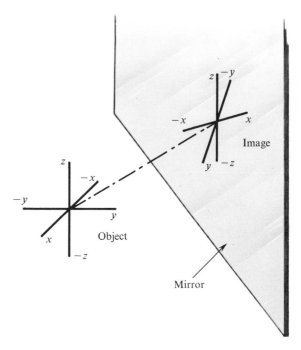

Figure 1-2 *Mirror symmetry.*

whose nature is such that the size, shape, and relative position of its parts on opposite sides of a median plane or about a center are the same possesses this symmetry; others do not. If one draws a pair of lines intersecting at right angles on a piece of paper and labels the ends of one line $+ x$ and $- x$ and the ends of the other $+ y$ and $- y$ and views this construction in a mirror held at rest vertically on the paper, it is evident that no imaginable rotation of the image in the plane will bring similar symbols into conjunction with those of the object. Interchanging the designations at the ends of one line or the other would be necessary to accomplish that purpose. This is what is meant by reversal of a coordinate, the changing from $+$ to $-$ and vice versa, by reflection. Similarly, if a construction of three mutually perpendicular wires in space, similar to the lines considered above, is viewed in a mirror, the image cannot be rotated to bring the lines into coincidence without reversing the labeling of one wire or of all three; and reversal of two will not do it. We will have occasion to invoke symmetry quite frequently in this book, notably in the cases of atoms and molecules and their more elementary constituents.

Another simple and very useful concept with which beauty of form is commonly associated is the regularly recurring sequence. Such a series of like objects or contours has indefinite extent only in our imagination. For many practical purposes this is not of great consequence, because the pattern persists over a large number of repetitions. The design is obvious to the eye or ear, and the property can be conceived as being indefinitely extended. The instances are legion. Such things as heart beats, clock ticks, or the sequence of days and nights recur in time; and fence posts, a footstep pattern on a beach, or beads on a string recur along a line. On a surface one thinks of ruled lines, networks or the great proliferation of wallpaper patterns, which, it is interesting to note, come in only a finite number of symmetry types. The property is observed in space as well. Here the honeycomb, the jungle-gym, or the pile of balls are familiar instances. Like the concept of symmetry, that of regular recurrence is capable of extension or contraction to any scale, and its application to wave motion and crystal structure is of great importance in atomic theory.

Relation of mathematics to science   1-4

Mathematics, according to the definition of Bertrand Russell, is the science concerned with the logical deduction of consequences from the general premises of all reasoning. It has to do with things such as numbers, points, vectors, etc., that are capable of quite precise definition; and with groups, which are the classes of relationships among such things, that possess special properties. The concepts of mathematics have evolved from generalization of the raw material of observation, and in consequence the connection between physical science and mathematics is a very close one—observation in general furnishing the material and stimulus for mathematical development, and mathematics in turn providing the convenient and appropriate expression for the results of scientific thought. The quantitative character of physical science is one of its outstanding characteristics; in consequence, mathematics is particularly appropriate and indeed ultimately indispensable for expressing scientific conclusions. The ordinary vernacular in which we carry on our common conversations has a rich vocabulary for expressing qualitatively fine shades of meaning, but it is highly impressionistic and ambiguous and can be used only with the greatest caution in scientific descriptions.

Because of its simplicity, precision, and generality mathematics is pre-eminently the language of science. Ordinary words must, of course, also be used to establish the connection between our observational experience and its precise embodiment in a mathematical statement. But these must usually be shorn of many of their connotations and redefined if they are to be precise. "Particle," for instance, is a word meaning a minute entity, but also carries with it implications of size, shape, hardness, etc. The term particle as used in physics refers to units of matter that are so excessively minute that such other properties as those listed above cannot be associated with them. Certain significant generic properties are, however, associated with physical particles, as will be brought out in the subsequent discussion. These properties differentiate particles into groups of various types. The primary property of a particle is excessive minuteness; it lacks extent in the ordinary sense, and resembles a point center from which emanate physically observable interactions with other particles.

Just as languages are composed of words and punctuation marks, mathematics is a language of symbols and signs of operation. Some of the symbols are numbers, such as the whole numbers 1, 2, 3, etc., which are precisely defined and may be taken as well understood. Other symbols are letters of alphabets which may be defined at will to represent specific numbers that may or may not be associated with certain physical or conceptual things; or each letter may represent a whole set or range of values that can be substituted for the letter at will. Thus x can represent a number of dollars, the position of the hand of a clock, or an undefined quantity capable of taking any numerical value, say, between 0 and 100. The signs, such as equality ($=$), addition ($+$), multiplication ($\cdot$) (often abbreviated by simple juxtaposition), indicate a relationship that exists between quantities or a process that is to be carried out with them. Thus $a + 1$ means 1 is to be added to a, $2a$ means that a is to be multiplied by 2, etc.

Turning from the symbols and signs to the more basic matter of the relation between mathematics and science (in other words the expression of the results of scientific thought in the language of mathematics), one sees that the sentences and paragraphs of this language are statements of relations between the measurable quantities that derive from scientific observation. Physical measurements all relate to the position of something—the hands of a clock, a ball on a billiard table, or an elephant on a hillside. These are necessarily specified, not absolutely but relative to something else. In the instances cited, the position of the hands is specified relative to the markings on the dial; that of the ball possibly relative to one corner of the table; and that of the elephant relative to the peak of the hill. Scientific statements in mathematical form simply relate such measurements to one another.

A man walking along a road marked with milestones can relate the distance he covers, say x, with the time interval shown by his watch, say t, and the relationship between x and t describes his progress along the road in terms of the time. Such a relationship between x and t is said to be a *functional relationship*; i.e., x may be said to be a "function of t," or indeed t may be considered a function of x. If the man looks at his watch just as he passes the milestones, the function consists of a discrete series of pairs of numbers (t_1, x_1) for milestone #1, (t_2, x_2) for #2, etc. (A number is written in a subscript position to indicate the serial number corresponding to the milestone in question.) In situations of this type where the process appears to be continuous, one may imagine the "milestones" or road markers to be closer and closer together. More and more sets of observations of x and t may be taken over a certain distance, so that one may take the inductive step of saying that, in principle, the observations could be made indefinitely close to one another. Thus, for any position x along the road, a time t can be associated with the man's progress, and a continuous functional relation between x and t results.

It is generally more convenient to display such a functional relation in graphical form rather than as a very large number of pairs of numbers. Thus, if one number of the pair, say x, is read from a vertical scale and the other, say t, from a horizontal one, and a dot placed on the diagram at the proper position for each such pair, this dense series of dots or points traces out a line (see Fig. 1-3) which represents the functional relation between x and t, commonly written in terms of letters as $x = f(t)$ or $x = x(t)$, and read x is a function of t. Another

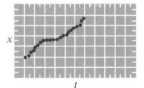

Figure 1-3 *Graphical representation of a function.*

interpretation of the diagram that immediately suggests itself is that such a set of pairs of values, or a two-dimensional diagram, can usefully represent the path of a man traversing a rectangular field where x represents the distance along one border and t along an adjacent border, the path being the functional relation expressing the trace of his footsteps.

The concept of the functional relation between two, or indeed several quantities, is a very basic one to the description of a particular physical phenomenon and to the generalized description or theory that represents a class of phenomena. The functional relation may be expressed as groups of numbers associated with one another as a result of measurement, or in terms of photographed tracks or constructed graphs. One may often also very usefully approximate such relations in algebraic form. For instance, if the man walks along the road at a uniform rate so that the distance traveled between any two times is equal to some constant number times the time, the relationship between x and t is said to be a linear one. The graph of the path is a straight line, and the algebraic expression of it is:

$$x = x_0 + a(t - t_0)$$

where x_0 is the starting point at the time the watch indicates t_0, and a is the constant walking speed. In other instances it may be possible to approximate the observed functional relationship with an expression such as:

$$x = x_0 + a_1(t - t_0) + a_2(t - t_0)^2 + a_3(t - t_0)^3$$

If such an algebraic relationship could be found approximating the actual observations, a number of advantages would result. In the first place algebraic techniques are available for dealing with such a function. Also such expressions provide an alternative form of understanding, which often aids in the disclosure of relations with still other observable quantities. This further increases the close relationship between physical quantities, and enhances our intellectual grasp of the phenomena represented. The simpler the form of expression for the functional relation, the more readily do we seem to appreciate it, and the more useful does it appear to be in extending our understanding.

1-5 *Elementary mathematical manipulation*

The emphasis in the present account of physical science is on the ideas and concepts involved, and minimal use is made of the mathematical language for derivation and exhibition. It is assumed that the elementary arithmetical processes are familiar, and that the simpler ideas of algebra and geometry require only brief review for ready reference. The present section is provided for the purpose of this review.

Exponentials and logarithms. A number written as a superscript of a quantity is known as an *exponent*: it indicates that the quantity is to be multiplied by itself a number of times equal to the exponent; thus a^2 is the same as $a \cdot a$ or $a^3 = a \cdot a \cdot a$. The exponent thus is the sum of the occurrences of the quantity in the product, and the product of two quantities such as $a^3 \cdot a$ is a^3a^1 or a^4, and a^2a^3 is a^5. In other words, products written in this way may be formed more simply by adding exponents. Multiplication of any quantity by 1 leaves the quantity unchanged, and similarly the addition of zero leaves a quantity such as an exponent unchanged. Hence any quantity with a zero exponent, which would otherwise be undefined, can logically be defined as 1 or unity. This understanding extends the significance of exponents to negative numbers. Thus a^{-4} is the reciprocal of a^4, or $1/a^4$, since the product of a^4 and a^{-4} is, by the addition of exponents, a^0 or unity. Similarly fractional exponents indicate what are called *roots*. For instance, $a^{1/2} \cdot a^{1/2} = a^1$, by the convention of adding exponents; hence, $a^{1/2}$ is that quantity which—when multiplied by itself—yields a. This is the definition of the square root of a. Similarly $a^{1/3}$ is the cube root of a, since $a^{1/3}$ multiplied three times by itself equals a. Since addition is generally an easier process to perform than multiplication, the use of the exponential nomenclature simplifies mathematical manipulation. It also affords considerable economy of writing or printing since 10,000,000,000,000 can be written more shortly as 10^{13} or 0.000,000,01 as 10^{-8}.

These considerations also provide a basis for the general system of effecting multiplication through the simpler medium of adding exponents called *logarithms*. As seems reasonable and may be rigorously shown, any number, say a, may be written as any other number, say b, with the exponent c which is determined by the choice of a and b. Thus $a = b^c$. The number b is then called the *base*, and the exponent c the *logarithm of a to the base b*. While b is quite arbitrary, two bases are in common use, and there are extensive tabulations of logarithms to these bases. They are $b = 10$ and $b = 2.7182818 \ldots$, the latter commonly called ϵ or the *base of natural logarithms* for reasons that will become evident in Sect. 17-4. In terms of either of these bases, if a number $a = b^c$ and another number $g = b^h$, then $a \cdot g = b^{c+h}$. On looking up c and h in the table and adding them together, one may use this number by reading the table in reverse order to find the number equaling the product ag. The multiplication process has thus been reduced to addition plus reference to the table of logarithms.

Binomial expansion. A further brief illustration of the combination of the simple processes of addition and multiplication furnishes a review of elementary algebra and also of certain formulae which are particularly useful in physics. If the quantity $(a + b)$ is multiplied by itself term by term, the following expression results:

$$
\begin{array}{r}
a + b \\
a + b \\
\hline
ab + b^2 \\
a^2 + ab \\
\hline
a^2 + 2ab + b^2
\end{array}
$$

$$(a + b)^2 = a^2 + 2ab + b^2$$

It may, of course, be simply verified that any numbers may be substituted for a and b on the two sides of this expression or equation and the equality remains true. If $(a + b)^2$ is multiplied again by $(a + b)$, one obtains:

$$
\begin{array}{r}
a^3 + 2a^2b + ab^2 \\
a^2b + 2ab^2 + b^3 \\
\hline
a^3 + 3a^2b + 3ab^2 + b^3
\end{array}
$$

If one proceeds to multiply this quantity by $(a + b)$ again, one sees certain regularities persisting which enables one to take an inductive step and to determine what the product of $(a + b)$ an indefinite number of times, say n, would be. The coefficient, which is the number appearing before any term, remains 1 for the first term; it is equal to $n/1$ for the second term; $n(n - 1)/1 \cdot 2$ for the third; $n(n - 1)(n - 2)/1 \cdot 2 \cdot 3$ for the fourth; etc. The exponent of a decreases by 1 for each term, and that of b increases by 1. Thus:

$$(a + b)^n = a^n + na^{n-1}b + \frac{n(n - 1)}{1 \cdot 2} a^{n-2}b^2 +$$

$$\frac{n(n - 1)(n - 2)}{1 \cdot 2 \cdot 3} a^{n-3}b^3 + \cdots\cdots\cdots + nab^{n-1} + b^n$$

Using the abbreviation:

$$n! = 1 \cdot 2 \cdot 3 \cdot 4 \cdot 5 \cdot 6 \cdot 7 \ldots\ldots\ldots\ldots n$$

which is read as *factorial n*, and noting that $n(n - 1)(n - 2)(n - 3) \cdots (n - m + 1)$ is equal to $n!/(n - m)!$, one obtains the general term in the expansion of $(a + b)^n$:

$$\frac{n!}{(n - m)!m!} a^{n-m}b^m$$

For the first term $m = 0$ [$0! = 1$], and thus it is a^n; for the second $m = 1$, and it is $na^{n-1}b$, and so on; for the last $m = n$, and the term is b^m.

The Bionomial Theorem is a very basic and important expansion, a particular use for which arises in mathematics and physics as a result of the fact that it leads naturally to a convenient form of approximation. Physical measurements can never be made with perfect precision; there are always errors due to the circumstances of observation, to the finite divisions of scales, etc. These inaccuracies or errors cannot in general be ignored. They may indeed combine in such a way as to be very significant. The error in a quantity that depends upon some measurement to a power will depend both upon the error in measurement, and upon the way this measurement enters the final result. Thus, let us say that b, representing for instance an error in the true value of a, is small in comparison with a itself. Then:

$$(a + b)^n = a^n \left(1 + \frac{b}{a}\right)^n$$

$$= a^n \left[1 + nx + \frac{n(n-1)}{1 \cdot 2} x^2 + \frac{n(n-1)(n-2)}{1 \cdot 2 \cdot 3} x^3 + \cdots \right]$$

where x is written for the fraction b/a. If the product (xn) is small, the successive terms decrease in magnitude with successive powers, and the retention of only a few of them may yield quite an acceptable approximation.

It may be shown that the expression:

$$(1 + x)^n = 1 + nx + \frac{n(n-1)}{1 \cdot 2} x^2 + \cdots + \frac{n!}{(n-m)!m!} x^m + \cdots$$

is true for any value of n positive or negative, integral or fractional, if x is less in absolute magnitude than 1, that is, if x lies between $+1$ and -1.

A particular instance which will later be seen to be useful in understanding why the logarithmic base ϵ is used so commonly in mathematics is that for which n is the reciprocal of x. When $1/n$ is substituted for x, the expansion becomes:

$$\left(1 + \frac{1}{n}\right)^n = 1 + 1 + \frac{\left(1 - \frac{1}{n}\right)}{1 \cdot 2} + \frac{\left(1 - \frac{1}{n}\right)\left(1 - \frac{2}{n}\right)}{1 \cdot 2 \cdot 3} +$$

$$\frac{\left(1 - \frac{1}{n}\right)\left(1 - \frac{2}{n}\right)\left(1 - \frac{3}{n}\right)}{1 \cdot 2 \cdot 3 \cdot 4} + \cdots \cdots$$

In imagination one may think of n becoming larger and larger and in consequence $1/n$ coming closer and closer to zero. In this limit of very large n, the reciprocals of n on the right become negligible, and the expansion of $(1 + 1/n)^n$ becomes:

$$\left(1 + \frac{1}{n}\right)^n = 1 + 1 + \frac{1}{2} + \frac{1}{6} + \frac{1}{24} + \frac{1}{120} + \frac{1}{720} + \frac{1}{5040} + \cdots$$

The sum of this series which is easily obtained to a high accuracy is the number ϵ, which is the base of natural logarithms mentioned earlier. Just the terms given here yield the approximation 2.71818.

Problems

1-1 If an equilateral triangle is drawn on a piece of paper and a single-sided vertical mirror is rotated about a vertical axis through the center, in how many orientations of the mirror does the figure consisting of parts of the center and image appear to be the original triangle? If the same observation is made with a square instead of a triangle, how many different mirror orientations are there?

1-2 The regular octahedron consists of eight equal equilateral triangles fitted together to form the surface of a solid. Give the number of each type of symmetry axis possessed by this solid. What are the additional symmetries of the tetrahedron not mentioned in the text?

1-3 Two glasses contain equal volumes, one of pure water and the other of pure alcohol. A spoonful of alcohol is taken from the first glass and stirred into the second glass of water. Then a spoonful of the mixture in the second glass is taken and stirred into the first glass of alcohol. The two volumes are now equal again; but which has the greater purity—the glass of mostly water or the glass of mostly alcohol? i.e., is there more alcohol in the water than there is water in the alcohol or is the opposite true?

1-4 A man says that when he looks in a mirror he finds left and right inverted, but not top and bottom. Since the mirror is a plane sheet of glass, he does not understand how it can differentiate between horizontal and vertical directions. Indeed it does not; for when he lies on his side, he still finds his left and right inverted, while his head and feet are not. Can you resolve his apparent problem?

1-5 A single layer of marbles is closely packed into a flat tray. How many vertical planes of symmetry may be drawn through any given marble?

1-6 There is an old problem with which you are probably familiar: "A tortoise and a hare agree to have a race over 100 yds. The tortoise has a start of 20 yds., but the hare runs twice as fast as the tortoise. At first sight the hare looks the obvious winner, but not if one argues thus: the hare runs 20 yds. in an effort to catch the tortoise, but the tortoise meanwhile has run 10 yds. and is still 10 yds. ahead. While the hare runs these 10 yds. the tortoise runs another 5 yds. and is thus 5 yds. ahead. The hare runs another 5 yds. and the tortoise is still $2\frac{1}{2}$ yds. ahead and so on. It seems that the hare can never quite catch the tortoise." If this is not true, indicate the fallacy in the argument.

1-7 A life insurance company grants policies to a number, say N_0, of elderly men. It is found that of the number remaining at the beginning of any year one tenth have died by the end of that year. Express N, the number remaining, as a function of t, the number of years elapsed. Is this a linear relationship?

1-8 Use the binomial theorem to multiply out $(x + y)^6$.

1-9 If Δx is small compared with x, find the approximate value of $(x + \Delta x)^7$.

1-10 What are the approximate values of $(1.001)^4$, $(1.001)^{1/4}$, $(1.003)^2$, $(4.004)^5$, $(1001)^8$, $(1001)^{-5}$, $1/1001$, $1/\sqrt{1001}$?

2 Concepts and units of physical measurement

2-1 Observation and measurement

Observation of the world, the solar system, and the universe beyond, is the most fundamental activity of science. Some observations are merely qualitative and lead to our concepts of the properties of matter, such as hardness, softness, wetness, texture, hotness, loudness, brightness, etc. Other observations are of a quantitative nature and involve the precise comparison of things in terms of geometrical shapes and numerical units. Both types of observation are important, as defining the kind of thing we are measuring and what its magnitude is. Upon the nature and quality of these observations depend the value and significance of the raw material out of which our scientific description of the world evolves, the clarity with which we understand what we are doing, the cogency that our description carries to others, and in consequence its eventual acceptability as an established fact.

Though broad qualitative observations are essential for an appreciation of the concepts in terms of which scientific description is expressed, it is the precise observations or measurements that provide the data for the quantitative description that is physical science. This raw material is ultimately reducible to the location of something in space. The basic requisite is thus a quantitative technique for specifying the position of a body relative to others. The specification of direction and the construction of measuring rods as well as other devices for precise observation and comparative measurement are essential. These instruments take many forms. Most commonly, data are derived from the position of a pointer on a dial, the level of a liquid on a scale, the shape of the trace of a beam or a pen on a surface marked with coordinate axes, or other such positioning of an indicating member relative to fiducial marks.

Most measurements must be made under conditions that are not static. Changes which may or may not be important take place during the measuring process; indeed, in a very fundamental sense the act of observation and measurement reacts on the system being measured, disturbing it to some extent. In the ordinary gross measurement of the position of the large bodies with which we commonly deal, this is generally of little importance. We can determine the position of a billiard ball on a table or a brick in a wall relative to our own position or to some other fiducial point with considerable accuracy by the use of measuring rods. The positions of inaccessible objects, such as a mountain peak, an airplane in the sky, or a planet, can be determined by triangulation. By this process, the position of some specified point associated with the object is located. To specify the position of an extended object such as a loose brick or an airplane, one must give its orientation about a point relative to some choice of directions in space. When one applies this measuring process to very small objects, one encounters a practical limit to precision, imposed by a residual random type of motion resulting from the thermal exchange of energy between the objects. This is a matter that will be considered in detail in Chap. 18. When striving for extreme precision in determining the positions of the atoms and their elementary constituents, we encounter a fundamental limitation, for the very act of making even the most delicate observation disturbs these minute entities so considerably that an indefiniteness persists as to either where they are, precisely, or how they are moving at the time of the measurement. This will be seen in Chap. 14.

Time and its measurement   2-2

Time is such a common word and the phenomena we associate with it are so deeply ingrained in our experience that it is difficult to be entirely objective about it. Our psychological appreciation of the continuous duration of experience furnishes us with a notion of the one-dimensional continuum of time. This notion is largely intuitive rather than complete and detailed; yet it forms the basis upon which our concept of time rests. The measurement or comparison of periods of time is particularly basic to scientific observation. We measure time, as we do everything else that appears to be continuous, in units which we choose quite arbitrarily. Many naturally occurring intervals of time that appear to be regularly recurring, as we judge them by our psychological sense of duration or by intercomparisons among them, provide readily available and convenient units. The period of rotation of the earth about its axis, of rotation of the moon about the earth, of rotation of the earth about the sun, as well as of vibration and rotation characteristic of atomic and molecular systems provide a wide range of alternative standards with which arbitrary time intervals can be compared. The sun dial was one of the earliest forms of time keeper. Rough secondary standards for measuring shorter intervals of time such as the hour glass and water clock or clepsydra have been in use for thousands of years. The pendulum clock came into use in the 13th and 14th centuries; and successive refinements in materials and techniques have resulted in the highly precise and reliable clocks in use today.

The motion of astronomical bodies is very regular, and provides a convenient time scale whose accuracy is quite adequate for most purposes. However, precise observations of the position of bodies in the solar system against the background of fixed stars show that there are departures from regularity in the rotation of the earth and in its circulation about the sun. The causes of some of these are recognized in terms of the irregular shape and plasticity of the earth and the effects of other astronomical bodies. Future observation and study will be necessary to provide an account of others which are as yet not completely understood. One of the most important types of information gained from the observation of the orbits of earth satellites is that which relates to the irregularity of the figure or shape of the earth; hence, experiments in this area will assist in our understanding of its rate of rotation and its reliability as a clock.

Certain periodic phenomena such as the oscillation of crystals in their natural periods are also highly reliable and regular when suitable precautions are taken to isolate them from disturbing influences. Electronic clocks can be constructed using these natural periods to control their rates. The periods of oscillation of such electronic clocks are very short, of the order of millionths of a second; hence they are particularly convenient for measuring very short time intervals. Finally, certain atomic phenomena can be used to provide highly regular basic time intervals. The oscillations in the relative positions of components of atomic or molecular systems which can be conveniently manipulated and used to govern electrical circuits provide clocks for the intercomparison of time intervals. These have periods of the order of 10^{-10} second, a convenient range for measuring the very short intervals of particular interest in atomic processes.

By international agreement, the *second* (sec.) has been chosen as the basic unit in which time is commonly measured. The constancy and reproducibility of atomic clocks are such that it has also been agreed to define the second in terms of the frequency of light emitted by a cesium atom. The atoms of cesium can be induced to make transitions between two stable energy states. In doing so, they absorb or emit radiation of a definite frequency (see, for example, Chap. 15). By defining this frequency to be exactly 9,192,631,770 oscillations per second, we obtain a fixed standard for the second. The choice of the above figure, instead of exactly 9×10^9, comes from an attempt to get the best possible agreement between this standard and a former standard based on astronomical measurements. The precision of the new standard is a few parts in 10^{11}. The minute is 60 seconds, and the hour is 3,600 seconds.

Because of the continuously progressive nature of our concept of time, it initially assumed a unique role among the variables used for physical descriptions. As time would appear to be uncontrollable, it naturally entered into equations describing the relative positions and motions of objects as the independent variable, the one in terms of which the functional relationships of science were most reasonably formulated. This tradition, or prejudice, had a profound effect upon the basic concepts of physics until the present century; it may well still exert subtle, and as yet unappreciated influences on our thinking. The advent of the principle of relativity, which will be considered in Chap. 7, has profoundly altered our concept of time and brought it more into accord with that of space.

Measurement of length and specification of relative position   2-3

Units and standards of length. The measurement of spatial intervals presents a problem which, in respect to the apparent continuity of the quantity being measured and the arbitrariness of the units that may be chosen, resembles the measurement of time. In other respects, however, it is rather different: spatial measurements can be reversed or are retraceable, whereas we intuitively measure the progress of time in a sense that we call forward. Also there are no simple, precise natural spatial intervals that are of a size convenient for common measurements. The scientific unit of length is the *meter* (m.). This was originally a quite arbitrary interval between two fiducial marks near the ends of a metal bar maintained at the International Bureau of Weights and Measures, at Sèvres, near Paris. This is approximately equal to 2.5×10^{-8} of the circumference of the earth at the equator; but the technical difficulties of establishing a unit in terms of the dimensions of the earth or the solar system are so great that such a definition is unacceptable for precise use.

By analogy with the case of electronic and atomic clocks, there exists a series of natural units of length that are excessively minute in terms of the meter, but are readily produced and easily compared with precision. Though not appropriate for everyday use, they are essential in precise laboratory measurements, particularly for measuring distances of the order of a millimeter (mm.) or less. These natural standards or units of length are the wave lengths of certain readily identifiable components of the light emitted by electric discharges through gases.

As with the modern standard of time, the precision, reproducibility, and availability of these atomic standards have led us, through international agreement, to define the basic unit of length, the meter, in terms of an atomic process. When an electric current is passed through a glass tube containing the most abundant isotope or form of the elemental gas krypton (Kr^{86}), several colors are emitted and can be separated. Each color is associated with a definite wavelength (distance between two successive equivalent points on the periodic light wave). The meter (m.) is defined to be exactly 1,650,763.73 times the wave length of an orange-red component of the radiation. The English yard, formerly an independent standard, is now defined to be exactly 0.9144 meter.

The comparison between standards of length can be made by means of precise microscopic comparators with an accuracy of about one part in 10^7. The subdivisions of the meter are the centimeter (cm.) (1/100 meter) and the millimeter (mm.) (1/10 cm., or 1/1000 m.). Rough measurements are frequently made to the nearest millimeter. The techniques for measuring length have an extensive history and involve much interesting practical detail, but this is of little particular interest in terms of physical principles.

Coordinates in a plane. The measurement of distance along a line or the specification of the spatial interval between two points on a line is clearly a matter of comparison of this interval with a standard of length. The result can be expressed in terms of a single number which, to the precision employed, states the number of meters and fractions thereof corresponding to the interval. Thus a single number specifies the position of a point on a line relative to some chosen fiducial point to which is assigned the number zero (0). A straight line is often said to represent a single *dimension* for this reason. Time is said to be one-dimensional, since a temporal interval can also be specified by a single number.

However, with a surface or a plane, two numbers are necessary to specify the position of a point. In other words, if a measuring rod is placed between an arbitrary fiducial point and any other point, the distance between them can be specified by one number, i.e., the number of rod divisions equal to the interval between them. However, to differentiate this particular point from all other points the same distance from the fiducial point requires a specification of the direction in which the measuring rod is laid, or the angle between the direction of the rod and some arbitrarily chosen direction in the plane.

There are many ways of specifying the fiducial points and lines, known as *coordinates*, in two dimensions. The two most common are (a) Cartesian coordinates and (b) polar coordinates. The former, named for the mathematician and philosopher Descartes, consists of two families of parallel straight lines intersecting one another at right angles (Fig. 2-1). An arbitrarily chosen intersecting pair, called the *axes*, constitutes the fiducial lines from which the distances to a point are measured. Thus if the axes are labeled x and y, a point at the intersection of any other two lines of the parallel families constituting the coordinates is determined by specifying the distances from the x and y axes. The member of the family of lines parallel to the y axis which passes through the point is the x coordinate of the point, say x_0; the y coordinate of the point, say y_0, is defined in an analogous way.

Alternatively, it is frequently more convenient to specify the position of a point in a plane in terms of two numbers that are associated with the system, known as polar coordinates. Cartesian coordinates have a special convenience in situations possessing a rectangular symmetry. Polar coordinates have that convenience in situations of circular symmetry, such as a rotation in which points pursue concentric circular paths about the point of rotation. The coordinate lines in this system are concentric circles about the fiducial zero point and straight lines or radii of these circles radiating from this point. The axes analogous to those of Cartesian coordinates are the fiducial point—a circle of zero radius—and an arbitrarily chosen radial line from which the angle with other radii is measured counterclockwise (Fig. 2-2). An angle is measured by the length of an arc of a circle of unit radius intercepted by the fiducial line and the line through the specified point. The unit angle when so defined is the angle for which the length of the intercepted arc is equal to the radius. It is called the *radian* (rad.). A common method of measuring angles employed by mariners, surveyors, and cartographers derives from the ancient Babylonian sexigesimal system, and is analogous

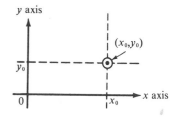

Figure 2-1 *Cartesian coordinates in a plane.*

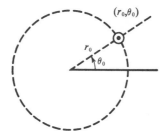

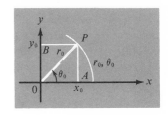

Figure 2-2 *Polar coordinates in a plane.*

Figure 2-3 *Relation between Cartesian and polar coordinates.*

to the division of the day into 24 hours, the hour into 60 minutes, and the minute into 60 seconds. In this system, the circumference of a circle is divided into 360 equal units called *degrees* (°); the degree is divided, as are hours, into 60 parts called angular minutes, and each angular minute into 60 angular seconds.

Evidently, since a point can be specified in either of two ways, i.e., Cartesian or polar coordinates, there must be a relation between the coordinates of a point in these two systems by means of which the specification in terms of one system may be transformed into the terms of the other. This relation is illustrated in Fig. 2-3.

The line OA, of length x_0, is one side of a right triangle of hypotenuse r_0 and the line AP of length y_0 is the other. The ratios of such sides to the hypotenuse are given special names in terms of the angle θ_0 for convenience, since they are used very frequently. Thus, y_0/r_0 is called $\sin \theta_0$, and x_0/r_0 is called $\cos \theta_0$. The ratio y_0/x_0 is called $\tan \theta_0$. Hence it is seen that:

$$x_0 = r_0 \cos \theta_0 \qquad \text{and} \qquad y_0 = r_0 \sin \theta_0$$

The values of sin and cos have been calculated and are listed in tables, as are those of tan; hence, if r_0 and θ_0 are given, x_0 and y_0 can readily be found. If one writes the ratio of y_0 to x_0, squares x_0 and y_0, and adds these together (recalling the property of a right triangle that $\sin^2 \theta_0 + \cos^2 \theta_0 = 1$), one obtains expressions for r_0 and θ_0 in terms of x_0 and y_0:

$$\tan \theta_0 = y_0/x_0 \qquad r_0{}^2 = x_0{}^2 + y_0{}^2$$

Thus, if x_0 and y_0 are given, the corresponding values of r_0 and θ_0 can be obtained by calculation and recourse to the prepared tables.

Vectors and Scalars. The concept of a *vector* represents a very simple and useful idea for the specification of the position of one point relative to another. A vector is the association of a number with a direction, or a directed magnitude, and hence is obviously a way of locating one point in terms of the position of another point. It is depicted graphically as an arrow; the length representing the number or magnitude and the direction of the arrow toward the head indicating the direction. Thus an arrow extending from a fiducial zero point to any other point serves, among other things, to locate the point graphically. The concept of vectors may be related to that of coordinates by the association of a unit vector with each coordinate. This is a vector of unit length directed along the coordinate axis in the increasing sense. Vectors are commonly differentiated from simple undirected magnitudes, or so-called *scalar* quantities, by drawing a line above or beneath the former, or by employing boldface type. Thus **i** and **j** are employed for unit vectors along the x and y axes, respectively. A point at a distance, x_0, from the origin along the x axis would be indicated by the product of the undirected magnitude x_0 and the unit magnitude direction indicator **i**, i.e., $x_0\mathbf{i}$. If the vector $y_0\mathbf{j}$ is added to this, then the direction of the terminal point P from the origin, or the resultant vector $\mathbf{r}_0$ is determined. Any number of vectors may be added together graphically by putting the arrows sequentially in the proper senses, or analytically by adding algebraically (with due regard to sense or sign) the magnitudes associated with the two directions **i** and **j**. Thus, if two vectors $\mathbf{r}_1$ and $\mathbf{r}_2$ are to be added together, this may be done graphically by placing the tail of one vector on the tip of the other as shown in Fig. 2-4(b), where $\mathbf{r}_3$ is the sum of $\mathbf{r}_1$ and $\mathbf{r}_2$. It is, however, usually more convenient to express $\mathbf{r}_1$ and $\mathbf{r}_2$ in terms of their x and y components. Thus

$$\mathbf{r}_1 = x_1\mathbf{i} + y_1\mathbf{j}$$
$$\mathbf{r}_2 = x_2\mathbf{i} + y_2\mathbf{j}$$

Then
$$\mathbf{r}_3 = \mathbf{r}_1 + \mathbf{r}_2 = x_1\mathbf{i} + y_1\mathbf{j} + x_2\mathbf{i} + y_2\mathbf{j}$$
$$= (x_1 + x_2)\mathbf{i} + (y_1 + y_2)\mathbf{j}$$

But expressing $\mathbf{r}_3$ in terms of its x and y components, one obtains

$$\mathbf{r}_3 = x_3\mathbf{i} + y_3\mathbf{j}$$

So
$$x_3 = x_1 + x_2$$
and
$$y_3 = y_1 + y_2$$

The magnitude of $\mathbf{r}_3$ is then $r_3 = \sqrt{x_3{}^2 + y_3{}^2}$ and the angle θ between $\mathbf{r}_3$ and the x axis is given by $\tan \theta = y_3/x_3$.

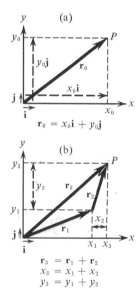

Figure 2-4 *(a) Cartesian vectors. (b) Addition of vectors.*

EXAMPLE. A soldier leaves his camp and marches 5 miles east, 10 miles southeast, 4 miles east, 11 miles in a direction 27° east of north, 3 miles north, and finally 15 miles west. What is his final distance and direction from camp?

The soldier's path is shown in Fig. 2-5, and, if it were accurately drawn to scale, the answers could be found by carefully measuring the length and direction of r_7. However, taking east as the x direction and north as the y direction, we may write the x and y components of r_7:

$$x_7 = x_1 + x_2 + x_3 + x_4 + x_5 + x_6$$
$$= 5 + 10 \,(\cos 45°) + 4 + 11 \,(\sin 27°) + 0 - 15$$
$$= 5 + 7 + 4 + 5 + 0 - 15$$
$$= 6$$

$$y_7 = 0 - 10 \,(\sin 45°) + 0 + 11 \,(\cos 27°) + 3 + 0$$
$$= 0 - 7 + 0 + 10 + 3 + 0$$
$$= 6$$

Then
$$r_7 = \sqrt{x_7{}^2 + y_7{}^2} = \sqrt{72} = 8.5$$

and
$$\tan \theta = \frac{y_7}{x_7} = 1 \qquad \text{and so} \qquad \theta = 45°$$

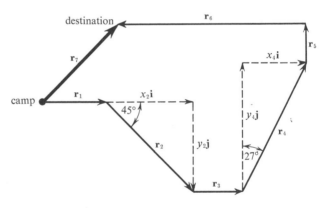

Figure 2-5 *The vectors r_1 through r_0 chart the route marched by a soldier. The resultant or sum of all these, r_7, shows the distance and direction of his destination from his starting point.*

Thus without resort to an accurate graph, the required answer is *8.5 miles northeast of the camp*. Notice that it does not matter in which order the vectors or their components are added.

Coordinates in space. We live and make our scientific observations not in a world of two dimensions, like that of a sheet of paper, but rather in a world of three dimensions that compose volumes rather than areas. It is simple, however, to extend the preceding ideas to provide a method of specifying the relative positions of points in three-dimensional space. Cartesian axes are readily generalized by erecting an axis, called the z axis, out of the paper from the origin of the x and y axes, which is then at right angles to each of them [Fig. 2-6(a)]. The three numbers necessary to specify the position of a point in three dimensions are then the three distances along the x, y, and z axes. The polar coordinates may be generalized to three dimensions in a similar way by erecting a perpendicular to the paper at the origin of the polar axes [Fig. 2-6(b)]. An arbitrary point in space is then specified by first giving the angle between this axis and a line through the origin to the point, then specifying the length of the line from the origin to the point, and finally specifying the angle between the fiducial line in the xy plane and the line joining the origin with the point in this plane lying immediately below the arbitrary point to be specified. By convention θ is used for the first angle, r for the distance from the origin 0 to the point P, and ϕ for the angle in the xy plane.

The vector concept is again readily generalized to three dimensions: arrows can point up or down out of the two-dimensional plane as well as lie within it; these can be added together by being placed base to tip, and the resultant can be thus determined. With Cartesian coordinates this is done by introducing a unit vector $\mathbf{k}$ in the positive z direction. A three-dimensional vector from the origin to the point (x_0, y_0, z_0) is then:

$$\mathbf{r} = x_0\mathbf{i} + y_0\mathbf{j} + z_0\mathbf{k}$$

and the sum of two vectors to the points (x_1, y_1, z_1) and (x_2, y_2, z_2) is, say, the vector to the point (x_3, y_3, z_3) or:

$$\mathbf{r_3} = \mathbf{r_1} + \mathbf{r_2} = x_3\mathbf{i} + y_3\mathbf{j} + z_3\mathbf{k}$$
$$= (x_1 + x_2)\mathbf{i} + (y_1 + y_2)\mathbf{j} + (z_1 + z_2)\mathbf{k}$$

Relations between three-dimensional Cartesian and polar coordinates. As with two dimensions, we may readily transform from one system of three-dimensional coordinates to another. Referring to Fig. 2-7, we see that

$$\mathbf{z_0} = z_0\mathbf{k} = r_0 \cos\theta_0\mathbf{k}$$

$$\mathbf{y_0} = s_0 \sin\phi_0\mathbf{j}$$
$$= r_0 \sin\theta_0 \sin\phi_0\mathbf{j}$$

$$\mathbf{x_0} = s_0 \cos\phi_0\mathbf{i}$$
$$= r_0 \sin\theta_0 \cos\phi_0\mathbf{i}$$

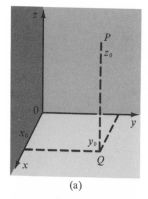

(a)

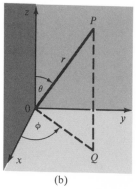

(b)

Figure 2-6 (a) Depiction of three-dimensional Cartesian coordinates. (b) Depiction of three-dimensional polar coordinates (spherical coordinates).

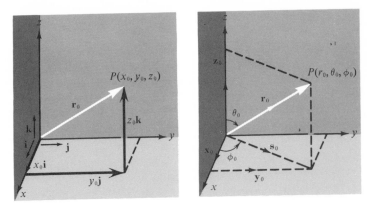

Figure 2-7   *Three-dimensional vectors.*

The components of a unit vector in the r_0 direction specified by the angles θ_0 and ϕ_0 along the three Cartesian axes are called the *direction cosines* of a vector in that direction. When multiplied by the magnitude of such a vector, they yield the magnitudes of its cartesian components. They are commonly designated by the symbol α.

$$\alpha_x = \sin\theta_0 \cos\phi_0 \qquad \alpha_y = \sin\theta_0 \sin\phi_0 \qquad \alpha_z = \cos\theta_0$$

By the Pythagorean theorem the sum of their squares is equal to unity.

This rather lengthy discussion of the location of a point in space is useful not only in accomplishing this particular purpose but also because it serves to introduce such useful concepts for the future as co-ordinate systems and vectors. Though the real physical objects to be described by a scientific theory have extent in space, and solid bodies have particular shapes as well, these can be thought of as an aggregate of closely packed points. The specification of a point, then is the first step in specifying the position of an actual object.

Location of an object in space. In the case of a two-dimensional object in a plane, an identifiable point of the object can be located by two coordinates, but the object can still rotate about the point. Hence there is an additional degree of freedom, and three numbers must be used to specify the position of the object. Two of these are the coordinates of the chosen point (x_0, y_0), and one may be an angle which indicates the direction of some identifiable axis in the body with respect to an axis in the plane. In the case of a solid in three-dimensional space (Fig. 2-8), which may for the moment be thought of as having an identifiable axis of symmetry, three coordinates will locate a chosen point on the axis in space. Two angles, e.g., θ_0 and ϕ_0 of the polar coordinate discussion,

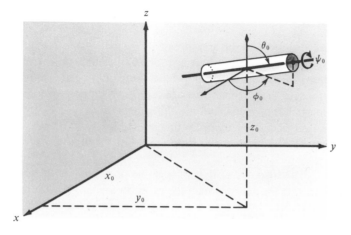

Figure 2-8 *Location of an extended body in space.*

then serve to define the inclination of the axis through the point relative to the Cartesian coordinates (or the direction cosines of the axis). Finally, the body may still be rotated about the axis without disturbing the other specifications, yielding yet another angular parameter for some line normal to the axis. Thus, six coordinates in all are required to specify the position of such a body. The axis of symmetry which was assumed for clarity is unnecessary, for the hypothetical cylinder could be firmly embodied in a solid of any shape; and when the cylinder was specified in location, the arbitrary body would be so specified as well.

Velocity and the concept of 2-4
time rate of change

All of the data that enter into the formulation of a physical description or theory derive fundamentally from such measurements of position as those mentioned in the foregoing discussion. Whether it be the relative position of two small objects that may be approximated as points in space, the position and orientation of some extended object, the height of the level of a liquid surface, or the position of a pointer on a dial, the principles that have been educed are the ones involved in making the necessary specification of this quantity to enable it to be incorporated satisfactorily into the desired description.

In general, however, the physical situation to be described is not a static one, but rather a dynamic one that changes with the time of observation. The previous section dealt with the matter of measurement without regard to when the measurement was made; one instant of time being the same as any other, the position of the hands of a clock would be unrelated to the measurement made. Actually it is more frequently the case that the very dependence of position on time is most important and is the essence of a description of the phenomena of greatest interest to us. The subject of *kinematics* is that which deals with the description of movement and the specification of positions that are themselves functions of time.

The simplest instance is that of a point or a particle which moves along a straight line. In this case the position x changes with the time, but with the time only; so x is a function of t; i.e., $x = x(t)$. As the hands of a clock move progressively around the dial through a series of values of t, the point moves along the line through a series of values of x (Fig. 2-9). The rate of covering x, or rate of motion, is called the *velocity*, and is customarily represented by the letter v. If the velocity is constant for the motion of a particle in this interval from x_b to x_a, then $(x_a - x_b)/(t_a - t_b)$ is the same all along the line, and the position of the particle within this interval may be written as:

$$(x - x_0) = \frac{(x_a - x_b)}{(t_a - t_b)} (t - t_0) = v(t - t_0)$$

If the particle started from the zero point on the line when the clock was started from zero then, $x_0 = t_0 = 0$ and $x = vt$.

Figure 2-9   *Motion of a particle in one direction.*

If the motion is not constant, which, in general, it will not be, v is itself a changing quantity and a function of the time; i.e., $v = v(t)$. Consider that the position x is specified at every instant, t, and at some time, t_1, it is at x_1; a very short time later, which will be written dt (d standing for "a small increment in"), it will be at $x_1 + dx$ (Fig. 2-10). The increment in position between the points in the spatial diagram is $(x_1 + dx) - x_1 = dx$ and the temporal interval is $(t_1 + dt) - t_1 = dt$. One may imagine that the interval, dt is steadily decreased, and in consequence, the spatial distance traversed during it becomes smaller and smaller for any ordinary type of motion. In the limit of this picture the ratio (dx/dt), whatever value it approaches, is taken as representing the velocity v at the point x_1.

The simplest situation is that of a constant velocity where the ratio $(x_a - x_b)/(t_a - t_b)$ has the same value for any choice of t_a and t_b and the corresponding positions along the line. The ratio (dx/dt) is then clearly also the same constant, and $v = dx/dt$ is the constant slope of the straight line giving the functional relation between position, x, and time, t, for the motion under consideration (Fig. 2-11).

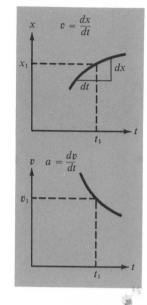

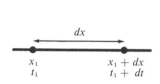

Figure 2-10   Closely spaced observations of the position of a particle moving along a line.

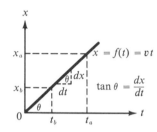

Figure 2-11   A constant velocity.

Figure 2-12   Motion with a variable velocity.

In general the motion will not proceed at a constant velocity, but v itself will be a function of the time. This means, of course, that x is a more involved function of the time than is given by the straight line relationship, but the slope of the curve or function relating x and t may be measured and represented as a function of the time (Fig. 2-12). The slope of this curve dv/dt, defined in the same manner as dx/dt, is called the *acceleration*. It is frequently written a. Of course, the acceleration may also be a function of the time, and so on.

The letter x has been chosen to represent any arbitrary single coordinate. But of course the velocity, being a directed quantity, is a vector with components generally in all three dimensions; the above discussion applies to each of the components separately or to their sum. Velocities and accelerations may be expressed in polar coordinates instead of Cartesian coordinates. This is particularly convenient in the case of rotational motion. If the motion is at a constant radius, an angle is continuously swept out by the moving point and the angular velocity $d\theta/dt$ is here designated by the letter ω (Fig. 2-13). The angular velocity ω may also be treated as a vector in the direction perpendicular to the plane in which the rotation takes place; by convention, its positive direction is that in which a right-hand screw would be advanced by the rotation.

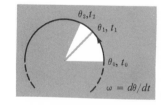

Figure 2-13   Angular motion.

The specification of x as $x(t)$ (read x of t) may be given in tabular form or in graphical form; the velocity v and acceleration a may be derived by taking differences or slopes. Such a problem is then completely specified in the terms that have been presented. The motion may take place along some tortuous curve in three dimensions and the object moving may not be a particle but an extended solid. The data may be thought of as secured by taking moving pictures of the process with two synchronized cameras so that the instantaneous position of the body can be measured at the time of exposure of each frame. The velocity and acceleration along the curve can be determined from the photographic data just as these quantities were derived for the motion along a straight line. The components of the velocity along the axes can be derived from the velocity along the curve by means of the direction cosines of the photographed trajectory:

$$v_x = v\alpha_x, \text{ etc.}$$

Finally, it may be that algebraic functional relationships between the variables x, v, a, etc., and t may be found that yield a satisfactory approximation to the experimental observations of the body's motion. Such instances are especially fruitful in the evolution of physical descriptions or theories, for they enable us to summarize the data of observation in succinct forms which are suggestive of significant relationships between the various measurable quantities. If it is possible to formulate an explicit functional relationship, one can make use of certain general mathematical results to relate the functions with their rates of change.

EXAMPLE. A ball is thrown into the air and its height, y, above the ground is periodically recorded simultaneously with the time, t, elapsed since launching. The following table of values is recorded:

t	0	0.10	0.20	0.21	0.22	0.25	0.30	0.40	0.60	1.00	sec.
y	2.000	4.05	6.0040	6.1939	6.3828	6.945	7.86	9.62	12.83	18.1	m.

This set of data is found to be in very good agreement with the formula $y = 2 + 21t - 4.9t^2$. What are the velocity and acceleration of the ball 0.2 sec. after launching?

There are three methods that could be used to solve this problem. In the first method the values from the table are used to plot a graph of y against t, as shown in Fig. 2-14. The slope of the graph at $t = 0.2$ is then the velocity v at this time. To calculate acceleration, it is first necessary to calculate the velocity thus for several times in the vicinity of $t = 0.2$, and then to plot v against t and again find the slope.

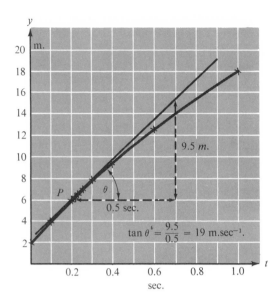

Figure 2-14 *Vertical displacement y in meters is plotted against time t in seconds. The
vertical velocity at time t = 0.2 sec. is the slope
of the graph at the point P. To the accuracy of
the graph, this is seen to be 19 m.sec.⁻¹.*

The second method is to estimate the ratio dy/dt for successively
smaller time intervals, dt, and thus estimate the limit of this ratio, which
is the instantaneous velocity v. Thus

$$\frac{y_{1.0} - y_{0.2}}{1.0 - 0.2} = 15.1 \qquad \frac{y_{0.6} - y_{0.2}}{0.6 - 0.2} = 17.1 \qquad \frac{y_{0.4} - y_{0.2}}{0.4 - 0.2} = 18.1$$

$$\frac{y_{0.3} - y_{0.2}}{0.3 - 0.2} = 18.6 \qquad \frac{y_{0.25} - y_{0.20}}{0.25 - 0.20} = 18.82 \qquad \frac{y_{0.22} - y_{0.20}}{0.22 - 0.20} = 18.94$$

$$\frac{y_{0.21} - y_{0.20}}{0.21 - 0.20} = 18.99$$

and apparently the limit $v = dy/dt \approx 19.0$. To find the acceleration
would then require finding the limit of dv/dt in a similar manner.

Such methods are useful when only a tabulated relationship between
y and t is known. But when an explicit functional relationship has
been determined, neither of these two methods would be used. The
faster, more accurate, and recommended method of solution is taken
up in Sect. 2-5.

2-5 Mathematical note; relation between a function and its rate of change

It is both interesting and useful to examine a general relationship that exists between the function of a variable, say t, and the function of t given by the rate at which the initial function changes with t. In terms of our definition of v as dx/dt, this is a consideration of the relation between x as a function of t and v as a function of t. It will be shown that if perpendiculars are dropped to the t axis from two points on the curve representing the dependence of v on t, then the area thus enclosed is equal to the difference in the values of x (of the curve of x as a function of t) corresponding to the two values of t chosen for dropping the perpendiculars.

The situation is represented in Fig. 2-15. Given the two figures, it is evident that the hatched area A can be thought of as approaching the sum of the vertical strips of area, $v_0(t_1 - t_0)$, $v_1(t_2 - t_1)$, $v_2(t_3 - t_2)$ etc., on through $v_{n-1}(t_n - t_{n-1})$, as the time intervals become smaller and smaller. If one writes dt for the equal time intervals, $(t_1 - t_0)$, $(t_2 - t_1)$, etc.,

$$A = v_0\, dt + v_1\, dt + v_2\, dt + \cdots\cdots v_{n-1}\, dt$$

Since by definition:

$$v = \frac{dx}{dt} = \frac{x(t + dt) - x(t)}{dt}$$

then:

$$v_0\, dt = x(t_0 + dt) - x(t_0) = x(t_1) - x(t_0)$$
$$v_1\, dt = x(t_1 + dt) - x(t_1) = x(t_2) - x(t_1)$$
$$v_2\, dt = x(t_2 + dt) - x(t_2) = x(t_3) - x(t_2)$$

etc. to

$$v_{n-1}\, dt = x(t_{n-1} + dt) - x(t_{n-1}) = x(t_n) - x(t_{n-1})$$

The sum of terms in the left-hand column is equal to A; when the right-hand column is added, the terms cancel in pairs except for the first and last: namely, $x(t_n)$ or x_n and $x(t_0)$ or x_0. Thus the area, A, under the rate curve between t_0 and t_n is equal to the difference in the ordinates corresponding to the values of t of the original function x.

$$A = x_n - x_0$$

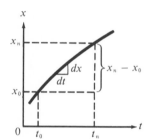

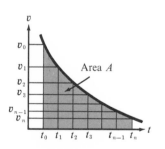

Figure 2-15 *Equality between* $x_n - x_0$ *and the area under the rate curve.*

This general conclusion is useful in many physical situations, helping us to envision the relation between functions, one of which represents the rate at which another changes as the independent variable assumes a range of values. If the function is an explicit one in an algebraic or trigonometric form, or, in general, if it can be said to be "analytic," equations embodying the above conclusion, which was demonstrated graphically in the accompanying figure, may be written.

Thus if x, for instance, may be represented as a power series of t, the rate of change of each term may be set down explicitly. Let us say: $x = t^n$, where n is a number. At some time later $(t + dt)$, x will become $(x + dx)$. Then by the binomial expansion in powers of the small quantity dt:

$$(x + dx) = (t + dt)^n = t^n \left(1 + \frac{dt}{t}\right)^n$$

$$= t^n \left[1 + n\frac{dt}{t} + \frac{n(n-1)}{2}\left(\frac{dt}{t}\right)^2 + \cdots \cdots\right]$$

and:

$$v = \frac{dx}{dt} = \frac{(x + dx) - x}{dt}$$

$$= nt^{n-1} + \frac{n(n-1)}{2} t^{n-2} dt + \cdots \cdots$$

As dt approaches infinitesimally small values, the terms beyond the first —all of which contain dt—vanish. Thus:

$$\text{if} \quad x = t^n \quad \text{then} \quad v = dx/dt = nt^{n-1}$$

Alternatively, of course, v could be given as a power or a series of power terms in t, and the area under this curve would be given by the end point ordinate difference for the corresponding x. If m is written for $(n - 1)$ in the preceding nomenclature, and the constant coefficient taken as unity for v, the coefficient of x becomes $1/(m + 1)$ and the above relation appears equivalently as follows:

$$v = t^m \quad \text{and} \quad x = \frac{1}{m + 1} t^{m+1}$$

Similar simple closed expressions relating a function and its rate of change, or the area under one curve and the end point ordinates of another can be obtained for such functions as the trigonometric sine and cosine functions or logarithmic and exponential functions.

EXAMPLE. Let us return to the problem given in Sect. 2-4; a vertical displacement y is given as a function of the time t: $y = 2 + 21t - 4.9t^2$, and it is required to find the velocity and acceleration at time $t = 0.2$, y being in meters and t in seconds.

The rate of change of a sum is the sum of the rates of change of each of the components. Thus

$$\frac{dy}{dt} = \frac{d(2 + 21t - 4.9t^2)}{dt} = \frac{d(2)}{dt} + \frac{d(21t)}{dt} - \frac{d(4.9t^2)}{dt}$$

$$= 0 + 21 - 9.8t$$

Thus at time $t = 0.2$, the velocity

$$v = dy/dt = 21 - 9.8(0.2) = 19.04 \text{ meter} \cdot \text{second}^{-1}$$

Similarly the acceleration a is found directly from the velocity expression:

$$a = \frac{dv}{dt} = \frac{d(21 - 9.8t)}{dt} = -9.8 \text{ meter} \cdot \text{second}^{-2}$$

Thus the acceleration is a constant 9.8 meter·second^{-2} in the downward (negative y) direction.

EXAMPLE. Water flows from a pipe line into a storage reservoir at an ever-increasing rate given by: $dV/dt = t^3/10000 + 14$, where V represents the volume of water in cubic meters and t the time in seconds. How much water is there in the reservoir after 40 seconds?

Using the rule given above for finding a quantity when given its rate of change, the volume is

$$V = \frac{t^4}{40000} + 14t + C$$

where C is an unknown constant. The reason for the appearance of this unknown constant is that the rate of change of any constant is zero; and hence, when given only the rate of change of a function, it is impossible to determine what, if any, constant term might have appeared in the original function. A moment of reflection, however, will disclose that, in the above situation, C represents the volume of water initially in the reservoir at time $t = 0$. This must obviously be known if the problem is to be solved. If the reservoir was initially empty, then $C = 0$ and

$$V = \frac{t^4}{40000} + 14t$$

which for $t = 40$ gives $V = 256 + 560 = 816$ m³. In such calculations the unknown constants will always be calculable from the initial conditions or the problem will be avoided, for example, by asking for the increase in volume.

Further reading:

Essen, L., "Accurate Measurement of Time," *Physics Today*, vol. 13, No. 7, p. 26 (1960).

Hudson, G. E., "Of Time and the Atom," *Physics Today*, vol. 18, No. 8, p. 34 (1965).

Lyons, H., "Atomic Clocks," *Scientific American*, vol. 196, No. 2, p. 71 (1957).

Problems

2-1 A car drives 10,000 m. in a direction 30° East of North. How far East and how far North has it travelled?

2-2 A dog runs North for 1 mi., then Southeast for 10 mi., and finally East for 1 mi.
(a) Sketch his path as a series of vectors.
(b) How many miles has he run?
(c) How far is he from his starting point? Assume $\sin 45° = \cos 45° = 0.7$.
(d) To go straight back to his starting point he must head at an angle θ West of North, where $\tan \theta = $?
$$\sin \theta = \text{?}$$
$$\cos \theta = \text{?}$$
(e) If he trots straight back at $\frac{5}{6}$ his running speed, will his return journey take more time than, less time than, or the same time as his run?

2-3 An object undergoes three displacements in a plane, r_1, r_2 and r_3, given by:
$$r_1 = \quad 2i - 3j$$
$$r_2 = -3i + 4j$$
$$r_3 = \quad i - 2j$$
Find its final position by adding the vectors any way you like.

2-4 A man is lost in a rectangular maze. He walks North for 5 m., East for 10 m., North for 2 m., West for 12 m., South for 20 m., East for 4 m., North for 6 m., East for 8 m., North for 5 m., West for 4 m., North for 2 m., East for 4 m., and finally North for 3 m. Using unit vectors i and j of length 1 m. in the East and North directions respectively, the exit is in a direction $(10i + 3j)$ from the man's starting position. Does the man reach the exit?

2-5 If one corner of a cube is taken as the origin of a rectangular coordinate system and three edges of the cube lie along the *x*, *y*, and *z* axes respectively, then taking unit vectors **i**, **j** and **k** in the *x*, *y* and *z* directions respectively, give the position vectors of the remaining seven corners of the cube. Take the length of a side as 2 units.

2-6 Two planes execute manoeuvers. At one instant, one plane is 300 m. directly above the other. The upper plane flies North for 400 m., West for 500 m., dives vertically 300 m. and then heads South. The lower plane in the same time flies East for 300 m., North for 600 m., West for 800 m. and then heads North. Show whether the planes are on a collision course. Take East as the *x* direction, North as the *y* direction and vertically up as the *z* direction, and use unit vectors **i**, **j** and **k** of length 100 m. Thus if the lower plane starts at the origin, then the upper plane starts with a displacement 3**k**.

2-7 The polar coordinates of a point are $(r, \theta, \phi) = (8, 30°, 45°)$. Find the Cartesian coordinates of the same point.

2-8 A particle has velocity components $v_x = 4$ m.sec.$^{-1}$, $v_y = -3$ m.sec.$^{-1}$ and $v_z = -13$ m.sec.$^{-1}$. What is the magnitude of its resultant velocity?

2-9 Two particles are ejected simultaneously from the same point, one with a constant velocity in the *y* direction of 40 m.sec.$^{-1}$ and the other with a constant velocity in the *x* direction of -30 m.sec.$^{-1}$. What is the separation distance of the two particles 10 sec. after ejection? What then is the angle between the *x* axis and the line joining the two particles? (Express the angle as a tangent.)

2-10 Two particles start simultaneously from rest at different points in the same *x*–*y* plane, one with a constant acceleration in the *y* direction of 40 m.sec.$^{-2}$ and the other with a constant acceleration in the *x* direction of -30 m.sec.$^{-2}$. What is the magnitude of the relative velocity of the two particles after 10 sec.? What angle does this relative velocity vector then make with the *x* axis? (Express the angle as a tangent.) Would the answers be different if the particles did not start in the same *x*–*y* plane?

2-11 A car races around a 200 m. diameter circular track with a constant angular velocity of 1.0 ra.sec.$^{-1}$. A second car, initially half a lap behind the first, is travelling with a constant angular velocity of 1.2 ra.sec.$^{-1}$. What is their angular separation after 5.7 sec.? What is their separation in meters around the track? Take $\pi = 3.14$.

2-12 A racing car moves at such a rate that its distance from the start in meters is always equal to ten times (the time elapsed in seconds)^2; i.e., $x = 10t^2$. What is the car's velocity and acceleration
(a) at the start?
(b) after 5 sec.?

2-13 As a spherical balloon is inflated, its radius *r* steadily increases. Show that its volume increases at $\frac{1}{2}r$ times the rate of increase of the surface area.

Hint: The volume of a sphere is $V = (\frac{4}{3})\pi r^3$.

The surface area of a sphere is $A = 4\pi r^2$.

Find the rate of increase of each with respect to the common variable r.

2-14 A rocket accelerates from a stationary start so that its velocity in meter seconds^{-1} is always equal to $10t^3$ after an elapsed time of t seconds.

(a) Find its position ⎫

(b) Find its velocity ⎬ 8 sec. after starting.

(c) Find its acceleration ⎭

2-15 $y = 7x^{12} + 9x^7 + x^5 - 4x^3 + 8$

(a) Find $\dfrac{dy}{dx}$

(b) Find z such that $\dfrac{dz}{dx} = y$.

3 The concepts of force and momentum and the relationship between them

3-1 Force and its measurement

The concept of *force*, as that which tends to bring about or change the motion of material things, comes very basically and intuitively from the kinesthetic experiences that result from muscular efforts—the pushing and pulling that move things about. In general, the effort that must be exerted increases with the size of the object, or more specifically with what has come to be called its *weight*. Weights of objects are compared by means of a balance, and for objects composed of the same material the weight is proportional to the size or volume. Man's ingenuity has for eons been exercised in the technology of moving weighty or massive objects. Such expedients as wedges, rollers, levers and screws were devised to facilitate the application of man's anatomical characteristics and musculature to moving objects of various sizes, shapes and weights.

Methods of comparison of forces on the basis of muscular sensation are of course scientifically unsatisfactory. They are qualitative rather than quantitative, and lack that objectivity upon which general acceptance must be based. However, the tendency for all bodies to fall and come to rest on the surface of the earth is appreciated even by animals. It was early used to compare weights, and hence indirectly to provide comparisons of forces. The commonest device for making these comparisons is the beam balance (Fig. 3-1), which consists of an arm resting stably upon a fulcrum such that comparatively free rotation may take place in a vertical plane about this support. The arm or beam is generally first adjusted so that it is itself in balance. The weight of objects may be compared by suspending two objects, one on the right and the other on the left of the fulcrum, so that the beam is again in balance. The weight of a third object is said to be equal to the weight of one of the two initially suspended objects if, when it is substituted for it, the equilibrium is undisturbed. Such manipulations may also be used to demonstrate the principle of the lever, or of moments; namely, that there is no tendency for a rotation of the beam about the fulcrum if the sum of the products of the weights and their distances from the fulcrum (taken positive along one arm and negative along the other, since the tendency to rotate is in opposite directions) is zero.

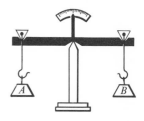

Figure 3-1 *Beam balance.*

Spring balances (Fig. 3-2) may also be used for comparison of weights, for the extension of a spring depends upon the magnitude of the weight that is suspended from it. Equal weights extend a spring by equal amounts. If the lower end of the spring is fitted with a pointer moving over a vertical scale, the displacement itself may be used as a fairly accurate measurement of the weight. The force acting upon weights under which these various equilibrium configurations are brought about is derived from the tendency of bodies to move downward toward the earth. This force is said to be gravitational, or due to the gravitational attraction of the earth. In the instance of the beam balance such forces are compared with one another. In the instance of the spring balance they are opposed by forces that arise from the distortion of the spring. The latter are found to depend upon many factors: the relative elongation, the material of the spring and its previous history, the temperature, etc. Hence, as a method of precise and reliable comparison, the spring is generally inferior to the beam balance.

The basic data entering our description of physical phenomena are the positions of objects and the rates of change of these positions. Thus forces, which are evidenced by their tendency to displace objects, provide a useful and unifying concept immediately applicable over a wide field of experience. The particular physical circumstances under which forces are observed to hold objects in static equilibrium or to move them about have lead us to differentiate among the causes of forces and to adopt assumptions regarding their nature and genesis. The various categories into which forces were divided, by the persons who first studied them and observed their effects, have tended to establish the historical categories of physical science, or "natural philosophy" as it was first called. Forces occurring between relatively rigid bodies are of the *contact type*, so called because they appear to be exerted over

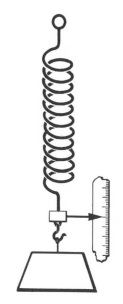

Figure 3-2 *Spring balance.*

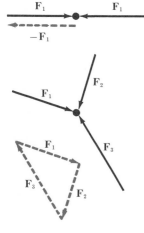

$$F_1 + F_2 + F_3 = 0$$

Figure 3-3 *Forces in static equilibrium.*

those areas where objects touch one another. Internal *elastic forces* arise as a result of the distortion of relatively rigid bodies. They also generally become evident at points of contact with other bodies. Forces that tend to oppose movement of one contact area over another are called *frictional forces*. There are internal forces (in addition to the elastic ones) opposing the distortion of relatively rigid bodies which are similar in nature to frictional forces, and are spoken of as *internal frictional forces*. The forces that support a ship or any body immersed in a fluid are known as *buoyant forces*. The *gravitational force* that tends to draw massive bodies together and thus to produce a downward pull on bodies near the surface of the earth has already been mentioned. There are also forces, which will be referred to later, that are said to be of *electrical* or *electromagnetic* nature. There are, as well, forces we do not identify in the case of large bodies, but which we must come to recognize as operative in atomic and nuclear processes. These will be described in connection with the structure of atoms and nuclei. The most immediately familiar forces arising in our own muscles have their genesis in chemical processes; although they may be classed as *muscular* or *biological forces* in this boundary area between the physical and biological sciences, a more fundamental description of them is given in terms of the atomic processes that take place in living tissue.

Conventionally, an arrow representing in magnitude and direction a force of any nature that is applied to a particle of matter or to a point of an extended body is called a vector. A force of equal magnitude but opposite direction, i.e., an oppositely directed arrow (or vector) of equal length applied to the same particle or point will just annul the first, and the combination represents no net force or no tendency for motion to ensue. Thus, the resultant of the two arrows is zero; as the particle or body remains at rest, the situation is said to be static. Clearly, any number of arrows can be placed end to end sequentially in space (Fig. 3-3); and if they are of the right length and disposed in a particular way, they can form a closed figure, with the head of the last arrow lying on the origin of the first. Here again, if the arrows represent forces, there would be no net force, no motion would take place, and the situation would be static. In the same way many different forces of various magnitudes and directions could be applied to different points of an extended body (Fig. 3-4); e.g., a balance beam; and if they were properly chosen and suitably disposed relative to one another, no tendency to rotate would ensue.

The *moment* of force, which gives rise to a tendency to rotate, is the product of the magnitude of the force and the length of the perpendicular from its line of action to the point at which the moment is taken. The direction of the moment, or the sense of rotation, is clearly about an axis perpendicular to the plane of the force and the point, in the sense indicated by the force vector. The condition for there being no tendency for an extended body to rotate is that the sum of the vector moments about any point be zero.

Thus, if $\mathbf{F}_1, \mathbf{F}_2, \mathbf{F}_3$, etc. are the vectors representing all the forces being applied, the condition that there shall be no translational motion due to them is that the sum $\mathbf{F}_1 + \mathbf{F}_2 + \mathbf{F}_3 \ldots = 0$. This is sometimes written more briefly as:

$$\sum \mathbf{F}_i = 0$$

where $\sum$ is the greek letter "sigma," standing for sum, and i is an index letter standing for all the individual designating numbers 1, 2, 3, etc. Similarly, the condition that an extended solid body should not rotate under the influence of a series of forces giving rise to the moments $\mathbf{T}_1$, $\mathbf{T}_2$, $\mathbf{T}_3$, etc., about a point is that:

$$\mathbf{T}_1 + \mathbf{T}_2 + \mathbf{T}_3 + \cdots = 0 \qquad \text{or} \qquad \sum \mathbf{T}_i = 0$$

where $\mathbf{T}$ is the Greek letter "tau." In general, of course, the forces from various sources that impinge on a body do not produce static equilibrium, but rather contribute to a sum, or resultant, which net force and moment give rise to translational and rotational motion.

EXAMPLE. A special beam balance is constructed with one arm twice the length of the other (Fig. 3-5). Assuming the beam itself to be weightless, calculate the weight that must be applied to the end of the longer arm in order to balance a weight force of 4 units at the end of the shorter arm. Also calculate the force of the supporting column on the beam and the force of the beam on this column.

If the length of the shorter arm is l, then the total clockwise moment or torque about the pivot is $(F_2 2l - F_1 l)$ where F_1 is 4 and F_2 is to be found. When the beam is balanced, this torque is zero and hence

$$F_2 2l = F_1 l$$

therefore

$$F_2 = \frac{F_1 l}{2l} = \frac{F_1}{2} = 2$$

Thus the required force on the longer arm is *2 units*. If F_3 is the upward force of the column on the beam, then this must exactly balance the downward forces—if the beam is not to move vertically. Hence

$$F_3 = F_1 + F_2$$

Thus the column provides an upward force of *6 units* on the beam. This force F_3 is a reaction to the equal but oppositely directed force F_4 that the beam exerts on the column.

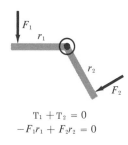

$$T_1 + T_2 = 0$$
$$-F_1 r_1 + F_2 r_2 = 0$$

Figure 3-4 *Moments of forces in static equilibrium.*

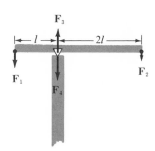

Figure 3-5 *Beam balance with unequal arms. For no rotation, $F_2 2l - F_1 l = 0$. For no displacement, $F_1 + F_2 - F_3 = 0$. Active and reactive forces $F_3 = F_4$.*

3-2 The concepts of mass and momentum; Galileo and Newton

The extension of these concepts to the motion of bodies under the influence of forces, which is the subject called *dynamics*, was made about three hundred years ago by Galileo Galilei (1564-1642) and Isaac Newton (1642-1727). Galileo of Pisa, who is best known popularly for his persecution for supporting the Copernican theory of the solar system (in which the earth and the planets are recognized as bodies circulating about the sun), was the first to recognize certain of the significant concepts of dynamics such as momentum.

To define the quantities of dynamics in an entirely satisfactory way one must anticipate certain observations that were not familiar to Galileo. If one makes precise measurements of the weight of an object, using the extension of a spring balance as observed at a number of different locations over the surface of the earth, it is found that the extension of the balance and hence the force attracting the body toward the earth varies somewhat from place to place. This is due to irregularities in the shape of the earth's surface and to variations in the material composing the earth's crust. However, this variation in downward force is found to be the same for all samples of any matter whatever; hence, weights compared with a beam balance always retain their same relationship to one another. On the other hand, it is intuitively reasonable and satisfying to think of an object as possessing an invariant property regardless of its location. Indeed objects do possess such a property: it is called *mass* and may be thought of as the amount of matter that is present. Two objects of the same mass exhibit the same weight on any balance at one location and are measured as producing the same force on the arm of a beam balance at any location. They will each extend a spring balance by equal amounts, even though this amount will vary with location.

The balance evidently provides an instrument for the intercomparison of masses and their measurement in terms of a standard. Though it is now known that matter is particulate, and is composed of atoms which would provide natural units of mass, this knowledge was unavailable when standards of mass were chosen; until very recently techniques of high precision were not available for the comparison of atomic masses. So, as in the cases of the other basic quantities length and time, an arbitrary standard of mass, the *kilogram* (kg.), was chosen. This standard took the form of a platinum cylinder maintained in the same reference laboratory as the standard meter. It weighs about as much as a cube of water 1/10 meter on a side, and is equivalent to about 2.2 pounds in the English measure of weight.

The *momentum* of a body, which is a very useful concept that we owe to Galileo, is defined as the product of the mass m and the velocity v of the body. A region of space in which forces of a given kind are found to act on bodies in that region is often called a *field*. Galileo observed the behavior of bodies in the gravitational field of the earth; or in other words, he observed the motion of bodies near the surface of the earth under the influence of the gravitational force operative between them and the earth. Galileo found that freely falling bodies acquired velocities proportional to their times of fall, i.e., v is proportional to t, or in the form of an equation: $v = at$, where the acceleration a is a constant, and in the case of free gravitational fall the constant a is generally written as g. Galileo found that the acceleration of a freely falling body depends on its size, shape, or material only to an extent that can be readily accounted for by the fact that air is a viscous fluid tending to retard motion taking place within it. Relative to gravitational forces, the viscous forces are much greater for objects of low density (paper, feathers, or balls of fluff) than for dense objects (rock, metal). Aside from this consideration, however, all freely falling bodies accelerate at the same rate g; this can be shown to be the case by evacuating the air from a region where the experiment is conducted.

Galileo likewise observed that an object thrown through the air, or a projectile shot from a crossbow or gun tends to follow a path that can be described by a simple algebraic functional relation between the vertical and horizontal coordinates, known as a *parabola* (Fig. 3-6). A

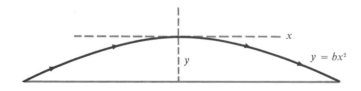

Figure 3-6   *Parabolic path of a projectile.*

parabola is a plane curve described by the cartesian equation $y = bx^2$, where b is a constant. Thus, neglecting air friction, the vertical coordinate y may be represented by a constant times the square of the horizontal coordinate x, if the origin of the coordinate system is taken at the point of greatest height to which the object arises. Galileo also recognized the appearance of a centrifugal type of force on rotating bodies;

he observed the simple harmonic motion of the swaying chandelier in the Cathedral of Pisa; and, according to his biographer Viviani, used the celebrated leaning tower in that city for the conduct of his experiments on falling bodies.

Newton extended, generalized and simplified the ideas developed by Galileo and integrated them with the formulation of the laws of planetary motion stated by Kepler on the basis of the astronomical observations of Tycho Brahe. The result was the concept of *inertia*—the tendency for a body to remain at rest or in a state of rectilinear motion with a constant velocity unless acted on by an external force. Another achievement of Newton was the formulation of the general dynamical law governing the motion of matter acted on by any forces. This states that the rate of change of momentum of a body is proportional to the net external force acting upon it; or, if the units are so chosen, the rate of change of momentum is equal to this force. This general law is seen to include the above concept of inertia as a particular case in which the net external force is zero.

Newton's third great contribution was his recognition of the form of the dependence of the gravitational force between two bodies upon the masses of these bodies and upon their separation. He found that motion of bodies near the surface of the earth, of the moon orbiting around it, and also of the earth and planets orbiting around the sun can all be described with great precision if the gravitational force is: (1) proportional to the masses of the attracting bodies; (2) inversely proportional to the square of their separation; and (3) directed along the line joining the bodies in a way representing an attraction between them. Further description of the general law of gravitation will be postponed until the consideration of planetary motion.

Newton's law of motion, which states that the force acting on a body is equal to the rate of change of its momentum, may be written symbolically as follows:

$$\mathbf{F} = \frac{d(m\mathbf{v})}{dt}$$

where $\mathbf{v}$ is the vector velocity of magnitude v. If the mass is constant and does not change with the time, $d(m\mathbf{v})$ is the same as $m(d\mathbf{v})$ and:

$$\mathbf{F} = m\frac{d\mathbf{v}}{dt} = m\mathbf{a}$$

where $\mathbf{a}$ is the vector acceleration and $\mathbf{F}$ is the net external force vector. The units, as may be seen by noting the nature of the quantities on the right-hand side of the equation, are kg.m.sec.$^{-2}$ which is abbreviated to the unit force, called the *Newton* (N.). The unit Newton is simply a shortened way of writing kg.m.sec^{-2}. A force of 1 Newton, when applied to a mass of 1 kg., will change its velocity at the rate of 1 m. per sec. per sec.

EXAMPLE. A sideways force of 10 Newtons is applied to a 4 kg. block resting on a smooth table (Fig. 3-7). What is the resultant acceleration of the block, and what is its momentum after 5 seconds?

The mass being constant, Newton's law may be written $F = ma$.

Hence: $$a = F/m = 10/4 = 2.5$$

The force F and mass m were expressed in mks units and hence the acceleration a, also in these units, will be 2.5 m.sec^{-2}. The momentum may be found by using the constant acceleration above to find the velocity, or by rewriting Newton's law:

$$F = \frac{d(mv)}{dt}$$

Since this rate of increase of momentum is here a constant, the total increase in momentum will evidently be Ft, where t is the time elapsed since the force was first applied. Thus, after a time $t = 5$, the momentum will be

$$mv = Ft = 10 \times 5 = 50$$

That is, the momentum after 5 sec. will be 50 kg.m.sec.$^{-1}$.

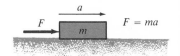

Figure 3-7 *A constant force F acting on a block of mass m produces an acceleration a in the direction of the force, where* $F = ma$.

Motion under the force of gravity at the earth's surface 3-3

Free fall. The case of a freely falling body, neglecting air friction, is readily described in terms of these concepts. The constant rate of acceleration downwards, which is the local gravitational constant, is the same for all bodies and is represented by the letter g. This quantity, as has been noted earlier, is not of precisely the same numerical value for all points on the earth's surface, because of the earth's rotation and of its irregular shape and heterogeneous composition. It is, for instance, a maximum in northern Norway, where the value is 9.83 m.sec.$^{-2}$, and a minimum in East Africa, where its value is 9.77 m.sec.$^{-2}$; 9.8 m.sec.$^{-2}$ is convenient to take as an approximate average value.

If a body of any mass is dropped from rest it acquires, at the end of a time t, a velocity of magnitude gt in a downward direction. Since we will adopt the convention of labelling all vertical axes in the upward direction positive, the above velocity at time t will be denoted by $-gt$. If thrown upward with a velocity v_0, the velocity after t seconds will be $v_0 - gt$. If thrown downward, the same expression will serve, but v_0, the initial velocity in the upward direction, will then be negative (Fig. 3-8).

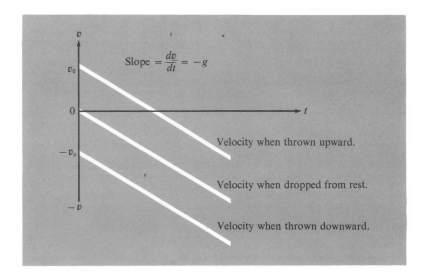

Figure 3-8   *Velocity as a function of time of free fall.*

If y is the coordinate axis chosen vertically upward, the position above the zero on this axis reached by the body at any time is equal to y_0, the position from which it starts at the zero of time when the clock is started, plus the distance traversed under the constant acceleration $-g$. Since v is the rate at which y changes, the considerations in the mathematical note of the preceding chapter pertaining to the relation between a function and its rate of change show that the difference between y at the time t and y_0 at the time $t = 0$ is equal to the area between the curve ($y = v_0 - gt$) and the axis of t bounded by the values $t = 0$ and $t = t$. Fig. 3-9 shows the situation graphically, or using the general algebraic expression from the preceding chapter ($v = t^m$ then $x = t^{m+1}/[m + 1]$), since:

$$v = v_0 - gt$$

$$(y - y_0) = v_0 t - \tfrac{1}{2}gt^2$$

If the body is dropped from rest, $v_0 = 0$; or if the body is thrown downward, v_0 is negative. In either case the magnitude of $(y - y_0)$ decreases parabolically, getting more negative with time. If the body is thrown upward, v_0 is positive, and v then becomes zero at the time $t = v_0/g$, which represents the greatest positive value achieved by $(y - y_0)$. On substituting this value of t in the equation for $(y - y_0)$, this maximum height of rise is seen to be $v_0{}^2/2g$. At the time $t = 2v_0/g$, $(y - y_0)$ is again zero, and from thereon it decreases steadily as the body falls past the point from which it was thrown with an ever-increasing velocity.

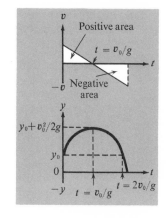

Figure 3-9 *v and y as functions of t for free fall.*

EXAMPLE. A man jumps horizontally out of a fifth floor window and lands in a fireman's net held at the level of the first floor windows. Assuming a height of 4 m. per floor, how long does it take the man to reach the net? What is his velocity on reaching the net? Could he decrease this velocity by jumping out of the window in an upward direction?

The initial velocity v_0 is zero here, and so is the final displacement y if distances are measured from the net. Hence it is possible to write:

$$y_0 = \tfrac{1}{2}gt^2$$

where y_0, the initial displacement, is 16 m. and g is 9.8 m.sec.$^{-2}$. Hence the time is:

$$t = \sqrt{2y_0/g} = \sqrt{32/9.8} = 1.8$$

Thus the man's fall takes 1.8 sec. His final velocity is given by:

$$v = v_0 - gt = -gt$$
$$= -9.8 \times 1.8 = -18$$

That is, his velocity on reaching the net is 18 m.sec.$^{-1}$, the negative sign merely indicating the downward direction. If the man were to jump in an upward direction, his initial trajectory would take him up a short distance and then, continually accelerating downward, he would fall back past his window, this time with a downward velocity equal to his initial upward velocity. It is apparent, then, that his velocity on reaching the net would be greater, not less, than if he had jumped horizontally out of his window.

Projectile. The first illustration was concerned with motion in the vertical direction only. In the case of a projectile, or a body thrown in an arbitrary direction, there will be a component of the initial velocity given it that is parallel to the surface of the earth. There is no gravitational force in this direction, and, if air viscosity and winds are neglected, the acceleration parallel to the earth's surface, say in the x direction, is zero. Thus, the velocity in that direction remains constant and equal to the initial x-velocity component customarily written v_{x0}. The distance traversed along the horizontal axis from the arbitrary starting point x_0 is then $(x - x_0) = v_{x0}t$. The complete statements for the accelerations, velocities and positions of a projectile, at a time t from the initial position (x_0, y_0) with the initial velocity components (v_{x0}, v_{y0}) are then:

	x direction	y direction
acceleration	$a_x = 0$	$a_y = -g$
velocity	$v_x = v_{x0}$	$v_y = v_{y0} - gt$
position	$x = x_0 + v_{x0}t$	$y = y_0 + v_{y0}t - \frac{1}{2}gt^2$

The graphical depiction of these functions of t presents nothing new; but the independent variable t may be eliminated between x and y, to display y as a function of x and the initial velocities, which is done in Fig. 3-10. The curve $y(x)$ is called the trajectory of a projectile.

$$(y - y_0) = \frac{v_{y0}}{v_{x0}}(x - x_0) - \frac{g}{2v_{x0}{}^2}(x - x_0)^2$$

$$(v_y - v_{y0}) = -\frac{g}{v_{x0}}(x - x_0)$$

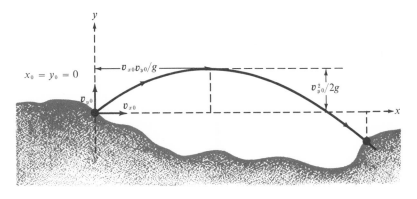

Figure 3-10 *Projectile trajectory.*

EXAMPLE. Neglecting the effects of air resistance, at what inclination should a ball be kicked or thrown in order to achieve the maximum possible range for a given initial velocity?

The last equation derived above expresses the range in terms of the velocities:

$$x - x_0 = \frac{v_{x0}}{g}(v_{y0} - v_y)$$

where, because of symmetry, the downward velocity $-v_y$ on landing must equal the initial upward velocity v_{y0}. Thus $v_{y0} - v_y = 2v_{y0}$ and:

$$(x - x_0) = \frac{2v_{x0}v_{y0}}{g}$$

Relating the initial velocity v_0 to its x and y components and to the inclination θ,

$$v_{x0} = v_0 \cos \theta \qquad \text{and} \qquad v_{y0} = v_0 \sin \theta$$

$$(x - x_0) = 2 \frac{v_0{}^2}{g} \cos \theta \sin \theta$$

$$= \frac{v_0{}^2}{g} \sin 2\theta$$

according to the trigonometric identity: $\sin 2\theta = 2 \sin \theta \cos \theta$. Hence the range $(x - x_0)$ is a maximum when $\sin 2\theta$ is a maximum, that is when 2θ is $90°$ and the inclination θ is $45°$.

EXAMPLE. A boy fires a stone from a slingshot directly at a monkey in a tree who simultaneously drops a coconut. The boy does not allow for any gravitational effects. How close to the coconut does the stone pass?

The important point in this problem is that since the stone and the coconut are launched simultaneously, they will travel for the same time t until the stone crosses the path of the coconut. This time is independent of any vertical acceleration, depending only on the original horizontal component of the stone's velocity and the horizontal distance between the boy and the monkey. Thus, if there were no gravitational force, the height of the stone when it hit the monkey would be

$$y = v_{y0}t$$

where v_{y0} is the initial vertical component of velocity and t is the time taken to travel the horizontal distance between the boy and the monkey. Considering now the effect of gravity, the height of the stone at the same time t will be

$$y = v_{y0}t - \tfrac{1}{2}gt^2$$

a height $\tfrac{1}{2}gt^2$ below the monkey. The coconut meanwhile will have fallen a distance $\tfrac{1}{2}gt^2$, its initial velocity being zero. Thus the stone will hit the coconut.

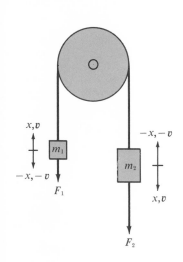

x, v

$-x, -v$

m_1

F_1

$-x, -v$

m_2

x, v

F_2

Figure 3-11 *Atwood's ma-chine.*

EXAMPLE. *Weights over a pulley* (*Atwood's Machine*). A further illustration of motion under the force of gravity which presents some novel points comes from considering the motion of two masses held together by a string or rope passing over a light pulley (Fig. 3-11). The force of gravity on each mass keeps the rope taut, and the rope itself keeps the two masses at a constant distance from one another so that they must move as a single unit. The rope is considered to be so light that its mass is negligible in comparison with those on either end, and the pulley so small and light that the force necessary to set it into rotation can be neglected. In short, the rope simply makes one mass move up at the same rate at which the other moves down; and the pulley simply reverses the sense of the forces, accelerations, velocities and displacements for one mass relative to the other.

The forces $F_1 = m_1 g$ and $F_2 = m_2 g$, while directed in the same sense, namely toward the earth, are oppositely directed with respect to the rope. The net or resultant force tending to move one mass down and the other up is:

$$F = F_2 - F_1 = (m_2 - m_1)g$$

By the definition of force as the rate at which the momentum changes:

$$F = (m_1 + m_2)\frac{dv}{dt}$$

Therefore, the rate at which the velocity of the masses changes, one down and the other up, is:

$$\frac{dv}{dt} = \frac{m_2 - m_1}{m_2 + m_1}g$$

This is clearly a constant which may be written a, and which is less than g in the ratio $(m_2 - m_1)/(m_2 + m_1)$. The acceleration g is a little large to measure easily by timing a falling mass with a stop watch; but Atwood's machine readily permits timing a motion accelerated at the much lesser rate a, whereby one can infer the value of g from the masses involved.

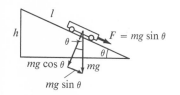

l

h

θ

θ

$F = mg \sin \theta$

$mg \cos \theta$

mg

$mg \sin \theta$

Figure 3-12 *Body on an in-clined plane.*

EXAMPLE. *The inclined plane.* Another illustration of the motion of a body under the influence of gravity is that of a mass placed upon a slope, or an inclined plane. Here it is somewhat more difficult to reduce the obscuring effects of incidental forces which it is not the present purpose to discuss. The most important of these is the frictional resistance to the sliding of the body on the plane. In order to move a body resting on a horizontal plane at a uniform rate, a force must be applied. The force required is found to be roughly proportional to the weight of the body, or the force with which the attraction of the earth presses it down upon the plane. If this force, which is associated with sliding friction, is written F_f, its ratio to the gravitational force mg, pressing it to the plane, is called the coefficient of friction. As has been stated, this ratio F_f/mg is approximately constant for two given surfaces of contact. The magnitude of this complicating force can be greatly reduced by mounting the body on wheels, since the friction at the bearings is generally considerably less than that between the larger surfaces of contact between the body and the plane.

If a body of mass m rests upon a plane having an inclination θ to the horizontal (Fig. 3-12), it can be seen that the force of gravity upon it may be resolved into two components: one along the plane, which is the direction in which motion can take place; and one at right angles to the plane, which simply serves to hold the body on the plane in the same way that the total gravitational attraction holds a body on a horizontal plane. By the triangular construction it is evident that the component along the plane is in the ratio of the lengths h and l. Or, since this ratio is $\sin \theta$, the force tending to move the body along the plane is $mg \sin \theta$. The rate a at which it will be accelerated down the plane is then given by: $ma = mg \sin \theta$ or: $a = g \sin \theta$.

If the frictional force is not negligible, it is evident that one must take into account the force F_f, which in magnitude is the coefficient of friction, say b, times the component of the gravitational force pressing the body to the plane; namely $mg \cos \theta$ (Fig. 3-13). Thus, the total force tending to produce the motion is $F = mg (\sin \theta - b \cos \theta)$ and the acceleration that results is:

$$a = g (\sin \theta - b \cos \theta)$$

By making measurements at two inclinations, θ_1 and θ_2, at which the measured accelerations are a_1 and a_2, both the gravitational constant g and the coefficient of friction b can in principle be determined.

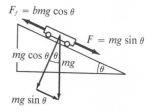

Figure 3-13   *Effect of friction.*

EXAMPLE. One can quite simply combine the inclined plane experiment with the principle of the Atwood's machine by mounting a small pulley at the top of the plane and connecting the mass on the plane with a freely hanging mass by means of a string or a rope (Fig. 3-14). If friction is neglected, the force along the direction of the rope and plane due to the attraction of the earth for m_1 is $m_1 g \sin \theta$ or $(m_1 g)(h/l)$. The force along the rope due to m_2 is $m_2 g$, and the total force tending to pull the mass up the plane is:

$$F = F_2 - F_1 = \left(m_2 - \frac{m_1 h}{l} \right) g$$

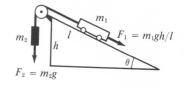

Figure 3-14   *Combination of the inclined plane and Atwood's machine.*

Since both masses connected by the rope must move as a unit, $F = (m_1 + m_2)a$. The acceleration downward of the mass m_2 (or upward of m_1) along the plane is:

$$a = \frac{m_2 l - m_1 h}{(m_2 + m_1)l} g$$

3-4 Rotational motion

The preceding illustrations, selected from various instances of the action of gravitational forces, have been given to convey some feeling of the nature of motion taking place under conditions in which the acceleration, or rate at which the velocity changes in magnitude, is constant in magnitude and direction. The Newtonian concept of force as rate of change of momentum—including the vectorial nature of the quantities force and momentum—is, of course, much more general and applies to cases: (1) where the acceleration is not constant, but varies in magnitude with the time; (2) where the vectors representing the force, velocity, and acceleration change in direction as well; and (3) where the mass of the body in question is not constant, but the changing momentum is contributed to not only by the changing velocity but also by the changing mass.

Consider as a simple and useful example of (2) above the common situation in which a mass is caused to rotate in a horizontal plane at a uniform angular rate about a central point or axis. For concreteness this may be thought of as a small, heavy object such as a metal ball, having a mass m, which is swung about rapidly at the end of a string or wire of length r. The path of the ball is circular, and as the mass of the ball does not change in this example, the force equation may be written again as:

$$\mathbf{F} = \frac{d(m\mathbf{v})}{dt} = m\frac{d\mathbf{v}}{dt}$$

In this case, however, $\mathbf{v}$ does not change in magnitude, but remains constant for a constant rate of rotation. By the definition of angular measure in Chap. 2, a distance, say s, along the circumference of the circular path, is equal to the product of the radius r and the angle θ subtended at the center by s. In other words, s, which is the position coordinate of the mass, is equal to θr. Hence, the magnitude of the velocity ds/dt is $r(d\theta/dt)$, or $r\omega$, since r is by definition constant and ω is the constant angular velocity.

However, the vector velocity **v** changes in direction. At the time t it is $\mathbf{v}_1$, and at a somewhat later time $t + dt$, it is $\mathbf{v}_2 = \mathbf{v}_1 + d\mathbf{v}$, where $\mathbf{v}_2$ is of the same length as $\mathbf{v}_1$, but rotated through the angle turned by **r**, namely ωdt. From the construction of Fig. 3-15, since **v** is perpendicular to the radius and the little vector change in velocity $d\mathbf{v}$ is in the limit of small dt perpendicular to **v**, then $d\mathbf{v}$ is parallel to **r** and inwardly directed. Since the angle between $\mathbf{v}_2$ and $\mathbf{v}_1$ is the same as that between $\mathbf{r}_2$ and $\mathbf{r}_1$, to which the velocities $\mathbf{v}_2$ and $\mathbf{v}_1$ are perpendicular, this angle is also $\omega\, dt$ and the vector $d\mathbf{v}$ is of length $v\omega\, dt$ and directed inwardly along **r**. Therefore, since the mass is constant, the magnitude of the force exerted by the string, $d(mv)/dt$, is $(mv\omega\, dt)/dt$, or $mv\omega$, and is directed inwardly along **r**. Thus, since $v = r\omega$, the force necessary to compel m to describe the circular path is given by: $\mathbf{F} = -m\omega^2\mathbf{r}$. This is the tension in the string holding the ball to the center of rotation. The magnitude of this force can be written variously and equivalently as: $m\omega^2r$, $m\omega v$, or mv^2/r as may be most suitable for a particular problem.

Instances of this force are all about us. It is a source of variation of the gravitational constant over the surface of the rotating earth; it is proposed as the equivalent of terrestrial gravity for astronauts in rotating space vehicles; it determines the bodily posture in skating figures, and the banking angle at turns in a road. When the adherence of mud to tires is less than this force, the mud flies off tangentially; the operation of centrifugal dryers and cream separators is based on it. If the rate of rotation ω is not uniform, or if other motions such as changes in r occur, there are other forces that result from these additional changes induced in the vector **v**. These are known as *Coriolis forces*. They are important in calculating trajectories of long-range missiles and in describing the motion of the circulating air masses that affect our weather.

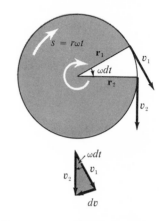

Figure 3-15 *Uniform circular motion at the angular velocity* ω.

EXAMPLE. The rotor of a helicopter has 4 blades, each of which is 2 m. in length, and makes 10 revolutions per sec. If the helicopter were to foul some overhead wires, and the tip of one blade, weighing 1 kg., were to be lost, what would be the resultant sideways force on the helicopter (Fig. 3-16)?

This is a situation in which symmetry has been lost. The centripetal force which must act on each blade as it rotates is usually balanced against the force required for the opposite blade, so that there is no net force on the helicopter body. But with the tip of one blade missing, the tip of the opposite blade requires a centripetal force which can now only be provided by the body of the helicopter. There is then a sideways force on the helicopter:

$$F = m\omega^2r$$

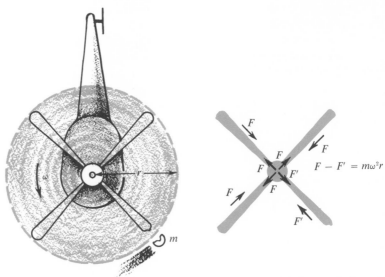

Figure 3-16 *The centripetal force F on each rotor blade of a helicopter is accompanied by an equal but oppositely directed force F on the helicopter body. If one of the centripetal forces decreases to F', because a tip is lost, then the forces on the helicopter body are no longer balanced, and there is a net force (F − F') on the body, equal to the centripetal force previously required for the lost tip.*

where $m = 1$ kg., $\omega = 2\pi \times 10$ rad.sec.$^{-1}$ and $r = 2$ m. Therefore:

$$F = 800\pi^2 = 7.9 \cdot 10^3$$

This force of about 8,000 Newtons is roughly equal to the weight of ten men. If this is the force on the helicopter when only the tip of a blade (1 kg $\approx$ 2.2 pounds) is lost, it is readily understandable why helicopters have their rotors inspected frequently. For a similar reason, large rotating machine parts such as flywheels are very carefully balanced.

EXAMPLE. *The conical pendulum.* Fig. 3-17a illustrates a *conical pendulum.* It consists of a heavy bob of mass m suspended by a light string of length l. The ball is swung around in a circle with angular velocity ω so that the string makes an angle θ with the vertical. Find the time T for one revolution of the pendulum.

There are only two forces acting on the bob, as shown in Fig. 3-17b, the tension F in the string and the weight mg of the bob. These do not balance, because there has to be a net inward force to provide the

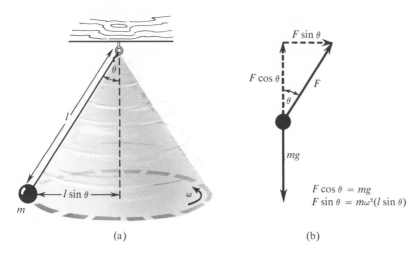

$$F \cos \theta = mg$$
$$F \sin \theta = m\omega^2(l \sin \theta)$$

(a)   (b)

Figure 3-17   (a) A conical pendulum consists of a heavy bob of mass m, which describes a circular orbit in the horizontal plane, supported by a light string of length l. (b) The horizontal component of the tension in the string provides the centripetal force necessary to maintain the circular orbit. The vertical forces are balanced.

centripetal acceleration. Thus we can say that the vertical weight force must be balanced by the vertical component of the tension F, or

$$mg = F \cos \theta$$

and the centripetal force must be the horizontal component of the tension F, or

$$m\omega^2(l \sin \theta) = F \sin \theta$$

$$\omega^2 = \frac{F}{ml} = \frac{g}{l \cos \theta}$$

Since there are 2π rad. in a circle, the time for one revolution will be

$$T = \frac{2\pi}{\omega} = 2\pi \sqrt{\frac{l \cos \theta}{g}}$$

This time is known as the *period* of the conical pendulum. It is interesting to compare it with the period of simple pendulum (cf. discussion in Chap. 6).

In this example, as in the previous one, the motion has been discussed from the point of view of a stationary outside observer. It was indicated that the imbalance of the forces results in a *centripetal* force which then provides the centripetal acceleration of the bob as it moves around the circle. To an observer moving around with the bob, there is no acceleration of the bob; to him the bob appears stationary. However, he does observe a tendency of all objects to fly outward, which he ascribes to some strange *centrifugal* force.

It may be shown that the most general type of displacement of a solid, or rigid body, resembles the type of motion we commonly associate with a screw; i.e., a displacement of all points of the body by a like magnitude and in a particular direction, together with a rotation of the necessary amount about an axis, parallel to the direction in which the displacement takes place. Thus, the most general type of motion to be described is linear displacement, together with rotation. The rate of change of momentum associated with the linear motion is a measure of the force in a particular direction which operates on the body. The rotational motion clearly is in response to one or more forces applied in a way that alters the orientation of the body. For example, in starting the rotation of a ball swung on a string, one moves one's hand in a small circle, changing the direction of the force inducing the rotational motion of the ball. Or one applies a twisting motion to a top to induce it to spin. Such twisting, or "circular-motion-inducing" forces are called *torques*; they were defined in Sect. 3-1 as the product of the force being applied multiplied by the perpendicular distance from the axis to the line of action of the force.

Fig. 3-18 represents the simple implications of this definition in terms of the consequent rate of change of angular velocity. For simplicity, a circularly symmetrical object such as the rim of a wheel of radius r and mass m, mounted on a frictionless axle, is considered the object whose angular velocity changes. The torque may be produced by a handle at some point along the rim to which a force varying in direction is applied; alternately it can be brought about by pulling with a force F, constant in direction, on a weightless rope which is wrapped about the wheel and unwinds during the application of the torque. First imagine that the mass m is all concentrated at one point on the rim. The force, by its definition in terms of changing momentum, is equal to $d(mv)/dt$, or in terms of the rate of rotation ω, $v = r\omega$ and $F = mr(d\omega/dt)$. In terms of the moment of the force or the torque T, which is equal to Fr,

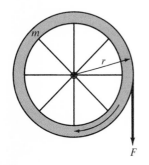

Figure 3-18   *Example of rotary motion.*

$$\mathbf{T} = (mr^2)(d\omega/dt) = (mr^2)\alpha$$

Since the angular velocity ω is an axially directed vector, contributions from all parts of the rim may be added algebraically. Hence, the above equation is applicable to any distribution of mass around the rim. The quantity mr^2 is called the *moment of inertia* of the wheel, and the quantity $mr^2\omega$ is called the *angular momentum*. **T** is clearly the rate of change of this quantity; hence, in analogy with the definition of force as the rate of change of momentum, torque is the rate of change of angular momentum, where α is the angular acceleration. If the axle of the wheel is to remain stationary, there must obviously be a force F acting on it, equal and opposite to the force F on the rim. However, such a force through the axis of rotation can have no torque about this axis. Likewise, centripetal forces cannot contribute to the torque about the axis.

EXAMPLE. A wheel of radius r_1 is rigidly connected to its axle of radius r_2, and its mass M is mostly concentrated in a heavy outer rim. As shown in Fig. 3-19, ropes are attached and wound around the wheel and the axle in opposite directions. A mass M_1 is then attached to the rope which hangs from one side of the wheel, and a mass M_2 to the rope which hangs from the other side of the axle. What is the acceleration of each mass when the system is released?

There are three systems to consider, each attached mass and the wheel which, unlike the wheel of Atwood's machine, is not to be considered massless. The three systems cannot easily be combined because of their different accelerations. Assume that the acceleration of M_1 is a_1 in a downward direction, and the tension in its rope is F_1. Similarly, assume M_2 moves upwards with an acceleration a_2, and its rope has a tension F_2. The angular acceleration of the wheel and axle may be taken as α. There is then an equation describing the motion of each system. For M_1 and M_2 independently, the net force equals the mass times the acceleration:

$$M_1g - F_1 = M_1a_1$$

$$F_2 - M_2g = M_2a_2$$

For the wheel, the net torque equals the moment of inertia Mr_1^2 times the angular acceleration:

$$F_1r_1 - F_2r_2 = Mr_1^2\alpha$$

Finally the accelerations are related:

$$\frac{a_1}{r_1} = \frac{a_2}{r_2} = \alpha$$

Taking the third equation, and substituting values of F_1, F_2, a_1 and a_2, found from the other three equations,

$$(M_1gr_1 - M_1r_1^2\alpha) - (M_2r_2^2\alpha + M_2gr_2) = Mr_1^2\alpha$$

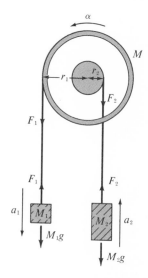

Figure 3-19 *Wheel and axle. The masses M_1 and M_2 are attached to the wheel and axle, respectively, by light ropes. The mass of the wheel is concentrated in the outer rim. F_1 and F_2 are the tensions in the two ropes.*

Concepts of force and momentum and their relationship 57

Then, collecting terms in α,

$$\alpha = \frac{(M_1 r_1 - M_2 r_2)g}{Mr_1^2 + M_1 r_1^2 + M_2 r_2^2}$$

and

$$a_1 = r_1 \alpha \qquad a_2 = r_2 \alpha$$

Of course, in assuming that M_1 would accelerate downwards and M_2 upwards, it was assumed that the torque $M_1 r_1$ would exceed the torque $M_2 r_2$. If this is not true, then the reverse motion will take place. The above equations will still be valid, however; α, a_1 and a_2 will merely turn out to be negative. Note that this general validity of the final results, independent of the assumed direction of motion, holds only if the forces and torques involved are independent of the direction of motion. Thus it does not hold if frictional forces are involved, because these change direction with the motion, always opposing it.

3-5 *The motion of masses that change with time*

There is finally the situation, referred to as case (3) in the preceding section, in which the mass whose position is being described is not constant, but also changes with time and the development of the phenomenon being observed. An instance of this would be the fall of a rain drop through moist air. In the course of its fall, it encounters additional water droplets and slowly increases in size. Another instance would be the initial stage in the flight of a rocket. The fuel is burning up and being ejected, which not only adds to the impulse of the rocket, but lightens it of its mass of fuel at the same time. As will be seen in Chap. 8, changing mass is also an important consideration in the case of bodies moving at very great velocities, where the requirements of relativity imply a significant change of mass with velocity. In such cases the momentum mv changes not only because of the change in $\mathbf{v}$ from $\mathbf{v}$ to $(\mathbf{v} + d\mathbf{v})$ in the time dt, but also by reason of the change in m from m to $(m + dm)$. Thus,

$$d(m\mathbf{v}) = (m + dm)(\mathbf{v} + d\mathbf{v}) - m\mathbf{v}$$

$$= \mathbf{v}\, dm + m\, d\mathbf{v} + d\mathbf{v}\, dm$$

and:

$$\mathbf{F} = \frac{d(m\mathbf{v})}{dt} = \mathbf{v}\frac{dm}{dt} + m\frac{d\mathbf{v}}{dt} + \left(\frac{d\mathbf{v}\, dm}{dt}\right)$$

The last term which is put in parenthesis is negligibly small for continuous processes in which both the rate of change of m and $\mathbf{v}$ are finite; for it is then of the order of dt, and vanishes in the limit of very small dt.

EXAMPLE. The application of this equation to the motion of a rocket during the period of burning fuel in free space is an interesting one. As there are no forces here due to air resistance or to gravitation, the only force experienced by the rocket and its unburned fuel must be just equal and opposite in sign to the rate at which the burning fuel carries away momentum, as it is ejected from the nozzle. The rate of decrease in mass of the rocket is $-dm/dt$; and if the constant nozzle velocity of the jet is V, the net velocity of the ejected fuel is this velocity minus the forward velocity of the rocket, or $(V - v)$. Thus the rate at which this carries momentum to the rear is $-(V - v)\,dm/dt$; if this is substituted for the force F in the above equation, which represents the rate of change of momentum of the rocket and its remaining unburned fuel, one obtains:

$$-(V - v)\frac{dm}{dt} = v\frac{dm}{dt} + m\frac{dv}{dt}$$

$$-V\frac{dm}{dt} = m\frac{dv}{dt}$$

The velocity at the end of an interval t is given by: $v = v_0 +$ sum of dv's in the interval. If the rocket starts from rest, v_0 is zero and: $v = \sum dv$, where $\sum$ stands for this sum. From the conservation of momentum equation $dv = -V(dm/m)$. Therefore:

$$v = -V\sum\frac{dm}{m}$$

In Sect. 17-4 it is shown that the change in a variable divided by the variable itself is equal to the change in the natural logarithm of the variable, i.e.:

$$\frac{dm}{m} = d\,[\ln(m)]$$

Hence, the equation for the velocity may be written:

$$v = -V\sum d\,[\ln(m)]$$

At the end of the time interval when the velocity is v, the mass is m; at the beginning of the interval when v is zero, the total mass of rocket and fuel may be written as the constant M. From the discussion in Sect. 2-5 the sum of the increments $d\,[\ln(m)]$ equals the difference between the value of $\ln(m)$ at the end and at the beginning of the interval. So the sum of the increments is $\ln(m) - \ln(M)$ or $\ln(m/M)$ and:

$$v = V\ln\left(\frac{M}{m}\right)$$

This is the explicit value of the velocity of the rocket in terms of its mass under the circumstances assumed. As m decreases from its initial value M, for which M/m is unity, and hence $\ln(M/m)$ is zero, the velocity increases. The velocity of the rocket is evidently equal to the velocity of fuel ejection when M/m is ϵ, when the mass m is M/ϵ or about 37 percent of its initial mass. Thereafter the velocity of the rocket increases further until the flow of fuel is stopped or the total fuel is expended.

Further reading:

HUNTOON, R. D., "Status of the National Standards for Physical Measurement." *Science*, vol. 150, No. 3693, p. 169 (1965).

Problems

3-1   In each of the experimental arrangements illustrated below, the spring balances, marked S, are to be considered to have negligible mass and to read directly in kilograms. Thus in the first case the actual tension in the string measured by the spring balance is 3×9.8 N., but the spring balance reads 3 kg. What is the reading of each of the other spring balances illustrated? (Neglect the weight of the spring balances themselves.)

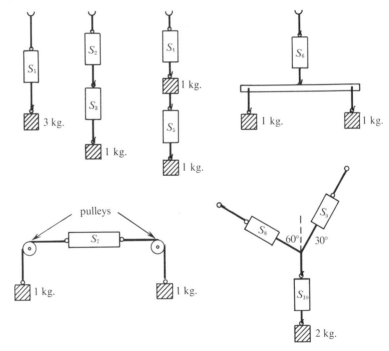

3-2   A beam balance has unequal arms, so that when an object is placed on the left balance pan the balancing mass on the right pan is M_R, and when the object is placed on the right pan the balancing mass on the left pan is M_L. Show that the true mass M of the object is $\sqrt{M_R M_L}$.

3-3   A sprinter of mass 80 kg. accelerates uniformly from a stationary start for the first 5 sec. of a race, at the end of which time his velocity is 10 m.sec.$^{-1}$. Calculate the force provided by his legs.

3-4   Explain why it is advisable, when catching a fast moving hard ball, to allow one's hands to move back with the ball. Use words which have already been defined to have precise physical and quantitative meanings, and if possible use an equation to summarize and quantify your explanation.

3-5   A firehose ejects $\frac{1}{10}$ m.^{3} of water per second with a velocity of 20 m.sec.$^{-1}$ at a wall. The density of water is 10^3 kg. m.$^{-3}$. Calculate the force on the wall, assuming the water is stopped completely by the wall and does not bounce back.

3-6   Explain the following paradox. A continuous chain hangs around a triangular block as shown. The weight of chain on the left side of the block is greater than that on the shorter right side. Therefore the chain will tend to move in the direction shown, overcoming any slight friction. (The length of chain hanging below the block is symmetrically placed, and its forces balance out evenly on both sides.) Since the chain is continuous, it seems that we have achieved the goal of the ancients—perpetual motion.

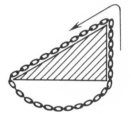

3-7   Neglecting air resistance, how long will it take a 1 kg. object to fall to the ground from the top of the Empire State Building (450 m.)? The object starts from rest. If a 2 kg. object is dropped, what will the answer be?

3-8   What momentum does the 1 kg. object of the previous problem have when it hits the ground? What is the momentum of the 2 kg. object?

3-9   The equations of free fall may be applied to any case of constant acceleration. In the general case of acceleration a in the x direction, they are written: $v = v_0 + at$ and $x - x_0 = v_0 t + \frac{1}{2}at^2$. From these two equations, derive one equation that does not contain the time t. Hence show that the product of the force F giving rise to the acceleration and the distance moved in the direction of that force is equal to the change in the square of the momentum p divided by twice the mass m; i.e., $Fx = (p^2 - p_0^2)/2m$.

3-10   For a given velocity of projection, there are in general two angles of inclination that will achieve the same range for a projectile. If one of these is θ, show that the other is $\frac{1}{2}\pi - \theta$.

3-11   A cannon is pointed so as to fire in the horizontal direction, and a 10 kg. cannonball is fired with a velocity of 100 m.sec.$^{-1}$. How far will the cannonball fall below the muzzle height in the first second? If the cannonball weighs 50 kg., how far will it fall in one second? If the velocity is increased to 1000 m.sec.$^{-1}$, how far will it fall in one second?

3-12 The Atwood's machine, discussed in Sec. 3-3, may be analyzed in terms of the tension in the rope and the forces on each mass in turn. Thus show that the acceleration of each mass is $\dfrac{m_2 - m_1}{m_2 + m_1}\, g$, as given by the simple treatment in the text.

3-13 A mass of 1 kg. is being whirled with constant angular velocity in a vertical plane on the end of a string 1 m. long. What is the smallest number of times per second the mass must go around if the string is to be kept taut?

3-14 A large station is constructed in space. To avoid possible undesirable physiological effects of prolonged weightlessness on the inhabitants, the station is to be rotated with a constant angular velocity. If the centrifugal force thus generated on the circumference of the space station of diameter 20 m. is to equal the force of gravity at the earth's surface, how many revolutions per second must the station make?

3-15 A man who crossed a road immediately after a car had passed claims that he was hit on the leg by a pebble dislodged from the tread of one of the rear tires. Road conditions at the time were excellent. Why would you doubt the accuracy of his statement?

3-16 When a car rounds a corner sharply, which tires tend to leave the road surface as a result of the centrifugal forces?

3-17 Derive an expression relating the optimum angle of bank of a curved section of roadway to the radius of curvature and the speed of the traffic.

3-18 What difference in the earth's gravitational acceleration as measured at the equator and at the poles is ascribable to the earth's rotation?

3-19 (a) Three garden rollers have the same diameter and total mass but different mass distributions. The first has most of the mass concentrated in a heavy outer rim; the second has most of the mass concentrated in a heavy weight suspended freely from the axle; and the third is a uniform solid cylinder. List the rollers in order, according to the ease with which they may be accelerated and decelerated.
(b) If the first roller mentioned above has a diameter of 1 m. and a mass of 100 kg., what force applied horizontally to the axle will give the roller an acceleration of 0.6 m.sec.$^{-2}$? What is the accompanying angular acceleration?

3-20 A man of mass m hangs from a light rope, the other end of which is wound onto a hollow drum of mass M and radius R. The drum is free to turn about a central axis. What is the angular acceleration of the drum if the man
(a) simply hangs from the rope?
(b) climbs up the rope at a rate such that his height relative to the drum remains constant?
(c) climbs up the rope with uniform velocity relative to the rope?

Work and energy and the conservation laws relating to momentum and energy   4

The concept of energy   4-1

In the preceding chapter we gave a precise quantitative meaning to the concept of force by using the definition proposed by Newton. Space and time intervals, and mass can be quantitatively measured in terms of several standards chosen for the three entities. The derived quantity velocity, as the ratio of a spatial to a temporal interval, extends these two concepts in a quantitative way to include the idea of motion, thus encompassing kinematics as well as statics. The inclusion of mass and the concept of inertia as the tendency of a mass to resist changes in its motion introduces the subject of dynamics. Since the quantities m and v entering the definition of momentum are themselves procedurally well-defined, momentum is also well-defined. And finally, Newton's definition of force as the rate at which momentum changes rests firmly upon previously defined quantities.

Of equal importance to the concepts of momentum and angular

momentum is that of *energy*. Prior to Newton's formulation of the laws of dynamics, Descartes, a great French mathematician and natural philosopher, and Leibnitz, an equally distinguished German scientist, engaged in a controversy as to whether the more significant property of a moving body was its velocity or the square of its velocity. Subsequently it has become clear that velocity to both the first and second powers appears in the definition of physically significant quantities: the velocity relates to the momentum and the square of the velocity relates to the kinetic energy; each of these provides an essential concept in the description of dynamic phenomena. Though the relationship between force and rate of change of momentum is the more direct initial approach to the definitions of dynamics, the concepts of work and energy are almost as intuitive. They have provided a more useful thread for tracing relationships among the various areas of physical science, uniting them into a single body of knowledge even prior to the advent of the atomic theory. In 1845, Robert Mayer, a German physician, recognized that energy is a significant entity which is conserved in a measurable way in the course of physical processes. This recognition was independently appreciated and re-emphasized by August Colding, a Dane; James Joule, an Englishman; and Herman Von Helmholtz, a German, a year or so later (1847).

Work is as immediately perceived by the senses as is force. The muscular effort required, or the degree of exhaustion experienced in pushing or pulling heavy objects about, uphill against gravity or against frictional, viscous or other retarding forces, is clearly related not only to the force overcome but also to the distance traversed. Hence one can establish as the scientific definition of the *work* done on a body the product of the net force on it in the direction of its motion and the distance traversed during the motion. Forces, of course, are classed for convenience in various categories; but the differences in type are irrelevant for the present purpose, and our only concern is with the magnitude of the component of the net force arising from all causes which oppose the displacement. As the force is more often than not a function of the time, or of the position of the body being moved, the work accomplished in traversing a given path is the sum of the individual increments of work associated with each small element of path. This is again an example of the function, or curve, and its associated rate function, or rate curve: the function here is the work; the spatial rate of doing work is the force (Fig. 4-1). The variable in this instance is the distance along the path; so the force which is the spatial rate at which work is done on the body in the course of impelling it along the path is:

$$F = dU/dx$$

where U is the energy expended. The unit of work is the *Joule* (J.), or

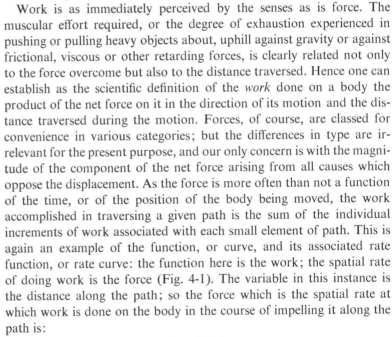

Figure 4-1 *The relation between force and spatial rate of change of energy in analogy with the relation between velocity and time rate of change of position.*

the work accomplished by the force of one Newton operating over the distance of 1 m.

EXAMPLE. A housewife, living in a three-story house with a young family, climbs up about twenty flights of stairs every day. If the height between floors is 3 m. and the housewife has a mass of 60 kg. (132 pounds), how much work does this entail?

In this case, horizontal motion does not require work, according to the definition above, because there is no horizontal component of force to oppose such motion. Therefore the total work done will be the product of the vertical force (the weight force mg) and the distance h moved against this force (a total of 60 m). Thus the total work done is:

$$U = mgh = 60 \times 9.8 \times 60 = 35,000 \text{ J.}$$

This is equivalent to performing about 120 "push-ups," or to "chinning a bar" about 120 times, assuming these raise the body by $\frac{1}{2}$ m. (Fig. 4-2). The calculation has neglected to consider any load that the

Figure 4-2 *The work done in raising a body is equal to the product of the weight of the body and the distance by which it is raised.*

housewife might be carrying, and any internal bodily work associated with the muscular exertions. Only the work done in raising, not lowering, the body has been evaluated.

Just as it was seen that forces were early categorized in terms of the phenomena with which they were associated, such as gravitational forces, mechanical contact forces, electrical forces, etc.; so is energy, or the work done by such forces frequently associated (for historical reasons or convenience in specification) with the particular phenomena being observed. Terms such as gravitational energy, energy of compression of a spring, or electrical energy are used. The fundamental unity provided by the concept of energy comes from the fact that the energy difference between two different physical configurations is equal to the sum of the products of each displacement and the force encountered in making that displacement for all of the bodies whose positions are altered–without regard to the nature or genesis of the forces being encountered. The unification of all areas of physics afforded by the concept of energy provides us with an intellectual grasp of the total phenomena of nature.

4-2 *Conservation of energy*

In introducing the discussion of energy, it is convenient to set aside, for the moment, consideration of energy transformations associated with the work done against such forces as those retarding motion in the presence of friction, viscosity or the permanent deformation of solid bodies. Such processes are said to be *nonconservative* for reasons that will be given later. The types of processes to be considered first, called *conservative*, are, for instance, the raising or lowering of a weight against the force of gravity, the elastic compression or elongation of a spring, the motion of a projectile, etc.

Consider, as an example of such a conservative process, the case of a projectile shot vertically upward against the force of gravity (Fig. 4-3). In Chap. 3 it was seen that the position of the projectile y, measured positively upward, and the value of the velocity v, again measured positively upward, are related to the time by the following equations:

$$v = v_0 - gt \qquad (y - y_0) = v_0 t - \tfrac{1}{2}gt^2$$

Here y_0 is the starting point when the clock is also started ($t = 0$) and the projectile is fired vertically upward with the velocity v_0. The time t

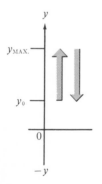

Figure 4-3   *Motion of a projectile shot vertically upwards.*

may be eliminated between these two expressions, and v may be displayed as a function of y. Thus:

$$(y - y_0) = \frac{1}{2}\frac{v_0^2}{g} - \frac{1}{2}\frac{v^2}{g}$$

If this equation is multiplied by mg on both sides:

$$mg(y - y_0) = \tfrac{1}{2}mv_0^2 - \tfrac{1}{2}mv^2$$

The left-hand side is the product of the displacement from y_0 to y and the constant force against which the displacement acts, namely mg. Thus, this is the work that would be done in raising the projectile from y_0 to y against the force of gravity; it is equal to the difference between the quantity $\tfrac{1}{2}mv^2$ at the beginning and at the end of the interval. This, of course, is true regardless of the point y achieved by the projectile. At its maximum height above y_0, as was seen in Chap. 3, $v = 0$ and $(y - y_0) = v_0^2/2g$. Thereafter the projectile falls back, and when $y = y_0$, again $v = v_0$; but then the projectile is traveling in the opposite direction. Throughout, however, the above relationship holds.

The equality between the work done in moving a body of mass m up or down in the presence of the gravitational force and the quantity $\tfrac{1}{2}mv^2$ strongly suggests the usefulness of a concept entailing an invariant quantity or one that may be said to be conserved; one which on the one hand takes the form of the definition of work $mg(y_0 - y)$, and on the other hand takes a form involving mass and the square of the velocity $\tfrac{1}{2}mv^2$. The quantity that emerges from these considerations as a new concept is called the *energy*; the work done by displacing the mass against its gravitational force, which is the product of the displacement $(y - y_0)$ and the force of gravity mg, is said to be the change—or more specifically the increase—in *potential energy* of the mass, i.e., its potential ability to accomplish further work in the course of a subsequent displacement. The potential energy increases as a body is raised and decreases as it is lowered, for in one case its return to the earth's surface could be used to accomplish greater work, and in the other its return could accomplish less. The product $\tfrac{1}{2}mv^2$ is called the *kinetic energy*, or energy of motion. The equation above represents the exchange of energy between these two forms for a freely moving body in the earth's gravitational field. The conservation of energy in this instance would be written as:

$$(mgy + \tfrac{1}{2}mv^2) = (mgy_0 + \tfrac{1}{2}mv_0^2) = \text{constant}$$

Instances of the exchange or transformation of energy among its various forms recur throughout physics. The equivalence between stored or potential energy and kinetic energy is implicit in Newton's relation between force and rate of change of momentum. If the equation $F = d(mv)/dt$ is multiplied on both sides by the small displacement dx, and it is recalled that $dx/dt = v$, the result for a constant mass is seen to be:

$$Fdx = mvdv$$

If the process is a conservative one, i.e., if there are no friction-like forces, then the work this force does in increasing the velocity of the mass is done at the expense of the energy stored within whatever source is available to it. This decrease in potential energy can be written $-dU_p$. The rate of change of U_p as a function of v is, of course, symbolically dU_p/dv; employing again the relationship between a function and its rate of change when this function and its rate of change can be expressed as a power of its variable, it is seen that:

$$dU_p/dv = -mv \text{ and } \qquad dU_p = -mvdv = -d(\tfrac{1}{2}mv^2)$$

The quantity $\tfrac{1}{2}mv^2$ has been called the kinetic energy U_k, and hence: $-dU_p = dU_k$, or $dU_p + dU_k = 0$. The energy withdrawn from the source that furnishes the force appears as energy of motion of the mass being impelled.

EXAMPLE. A man pushes a stalled car for a distance of 20 m., as a result of which it achieves a velocity of 7 km. per hr.$^{-1}$ (about 4 miles per hr.). If the car has a mass of 1500 kg. (about $1\tfrac{1}{2}$ tons) and there is no friction to consider, with what constant force did the man push? (Fig. 4-4)

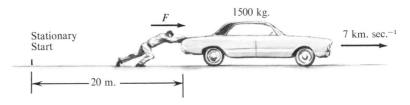

Stationary Start

F

1500 kg.

7 km. sec.$^{-1}$

20 m.

Figure 4-4   *The work done by a force in pushing a car is equal to the increase in the car's kinetic energy, if frictional forces are negligible.*

The kinetic energy of a 1500 kg. car travelling with a velocity of $7000/3600$ m.sec.$^{-1}$ is:

$$U = \tfrac{1}{2} \times 1500 \times (70/36)^2 \approx 3000 \text{ J.}$$

which will also be the work done by the man; hence the force over a distance of 20 m. must be:

$$F = 3000/20 = 150 \text{ N}.$$

EXAMPLE. The force F necessary to compress a spring is proportional to the distance x by which it is compressed; i.e., $F = kx$, where k is a constant (Fig. 4-5). What is the potential energy stored in such a compressed spring?

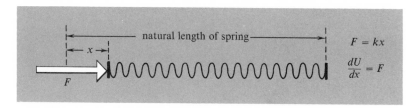

Figure 4-5 *The force necessary to compress a spring is proportional to the distance compressed. The spatial rate of increase of potential energy is equal to this force.*

The rate of increase of potential energy with compression of the spring will equal the rate at which work is simultaneously done on the spring. But the latter rate is just the force F which does the work. Thus:

$$\frac{dU}{dx} = \frac{dW}{dx} = F = kx$$

and application of the mathematical rule for finding a function when given its rate of change yields:

$$U = \tfrac{1}{2}kx^2$$

Thus a spring compressed a distance x has potential energy $\tfrac{1}{2}kx^2$ stored in it, where the constant k is a property of the spring.

EXAMPLE. A catchment area of 4000 km.² (about 1,500 square miles) has an annual rainfall of $\tfrac{1}{2}$m. (20 in.). Thirty per cent is lost by evaporation and 20 per cent through seepage. The remaining water is trapped by a dam and from thence drops 250 m. to a power station, where the kinetic energy of the water is employed to drive generators of electricity (Fig. 4-6). What is the average output capacity of the power station?

The total volume of water trapped per year is:

$$V = \tfrac{1}{2} \times \tfrac{1}{2} \times 4 \times 10^9 = 10^9 \text{ m.}^3$$

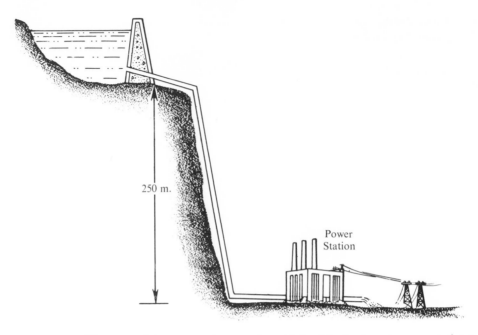

Figure 4-6 *The potential energy of water in a high altitude dam is converted into kinetic energy when the water falls down a pipe to the power station. In doing work to drive generators, the kinetic energy is converted into electrical energy.*

the mass of which, assuming a water density of 10^3 kg. m.$^{-3}$, is:

$$M = 10^9 \times 10^3 = 10^{12} \text{ kg.}$$

The potential energy of this water and hence the work done by it in falling 250 m. is then:

$$W = 10^{12} \times 9.8 \times 250 \approx 2.5 \times 10^{15} \text{ J.}$$

This work is expended over a full year, or $365 \times 24 \times 3600 \approx 2.5 \times 10^7$ sec. Hence the power or time rate of doing work is:

$$\frac{dW}{dt} = \frac{2.5 \times 10^{15}}{2.5 \times 10^7} = 10^8 \text{ W.}$$

1 Watt (W.) being a Joule per second. The above power can alternatively be written as 10^5 kW. or 100 MW.

EXAMPLE. A boy slides down a very slippery bannister. If he starts from rest and drops a height of 3 m. what is his velocity at the bottom?

This problem could be solved by assuming some slope of the bannister, by deriving the acceleration down the bannister, taking the distance moved down the bannister in the direction of the acceleration, and finally by using the equations derived for constant acceleration to solve for the final velocity. It is, however, much easier and quicker to use the conservation of energy principle. Thus at the top, the boy has only potential energy mgh, where m is his mass, g the acceleration due to gravity (9.8 m. sec.$^{-2}$), and h his height above the finishing point (3 m.); at the bottom he has only kinetic energy $\frac{1}{2}mv^2$, where v is his final velocity. If energy is conserved, the two energies are equal.

$$\tfrac{1}{2}mv^2 = mgh$$

Therefore:
$$v = \sqrt{2\,gh} = \sqrt{2 \times 9.8 \times 3}$$
$$\approx 7.7 \text{ m. sec.}^{-1}$$

The concepts of kinetic energy and potential energy are not restricted to linear motions. A rotating wheel, having a moment of inertia I about its axis, has rotational kinetic energy $\frac{1}{2}I\omega^2$ where ω is the angular velocity. Potential energy may be stored in a spiral spring, when, analogous to the second example of the above set, the energy will be of the form $\frac{1}{2}k\Theta^2$, where Θ is the angle of compression or extension and k is a constant of the spiral spring. Such potential energy is familiar to us as the source of energy for all "clockwork" mechanisms.

EXAMPLE. As an example involving both types of kinetic energy, consider a garden roller, most of whose mass m resides in a heavy rim of radius r. A man commences to roll this down a hill of height h, with velocity v_0; but he has scarcely started when he loses hold of the roller and it runs freely to the bottom of the hill (Fig. 4-7). What is the velocity v of the roller at the bottom of the hill, neglecting any frictional effects?

The initial energy is $(\frac{1}{2}mv_0^2 + \frac{1}{2}I\omega_0^2 + mgh)$, where the moment of inertia of the roller is $I = mr^2$ and its initial angular velocity is $\omega_0 = v_0/r$. The final energy of the roller is $(\frac{1}{2}mv^2 + \frac{1}{2}I\omega^2)$, where the final angular velocity is $\omega = v/r$. Equating the two energies:

$$\tfrac{1}{2}mv_0^2 + \tfrac{1}{2}(mr^2)v_0^2/r^2 + mgh = \tfrac{1}{2}mv^2 + \tfrac{1}{2}(mr^2)v^2/r^2$$

which simplifies to:

$$mv_0^2 + mgh = mv^2$$

and hence:
$$v = \sqrt{v_0^2 + gh}$$

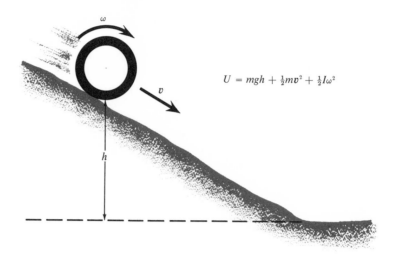

Figure 4-7 *A roller of mass m and moment of inertia I rolls down a hill with velocity v and angular velocity ω. When the roller is at a height h, its total energy U is the sum of the potential (mgh), linear kinetic (½mv²), and rotational kinetic (½Iω²) forms. I and ω are related to m and v by the radius of the roller.*

Earlier in this section certain types of phenomena, in which energy is clearly exchanged, were excepted as being nonconservative processes. This category of processes involves the generation or flow of heat. Heat is evidenced to us through our skin by the sensations of hot and cold, which we describe in terms of high and low temperatures. Such a simple qualitative understanding is adequate for present purposes. These processes are excluded from this discussion not because they represent situations in which energy is not conserved, but because forces of a nonconservative nature, experienced by the large bodies with which experiments are conducted, cannot be simply and uniquely specified in terms of the spatial and temporal variables describing the positions of these bodies; in consequence, these processes do not lend themselves to an elementary presentation. A description of heat in terms of atomic and molecular phenomena will be presented later (Chap. 18). Here a brief summary will suffice to present the essential features of nonconservative processes.

It was early recognized that there were processes in which the work done did not result in the gross motion of bodies, and in which energy disappeared from the mechanical form. These processes involve frictional forces where, by sliding or rolling, bodies generate heat; their temperatures rise. They become hot to the touch. Some examples are:

a boring or filing operation, the rubbing of two objects against one another, or the sliding of a heavy weight horizontally over a rough surface. Joule and Helmholtz recognized quantitatively that the amount of heat generated—which they measured by the mass and other physical properties of the substance concerned times its rise in temperature—was proportional (or equal in the proper units) to the amount of mechanical energy, kinetic or potential, that disappeared. Thus energy is not conserved in quite the same sense in dissipative processes as in conservative processes, since it is found that energy in the form of heat cannot be completely recovered and transformed back into the mechanical form. However, allowing for the fact that the dissipative process permits only one direction for the complete transfer of energy, the exchange in that direction represents a quantitative process in which the same amount of mechanical energy, when completely transformed by a frictional process into heat, raises a given mass of a substance in temperature by the same amount on any arbitrary scale. When this process is regarded from an atomic point of view, the fundamentally conservative nature of all processes of energy interchange becomes evident; the one-directional nature, corresponding to the so-called "flow of heat" from a hot to a cold body in contact, becomes reconcilable with the principle of energy conservation.

On the basis of a more refined consideration of physical processes in terms of constituent atoms and their interactions with one another, "heat energy" ceases to be a useful fundamental concept; it is more illuminating to consider heat in terms of the kinetic energy of atomic systems. Dissipative processes and the tendency for bodies in contact to come to the same temperature take on a different aspect from the atomic point of view. It is recognized that a vastly complex system of an enormous number of minute components is being observed which, in conforming to the distribution of energy among them that is most likely to occur under the circumstances, gives rise to the apparent phenomena of energy dissipation and thermal flow. The conservation of energy as a general principle pervades all common mechanical phenomena, and yields great insight into atomic processes. When viewed in terms of elementary physical particles, it extends with equal validity throughout all the physical processes that we know: mechanical, electrical, gravitational, atomic, nuclear, and cosmic; it is one of the most general and useful physical laws or principles of physical science.

The two categories of conservative and dissipative processes do not represent the division of all physical phenomena neatly into two types. Conservative macroscopic processes are actually idealizations of mechanical processes which present very useful, if strictly unrealizable, descriptions. There are frictional or viscous forces present in any common process. The air is set in motion by a falling body and energy is thus lost to the particular process under consideration, though the fractional loss may be negligible for very dense bodies. Friction is always present to some extent in wheels and pulleys, and even in the best lubricated sliding surfaces. If one recognizes such causes of energy loss from simple mechanical form, engineering calculations can be carried out to any desired degree of precision. To a first approximation friction may often be neglected, but precise calculations require its inclusion.

EXAMPLE. A boy on roller skates comes to the start of a steep downward slope with velocity v_0. He rolls without effort down the slope and reaches the bottom with velocity v. If his mass is m, and the slope is of length s, and of height h, find the constant frictional force.

The energy at the start is partly potential (mgh) and partly kinetic ($\frac{1}{2}mv_0^2$). The energy at the bottom is entirely kinetic ($\frac{1}{2}mv^2$). These energies must differ by the work done by frictional forces, which always oppose the motion.

$$(\tfrac{1}{2}mv_0^2 + mgh) - \tfrac{1}{2}mv^2 = F \cdot s$$

Therefore:

$$F = \frac{\frac{1}{2}m(v_0^2 - v^2) + mgh}{s}$$

4-3 *Conservation of momentum and angular momentum*

Energy is not the only quantity that obeys a conservation law. Among the quantities that occur in mechanics, momentum and angular momentum both obey similar laws. As these quantities are likewise capable of meaningful extension into the realm of atomic processes, the conservation of momentum and of angular momentum are of equal significance to the conservation of energy as guiding principles and unifying laws in both the large scale and the atomic description of physical phenomena. From the definition of force as the rate at which momentum changes, it is clear that if no net force is applied to the body being considered, the momentum remains unchanged. If one enlarges one's view to consider two bodies which exert forces on one another, as in the case of the earth exerting its gravitational attraction on a mass, or in the case of two bodies colliding with one another in free space, there are two forces to be considered: one on each body, exerted by the other. If these are the only two bodies, and there are no others present to exert forces of any nature, the two forces that are present must just balance one another. Newton expressed this by saying that to every action (force) there is an equal and opposite reaction (opposing force). If the force on body 1, $\mathbf{F}_1$, is equal and opposite to that on body 2, $\mathbf{F}_2$, then the momenta change equally and oppositely during any time interval, and the total momentum remains constant.

$$\mathbf{F}_1 = -\mathbf{F}_2 \qquad \mathbf{F} = \frac{d(m\mathbf{v})}{dt}$$

hence:

$$\frac{d(m_1\mathbf{v}_1)}{dt} = \frac{-d(m_2\mathbf{v}_2)}{dt}$$

or:

$$\frac{d(m_1\mathbf{v}_1 + m_2\mathbf{v}_2)}{dt} = 0$$

and $(m_1\mathbf{v}_1 + m_2\mathbf{v}_2)$ is constant. The argument may, of course, be extended to any number of bodies; hence the total momentum of any system of bodies not acted on by any force external to them remains constant.

Momentum, unlike energy, is a vector quantity. Its direction is that of the velocity, and its magnitude is that of the product of m and the magnitude of $\mathbf{v}$. Its conservation, or constancy, depends on its remaining the same in both magnitude and direction, which in turn implies that its components along each of the three coordinate axes remain constant separately. Thus the x, the y, and z components of the momentum of any system of particles or extended bodies all remain constant, provided, of course, that all the interacting bodies are always taken into account in the calculation. Since momentum is a vector quantity, it does not manifest quite the protean properties of energy, a concept that has taken on a plurality of forms throughout the divisions of physical science. Likewise there is no analog in the case of momentum to the nonconservative macroscopic (large scale) situations in which energy seems to disappear from the mechanical form. All phenomena, both macroscopic and atomic, agree with this simple form of the conservation of momentum.

EXAMPLE. A rocket explodes into three pieces; one piece of mass m_1 moves vertically up with velocity v_1, a second piece of mass m_2 moves to the right with velocity v_2. Find the velocity (including its direction) of the third piece of mass m_3, if the original velocity of the rocket was v vertically upwards. (Fig. 4-8).

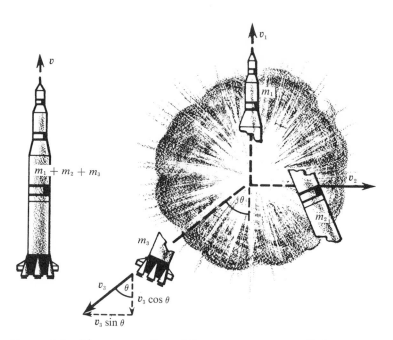

Figure 4-8 *The conservation of linear momentum applied to an exploding rocket: the total upward momentum of the pieces equals the initial upward momentum of the whole. The total sideways momentum of the pieces equals the initial sideways momentum of the whole, which in the above case was zero.*

The initial velocity and the velocities of the first two pieces involve only two directions. Simple reasoning then dictates that the third piece must travel on a plane encompassing these two directions; otherwise it would have a component of momentum out of this plane which could not be balanced by the momenta of the whole rocket or of the other pieces. Assume then that the third piece travels downward and to the left at an angle θ to the vertical. Then equating the original and the final vertical momentum components,

$$(m_1 + m_2 + m_3)v = m_1 v_1 - m_3 v_3 \cos \theta$$

Similarly, equating the horizontal momentum components,

$$0 = m_2v_2 - m_3v_3 \sin \theta$$

Rearranging these equations,

$$m_3v_3 \cos \theta = m_1v_1 - (m_1 + m_2 + m_3)v$$

and
$$m_3v_3 \sin \theta = m_2v_2$$

Dividing the last equation by the first then gives:

$$\tan \theta = \frac{m_2v_2}{m_1v_1 - (m_1 + m_2 + m_3)v}$$

The value for v_3 may be found by squaring both equations. Then using the identity $\sin^2 \theta + \cos^2 \theta = 1$,

$$(m_3v_3)^2 = (m_2v_2)^2 + (m_1v_1)^2 + (m_1 + m_2 + m_3)^2v^2$$
$$- 2m_1v_1(m_1 + m_2 + m_3)v$$

and hence:

$$v_3 =$$

$$\frac{1}{m_3} \sqrt{(m_1v_1)^2 + (m_2v_2)^2 + (m_1 + m_2 + m_3)^2v^2 - 2m_1v_1(m_1 + m_2 + m_3)v}$$

EXAMPLE. *The ballistic pendulum.* This is an instrument used for the determination of the velocity of a bullet. A heavy wooden block is suspended by two cords, and is free to swing as a pendulum in the plane of the two cords, as shown in Fig. 4-9. A bullet fired at the block will become embedded in it and transfer momentum to it. Thus if v

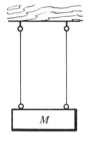
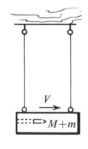
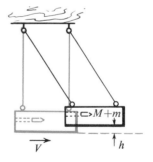

The momentum $(M + m)V$ of the block plus the bullet after the collision equals the momentum mv of the bullet before the collision.

The potential energy $(M + m)gh$ at the top of the swing equals the kinetic energy $\frac{1}{2}(M + m)V^2$ at the bottom of the swing.

Figure 4-9   *The ballistic pendulum is used to determine the velocity of a bullet.*

is the initial velocity of the bullet of mass m, and V is the velocity of the block of mass M plus the embedded bullet immediately after the bullet has come to rest in the block, then by the conservation of momentum:

$$mv = (M + m)V$$

The velocity is most easily determined by measuring the height to which the wooden block rises, for, by the conservation of energy, if the block rises to a height h above its equilibrium position, then:

$$\tfrac{1}{2}(M + m)V^2 = (M + m)gh$$

These equations may be combined to yield:

$$v = \frac{M + m}{m}\,V = \frac{M + m}{m}\,\sqrt{2gh}$$

Notice that it was not assumed that energy was conserved when the bullet struck the block; indeed the amount of energy lost in the form of heat may readily be estimated from the difference in kinetic energies before and after the collision.

Angular momentum is a quantity that is also conserved. It is, of course, a measure of the rotational motion taking place, being the product of the moment of inertia, I, and the angular velocity, ω. Its rate of change with time is the torque, which is the product of the force being exerted times the perpendicular distance from the line of action of the force to the point about which the tendency to change the rate of rotational motion is being calculated. It is a vector quantity like the angular velocity, and its positive direction is chosen by convention to be that in which a right-hand screw would tend to advance under the influence of the twist induced by the torque. If the forces between any two interacting particles are co-linear and opposite in magnitude (as symmetry conditions would lead us to conclude they must be), the torque exerted at any point by the two together is equal to zero or vanishes for any point that can be chosen (Fig. 4-10). The argument can, of course, be extended to any number of interacting particles, and if all are duly taken into account, the total angular momentum remains constant with the time just as does the total momentum. All physical phenomena so far observed are in agreement with the conservation of angular momentum, as they are with the conservation of linear momentum. Being a vector quantity, the total angular momentum, whatever its constant value, remains constant in both magnitude and direction, i.e., there is no tendency for the total angular momentum about any of the three axes to change with time.

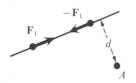

Figure 4-10 *If two particles exert equal but opposite forces on one another along the line joining them, then the torque exerted by these forces upon a particle situated at any arbitrary point such as A must vanish; for by definition the torque is $(\mathbf{F}_1 - \mathbf{F}_1)d$.*

EXAMPLE. A boy stands on a turntable and holds a dumbbell of mass m in each hand. He holds his arms out horizontally to the side so that the dumbbells are a distance $2r$ apart. If the boy has a moment of inertia I about the turntable axis, and the turntable rotates with angular velocity ω_0, what will be the angular velocity ω of the turntable if the boy pulls the dumbbells in close to his body (Fig. 4-11)?

Since angular momentum must be conserved, and since each dumbbell has an initial moment of inertia mr^2 about the turntable axis and a final moment of inertia which is negligibly small about this axis, then:

$$(I + 2mr^2)\omega_0 = I\omega$$

Therefore:

$$\omega = \left(1 + \frac{2mr^2}{I}\right)\omega_0$$

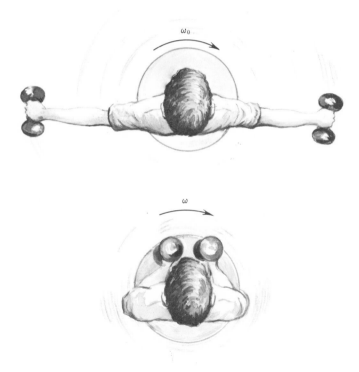

Figure 4-11 *The angular velocity of a boy on a turntable increases when he pulls his outstretched arms in.*

EXAMPLE. The boy equipped as he was in the above example, but now at rest, can alter his orientation by the following procedure: he extends the dumbbells, rotating his spine through the angle θ; then lowers the dumbbells and rotates his spine back through the same angle. If I_l is written for the moment of inertia of the lower portion of his body and the turntable, and I_{ue} for the moment of inertia of the upper portion of his body with the dumbbells extended, the conservation of angular momentum during the first movement yields:

$$I_l \omega_l = I_{ue} \omega_u$$

where ω_u and ω_l are the respective angular velocities of the upper and lower portions of his body. As both portions rotate for the same time, say t, the angles turned through by each are:

$$\theta_l = \omega_l t \quad \text{and} \quad \theta_u = \omega_u t$$

So:

$$I_l \theta_l = I_{ue} \theta_u$$

During the second motion, the argument is the same; but I_{ue} must be replaced by the moment of inertia with the dumbbells retracted, which will be written as I_{ur}. I_l remains the same, and if the angles are written as $\theta_{l'}$ and $\theta_{u'}$ during the second motion:

$$I_l \theta_{l'} = I_{ur} \theta_{u'}$$

The sums $\theta_l + \theta_u$ and $\theta_{l'} + \theta_{u'}$ are each equal to the maximum angular distortion about the boy's spine, say θ; if the equations are solved for the difference $\theta_u - \theta_{u'}$ in terms of θ, the result is:

$$\theta_u - \theta_{u'} = \left(\frac{I_l}{I_l + I_{ue}} - \frac{I_l}{I_l + I_{ur}} \right) \theta$$

If $I_l = I_{ur}$, and $I_{ue} = 2I_{ur}$, the angle turned through during the motions is $\theta/6$. Of course, in the case of an astronaut in free space, the extension or retraction of arms and legs can take the place of dumbbells, and a change of orientation can be accomplished by bodily movements alone. The cat, who is more flexible muscularly than man, can be held upside down by the fore and hind paws a few feet above the ground; when it is released, it can turn over sufficiently to light on its paws.

EXAMPLE. *The top.* The top is a particularly important example of the conservation of angular momentum, because it exemplifies the behavior of any spinning object in a force field. As such it has important application to the discussion of rotating atomic and nuclear particles, which will be found in Chap. 11. Consider a top of mass m which, when viewed from above, is spinning in a counterclockwise direction with angular momentum $\mathbf{L}$ (Fig. 4-12). By convention, this is indicated by a vector of length L that points upward along the axis of the top. If the top is not upright, then the weight force mg vertically down will provide a torque $\mathbf{T}$ about the base of the top, which must tend to produce an increase in angular momentum in the direction of that torque. This direction will always be perpendicular to the direction of $\mathbf{L}$; hence the torque can never change the magnitude of $\mathbf{L}$, but only its direction. It is seen that $\mathbf{L}$, and hence the axis of the top, will precess around in a circle about the vertical. In Fig. 4-12 (a), the center of mass of the top is seen to be at a distance r from the vertical. Consequently the torque is of magnitude:

$$\mathbf{T} = mgr$$

This is, then, the magnitude of the time rate of change of angular momentum $d\mathbf{L}/dt$. In Fig. 4-12(b) the angular momentum is depicted as precessing about the vertical with angular velocity

$$\Omega = \frac{d\phi}{dt} = \frac{d\mathbf{L}/\mathbf{L} \sin \theta}{dt} = \frac{d\mathbf{L}/dt}{\mathbf{L} \sin \theta}$$

$$= \frac{mgr}{\mathbf{L} \sin \theta} = \frac{mgh}{\mathbf{L}}$$

where h is the distance from the center of mass to the base of the top, and $r = h \sin \theta$. For the top shown, the mass is concentrated in the rim of radius R and hence the moment of inertia: $I = mR^2$ and the angular momentum: $\mathbf{L} = I\omega = mR^2\omega$

Hence:
$$\Omega = \frac{mgh}{mR^2\omega} = \frac{gh}{R^2\omega}$$

Notice that Ω is not a function of θ, but is inversely proportional to the spin angular momentum of the top. Thus as the spin of a top decreases, the precessional angular velocity will increase, as is commonly observed. It can also readily be seen why, when a top falls over and rolls on the ground, the direction of roll is opposite to the direction of precession.

The three conservation laws of energy, momentum, and angular momentum express our knowledge of the motion of massive particles and extended bodies. They are the basis for answering any questions concerning the future locations and motions of any system of interacting bodies if the present locations and motions are given. This, of course, is not to say that these conservation laws constitute all of physics. As mentioned in Sect. 4-1, our observations of the circumstances under which forces appear, which redistribute momentum among bodies, and

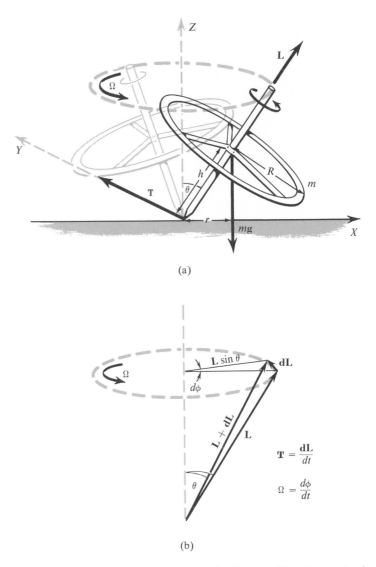

(a)

(b)

Figure 4-12 (a) Spinning top. The Torque **T**, of magnitude mgr, is horizontal and perpendicular to **L**. It causes **L**, and hence the top axis, to precess as indicated by the dashed circle. (b) The angular momentum vector **L** does not change in magnitude, but only in direction.

under which energy is exchanged between its various forms have directed the course of intellectual exploration that has led to our present understanding of physical phenomena. Our present description is in terms of elementary particles that obey these conservation laws and others we will encounter in later chapters.

The application of the conservation laws clearly requires that all interacting bodies be included in the considerations, that all forms of energy embodiment are specifically taken into account, and that only those energy transformations are postulated as are found by observation to take place. The last limitation is of importance in macroscopic thermal processes where the concept of heat energy is employed. When phenomena are described in terms of elementary atomic processes this limitation on the interconversion of energy is removed.

The requirement that all interacting bodies be included means, when strictly interpreted, that all problems are impossibly complex. For every atom in the universe, in principle, affects every other one, e.g., by the gravitational force between them. Theoretically this is true, but in practice—since our observations and measurements can be made with only finite precision—the gravitational effects of very distant bodies can be ignored as being too small for us to observe. It is in most cases possible to define in scope and nature the considerations that must be included in any problem and, thus, to reduce it to a manageable one. One may, for instance, in the case of our solar system, imagine it to be enclosed in a gigantic membrane-like envelope, isolating it from the rest of the universe. The mutual gravitational effects of the sun, its planets, and their satellites may then be considered in isolation and the conservation laws applied to this finite number of bodies to determine their motions. These calculations will, of course, be in error to the extent that the envelope is permeable to the exchange of energy with other celestial objects, but in this instance all other objects are at such a great distance that the motions of the bodies within our solar system are unaffected by them within the precision of our observations. We can conclude, however, that outer space, and its contents, whatever these may be, do not appear to determine any preferred direction in space toward which the envelope and its contents would tend to move, or along which its angular momentum would tend to align itself; nor is there any preferred point in time in relation to which the conserved quantities would tend to change.

In regard to the second limitation: namely, that all forms of energy must be taken into account, again the matter is one of seeking simplicity by judicious and acceptable approximation. In the case of our hypothetically enveloped solar system, the model is adequate for kinetic and gravitational energy, but not if radiant energy—such as that constantly emanating from the sun and stars—is included. For through this mechanism there is a constant exchange of energy in the radiant form between the external and internal regions separated hypothetically by the envelope. A different simplifying model must be sought if the conservation laws are to yield an adequate approximation to our observations in this instance. Indeed, the extension of the boundaries of our knowledge of physics has often come about through our recognition of the inadequacy or inaccuracy of the models and approximations we have introduced to make our observations agree with the conservation laws.

As an imaginary instance, consider an unexplained motion of our solar system which could possibly be accounted for by the presence of a hitherto undiscovered mass just beyond our hypothetical enveloping surface. By an expansion of the surface outward to include the mass within our gravitating system, an explanation accounting for our observation could be brought about. In a rather analogous way, new types of phenomena have been inferred from observations that were not simply accounted for in terms of the conservation laws and the extent of the energy concept existing at that time. These phenomena have later been included within the energy and momentum conservation pattern by extending the energy concept. To the initial categories of kinetic energy, gravitational energy, and the various forms of mechanical potential energy have been added the energy of interaction of electric charges, at rest and in motion; the energy associated with mass; and various energies associated with the interaction of elementary atomic and nuclear particles. The identification and incorporation of these various forms of energy within the framework of our basic concepts permits the conservation of energy principle to maintain its form and significance, while at the same time to vastly extend its range of applicability. The coordination and unification of the areas of physical science that have ensued has been a major factor in improving our understanding of the structure of matter and the world about us.

4-4 Impact of one body on another as an illustration of the conservation laws

A grasp of such simple general principles as the mechanical or dynamical conservation laws comes only through extensive experience with them and observation of their application in many instances. An illuminating example, requiring only very simple algebra, is the one in which the motion of two colliding particles or mass points is examined. By *mass point* is meant a massive body of negligible extent in space. The only forces considered are those between the two bodies; all the rest of the universe is neglected. The collision may be considered to occur between two smooth elastic spheres; or, more approximately, because of the effect of rotation and friction, to occur between two billiard balls on a smooth level table. By *collision* is meant an interaction which effectively takes place during a limited period of time; except during this brief period, the bodies are without effect on one another's motion. Long-range forces, i.e., gravitational or electrical attraction, are not here considered. We are rather considering the contact type of force between two solid objects. The analysis is applicable to long-range forces as well, but in these cases the potential energy as a function of separation must be taken into account, which adds an unnecessary complication. Perfectly smooth billiard balls that cannot transfer torque from one to another at impact are an approximate example. Rotary motion could, of course, be included in the analysis, at the expense of some additional complication.

Consider first that the only motion that takes place is along a single axis, say the x axis, and that it consists of a ball of mass m_a moving with a velocity v_0 along the positive x axis, encountering a mass m_b at rest (Fig. 4-13a). The total momentum is in the x direction, and is equal in magnitude to $m_a v_0$. After the collision each ball will, in general, be moving with presently unknown velocities along x, which may be represented by v_a and v_b respectively (Fig. 4-13b). The conservation of momentum states that:

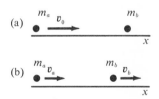

$$m_a v_a + m_b v_b = m_a v_0$$

The conservation of angular momentum is represented by the same equation multiplied on both sides by the distance from the x axis to an arbitrary point P; but as this constant factor is common to the two sides, it introduces no new condition in this example. How the conservation of energy is stated for this example depends on the further properties specified for the masses. If they are perfectly elastic, so that at contact each distorts and stores energy in the potential form (as elastic distortion at impact), and this is subsequently all returned to kinetic energy of linear motion afterwards, then the sum of the $\frac{1}{2}mv^2$ terms for each mass before the collision and after the collision is the same. If energy is lost from this form to vibratory motion of each mass (which eventually is damped down, and results in the heating of each), a quantity of energy, say $-Q$, is lost from the $\frac{1}{2}mv^2$ form. If there is an explosive cap between the masses at impact, which upon detonation liberates a quantity of energy, say Q, into the kinetic form, which in turn adds to the

Figure 4-13 *(a) Initial condition of collision example. (b) Final condition of collision example.*

total quantity, then the energy Q must be added to the $\frac{1}{2}mv^2$ term. In general, then, the conservation of energy states:

$$\tfrac{1}{2}m_a v_a{}^2 + \tfrac{1}{2}m_b v_b{}^2 = \tfrac{1}{2}m_a v_0{}^2 + Q$$

The two equations for the conservation of momentum and energy can be used to determine the only two unknown quantities, v_a and v_b, by eliminating first one and then the other between them. It is found that:

$$\frac{v_a}{v_0} = \frac{m_a}{m_a + m_b}\left\{1 - \frac{m_b}{m_a}\left[1 + \frac{(m_a + m_b)}{m_b}\frac{Q}{\frac{1}{2}m_a v_0{}^2}\right]^{\frac{1}{2}}\right\}$$

$$\frac{v_b}{v_0} = \frac{m_a}{m_a + m_b}\left\{1 + \left[1 + \frac{(m_a + m_b)}{m_b}\frac{Q}{\frac{1}{2}m_a v_0{}^2}\right]^{\frac{1}{2}}\right\}$$

Since the square root of a negative quantity does not have a physically meaningful value, it is evident that the square bracket of the above expressions can never be less than zero. This means that the fraction of the kinetic energy lost at a collision, $-Q/\frac{1}{2}m_a v_0{}^2$, can never be greater than $m_b/(m_a + m_b)$. If it is equal to this quantity, then the square bracket is zero and the final velocities are seen to be equal to one another, each being equal to $m_a/(m_a + m_b)$ times the initial velocity of m_a. This situation is thus a collision in which m_a and m_b stay together, sticking like balls of putty. This is the extreme case of the perfectly inelastic collision when the maximum possible kinetic energy disappears; the maximum possible energy loss, $[m_b/(m_a + m_b)]\frac{1}{2}m_a v_0{}^2$, evidently varies from a negligible amount if m_b is very small compared to m_a, to nearly the total amount initially present if m_b is very large compared to m_a.

If less than the maximum amount of energy disappears from the kinetic form, it is seen that the final velocities differ, and the bodies proceed along the x axis at different rates. If no energy is lost ($Q = 0$):

$$\frac{v_a}{v_0} = \frac{m_a - m_b}{m_a + m_b} \qquad \frac{v_b}{v_0} = \frac{2m_a}{m_a + m_b}$$

From these equations it is seen that m_a is brought to rest under this condition if $m_a = m_b$, and m_b then proceeds on with the initial velocity of m_a. Indeed, setting the expression for v_a equal to zero, it is seen that the general condition on Q for bringing m_a to rest is:

$$Q = \frac{m_a - m_b}{m_b}\,\tfrac{1}{2}m_a v_0{}^2$$

If $Q = 0$, the condition is $m_a = m_b$; if Q is greater than zero, m_a may be stopped only if m_a is greater than m_b; and if Q is less than zero, m_a may be brought to rest only if m_a is less than m_b. The mass m_b will, of course, always be projected forward, but m_a may move in either direction or remain at rest, depending on Q and on the ratio m_a/m_b.

The foregoing discussion can readily be generalized to include the case in which m_b as well as m_a is initially in motion along x. This is done simply by subtracting the initial velocity of m_b vectorially from all the velocities, both initial and final, of the problem (Fig. 4-14). The equations stating the conservation laws remain in just the same form, with the understanding that $v_0 = v_{0a} - v_{0b}$. The conditions are then precisely the same as before, as long as we keep in mind that the constant velocity v_{0b} is to be added to all velocities (seen in the preceding problem) after collision. So, when conditions for bringing m_a to rest are specified in the initial circumstances, these same conditions bring m_a to the velocity v_{0b} in the new circumstances. And the condition that the velocity of m_a after the collision should be zero in the new situation is that $v_a = v_{0b}$.

EXAMPLE. A baseball of mass m is thrown with a velocity v_0. It is struck by a bat of mass M, moving with velocity V_0; $-Q$ is the energy lost in the collision. Find the final velocities v of the ball, and V of the bat.

This problem is most easily solved by considering the bat at rest, and the ball travelling toward it with a relative velocity of $v_0 + V_0$. Then according to the equations derived above, subtracting $-V_0$ from all velocities:

$$\frac{v + V_0}{v_0 + V_0} = \frac{m}{m + M}\left\{1 - \frac{M}{m}\left[1 + \frac{m + M}{M}\frac{Q}{\frac{1}{2}m(v_0 + V_0)^2}\right]^{\frac{1}{2}}\right\}$$

and

$$\frac{V + V_0}{v_0 + V_0} = \frac{m}{m + M}\left\{1 + \left[1 + \frac{m + M}{M}\frac{Q}{\frac{1}{2}m(v_0 + V_0)^2}\right]^{\frac{1}{2}}\right\}$$

from which v and V may readily be found. They will, of course, turn out to be negative, because they are in the opposite direction to v_0. Notice that the velocity V_0 was added to all velocities occurring in the two equations.

Full generality can finally apply to the collision of two masses, if we recognize that each mass may possess arbitrary components of velocity in the directions of y and z without those components necessarily affecting the overall results, since neither mass exerts a force on the other in these directions. Thus there is no change of momentum or velocity in these directions as a result of the encounter, and the velocity components in these directions remain the same after collision as they were

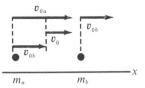

Figure 4-14 *Initial conditions when both masses are in motion, with velocities v_{0a} and v_{0b}. The velocity v_{0b} of mass m_b is first subtracted to give velocities $v_0 = v_{0a} - v_{0b}$ for m_a and $v_{0b} - v_{0b} = 0$ for m_b. This problem is solved, and then the velocity v_{0b} is added back for each mass to give the final solution.*

before collision. Of course the condition that there be a collision of this sort at all requires that the starting positions of the bodies in space be chosen—in regard to their vector velocities—so as to ensure that they will encounter one another, in a way that the line joining the centers of mass at the instant of impact coincides with the x axis.

Further reading:

EISENBUD, L., On the "Classical Laws of Motion," *American Journal of Physics*, vol. 26, p. 144 (1958).

FEINBERG, G. and GOLDHABER, M., "The Conservation Laws of Physics," *Scientific American*, vol. 209, No. 4, p. 36 (1963).

WIGNER, E. P., "Symmetry and Conservation Laws," *Physics Today*, vol. 17, No. 3, p. 34 (1964).

Problems

4-1 The rate of doing work, or the rate of expenditure of energy, is known as the power. Show that a constant force F pushing a body with velocity v is thereby using power $P = Fv$.

4-2 A man walks steadily, so as to maintain his height constant on a downward moving escalator. He claims that he is doing just as much work as if the escalator were stationary. An observer argues that the man does no work, because his height does not change and therefore there is no motion against the gravitational force. Show who is right and show all the applicable forces on a diagram.

4-3 Show that the work dW done by a gas when it expands by an amount dV is given by the relation $dW = PdV$. (Define what one means by the work done, and show that it is equal to the product of the pressure times the change in volume.)

4-4 A car moving at 30 mi./hr. slams on its brakes and stops in 100 ft. If it is assumed that the effect of braking is to apply a constant retarding force, how far will the car go if it brakes with an initial speed of 60 mi./hr.?

4-5 (a) A simple pendulum reaches the highest point of its swing. At this moment the value of g (the acceleration due to gravity) is miraculously increased by a factor of 100 (i.e., new value of $g = 100 \times$ old value of g). By what factor will the velocity at the lowest point of the swing be increased or decreased (show which), if it changes at all?
(b) If instead of g changing, the mass of the bob is increased by a factor of 100 while the bob is at the highest point of its swing, what is the effect again on the velocity at the lowest point of the swing?

4-6 A pendulum bob is released from a height *h* above the lowest point of its swing. When it reaches its lowest point, a peg catches the string at its mid point, effectively halving the length of the pendulum. To what height will the bob now rise on the right hand side of its swing? Show your reasoning.

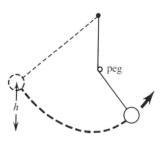

4-7 A mass *m* is swung in a circle of radius *r* about a horizontal axis by means of a string.
(a) Considering the effect of gravity, how is energy conserved?
(b) Write down the relation between the velocity v_0 at the top of the swing and the velocity v at the bottom of the swing.
(c) How much work per cycle is done by the force with which the string pulls? Explain your reasoning.

4-8 A car at the bottom of a hill of height 200 m. is towed to the summit, a distance of 1000 m. by road. At the summit the tow rope breaks and the car rolls back down the road to the bottom where it is stopped by a large rock. If a constant frictional force of 50 N. opposes the car's motion, how much energy is dissipated in towing the car? What is the total energy dissipated by the time the car is finally stopped? The mass of the car is 500 kg.

4-9 It is asserted that the total momentum of a system of objects is conserved (i.e. remains a constant) if no external forces act on the system. If a ball is shot vertically into the air, what objects are included in the system in which momentum is conserved? Describe the motion of the objects involved between the time the ball is thrown upwards and the time it returns to the earth. How is momentum conserved when a ball bounces repeatedly on the ground? How is it conserved in a tennis rally?

4-10 A boy of mass 35 kg. is sliding across a frozen pond with a speed of 10 m.sec.$^{-1}$ on a sled of mass 5 kg. A boy of mass 20 kg. drops onto the sled as it passes him. What is the speed of the sled and boys afterward?

4-11 It is observed in Russia that rivers that flow approximately North or South have a very steep right bank. Give a plausible explanation.

4-12 A man sits on a stationary frictionless turntable. The moment of inertia of the turntable plus everything on it is *I*. The man now spins a top on the turntable at a rate of 20 revolutions per second in a clockwise direction. If the top has a moment of inertia *I*/1200, describe the motion of the turntable. Give a quantitative as well as a qualitative answer and show your reasoning.

4-13 Explain the stability of a bicycle and show how and why it can be steered by the rider merely leaning to one side or the other.

4-14 A ball of mass m_1, travelling with velocity v_0, makes a head-on collision with a stationary ball of mass m_2. Both balls then move on in the same direction m_1 with velocity v_1, and m_2 with velocity v_2.

If $m_1 = 8$ kg., $m_2 = 6$ kg., $v_0 = 10$ m.sec.$^{-1}$, and $v_1 = 4$ m.sec.$^{-1}$, find the value of v_2 and hence show whether energy is gained, conserved, or lost in the collision.

4-15 Two identical plastic balls are suspended by long threads of equal length from a common support so they are in contact with one another. One of the balls is drawn away to such an extent that it rises 0.1 m. above its lowest position and is released. When it impinges on the other ball, the latter is observed to swing on in an arc that carries it 0.081 m. above its lowest position. What fraction of energy is lost from the mechanical form? To what height will the first ball return, and in which direction?

The universal law of gravitation and the motion of bodies under its influence 5

The universal law of gravitation 5-1

One of the first recorded impetuses to man's scientific thinking came from observations of the motion of the sun and the planets against the fixed position of the stars. These phenomena, that were associated with earthly seasons, provided imaginative men with inexhaustible material for speculation; they provided the practical minded with a method for measuring intervals of time. The sun and moon appear to move quite steadily among the stars, the moon completing its circuit about once a month, and the sun once a year. The apparent motion of the planets, viewed from the earth, however, is quite complicated; because of the earth's own motion, they at times appear to move forward, and at other times backward among the stars. Because of the apparently fixed position of the earth, and because of man's natural tendency to consider himself at the center of things, it was natural for the early thinkers to accept the apparent motion of these bodies about the earth, and to regard earth as a center. In the second century A.D., Claudius Ptolemy issued a dictum that led to the so-called Ptolemaic system. This system accounted for the complexities of the apparent motion of the heavenly bodies in terms of a geocentric hypothesis, and was current for nearly 1400 years, until the time of Copernicus, Kepler, and Newton.

Babylonian astronomers long before the dawn of recorded history doubtless observed the motion of the bodies in our solar system against the background of the distant stars; the earliest records show that they were adept at timekeeping by this means. The earth, however, was generally considered flat. While there were some doubts expressed in this regard, it was not until nearly the advent of the Christian era that good evidence was presented for the roundness of its surface. Still another millennium and a half elapsed before this view was generally accepted, and was convincingly demonstrated by the circumnavigation of the globe. An observation made by Eratosthenes, the librarian of Alexandria, about 200 B.C., could have greatly expedited the acceptance of the sphericity of the earth, if it had been more widely known and understood. He observed that, at Aswan, on the Upper Nile at midsummer noon, a gnomon* cast no shadow except for that cast by the bob itself, whereas at Alexandria, 5000 stadia (500 miles) to the north at the mouth of the Nile, the gnomon cast a shadow equal to $\frac{1}{8}$ of its length at the same time of day and year. Fig. 5-1 shows the geometry involved. The sun is so far away that its rays may be considered to be parallel. At midsummer noon it is directly overhead at Aswan, whereas

*A wire or thread attached to a fixed support at its upper end and stretched tautly in the vertical direction by a small, heavy bob at the lower end.

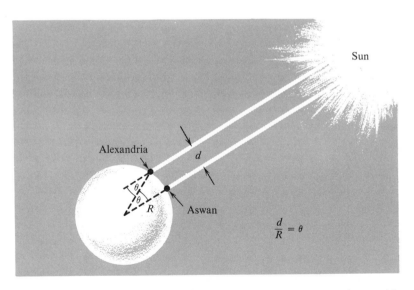

Figure 5-1   *Eratosthenes' observation on the curvature of the earth's surface.*

at Alexandria it lies to the south of the vertical by an angle at the center of the earth equal to that subtended by the distance between these cities. Eratosthenes interpreted his observations correctly and inferred that 5000 stadia represented $\frac{1}{8}$ of the radius, or about 1/50 of the circumference of the earth. The result was, then, that the circumference was 250,000 stadia. This is a very good approximation of its true value of about 24,000 miles, when the conversion factor from ancient stadia to miles is taken as 1/10.

More evidence than was available to the world during the beginning of the Christian era was necessary to persuade people that their earth was not the center of the universe. The foundation of the correct concept of the solar system was laid by the careful and accurate observation of the astronomer Tycho Brahe. Copernicus had proposed and advanced persuasive arguments for the heliocentric hypothesis, i.e., the theory that all the planets including the earth rotate about the sun. But it was Johannes Kepler who, on the basis of Tycho Brahe's observations, convinced the small body of scientific thinkers at the end of the 16th century that the sun lay at the center of the celestial bodies, which revolved around it. Kepler stated his conclusions in the form of three laws: (1) Each planet moves in an ellipse, with the sun at one of its foci; (2) The radius vector joining the planet and the sun sweeps out equal areas in the plane of the orbit in equal times; (3) The squares of the times taken to complete a revolution are proportional to the cubes of the semi-major axes for all the planetary orbits.

It remained, however, for Isaac Newton, nearly 100 years later, to demonstrate that these laws embodying the description of planetary motion were the consequences of a simpler law stating the nature of the forces that exist inherently between any two masses. This universal law of gravitation, propounded by Newton, together with the dynamical conservation laws which were discussed in Chap. 4 provide the basic description for the motion of the earth, the planets and their satellites, comets, projectiles, and rockets. This general law of gravitation formulated by Newton accounted in detail for the celestial observations which had been made with increasing precision during the preceding century. It states that the force attracting any two particles of masses m_1 and m_2, which are a distance r apart, lies along the line joining m_1 and m_2; the force is proportional in magnitude to the product of the masses, and inversely proportional to the square of the separating distance. Thus the magnitude of the force is proportional to $m_1 m_2 / r^2$. The general law is true regardless of the particular units chosen for mass and distance. But if the commonly accepted units of kilograms and meters are chosen for these quantities, and the magnitude of the force for a particular set of values of masses and separation is measured in Newtons, the numerical value of the constant of proportionality in these units is obtained. This constant—which is a universal constant applying in all instances of the gravitational attraction of masses—is commonly written as G. The universal law of gravitation would thus be written:

$$F = G \frac{m_1 m_2}{r^2}$$

The numerical value of G in units of Newton·meter squared per kilogram squared must be found from experimental observation. It cannot be determined very simply from observing the motion of the earth about the sun or the moon about the earth, because even though the distances involved can all be measured with considerable accuracy, the masses of these bodies are not known from independent measurements. Measuring the force exerted on a kilogram at the earth's surface, which is the same as measuring g (the acceleration of gravity at the earth's surface), yields the product of G and the mass of the earth M_e, if the radius of the earth is separately measured. Measuring the relative positions of the earth and moon during a month yields the product GM_eM_m, where M_m is the mass of the moon; measuring the relative positions of the sun and earth during a year yields the product GM_eM_s, where M_s is the mass of the sun. The four unknown quantities G, M_e, M_s, M_m cannot be separately determined from the three relations obtained from these measurements. However, the small effect of the sun on the moon's motion yields a relation evidently involving G, M_s, and M_m; this fourth relation, which introduces no additional unknown, does provide a way of separately arriving at the values of all four unknown quantities. Because of the smallness of the effect of the sun on the moon's motion, which can be understood by referring to Table 5-1 (which gives the values of the planetary masses and average distances of separation), we see that the precision of the value of G thus obtained is not great.

One could also measure G directly on the surface of the earth by rolling a large massive sphere up close to a mass suspended freely by a long fiber, and by observing the deflection of the fiber from the vertical caused by the presence of the sphere. A sphere is postulated because, as Newton showed, spheres of uniform density attract one another gravitationally as if the masses were all concentrated at their centers. The angular deflection, which would be d/l of Fig. 5-2, would then be given by $(m/r^2)/(M/R^2)$. If this is written in terms of the densities (masses per unit volume) of the material of the sphere ρ_s, and of the earth ρ_e:

$$\frac{d}{l} = \frac{\rho_s r}{\rho_e R}$$

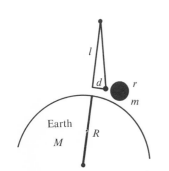

Figure 5-2 *Terrestrial measurement of the universal constant of gravitation.*

Table 5-1   Solar and planetary data

	mass (kilograms)	radius (meters)	density
Sun	1.983×10^{30}	6.953×10^{8}	1.42×10^{3}
Earth	5.983×10^{24}	6.378×10^{6}	5.52×10^{3}
Moon	7.355×10^{22}	1.738×10^{6}	3.36×10^{3}

	mean dists. from sun	earth masses	periods (days)
Sun		329390.	
Mercury	0.58×10^{11}	0.0549	87.97
Venus	1.08×10^{11}	0.8073	224.70
Earth	1.49×10^{11}	1.000	365.26
Mars	2.28×10^{11}	0.1065	686.98
Jupiter	7.78×10^{11}	314.5	4,332.59
Saturn	14.26×10^{11}	94.07	10,759.20
Uranus	28.69×10^{11}	14.40	30,685.93
Neptune	44.95×10^{11}	16.72	60,187.64
Pluto	59.00×10^{11}	—	90,885.
Moon	3.84×10^{8} (from Earth)	0.01228	27.322

$G = 6.670 \times 10^{-11} \text{ N.m.}^{2}\text{kg.}^{-2}$

Since the densest convenient material is little over twice that of the earth, and the radius of the earth is about 4000 miles, the radius of the sphere r would have to be 2 miles to cause a deflection of 1/1000. Thus this simple direct experiment is not feasible; therefore, ingenious experimental expedients and refinements must be resorted to, in order to achieve a result of even modest accuracy (See the Torsion Pendulum example of Sect. 6-2). It is regrettable that this important physical constant is not more accurately known, for it is a measure of one of the most fundamental interactions between samples of matter that is known to us. Possibly the most significant challenge to physicists today is to devise some experimental technique that would furnish a value for the universal constant of gravitation which would be several orders of magnitude more precise than the values furnished by techniques that have so far been employed. The presently accepted value for this constant from the best modern measurement is:

$$G = 6.670 \times 10^{-11} \text{ N. m.}^2 \text{ kg.}^{-2}$$

The accuracy is about 1 part in 1000; an uncertainty of about ± 6 in the place where the zero occurs in the number above. It is intriguing that the law of gravitation involves only one property of a body, namely its mass. Shape, density, chemical constitution, or other properties are irrelevant. This characteristic is common to both gravitation and inertia; the parallelism suggests that there is a more profound relationship between acceleration in general and the properties of a gravitational field than we have as yet appreciated. The experimental equivalence of acceleration and gravitation (which will be referred to again in Chap. 8, dealing with the theory of relativity) is a basic observation which has led to some very surprising—but well established and useful—conclusions. However, it is unlikely that our understanding of these matters is as yet nearly complete.

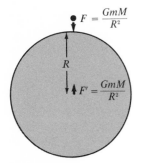

EXAMPLE. An apple of mass 0.15 kg. drops from a tree to the earth (Fig. 5-3). Describe the motion of the apple and the earth. Treat the earth as a mass point, and refer to the table of solar and planetary data.

The apple of mass m is a distance R from the center of the earth of mass M and radius R; hence the force on the apple is:

$$F = \frac{GmM}{R^2}$$

Consequently the acceleration of the apple toward the earth is:

$$a = \frac{F}{m} = \frac{GM}{R^2} = \frac{6.670 \times 10^{-11} \times 5.983 \times 10^{24}}{6.378 \times 10^6 \times 6.378 \times 10^6}$$

$$\approx 9.8 \text{ m.sec.}^{-2}$$

The force on the earth is the same as that on the apple:

$$F' = \frac{GmM}{R^2}$$

Consequently the acceleration of the earth toward the apple is:

$$a' = \frac{F}{M} = \frac{Gm}{R^2} = \frac{6.670 \times 10^{-11} \times 0.15}{6.378 \times 10^6 \times 6.378 \times 10^6}$$

$$\approx 2.5 \times 10^{-25} \text{ m.sec.}^{-2}$$

Figure 5-3 *An apple falls toward the earth. The forces on the apple and the earth are equal and opposite; so the earth also falls toward the apple.*

which, of course, is much too small to be detectable. All motion ceases the instant the apple hits the earth, if the apple does not bounce.

EXAMPLE. If a space ship were to travel away from the earth along a path so that the ship always lay on a direct line from the earth to the sun, at what distance from the earth would the net gravitational force on the ship become zero, if we neglect the presence of other planets?

The net gravitational force on the space ship is, according to Fig. 5-4:

$$F = \frac{GmM_e}{d^2} - \frac{GmM_s}{(R - d)^2}$$

where M_e is the mass of the earth, M_s the mass of the sun, and m the mass of the space ship; R is the radius of the earth's orbit (which is assumed to be constant), and d is the distance of the ship from the center of the earth. When the force is zero, then:

$$M_s d^2 = M_e(R - d)^2 = M_e R^2 - 2M_e Rd + M_e d^2$$

and hence:

$$(M_s - M_e)d^2 + 2M_e Rd - M_e R^2 = 0$$

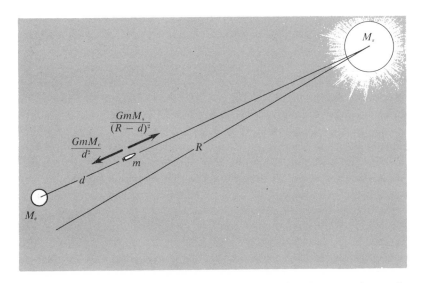

Figure 5-4 *A spaceship travelling along a direct line between the earth and the sun experiences a gravitational force due to each. At some distance d from the earth, the net force becomes zero.*

This is a quadratic equation, the solutions of which are:

$$d = \frac{-2M_eR \pm \sqrt{4M_e^2R^2 + 4(M_s - M_e)M_eR^2}}{2(M_s - M_e)}$$

$$= \frac{-M_eR \pm \sqrt{M_sM_e}\,R}{M_s - M_e}$$

The negative solution is physically meaningless, and hence the required distance is:

$$d = \left(\frac{\sqrt{M_sM_e} - M_e}{M_s - M_e}\right)R = \left(\frac{\sqrt{M_s/M_e} - 1}{M_s/M_e - 1}\right)R$$

and since M_s/M_e is much greater than 1, this may be written approximately as:

$$d \approx \frac{\sqrt{M_s/M_e}}{M_s/M_e}R = \sqrt{\frac{M_e}{M_s}}R$$

Substitution of the values given in the table of solar and planetary data (Table 5-1) then shows the distance d to be approximately 2.6×10^8 m.

5-2 Gravitational potential energy and the relation between "G" and "g"

The energy concept permits simpler statements of problems and their solutions than does a law of force. This obtains in all areas of physical science. Greater simplicity also contributes significantly to our innate understanding of the phenomena observed, and of the principles which formulate our explanation or description of them. The quantitative statement of the force of attraction between two masses may be converted into a quantitative statement of the work done in displacing those masses, relative to one another; i.e., a statement of the potential energy—in this case gravitational potential energy—stored or released in such a displacement. Since the force lies along the line of centers, the motion of either mass at right angles to this line requires no work, the force in this direction being zero. The work done, or the potential energy being stored or increased upon increasing the separation r by a small amount dr, is given by:

$$dU_p = -Fdr = G\frac{m_1m_2}{r^2}dr$$

since the rate at which the potential energy increases with r, namely (dU_p/dr), is Gm_1m_2/r^2. The negative sign is placed before F in the preceding equation, since F was earlier designated positive in cases of attraction or decreasing separation. This, then, is another example of the now familiar relation between a function, U_p in this case, and its rate of change, $(dU_p/dr) = Gm_1m_2/r^2$ in this case (Fig. 5-5). Since the rate of change is proportional to r^{-2} in this case, the general formula given in the mathematical note of Chap. 2 yields:

$$U_p = -G\frac{m_1m_2}{r}$$

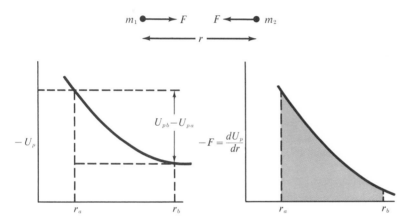

Figure 5-5   *Area under the rate curve equals the difference in ordinates of the function applied to gravitational force and to potential energy.*

This may be stated in words by saying that the area under the curve representing the force between r_a and r_b (where r_b is greater than r_a) is equal to $-Gm_1m_2(1/r_b - 1/r_a)$. Since r_b is greater than r_a, this quantity as a whole is positive (as of course it must be since work is done), and energy is stored in the gravitational form when the separation between m_1 and m_2 is increased. The reverse would be the case, and the masses would gain kinetic energy at the expense of potential energy, if the force of attraction were to accelerate them freely toward one another.

The law of gravitational attraction as stated refers to point masses. To illustrate, we can see from the table of planetary parameters that the sun and the planets have dimensions of the order of 10^{-2} to 10^{-6} times their separations. However, if one wishes to sum up the gravitational effects of all the small elements of mass that make up the totality of the earth upon some mass that is near to its surface, one appears to be faced with a problem of enormous complexity. Yet if g (the gravitational acceleration at the surface of the earth) is to be related to the general constant G, or if the gravitational effects between any extended bodies are to be calculated from the law that has been given for massive particles only, such calculations must be made. It was probably the difficulty presented by this problem that caused Newton to delay the announcement of his general theory of gravitation for 20 years or so, after he had realized that his concept of the gravitational effect between point masses provided an excellent description of planetary motion.

For a body of any shape, and one in which the density, or mass per unit volume, varies arbitrarily throughout its volume, the problem is indeed one of great difficulty. It requires laborious numerical calculations to achieve even a crude approximation of the total gravitational field, or of the gravitational potential energy of a unit test mass as a function of position. However, many simple geometries have lent themselves to mathematical analyses.

In particular, a spherically symmetrical distribution of mass, for example, a sphere of uniform density, or a sphere made up of concentric spherical shells of uniform density (the density may vary from shell to shell), presents a geometry which leads to a very simple result and furnishes quite a good approximation of gravitational phenomena near the surface of the earth. In such a geometrical configuration, the total gravitational effect is the same as the one that would be produced if the entire mass of the sphere were concentrated at its center. This conclusion was eventually demonstrated by Newton; it led to the assured application of the law of gravity to practical situations. A proof of this statement is given in a supplementary mathematical section at the end of this chapter.

This result immediately establishes a connection between the universal constant G and the gravitational constant g at the earth's surface. If the mass of the earth is M, and its radius is R, the force of attraction on a mass m, a distance y above the surface shown in Fig. 5-6 is:

$$F = G \frac{Mm}{(R + y)^2}$$

If y is small compared to R, which is generally the condition met in phenomena that occur close to the earth's surface, the factor $(R + y)^{-2}$ can be expanded by the binomial theorem, the terms of which rapidly decrease in magnitude:

$$(R + y)^{-2} = R^{-2}\left(1 + \frac{y}{R}\right)^{-2} = R^{-2}\left[1 - 2\left(\frac{y}{R}\right) + 3\left(\frac{y}{R}\right)^2 \ldots\right]$$

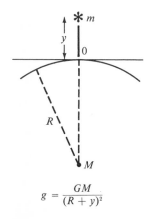

$$g = \frac{GM}{(R + y)^2}$$

Figure 5-6 *Relation between g and G in terms of the mass and radius of the earth.*

If y is less than 2 miles above the earth's surface, $(2y/R)$ is less than 10^{-3}, and $F = GMm/R^2$ to within 1 part in 1000. Since this force is equal to mg in terms of the gravitational constant g, it is seen that to a close approximation:

$$g = \frac{GM}{R^2}$$

in the immediate neighborhood of the surface of the earth. The same conclusion can, of course, be reached by equating potential energies—as given by the general law and the specific case of phenomena taking place at the earth's surface—rather than by equating forces, as has just been done.

EXAMPLE. *The total potential energy of the sun-earth-moon system.* Referring to Fig. 5-7, M_s, M_e, and M_m are the masses of the sun, earth, and moon, respectively; R is the radius of the earth's orbit, and r is the radius of the moon's orbit. Both orbits are assumed to be circular. r is so much less than R, that the position of the moon in its orbit does not affect the approximate calculation. In other words, the moon may be considered to be a distance R from the sun.

The potential energy of the earth-moon system is:

$$U_p = -\frac{GM_eM_s}{r}$$

The potential energy of the sun-earth system is:

$$U_p' = -\frac{GM_sM_e}{R}$$

and finally the potential energy of the sun-moon system is:

$$U_p'' = -\frac{GM_sM_m}{R}$$

Hence the total potential energy of the sun-earth-moon system is:

$$U_p + U_p' + U_p'' = -\frac{GM_eM_m}{r} - \frac{GM_s(M_e + M_m)}{R}$$

which, using the values from the table of solar and planetary data, is found to be:

-6.67×10^{-11}
$$\left[\frac{5.98 \times 10^{24} \times 7.36 \times 10^{22}}{3.84 \times 10^8 \times 3.84 \times 10^8} + \frac{1.98 \times 10^{30} \times 6.06 \times 10^{24}}{1.49 \times 10^{11} \times 1.49 \times 10^{11}}\right]$$
$= -6.67 \times 10^{-11} [2.99 \times 10^{30} + 5.40 \times 10^{32}]$
$= -6.67 \times 10^{-11} \times 5.43 \times 10^{32}$
$= -3.62 \times 10^{22}$ J.

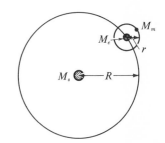

Figure 5-7   *The total potential energy of the sun-earth-moon system is the sum of the potential energy terms due to each pair of bodies.*

Notice that the magnitude of the potential energy associated with the sun and earth exceeds that associated with the earth and moon by a factor of more than 100.

EXAMPLE. *The acceleration due to gravity on the surface of the moon.* The acceleration due to gravity on the surface of any spherically symmetric planet or other body of mass M and radius R is:

$$g = \frac{GM}{R^2}$$

For the planet earth, the value is 9.80 m.sec.$^{-2}$. For the moon the value is:

$$g = \frac{6.67 \times 10^{-11} \times 7.36 \times 10^{22}}{1.74 \times 10^6 \times 1.74 \times 10^6} = 1.62 \text{ m.sec.}^{-2}$$

Thus all objects will weigh less on the moon than they would on the earth, by a factor of approximately 6. The force necessary to impart a given acceleration to an object will, of course, be the same for observers on both bodies, because this depends on inertia or mass, a property that does not change.

5-3   *Gravitational field strength and potential*

The term *field* has already been used in a general sense to indicate the field of influence of a massive body, or the region in which other massive bodies would experience a gravitational attraction due to the first body. The concept may be given quantitative embodiment by defining a *field strength* Γ at any given point as the gravitational force that a unit mass would experience if placed at that point. The field strength is obviously a vector quantity, the direction of the vector being that of the corresponding force. This quantitative use of a field is mathematically convenient. For example, once we have educed the field strength Γ (at any given point) due to some complex system of neighboring masses, we immediately know the force $\mathbf{F}$ on any object of mass m, when it is placed at that same point. $\mathbf{F}$ is the product of the field strength and the mass of the body:

$$\mathbf{F} = \Gamma m$$

The field strength at distance r from a spherical mass M is evidently given as:

$$\Gamma = G \frac{M}{r^2}$$

The field may be regarded as a physical attribute of any massive body, emanating from it and pervading all space, through which any other massive body is influenced. For example, by careful measurements it is possible to determine the gravitational field strength at any point on the earth's surface; the entire field over the earth's surface can be mapped. The force on a massive body at any point on the earth's surface is then known, although the distribution of mass within the earth which gave rise to this field was never determined.

The field concept will later be applied to other types of force, field strength always being defined as the force per unit quantity that is acted upon. The gravitational field, however, is unique in that the quantity acted upon, i.e., the mass, is also identified with the property inertia. Thus as the gravitational and inertial masses are the same, the gravitational field strength or force per unit mass may be identified with the acceleration. So over the earth's surface, the magnitude of the vector Γ is simply g, the acceleration due to gravity.

Just as it is convenient to discuss forces in terms of their related fields, it is also convenient to define a gravitational *potential* Φ at any given point as the change in gravitational potential energy when a unit mass is brought from a great distance to that point. Then if an object of mass m were brought to that point, the resultant gravitational potential energy would be:

$$U_p = \Phi m$$

The potential at distance r from a mass M is evidently given as:

$$\Phi = -G\frac{M}{r}$$

The gravitational potential is obviously a scalar quantity; hence several such potentials may be added algebraically.

EXAMPLE. A small planet of mass M has 6 distant moons, each of mass m, evenly distributed around a circular orbit of radius r. What are the values of the gravitational field strength, force, potential, and potential energy at the planet due to the moons; and what are the values of the same quantities at any one moon due to the planet and the other moons? (See Fig. 5-8a)

On the planet, the field strength due to any one moon is of magnitude Gm/r^2 and is directed outward toward the moon. The diametrically opposite moon produces an equal but oppositely directed field strength. Therefore, the net field strength due to all moons must be zero. In consequence, the force on the planet must also be zero. The potential at the planet due to any one moon is $-Gm/r$, and is a scalar quantity.

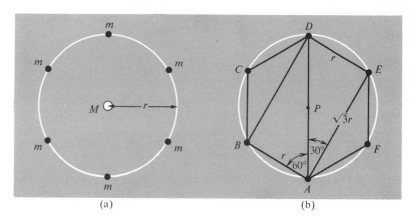

A planet of mass M has 6 moons, each of mass m, evenly distributed around a circle of radius r.

The moons are seen to lie on a hexagon of side r. The angles ABD and AED are right angles, from which the other dimensions follow.

Figure 5-8 *Calculations of fields and potentials are frequently simplified by the application of symmetry principles.*

Hence the net potential due to the six moons is $\Phi = -6Gm/r$, and the net potential energy is $U_p = -6GmM/r$.

In Fig. 5-8b, the moons are seen to lie on a hexagon, and the distance between neighboring moons is r. The angle ABD is an angle within a semicircle and, by an elementary rule of geometry, is therefore a right angle. Hence the angle BAD has a cosine of magnitude $BA/AD = r/2r = \frac{1}{2}$. Therefore the angle BAD is 60°. Similarly, the angle AED is a right angle, and the sine of the angle EAD is $r/2r = \frac{1}{2}$. Therefore the angle EAD is 30°. Also the side AE of the triangle AED is of length $\sqrt{(2r)^2 - r^2} = \sqrt{3}\,r$.

The potential at the moon A due to the planet P is $-GM/r$, and that due to the moon D is $-Gm/2r$. The moons B and F each contribute a potential $-Gm/r$, and the moons C and E, at distance $\sqrt{3}r$, each contribute a potential $-Gm/\sqrt{3}\,r$. Thus the total potential at A is:

$$\Phi = -\frac{GM}{r} - \frac{Gm}{2r} - \frac{2Gm}{r} - \frac{2Gm}{\sqrt{3}r}$$

$$= -\frac{Gm}{r}\left[\frac{M}{m} + \frac{1}{2} + 2 + \frac{2}{\sqrt{3}}\right] = -\frac{Gm}{r}\left[\frac{M}{m} + 3.655\right]$$

The potential energy of a moon is therefore:

$$U_p = -\frac{Gm^2}{r}\left[\frac{M}{m} + 3.655\right]$$

Because of the symmetry, the net field strength at A must be radially inward, any components perpendicular to this direction cancelling out. Therefore it is only necessary to sum all components in this direction. Those due to the planet P and the moon D are GM/r^2 and $Gm/(2r)^2$ respectively; those due to the moons B and F are each $(Gm/r^2) \cos 60°$; and those due to the moons C and E are each $[Gm/(\sqrt{3}r)^2] \cos 30°$. The net field strength is then:

$$\Gamma = \frac{GM}{r^2} + \frac{Gm}{4r^2} + \frac{2Gm}{r^2}\frac{1}{2} + \frac{2Gm}{3r^2}\frac{\sqrt{3}}{2}$$
$$= \frac{Gm}{r^2}\left[\frac{M}{m} + \frac{1}{4} + 1 + \frac{\sqrt{3}}{3}\right] = \frac{Gm}{r^2}\left[\frac{M}{m} + 1.827\right]$$

in a direction radially inward. The net force, also in this direction, is then:

$$F = \frac{Gm^2}{r^2}\left[\frac{M}{m} + 1.827\right]$$

EXAMPLE. Determine the effect on g, the acceleration due to gravity, of a large spherical cavern of radius 100 meters, immediately below the surface of the earth where g is to be measured. Consider the density of the earth to be uniform. (See Fig. 5-9.)

It has been shown that g is simply the value of the gravitational field strength Γ measured near the surface of the earth. Consider first the general problem of a hole of radius r whose center lies a distance d below the surface of the earth of radius R and mass M. Imagine that the hole, if filled with earth, would contain a mass m. Then the field strength at the surface of the earth, now of mass $(M + m)$, would be $G(M + m)/R^2$. But this must be the sum of the field strengths due to the filled hole of mass m, and to the true earth of mass M. As both field strengths have the same direction they may be added algebraically to yield:

$$\frac{G(M + m)}{R^2} = \frac{Gm}{d^2} + \Gamma$$

Therefore:

$$g = \Gamma = \frac{G(M + m)}{R^2} - \frac{Gm}{d^2}$$

Elsewhere on the planet, the hole would have little effect, and the value of g would be GM/R^2. Hence the change in g, on moving over the hole is:

$$\frac{GM}{R^2} - \left[\frac{G(M + m)}{R^2} - \frac{Gm}{d^2}\right] = Gm\left(\frac{1}{d^2} - \frac{1}{R^2}\right)$$

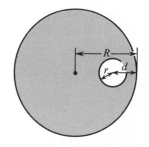

Figure 5-9 *The presence of a spherical cavern of radius r, whose center lies a distance d below the surface of the earth, will affect the value of g measured in its vicinity on the surface of the earth.*

and the fractional change in g is:

$$\frac{Gm[1/d^2 - 1/R^2]}{GM/R^2} = \frac{m}{M}\left(\frac{R^2}{d^2} - 1\right)$$

If the earth is of uniform density, then the mass of a sphere is proportional to the cube of its radius, and m/M may be written r^3/R^3. Also, since R^2/d^2 is much greater than 1, the fractional change in g becomes approximately r^3/Rd^2, which for $r = d$ simplifies to r/R. Thus in the situation above, the answer is that g decreases by an amount:

$$(r/R)g = (100/6.4 \times 10^6)9.8 = 1.5 \times 10^{-4}\text{m.sec.}^{-2}$$

or the percentage decrease in the value of g is $(r/R) \times 100 = 1.5 \times 10^{-3}\%$.

5-4 *Motion of planets and satellites*

The universal law of gravitation, together with the mechanical conservation laws, provides a completely adequate description of the motion of planets and satellites, except for small frictional or viscous retarding forces and for the complexity of calculations for close satellites where the departure of the earth from spherical symmetry becomes important. We can readily see, if we refer to the numerical values of the planetary parameters listed in Table 5-1, that although there are many bodies in the solar system, each planet may be considered to rotate about the sun independently of all the others. Since the conservation of energy is a starting point in determining the motion that takes place, a comparison of the mutual gravitational energies between pairs of celestial bodies is a good indication of the magnitude of the effects to be expected. Since the sun is of the order of a million times as massive as each of the four small close planets, and since the average distance between any two of these small planets is comparable to the separation of a planet from the sun, the perturbing effects of these on one another should be smaller in comparison with the effect of the sun, by a factor of about 10^6. Of the four larger and more distant planets, the ratio of mass-to-orbit radius is greater by a factor of about 6 for Jupiter than for Saturn, which is next in order. But the perturbing gravitational energy of Jupiter and the earth is only of the order of 10^{-4} times that of the sun and earth. The effect of this is small, but detectable.

Similarly, for the earth-moon system the perturbing effect of the sun is small, and the effects of the other planets are still smaller. So that to an excellent approximation, the rotation of a planet about the sun or of the moon about the earth may be considered a motion taking place solely under effects attributable to the two bodies concerned.

For the moment, consider a situation in which (1) the total linear momentum of the system is zero, and (2) one of the bodies is very much heavier than the other, and hence will tend to remain fixed while the lighter body moves around it. Of course the heavier body will have to move a little in the direction opposite to that of the lighter body's motion, if the total linear momentum is to remain zero. However, because its mass is so much greater, its velocity (and hence its excursion) will be very much smaller. This is the situation presented by a planet as it moves around the much heavier sun.

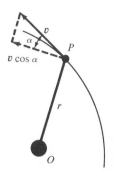

Conservation of angular momentum and Kepler's Second Law. The angular momentum L of the system must be conserved because there are no external torques acting upon it. Referring to Fig. 5-10, if v is the velocity of the light body P (of mass m), r the length of the radius vector OP from the fixed heavy body O (of mass M) to the moving light body, and α the angle between v and the perpendicular to the radius vector, then the velocity perpendicular to the radius vector is $v \cos \alpha$. Hence the angular velocity ω about the center of rotation O will be $v \cos \alpha/r$, and the angular momentum will be:

Figure 5-10 *The angular velocity ω of the light body P about the heavy body O is $v \cos \alpha /r$, since $v \cos \alpha$ is the component of the velocity v perpendicular to the radius vector OP of length r.*

$$L = mr^2\omega = mr^2 \frac{v \cos \alpha}{r} = mrv \cos \alpha$$

The area A traced out by the radius vector OP, in a time t, is shown crosshatched in Fig. 5-11. It is approximately the same as the area of the heavy black triangle. The areas are in fact identical for infinitesimally small movements. This is a simply half of the product of the base and the height of the triangle, or $dA = \frac{1}{2} (v \cos \alpha)rdt$. So the area traced out in unit time is $\frac{dA}{dt} = \frac{1}{2}rv \cos \alpha = \frac{L}{2m}$. Thus the rate at which the radius vector sweeps out area is constant. This is Kepler's second law.

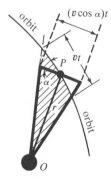

Conservation of energy and Kepler's First Law. The energy in kinetic form, on the assumption that the heavier body is at rest, is $\frac{1}{2}mv^2$; the potential energy of gravitational attraction has been seen to be $-GmM/r$. Hence the total constant sum of these energies, which is written U, is:

Figure 5-11 *Area traced out by radius vector OP in time t (shown cross-hatched) is approximately the same as the area of the heavy black triangle. $A = \frac{1}{2}(v \cos \alpha)tr$.*

$$\tfrac{1}{2}mv^2 - G\frac{mM}{r} = U$$

Eliminating the velocity v through the use of the expression for the constant angular momentum L, this expression for the conservation of energy may be written:

$$r^2 + \frac{GmM}{U}r - \frac{L^2}{2mU\cos^2\alpha} = 0$$

Recalling that the solution of a quadratic equation of the form $ax^2 + bx + c = 0$ is $x = [-b \pm (b^2 - 4ac)^{1/2}]/2a$, it is seen that r may be written in either of the two following forms:

$$r = \frac{1}{2}\left[-\frac{GmM}{U} - \left(\frac{G^2m^2M^2}{U^2} + \frac{2L^2}{mU\cos^2\alpha}\right)^{1/2}\right]$$

or:

$$r' = \frac{1}{2}\left[-\frac{GmM}{U} + \left(\frac{G^2m^2M^2}{U^2} + \frac{2L^2}{mU\cos^2\alpha}\right)^{1/2}\right]$$

Thus it is seen that there are two different values for the length of the radius vector for a given set of parameters (m, M, G, U, L, and $\cos\alpha$). This may be related to the fact that there are two values of α that give the same value of $\cos\alpha$. As we see if we compare Fig. 5-10 with Fig. 5-12, the angle between the radius vector and the normal to the orbit is the same as that between the velocity vector and the normal to the radius vector. Hence the second value r' represents a radius vector that locates the angle $-\alpha$, or α, on the other side of the normal, PN, to the orbit at the point P, as shown in Fig. 5-13.

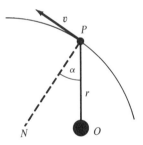

Figure 5-12   *The angle α, between the tangent to the orbit and the perpendicular to the radius vector, is also that between the radius vector and the perpendicular to the orbit, since the angle between any two lines is the same as the angle between their perpendiculars.*

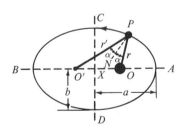

Figure 5-13   *Elliptical orbit of planetary motion of a light body P about a massive body at the point O. O and O' are the two foci of the ellipse.*

If the two solutions are added together, the second terms cancel and it is found that:

$$r' + r = -\frac{GmM}{U}$$

The sum of the two radius vectors is thus seen to be constant. Since the radius vectors are positive, it is evident that the energy U must be negative. This means that the kinetic energy term in the expression for U, in this case, cannot exceed the magnitude of the gravitational potential energy term. The curve which is the locus of a point, the sum of whose distances from two fixed points is constant, is called an ellipse. Thus it is evident that for negative values of the total energy, the path of m is elliptical; this is Kepler's first law.

The size and shape of the orbit. The ellipse has two axes of symmetry, both of which are perpendicular to the orbit. These are the lines AB and CD of Fig. 5-13. As a point proceeds along the curve, the angle α increases from the value zero at A to its maximum value at C, and again decreases to zero at B. The major axis AB through the two foci O and O' is determined by the total energy U. For:

$$2a = AO' + BO' = AO' + AO = r' + r = -\frac{GmM}{U}$$

The length of the minor axis $2b$ depends upon the angular momentum of the system as well as upon its energy. Fig. 5-14 shows the geometry for a point on the curve and on the minor axis where the value of α is maximum. From the figure:

$$2b = 2[(OC)^2 - (OX)^2]^{1/2}$$

Since OC and $O'C$ are equal, and their sum is equal to $r + r'$, which is the constant $-(GmM/U)$, then $OC = -(GmM/2U)$. Also OX is evidently equal to $(r' - r)/2$ when α is zero. Using these relations and the expressions for r' and r:

$$2b = 2\left[\left(\frac{G^2m^2M^2}{4U^2}\right) - \frac{1}{4}\left(\frac{G^2m^2M^2}{U^2} + \frac{2L^2}{mU}\right)\right]^{1/2}$$

$$b = L(-2mU)^{-1/2}$$

Thus the length of the major axis of the orbit is determined by the energy and that of the minor axis by both energy and angular momentum.

Obviously the largest value that the minor axis can have is equal to the value of the major one, in which case the ellipse becomes a circle. The corresponding maximum value for L, which is found by equating a and b, is then:

$$L_{\max} = Gm^2M(-2mU)^{-1/2}$$

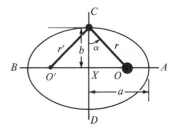

Figure 5-14 *The lengths of the major axis 2a and minor axis 2b of an elliptical orbit are determined by the total energy E and the angular momentum L.*

It is also seen on referring to the expressions for r and r' that this is the largest value L can have and still avoid the square root's becoming negative.

If the ratio of b to a for a general elliptical orbit is inspected, it is seen to be proportional to $(-U)^{1/2}$ if L is constant. Thus if the energy in the mechanical form U were to be decreased through frictional forces and to assume a larger negative value, the ratio (b/a) would increase toward unity; or, the orbit would become more circular. The planetary orbits and the lunar orbit are nearly circular, as would be the expected result from tidal motion and other viscous impediments continuously converting mechanical energy into heat during the life of the solar system. The orbits of earth satellites that pass through the atmosphere during their revolutions also tend to become successively more circular because of the loss of energy caused by the atmosphere's viscous drag on their motion.

The preceding discussion of orbit sizes and shapes has been limited to those cases in which the total energy was negative; or, in other words, to those cases in which the amount of kinetic energy was smaller than the magnitude of the negative gravitational potential energy. The limit of these cases is that for which U becomes so small that it approaches zero. This condition applies to an orbit whose major axis increases in proportion to $(1/-U)$ to a very great value. The two sides of the orbit tend to become parallel with the separation $2b$, which increases evidently as $(1/-U)^{1/2}$ for a constant angular momentum L. This is the parabolic orbit shown in Fig. 5-15, where r' becomes an infinite quantity and the potential energy and kinetic energy both become zero at this great distance from the focus O. This is the limiting case between positive and negative values of the total energy U.

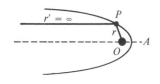

Figure 5-15 *Parabolic orbit obtained for zero binding energy. The two sides of the orbit become parallel at infinity, when the velocity of the light body P is zero.*

Finally there are the orbits of comets and interplanetary vehicles that have finite positive energies at great distances, i.e., they have a positive value for the total energy U. These orbits would be the only ones possible if the force between the two bodies were repulsive rather than attractive. These orbits are such that the line intersecting a point P at the angle $-\alpha$ with the normal to the orbit diverges from the major axis, and must be projected back to meet it, as illustrated in Fig. 5-16. The solid curve on the left represents the orbit for an attractive force between P and O, or a repulsive force between P and O'; the symmetrically placed dashed curve represents an orbit which would be generated by a repelling force emanating from O, or an attracting force emanating from O'. The previous derivation of the elliptical orbits need only be altered by changing the sign of the backward projected radius vector r' to obtain the equation of these orbits. Thus:

$$r' - r = \frac{GmM}{U}$$

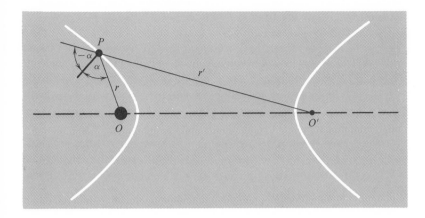

Figure 5-16 *Hyperbolic orbit obtained for a total energy which is posi-*
tive. The light body P is deflected, but never captured into a bound orbit.
O' would be the second focus for the hypothetical case of a negative
gravitational force, or for −G.

This equation describes the third type of conic section known as a
hyperbola. A hyperbola is defined as the locus of points, the difference
between whose distances from two fixed points is a constant.

The period of the orbit and Kepler's Third Law. Kepler's third law follows simply and directly from three of the relations already derived.
First it was seen that, for any orbit, the area traced out in unit time by
the radius vector joining the fixed heavy body and the moving light body
is $L/2m$. So the time taken to complete a revolution is $T = A/(L/2m)$,
where A is the area of the ellipse. The area A of an ellipse is πab, where
$2a$ and $2b$ are the respective lengths of the major and minor axes. Then
inserting the values already found for $2a$ and $2b$, it is seen that:

$$T = \frac{\pi}{4}\left(\frac{GmM}{-U}\right)\left(\frac{L}{\sqrt{-\frac{1}{2}mU}}\right)\left(\frac{2m}{L}\right)$$

which may be written:

$$T^2 = \frac{4\pi^2}{GM}\left(\frac{G^3m^3M^3}{-8U^3}\right) = \frac{4\pi^2}{GM}a^3$$

The proportionality between T^2 and a^3 is Kepler's third law, since the
term $4\pi^2/GM$ is constant for all the planets.

Planetary motion in which both masses are finite. In the preceding discussion it has been assumed that the heavier mass was so great that, in
effect, it did not move at all. Clearly this is an approximation that is not
strictly true; the motion of the more massive body should be taken into

consideration, if we are to give a complete account. The two bodies of masses m_1 and m_2 and velocities v_1 and v_2 are shown in Fig. 5-17. If the total momentum is to remain at a constant value, which may be chosen to be zero, then the two bodies must move in opposite directions with equal momenta; so that $m_1v_1 = m_2v_2$, and v_1 and v_2 make the same angle with the line joining m_1 and m_2. Since m_1 and m_2 move in opposite directions, it follows that there must be some point on the line joining them that is instantaneously at rest. This is the point O, shown in Fig. 5-17. In a short time interval dt, the bodies will have moved distances v_1dt and v_2dt, such that the new line joining them intersects the original line at O. Another way of stating this is to say that the bodies have equal angular velocities about O.

$$\frac{v_1 \cos \alpha}{r_1} = \frac{v_2 \cos \alpha}{r_2} \qquad \text{and} \qquad v_1 = \frac{r_1}{r_2} v_2$$

which, together with the condition $m_1v_1 = m_2v_2$, gives:

$$m_1r_1 = m_2r_2 = m_2(r - r_1)$$

where the distance between the two bodies is $r = r_1 + r_2$. This leads to:

$$r_1 = \frac{m_2r}{m_1 + m_2} \qquad r_2 = \frac{m_1r}{m_1 + m_2}$$

In agreement with the earlier treatment, if m_2 is much greater than m_1, then $r_1 \approx r$ and $r_2 \approx 0$.

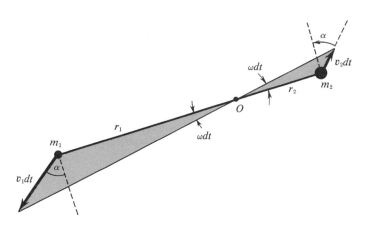

Figure 5-17 *The line joining two mutually attractive bodies (masses m_1 and m_2) rotates about a point O such that $r_1 = m_2r/(m_1 + m_2)$ and $r_2 = m_1r/(m_1 + m_2)$, where $r = r_1 + r_2$.*

The mutually attractive force on each body is:

$$F = \frac{Gm_1m_2}{r^2}$$

which can be written for m_1 in terms of r_1 as:

$$F_1 = G\left(\frac{m_2}{m_1 + m_2}\right)^2\left(\frac{m_1m_2}{r_1^2}\right) = G\frac{m_1m_2'}{r_1^2}$$

where:

$$m_2' = m_2\left(\frac{m_2}{m_1 + m_2}\right)^2$$

Thus m_1 obeys an inverse square law of force as it orbits about O; but the central mass m_2 is effectively modified to the value m_2'. The earlier equation derived for a stationary central mass M can then be taken over completely by writing r_1 for r, m_1 for m, and m_2' for M. Thus:

$$r_1^2 + \frac{Gm_1m_2'}{U_1}r_1 - \frac{L_1}{2m_1U_1\cos^2\alpha} = 0$$

where $L_1 = m_1r_1v_1\cos\alpha$ and $U_1 = \frac{1}{2}m_1v_1^2 - Gm_1m_2'/r_1$. Similarly the orbit equation may be used for the motion of mass m_2, if m_1 is replaced by:

$$m_1' = m_1\left(\frac{m_1}{m_1 + m_2}\right)^2$$

and r by r_2, etc. Of course the total angular momentum $L = L_1 + L_2$ and the total energy $U = U_1 + U_2$ remain constant, as can be seen by forming these quantities. The orbits of two mutually attractive bodies are shown in Fig. 5-18.

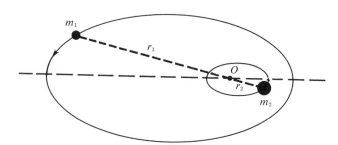

Figure 5-18 *The orbits of a mutually attractive light body (mass m_1) and a heavy body (mass m_2) moving about a point O which is a focus of both ellipses.*

The apparent restriction of choosing the net momentum of a system to be zero, so that there is a stationary point O about which both masses can rotate, is not in fact a limitation. If the system has net momentum p in some given direction, then, since the total mass of the system is $m_1 + m_2$:

$$p = (m_1 + m_2)V$$

where V is the net velocity of the system in the given direction. By subtracting this constant velocity vectorially from both v_1 and v_2, the velocities of both m_1 and m_2 about the center of motion O are obtained. Thus the linear and rotational motions may be separated, and the latter remains in accord with the description that has been given:

EXAMPLE. A comet is observed as it passes through our solar system. Its closest approach to the sun is a distance r of 6.67×10^{10} meters, at which time it has a velocity v of 6.20×10^4 m.sec.$^{-1}$. Will the comet ever return to our solar system, and if so, when? (See Fig. 5-19)

The total energy of the comet, of mass m say, is the sum of the kinetic and potential forms:

$$U = \frac{1}{2}mv^2 - \frac{GmM}{r}$$

$$= m\left(\frac{v^2}{2} - \frac{GM}{r}\right)$$

$$= m\left(\frac{38.4 \times 10^8}{2} - \frac{6.67 \times 10^{-11} \times 1.98 \times 10^{30}}{6.67 \times 10^{10}}\right)$$

$$= m\,(19.2 \times 10^8 - 19.8 \times 10^8)$$

$$= -m \times 6 \times 10^7 \text{ J., if } m \text{ is in kg}$$

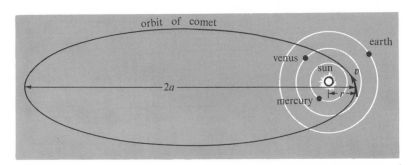

Figure 5-19 A measurement of the distance r of closest approach of a comet to the sun, and of the comet's velocity v at this point is sufficient to determine the length 2a of the major axis of the orbit, and hence the period T of the orbit.

Because the total energy is negative, the orbit must be a closed ellipse and the comet will return. The period T of the motion is expressed as a function of the semimajor axis a, which in turn is expressed as a function of the total energy U by the following equations:

$$T = 2\pi \sqrt{\frac{a^3}{GM}}$$

where $a = -GmM/2U$. Hence:

$$T = 2\pi \sqrt{\frac{G^2M^2}{4}\left(\frac{-m}{2U}\right)^3} = \frac{\pi GM}{(-U/m)\sqrt{-2U/m}}$$

$$= \frac{\pi \times 6.67 \times 10^{-11} \times 1.98 \times 10^{30}}{6 \times 10^7 \sqrt{12 \times 10^7}} \approx 0.63 \times 10^9 \text{ sec.}$$

$$= \frac{0.63 \times 10^9}{3600 \times 24 \times 365} \approx 20 \text{ years}$$

Notice that, because the difference of two approximately equal quantities is taken in deriving the total energy, the results are only accurate to one figure—although the initial data were accurate to three figures. This is clearly unfortunate; whenever possible, the observations should be made in a way that will avoid such degradation in the precision of the result.

EXAMPLE. *The axis of the earth-moon system.* Since the earth does not have infinite mass, it must describe an orbit of small radius r (Fig. 5-20) in order to balance the linear momentum of the moon which constantly changes direction: This motion of the earth is, of course, independent of its rotation and its motion about the sun. From the equations in the text, if R is the distance between the earth and the moon, and M and m are the masses of the earth and moon respectively, then:

$$r = \frac{mR}{M+m}$$

$$= \frac{7.4 \times 10^{22} \times 3.8 \times 10^8}{6.0 \times 10^{24} + 7.4 \times 10^{22}} = \frac{7.4 \times 3.8 \times 10^6}{6.1}$$

$$= 4.6 \times 10^6 \text{m.}$$

This value should be compared with the earth's radius, which is about 6.4×10^6 meters. Thus the earth, as it moves around the sun, "wobbles" about an axis that is displaced from the earth's rotational axis by approximately two-thirds of the earth's radius.

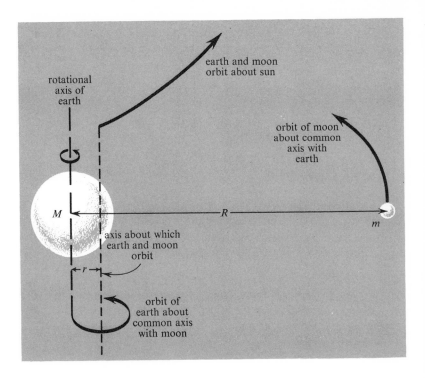

Figure 5-20 *Orbital motion of the moon and the earth about a common axis.*

EXAMPLE. *Total orbital energy and angular momentum of the moon.* If the moon's orbit is assumed to be circular, then the radius $(R - r)$ of the orbit is related to the total orbital energy U by the formula:

$$2(R - r) = \frac{GmM}{-U}$$

where m and M are the mass of the moon and the earth respectively. Therefore:

$$U = \frac{-GmM}{2(R - r)}$$

$$= \frac{-6.7 \times 10^{-11} \times 7.4 \times 10^{22} \times 6.0 \times 10^{24}}{2 \times 3.8 \times 10^{8}}$$

$$= -3.9 \times 10^{28} \text{ J}.$$

For a given energy U, the angular momentum is a maximum for a circular orbit and has been shown to be:

$$L = GM \sqrt{\frac{m^3}{-2U}}$$

$$= 6.7 \times 10^{-11} \times 6.0 \times 10^{24} \sqrt{\frac{(7.4 \times 10^{22})^3}{7.8 \times 10^{56}}}$$

$$= 4.0 \times 10^{14} \sqrt{5.2 \times 10^{38}}$$

$$= 2.9 \times 10^{34} \text{ kg.m.}^2\text{sec.}^{-2}$$

Escape velocity and space travel. For circular orbits:

$$r = r' = \frac{GmM}{-2U}$$

where:

$$U = \frac{1}{2} mv^2 - \frac{GmM}{r}$$

If the value obtained for U in the first equation is now substituted in the second equation, then:

$$-\frac{GmM}{2r} = \frac{1}{2} mv^2 - \frac{GmM}{r}$$

which leads to:

$$v = \sqrt{\frac{GM}{r}}$$

The velocity for a satellite which is put into an orbit of radius just a little greater than the earth's radius R is evidently given approximately by $\sqrt{GM/R}$. Using the values: $G = 6.67 \times 10^{-11}$ Newton·meter²·kilogram^{-2}; $M_{earth} = 5.98 \times 10^{24}$ kg.; $R_{earth} = 6.38 \times 10^6$ m. We find the velocity to be 7.9 km. per sec. The time to make a complete circuit of the earth is the circumference divided by this velocity, or 84.5 minutes. If the satellite were as much as 30 miles above the surface, the velocity would differ from the given value only by about one percent.

The velocity of a satellite in orbit close to the earth is not much less than the velocity which would enable a rocket, unimpeded by the earth's atmosphere, to escape entirely from the earth's gravitational attraction and to traverse outer space. Since the gravitational potential energy of a mass m on the surface of the earth is $-GmM/R$, the energy that would have to be supplied for a satellite to move vertically against gravity to a very great distance, at which the gravitational energy would rise from

$-GmM/R$ to approximately zero, would be GmM/R. Setting this equal to the initial kinetic energy assumed to be imparted to it:

$$\frac{1}{2}mv^2 = \frac{GmM}{R}$$

or:

$$v = \sqrt{2GM/R}$$

This is $\sqrt{2}$ times the orbital velocity, or about 11.2 kilometers per second.

Of course, if the interplanetary vehicle is to go from the earth to the moon, and to land on the latter body without a damaging impact, it must be equipped with a retarding rocket that will reverse the velocity it will acquire in falling freely to the moon's surface. This is clearly the velocity given by:

$$\frac{1}{2}mv^2 = \frac{GmM_m}{R_m}$$

where the subscripts m refer to the moon. This is in the ratio $(M_mR_e/M_eR_m)^{1/2}$ to the velocity of escape from the earth. Inserting the values from the table of solar and planetary data, we find this value to be a little over two-tenths of the escape velocity from the earth, or 2.37 km. per sec. One may visualize the basic problem of space travel in terms of the gravitational potential surface due to the celestial bodies, as shown in cross-section in Fig. 5-21. Each body in this picture—sun, planet, and moon—is at the bottom of a funnel-like well, the base of which is the surface of the body; the walls are generated by rotating the potential curve GM/r about the vertical axis. The flaring lips of these funnels fit smoothly together in what is nearly a horizontal zero-potential plane, stretching throughout space, except where the presence of these masses disturbs it. The depth of each funnel is, of course,

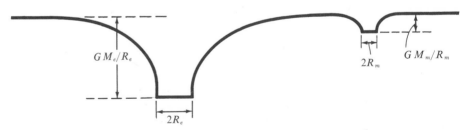

Figure 5-21 *Schematic section through the potential energy surface along the earth-moon line.*

GM/R, where M and R are the mass and radius respectively of the body. To navigate from the surface of any body to that of any other, enough energy (GmM/R) must be supplied to lift the space vehicle of mass m up from the surface, and out of the local funnel. The vehicle must then be directed toward the desired objective, and on its way it must avoid coming so close to undesired bodies as to fall onto, or to come too close to their surfaces. Finally, on reaching its objective, it must be able to slow up its descent into this terminal funnel to such an extent that the impact is tolerable. These funnels or dimples in the potential surface move about through space with the motion of the planets and the moon. The astronaut must have a thorough knowledge of the changing spatial potential landscape for successful navigation.

Supplementary mathematical section   5-5

The following is proof that the gravitational potential energy of a mass m, in the external neighborhood of a uniform spherical shell of mass M, is the same as it would be if M were concentrated at the center of the shell.

Consider the ring section of the spherical shell that would be cut out by two close planes perpendicular to the line from the mass m to the center of the shell, as shown in Fig. 5-22. This is the ring that would be

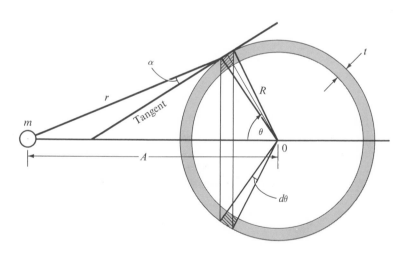

Figure 5-22   *Section through the center of a spherical shell in the plane of an external point mass m.*

swept out by rotating the segment subtended by the angle $d\theta$ at the angle θ with the line mO about this line. Every part of this ring is at the distance r from m; if the thickness of the shell is t, its cross-sectional area is $tR d\theta$, and its volume is this times its length, which is $2\pi(R \sin \theta)$. Thus the volume of the ring is $2\pi R^2 t \sin \theta d\theta$. If the mass per unit volume of the material of the shell is ρ, the mass of the ring is $2\pi\rho R^2 t \sin \theta d\theta$. The potential energy of the mass m due to the mass of the ring is then:

$$dU_p = -\frac{Gm}{r}(2\pi\rho R^2 t \sin \theta d\theta)$$

The volume of the whole shell is its area, $4\pi R^2$, times t. Hence its mass M is given by $4\pi R^2 t\rho$. Therefore, the potential energy of the mass m and the ring is:

$$dU_p = -GmM \frac{\sin \theta d\theta}{2r}$$

From the triangle formed by R, A, and r, and from the trigonometric relation that sides are proportional to the sines of opposite angles:

$$\frac{r}{\sin \theta} = \frac{A}{\sin (\pi/2 + \alpha)} = \frac{A}{\cos \alpha}$$

The last equality results from the fact that the sine of any angle plus a right angle is the same as the cosine of the angle. Also, the change in r between the two edges of the ring dr is $(R d\theta) \cos \alpha$, which is the projection of the ring width along the circumference on the direction r, making the angle α with the circumference at that point.

Therefore:
$$\frac{\sin \theta d\theta}{2r} = \frac{\cos \alpha}{2A} \frac{dr}{R \cos \alpha} = \frac{dr}{2AR}$$

and:
$$dU_p = \frac{-GmM}{2AR} dr$$

The rate at which U_p changes with r is thus the constant $-(GmM/2AR)$, and the value of U_p for the whole shell is the area under the rate curve, which is the straight line at this height, and the difference between the two limits of r, namely, $(A + R)$ and $(A - R)$. This difference is clearly $2R$; so the potential energy of the mass m, and the shell of mass M with its center at the distance A is:

$$U_p = \frac{-GmM}{A}$$

This is the same as if the mass M were concentrated at A. A sphere made up of spherical shells of uniform density clearly has a mass equal to the sum of the masses of the shells; and, as each of these has the same effect as if it were located at its center, the potential energy of a mass m at the distance A from such a sphere of mass M is evidently given by the same expression as has been derived for one shell.

Further reading:

ADAMS, C. C., *Space Flight*, McGraw-Hill Book Company (1958).

DICKE, R. H., "Gravitational Theory and Observation," *Physics Today*, vol. 20, No. 1, p. 55 (1967).

DICKE, R. H., "The Eötvös Experiment," *Scientific American*, vol. 205, No. 6, p. 84 (1961).

EHRICKE, K. A. and GAMOW, G., "A Rocket Around the Moon," *Scientific American*, vol. 196, No. 6, p. 47 (1957).

KOLOSSVARY, B. G., "Eötvös: Balance," *American Journal of Physics*, vol. 27, No. 5, p. 336 (1959).

Problems

5-1 (a) "A body which is well removed from any other bodies in space is almost weightless and massless." Very briefly discuss the truthfulness of this, giving reasons for your conclusions.
(b) "The gravitational forces on two mutually attracting bodies are equal to one another. Therefore if I throw a ball in the air, it attracts the earth with a force equal to that with which the earth attracts it. Therefore the acceleration of the ball will equal the acceleration of the earth." Is this statement correct? If not, what is wrong with it?

5-2 Two spherical space ships, each 4 m. in radius and of 10^4 kg. of mass are travelling on parallel paths some distance apart. When they are drawn together by the gravitational force between them, show that the impact is less than if one had fallen through a height of about 10^{-8} m. to the surface of the earth.

5-3 Three masses, 3, 5 and 7 kg., are placed at the corners of an equilateral triangle with a distance of 2 m. between any pair of masses. Calculate the total potential energy of the system. Assume the Universal gravitational constant to be $G = 7 \times 10^{-11}$ J. m. kg.$^{-2}$.

5-4 The density of oil is about one fifth that of rock. If the subterranean cavern of Sec. 5-3 be filled with oil, thus representing an oil basin, deduce a formula for the fractional change in g to be expected on moving over this oil basin of radius r and depth d.

5-5 (a) What is the magnitude and direction of the gravitational force on each of the masses in the figure?
(b) What is the field strength and the potential at each mass, due to the presence of the others?
(c) What is the total potential energy of the system?

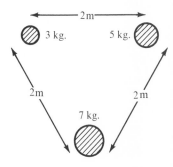

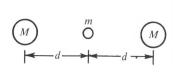

5-6 (a) If the earth, of radius 6.4×10^6 m., is assumed to consist of a spherical core of iron of density 8.0×10^3 kg.m.$^{-3}$ surrounded by a shell of rock of density 4.0×10^3 kg.m.$^{-3}$, calculate the radius of this iron core that will yield the value of $g = 9.8$ m.sec.$^{-2}$ at the earth's surface. Assume the universal gravitational constant G to be 6.7×10^{-11} N.m.^{2}. kg.$^{-2}$.

(b) Show that the above distribution of density then gives approximately the correct average density of 5.5×10^3 kg.m.$^{-3}$ for the earth.

5-7 Derive the relationship between velocity and radius for a circular orbit by use of the formula for centripetal force.

5-8 What is the radius of the orbit of a satellite that remains fixed above one point of the earth's surface? Can any point on the earth's surface be thus perpetually surveyed? Explain.

5-9 Show that, for an orbit of zero angular momentum, the central body would be at the extreme end of the orbit. Of course such an orbit would be unrealizable in practice because the orbiting body would have to pass through the central body; however, this difficulty is to be ignored.

5-10 When light is reflected from a smooth surface, the reflected rays leave the surface at the same angle as the incident rays, only on the opposite side of the normal to the surface. What would be the ideal shaped reflector for collecting all the light emitted from a point source and focussing it onto another point? (This is also the principle of a "whispering gallery"). What would be the ideal shape for a reflector to produce a parallel beam of light from a point source?

5-11 What is the value of the gravitational potential experienced by a satellite moving in a circular orbit with velocity v?

5-12 If one of the space ships described in the second problem were to be orbiting the earth with a period of 100 min. and were to fire a rifle bullet of mass 10^{-2} kg. at 10^3 m. sec.$^{-1}$ at right angles to its path, through what angle would its trajectory be turned?

5-13 An artificial earth satellite A is observed to make one revolution around the earth in two hours. A second satellite B is observed to take 8 hrs. to complete one revolution about the earth. What is the ratio of the distances r_A/r_B from the center of the earth to each satellite?

5-14 Show that, for two finite mutually attracting orbiting masses, the sum of their individual energy terms, as derived in the text, does in fact give the expected total energy of the system.

5-15 Given that the moon's radius is about $\frac{1}{4}$ that of the earth, and the moon's mass is about $\frac{1}{80}$ that of the earth, find the approximate ratio of the values for (a) the "acceleration due to gravity" on the two surfaces and (b) the "escape velocity" for the two surfaces. You may neglect the effect of either sphere on conditions at the other.

Simple harmonic motion and waves 6

The planetary motion considered in the preceding chapter is characterized by a regularly recurring configuration of the two masses, with periods of time varying from 84.5 minutes for a close earth satellite to a month in the case of the earth and moon, or to about 165 years in the case of the rotation of the most distant planet, Neptune, about the sun. Except in the case of the satellite penetrating the earth's atmosphere, the rate of energy loss from the kinetic and potential forms to the form of heat is very small. In the instances of the motion of common objects in laboratories or elsewhere on the surface of the earth, the frictional and viscous forces tend to reduce much more rapidly the amplitude of any motion generated. This is certainly just as well, for it provides a world to live in where objects tend to stay at rest. The book remains on the table, the table stays in place in the room, the components of the house and the materials of the earth's crust are all retained in fixed relative positions by frictional forces. In many instances the frictional forces are so great in comparison with any others that any impulse applied results simply in a subsequent static situation differing from the first only by a slight displacement. If some kinetic energy is imparted to a book lying on a table, it moves under the influence of the retarding force of friction along the table top; after an amount of work equivalent to the initial kinetic energy is done against the frictional force, the book comes to rest a few inches or feet away. On the other hand, wind soughing about the house will make its windows rattle and its fabric vibrate—particularly if it is lightly built. These vibrations will, however, rapidly die down when the wind falls and ceases to supply the energy necessary to maintain them.

Instances of such vibratory or oscillatory motion are seen on every hand. The familiar oscillations of the pendulum of a clock are maintained by the energy stored from winding a spring or raising a weight. The oscillations imparted to the beam of a balance, or to a mass suspended by a spring, slowly die down with time. The oscillatory motion of a paddle dipping into a liquid gives rise to waves on its free surface. Metal bars and taut strings also readily exhibit this type of vibratory motion. All of the information that reaches our ears comes in the form of vibrations in the air. This information has acquired vibratory motion from vocal chords, the diaphragms of loud speakers, musical instruments, or from the shocks and vibratory impulses imparted to the air by objects around us. The telephone, telegraph, radio, radar, and television all involve the transmission of electromagnetic oscillations; our vision results from the impinging upon our retinas of the still higher frequency electromagnetic waves that we call light.

This type of motion is so omnipresent and so pervasive throughout our physical experience that it merits careful consideration on its own account. Its study also provides us with the important concepts of both harmonic or oscillatory motion and of wave motion, which is the propagation of oscillatory effects from one place to another. These concepts are important for the description of large-scale phenomena, and are extensible to the description of phenomena on an atomic scale as well. The inclusion in our considerations here of frictional or viscous forces, which are said to "damp" such motion through the conversion of mechanical energy into the form of heat, would unduly complicate this presentation without contributing to our understanding. In many instances, indeed, the effects of such nonconservative forces may be reduced to present only a very small correction to the results obtained when these effects are omitted from consideration entirely. For these reasons, then, this aspect of real vibratory motion is here neglected.

All oscillatory motion is characterized by the alternate conversion and reconversion of energy between two forms. In the case of the free pendulum the forms are kinetic and gravitational potential energy; in that of the balance wheel of a watch the forms are kinetic energy of rotation and potential energy of distortion in the spring; in the case of sound waves there is the kinetic energy of air motion and the potential energy stored in the compression of air; etc. A picture is always helpful: one may, for specificness, consider a marble or a ball bearing released on the inner surface of a smooth bowl, such as that shown in section in Fig. 6-1. It rolls from rest down the side, acquiring its maximum kinetic energy at the bottom. Then it mounts the opposite side, gradually losing kinetic energy and gaining gravitational potential energy until it comes to rest at the same height as that at which it was released. The motion then repeats in the opposite sense, and alternates indefinitely. The

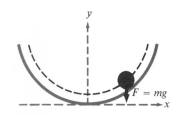

Figure 6-1   *Ball oscillating in a bowl.*

difference between the potential energy of the ball at any point at a height y above the bottom and its potential energy exactly at the bottom is mgy, where m is the mass of the ball. The law of conservation of energy then states that:

$$\tfrac{1}{2}mv^2 + mgy = U$$

Here the rotational energy of the ball has been neglected; v is its velocity along the inside of the bowl, and U is the constant total energy. If the height of the point of release is y_0, then $U = mgy_0$, and the velocity at the bottom is given by: $v = \sqrt{2gy_0}$.

The effect of the shape of the bowl on the character of the motion has not been mentioned. An important general conclusion can be reached for oscillations of small amplitude by considering the motion in a bowl of any shape, provided only that the shape of the bowl resembles that of the figure in symmetry about the y axis and in tangency at the xy origin. It should be noted that potential energy, which is proportional to y, is represented graphically as a function of the lateral displacement x by the bowl contour, as shown in Fig. 6-2.

An arbitrary curve such as the bowl contour may be expressed as an ascending power series in x in the neighborhood of the origin.

$$y = a_0 + a_1x + a_2x^2 + a_3x^3 + a_4x^4 + \cdots\cdots\cdots$$

The a's are arbitrary, and by choosing them properly, any curve of this nature can be closely approximated. In the present case, since the origin is on the curve: $a_0 = 0$. Also, since the curve is symmetrical (i.e., y has the same value for $+x$ as it has for $-x$, for any value of x), odd powers of x that would add to y for x positive, and subtract from it for x negative, must not appear; i.e.: a_1, a_3, a_5, etc. must all be zero, or:

$$y = a_2x^2 + a_4x^4 + \cdots\cdots$$

Finally, if the coefficients of the powers of x—namely, the a's—are not too greatly different from one another in magnitude, the successive terms in the series decrease rapidly in magnitude for small values of x and

$$y = a_2x^2\left(1 + \frac{a_4}{a_2}x^2 + \cdots\cdot\right)$$

becomes approximately

$$y = a_2x^2$$

The argument is indeed a very general one, and one not limited to the specific example of the bowl. If the nature of the potential energy stored in any system as a result of some disturbance from its equilibrium posi-

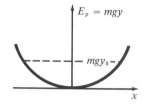

Figure 6-2 *The contour of a bowl forms a graphical representation of the potential energy mgy as a function of the lateral displacement x.*

tion resembles the contour of the curve in symmetry and in magnitude of the coefficients (the a's), a good approximation to the potential energy for displacements of small amplitudes is that the potential energy is proportional to the square of the displacement. The general relation between a function and its rate of change (a relation that has already been referred to so frequently) then states that the force that resists a small displacement from equilibrium is proportional to the displacement:

$$U_p = ax^2$$
$$F = -dU_p/dx = -2ax$$

The minus sign indicates that the force is in the opposite direction to the lateral displacement x. It is usual to use another constant k, such that $k = 2a$. Then

$$U_p = \tfrac{1}{2}kx^2$$
$$F = -kx$$

This is an empirical law long known in physics as *Hooke's Law*. The general form of the conservation of energy equation for small oscillations of a mass m, let us say, along the x axis, under the influences of a restoring force equal to k per unit displacement, is:

$$\tfrac{1}{2}mv_x^2 + \tfrac{1}{2}kx^2 = U$$

6-2   *Simple harmonic motion*

The type of motion implied by the equation for the conservation of energy that has just been developed is called *simple harmonic motion*. It is a simple periodic motion in which a given displacement x, and the associated velocity dx/dt, or v_x, recur at regular intervals of time T, known as the *period* of the motion. The sine and cosine functions introduced in Chap. 2 will now be shown to accurately describe simple harmonic motion as a function of the time t. Since the cosine of an angle has a maximum possible value of 1, which recurs at angular intervals of 2π, the expression for the displacement

$$x = A \cos\left(2\pi \frac{t}{T}\right)$$

will have maxima equal to A which will recur at intervals of time T, as $t = 0, T, 2T, 3T$, etc. This periodicity is illustrated in Fig. 6-3. A is

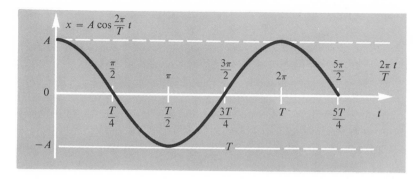

Figure 6-3   *The displacement of simple harmonic motion has a regularly recurring pattern, as exhibited by the cosine function above. A is termed the amplitude, and T the period of the motion.*

termed the *amplitude* of the motion. It is shown in the supplementary section of this chapter that the velocity v_x or dx/dt will then be given by:

$$v_x = \frac{dx}{dt} = -\frac{2\pi}{T} A \sin\left(2\pi \frac{t}{T}\right)$$

as illustrated in Fig. 6-4. Inserting these values for x and v_x in the equation for the conservation of energy, it is seen that:

$$\frac{1}{2} m \frac{4\pi^2}{T^2} A^2 \sin^2\left(2\pi \frac{t}{T}\right) + \frac{1}{2} kA^2 \cos^2\left(2\pi \frac{t}{T}\right) = U$$

If the period T has a value such that $m(4\pi^2/T^2) = k$, or

$$T = 2\pi \sqrt{\frac{m}{k}}$$

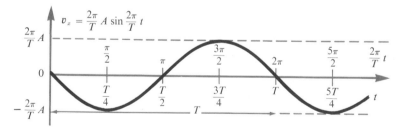

Figure 6-4   *The velocity of simple harmonic motion may be described by a negative sine function, with maxima occurring at the same interval T as they do for the displacement.*

then:

$$U = \frac{1}{2} kA^2 \left[\sin^2 \left(2\pi \frac{t}{T} \right) + \cos^2 \left(2\pi \frac{t}{T} \right) \right] = \frac{1}{2} kA^2$$

which is indeed constant. Thus the above relationships satisfy the conditions, and accurately describe the motion. The sine function would have done as well as the cosine function for x; the corresponding function for v_x would then have been the cosine function. The reciprocal of the period, the number of complete cycles in unit time, is called the *frequency*, and is written ν (nu). Thus

$$\nu = \frac{1}{T} = \frac{1}{2\pi} \sqrt{\frac{k}{m}} \quad \text{and} \quad x = A \cos (2\pi\nu t)$$

In Fig. 6-3 the displacement x is taken as maximum, namely a, at the time $t = 0$, by choosing the cosine function for it. If the sine function had been chosen for the displacement it would have been zero at the time $t = 0$. The displacement passes through alternate maxima in the positive and negative directions. At these maxima all the energy is stored in the potential form, and the system is at rest. We see that the curve for the velocity v_x crosses the axis at these times, and hence is zero. On the other hand, when the excursion is zero the energy is all in the kinetic form, and v_x has its maximum value, namely $(2\pi/T)A$. The energy is exchanged continuously between these two forms in the course of the motion.

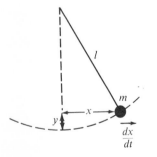

Figure 6-5 *A simple pendulum having a bob of mass M and string of length l.*

EXAMPLE. *The simple pendulum.* As a useful example of this type of motion, consider a simple pendulum formed by a small bob of mass m at the end of a long string of length l, fastened to a rigid support at its upper end. Let the bob be drawn aside from the equilibrium position, so that it is raised vertically by a distance y. The potential energy stored in the system is then this distance times the force of gravity on m, namely mgy. For small displacements, however, the motion takes place mostly in the horizontal or x direction; in order to solve the problem, the potential energy should be expressed in terms of x rather than of y. From Fig. 6-5, and using Pythagoras' theorem for the right triangle, we see that:

$$y = l - (l^2 - x^2)^{1/2} = l[1 - (1 - x^2/l^2)^{1/2}]$$

where x is the horizontal displacement from the position of equilibrium. If x is small compared with l, then x^2/l^2 is very small compared with 1, and the binomial theorem may be usefully employed. Thus:

$$(1 - x^2/l^2)^{1/2} = 1 - \tfrac{1}{2}x^2/l^2 + \text{much smaller terms}$$

which may be neglected. Thus the potential energy is given by:

$$U_p = mgy = mgl[1 - (1 - \tfrac{1}{2}x^2/l^2)] = \tfrac{1}{2}mgx^2/l$$

and the kinetic energy is given by:

$$U_K = \frac{1}{2} m \left(\frac{dx}{dt}\right)^2$$

where the velocity of the bob, being mostly in the horizontal or x direction, has been written as dx/dt. The conservation of energy equation is then:

$$\frac{1}{2} m \left(\frac{dx}{dt}\right)^2 + \frac{1}{2} \frac{mg}{l} x^2 = U$$

which is of the simple harmonic form

$$\frac{1}{2} m \left(\frac{dx}{dt}\right)^2 + \frac{1}{2} kx^2 = U$$

where k is represented by mg/l. The period of the motion is therefore

$$T = 2\pi \left(\frac{m}{k}\right)^{1/2} = 2\pi \left(\frac{l}{g}\right)^{1/2}$$

and the frequency is the reciprocal of this:

$$\nu = \frac{1}{2\pi} \left(\frac{g}{l}\right)^{1/2}$$

The period (and frequency) are independent of the mass of the bob. They depend only on l and g. Thus a measurement of T and l yields the value of the gravitational constant g. The amplitude of motion A in the expression for the horizontal displacement as a function of time t is determined by the initial horizontal displacement. If the bob starts from rest with an initial displacement x of value A, then

$$x = A \cos 2\pi\nu t = A \cos 2\pi t/T$$

and the total energy of the system, which is continually transferred between the potential and the kinetic forms, is simply the original stored potential energy

$$U = \frac{1}{2} kA^2 = \frac{1}{2} \frac{mg}{l} A^2$$

Angular simple harmonic motion. Simple harmonic motion is not restricted to linear motion; as one might expect, periodic rotational motion of a body about some fixed axis may be described by means of a set of equations completely analogous to those already derived for linear motion. Thus the total energy equation for rotational simple harmonic motion is

$$\frac{1}{2} I \left(\frac{d\theta}{dt}\right)^2 + \frac{1}{2} f \theta^2 = U$$

where I is the moment of inertia of the body rotating about some given axis, θ is the angle of deflection from the equilibrium position, and f is the restoring torque $\mathbf{T}$ per unit angular displacement; i.e.,

$$\mathbf{T} = -f\theta$$

The period of the angular motion, also by analogy, will then be

$$T = 2\pi \left(\frac{I}{f}\right)^{1/2}$$

and the frequency

$$\nu = \frac{1}{2\pi} \left(\frac{f}{I}\right)^{1/2}$$

EXAMPLE. *The Torsion Pendulum.* The torsion pendulum is a device that has been basic in technology and instrument design throughout the history of modern scientific measurement. Its simplicity, sensitivity, and versatility have led to its employment in basic measurements of mechanical, gravitational, electric, and magnetic forces. As a second illustration of simple harmonic motion, its application in the measurement of the universal constant of gravitation can be presented. The torsion pendulum consists of a mass suspended from a rigid support by a fiber that elastically resists twisting, so that potential energy can be stored in it by applying a torque to the supported mass about the fiber axis. In the particular kind of torsion pendulum used in the determination of G, the supported mass is a very light horizontal wire or stiff fiber with two small massive spheres affixed to either end of it. The light wire is supported from the center by a very fine, long vertical quartz fiber. The whole apparatus is enclosed, so that it is insulated to the greatest possible extent from disturbances arising from its surroundings. The angular deflection is measured by observing a beam of light reflected from a small mirror attached to the center of the wire beam, as shown in Fig. 6-6.

The deflection is produced by disposing two larger masses symmetrically with respect to the pendulum, first so that the gravitational forces induce a torque in one direction, and then in such a way that the opposite torque is produced. Considering here just the effects of the nearest masses disposed as shown in Fig. 6-7(a), the torque induced by

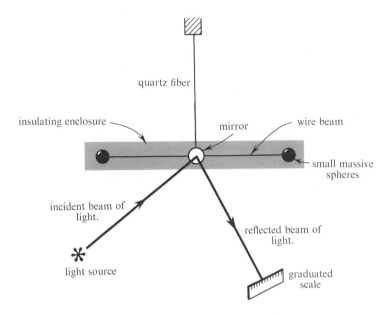

quartz fiber

insulating enclosure

mirror

wire beam

small massive spheres

incident beam of light.

reflected beam of light.

light source

graduated scale

Figure 6-6   *Torsion pendulum. The position of the pendulum is indicated by a spot of light on the graduated scale.*

the mass M attracting the near small mass m is: $(GMm/S^2)d$. From the mass combination at the other end, a like torque is generated. And, if the restoring torque of the quartz fiber per unit angular displacement is f, the angular displacement θ due to the gravitational attraction between the m's and the M's is:

$$\theta = \frac{2GMm}{S^2}\frac{d}{f}$$

The difference between this and the displacement when the masses M are moved to the positions of Fig. 6-7(b) is 2θ. The constant f can be determined from a separate experiment in which the period T of free torsional oscillation of the pendulum is measured. The total moment of inertia of the two masses m rotating about the central fiber at distance d is $I = 2md^2$. Then

$$f = \left(\frac{2\pi}{T}\right)^2 I = \frac{8\pi^2 md^2}{T^2}$$

Using this value for f, the value of G is determined as:

$$G = \frac{4\pi^2 S^2}{MT^2}\frac{d}{}\theta$$

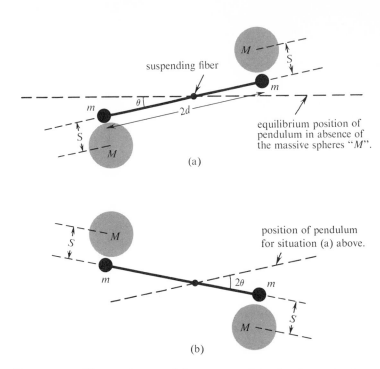

Figure 6-7 *The torsion pendulum, as used in the determination of the gravitational constant G. The massive spheres M are first placed as shown in position (a), and then as shown in position (b). The difference 2θ in angular deflection of the pendulum for the two situations is measured.*

In this expression, S, d, θ, M, and T can all be measured; hence the value of G can be found. As was mentioned in Chap. 5, the experiment is difficult to perform with accuracy because G is so small. The larger the gravitational energy represented by the proximity of the masses, the greater the relative precision or accuracy that can ultimately be attained in its measurement. The magnitude of the masses can not be increased indefinitely in order to increase the torque they produce, since, as indicated in Chap. 5, even the densest of available materials eventually reach large sizes: when their sizes become comparable with the length $2d$ of the bar, the net torque is lessened by the attraction of these masses for the more distant of the small masses. In order to obtain angular displacements that are large, f must be small, and the period T large; hence long times are inevitably involved in precise measurements of the small energy concerned. This is an example of a very general principle which is applicable to energy measurement.

Phase. The general behavior of any simple harmonic oscillatory system, such as the simple pendulum, may be completely described by specifying the amplitude A and the period T (or frequency ν) of the motion. However, if the exact state of the system (e.g., the displacement) is required at some given time t, then it is necessary to know the starting conditions (at time $t = 0$). Consider two identical oscillators of period T, each of which is started from its point of maximum positive displacement ($x = +A$). But oscillator number 1 is started a time t_0 later than oscillator number 2. If it is decided to measure time from the moment of starting oscillator 1, then its displacement x_1 at any later time t will be given by the expression

$$x_1 = A \cos\left[\frac{2\pi}{T} t\right]$$

At the same time t, however, the time elapsed since starting oscillator 2 will be $(t + t_0)$, and so its displacement x_2 will be given by the expression

$$x_2 = A \cos\left[\frac{2\pi}{T} (t + t_0)\right]$$

$$= A \cos\left[\frac{2\pi}{T} t + \frac{2\pi}{T} t_0\right]$$

which may be written

$$x_2 = A \cos\left[\frac{2\pi}{T} t + \phi\right]$$

where the constant ($\phi = 2\pi t_0/T$) is termed the *phase angle*. At any given time, the displacement x_2 of oscillator 2 may be found by inserting this phase angle ϕ in the expression for the displacement x_1 of oscillator 1. Note that $A \cos \phi$ is the displacement of oscillator 2 when oscillator 1 is started (at time $t = 0$). When $\phi = 0$, 2π, 4π, etc., the motions of the two oscillators coincide, and they are said to be *in phase*. When $\phi = \pi$ (or 180°), 3π, 5π, etc., the two oscillators are said to be in *opposite phase*, or *180° out of phase*.

EXAMPLE. *Phases of a piston engine.* As an illustration of phase angles, consider an eight cylinder diesel engine, in which the piston of each cylinder completes one cycle (from the top of the cylinder to the bottom and back up to the top) in a time equal to the period T. The motion of each piston is shown in Fig. 6-8 as a function of the time t. The top of the stroke is the position of maximum displacement $+A$; the bottom of the stroke corresponds to a displacement of $-A$. Although all pistons oscillate in an identical manner, no two oscillations are in phase. The

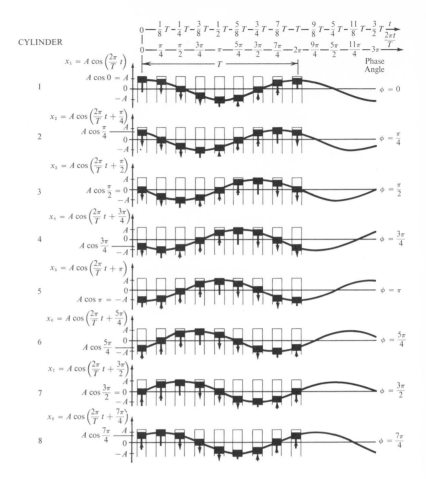

Figure 6-8 *Phase angles φ for an 8-cylinder diesel engine. The displacement x of each piston is shown as a function of time t. The oscillation of consecutive pistons differ in phase by $2\pi/8 = \pi/4$, or 45°.*

relative timing of the oscillations is adjusted so that the pistons reach their maximum displacements in a regular sequence: 1, 2, 3, 4, 5, 6, 7, 8, 1, 2, 3, etc., with equal intervals of time between each. There being 8 pistons, these time intervals must be $T/8$, and the phase angles for the oscillations of any two successive pistons must differ by $2\pi/8 = \pi/4$ or 45°. Thus if the phase angle for the oscillation of piston 1 is taken as 0, then $\pi/4$ will be the phase angle for the oscillation of piston 2, $\pi/2$ for piston 3, $3\pi/4$ for piston 4, etc., up to $7\pi/4$ for piston 8. The phase angle of $8\pi/4 = 2\pi$ is equivalent to zero phase angle, and corresponds again to the oscillation of piston 1.

EXAMPLE. *Phase difference between displacement and velocity in simple harmonic motion.* It is instructive to consider the separate oscillations of the displacement and the velocity already discussed for simple harmonic motion. The displacement changes from its maximum positive value $+A$ to a value of zero in a time equal to a quarter of the period, (or $T/4$). The velocity simultaneously changes from zero to its maximum negative value, as shown in Fig. 6-9. Thus the velocity oscillation *leads* the displacement oscillation by a phase angle of $2\pi/4 = \pi/2$ or $90°$. Of course it could be stated alternatively that the displacement oscillation leads the velocity oscillation by a phase angle of $2\pi - \pi/2 = 3\pi/2$ or $270°$.

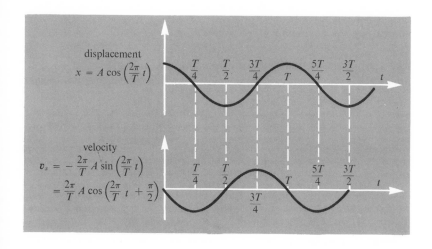

Figure 6-9 *The velocity oscillation leads the displacement oscillation of simple harmonic motion by a phase angle of $\pi/2$ or $90°$.*

Wave motion   6-3

The phenomenon of wave motion within volumes of matter or on the interfacial surfaces separating gases, liquids, or solids is closely related to the phenomena of the vibratory or oscillatory motion of discrete component masses comprising a physical system in near-equilibrium. As in the case of simple harmonic motion, we find examples of wave motion all about us; many of them are directly perceptible to our hearing as well as to our sight and touch. Travelling waves are observed in taut strings and wires shaken or disturbed by winds, or bowed as in musical instruments. They are felt as earth tremors, and as vibrations due to heavy machinery; they are felt in the vibrations of musical instruments. Sound, as it comes to our ears through the air, is directly perceived. The waves on water surfaces are well known to everyone. The colors exhibited by thin films of transparent liquids or solids are due to the wave nature of light. Wave motions of large amplitude, such as explosive waves in the atmosphere or breaking waves at sea, represent complex processes that are difficult to describe. But small amplitude waves, like small amplitude harmonic oscillations, can be understood and described simply and generally in terms of the concepts already introduced. The ideas that become familiar when we study the basic phenomena of wave propagation are of great value in describing many large-scale phenomena. They also provide an essential conceptual background for the development of atomic theory.

Waves propagated along stretched strings or over the surfaces of liquids provide particularly familiar examples, which may be used to illustrate the principal generic properties of this type of motion. These concepts can then be extended to waves travelling through the bulk of some medium, and then to light and electromagnetic waves—where the displacement phenomena are not as obvious and where the wave motion and its detailed characteristics must be inferred indirectly. The simplest prototype of wave motion is a regularly recurring periodic disturbance, of considerable spatial and temporal extent, generated by some continuing local harmonic disturbance. In the case of such waves on wires or over surfaces, the disturbance can be seen to travel along with a measurable velocity; the displacement at any one instant of time is a replica of the unit spatial displacement pattern, which frequently takes the shape of a simple sine curve. Also, at any one point in space, an observer is presented with a regular repetition (in time) of the displacement pattern, in general resembling a simple harmonic motion of displacement as the wave passes by. Thus the disturbance is characterized by a function of both space and time, such that whatever its value may be at a point x_1 and a time t_1, this same value will be propagated in the direction of the advancing wave, and will occur at a neighboring point, say x_2, at a later time t_2. If the wave velocity is c, then $t_2 = t_1 + (x_2 - x_1)/c$, or $(t_2 - x_2/c) = (t_1 - x_1/c)$. Hence the displacement function for wave motion can be written very generally as a function of the composite variable $(t - x/c)$, where t is the time and c is the velocity of propagation of the wave pattern along the x axis. If the magnitude of the disturbance constituting the wave depends upon the temporal and spatial variables t and x only through being a function of $(t - x/c)$, then the disturbance will remain the same in magnitude if the quantity in parenthesis is unchanged. The entire pattern, whatever its details, appears then to move along with the velocity $dx/dt = c$. The negative sign in the term within parenthesis $(t - x/c)$ clearly refers to a velocity in the positive x direction. A positive sign in the parenthesis would refer to a wave moving in the direction of $-x$ with the velocity c.

Simple harmonic waves   6-4

Much as in the case of the simple harmonic motion of discrete bodies, it is possible to simplify the discussion considerably by restricting consideration to small-amplitude waves for which the sine and cosine functions provide excellent approximations to actual disturbances. Quite arbitrarily shaped waves can indeed be represented by sums of separate simple periodic disturbances of suitably chosen frequencies and amplitudes. The sine or cosine wave of Fig. 6-10 can be considered either an instantaneous photograph of the contour of a travelling wave, in which case the horizontal axis is the distance travelled x; or it may be considered the displacement observed at some fixed point in space, in which case the horizontal axis is the time t.

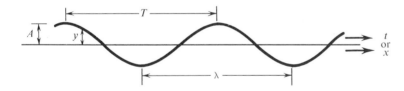

Figure 6-10   *Travelling wave.*

The spatial distance between corresponding points of displacement, or the length of the repetitive-pattern unit is called the *wave length*, and is customarily written λ (lambda). To a stationary observer the time interval between recurrences of the periodic displacement pattern is called the *period T*. Clearly these are related by the equation $\lambda = cT$, since the wave length travels past a stationary observer with the velocity c in the time T. The reciprocal of the period is called the *frequency, v*.

The expression for a travelling simple harmonic wave can then be written in terms of these quantities, using either the sine or cosine function:

$$y = A \sin 2\pi \left(\frac{t}{T} - \frac{x}{\lambda}\right) \qquad \text{or} \qquad A \cos 2\pi \left(\frac{t}{T} - \frac{x}{\lambda}\right)$$

$$y = A \sin 2\pi\nu \left(t - \frac{x}{c}\right) \qquad \text{or} \qquad A \cos 2\pi\nu \left(t - \frac{x}{c}\right)$$

$$\frac{\lambda}{T} = \lambda\nu = c$$

A is the maximum amplitude of the disturbance.

The velocity c, with which the wave is propagated, is one of its most important physical characteristics. All waves, of course, do not travel with the same velocity, and one must either investigate experimentally the factors that determine the velocity of propagation in particular instances, or else deduce these factors in simple cases from general physical principles such as those introduced in previous chapters. In the case of waves on stretched strings, for instance, it is found experimentally that the more tightly the string is stretched, the faster they travel. They travel more slowly if the string is heavy than they do if it is light. The rate at which the momentum of an elementary segment of the string or wire changes with the time is equal to the force tending to displace it; consequently, it may be shown that the velocity with which a wave is propagated along the string or wire is given by the square root of the ratio of the tension in the string to the mass of the string per unit length.

The speed with which sound travels in air is found to be proportional to the square root of the temperature. And again, upon applying the principles of mechanics we can show that this velocity must be proportional to the square root of the ratio of the pressure of the air to the mass per unit volume or density. These results are concordant; they simply say the same thing in two different ways because of the relation between pressure, density, and temperature, called the gas law, which will be mentioned in Chap. 18.

Waves that travel over a water surface are found to proceed at different speeds depending upon their wave length or frequency. There are two kinds of these: one is the very small ripples whose physical properties are determined primarily by the surface forces of the liquid; the other kind is the larger waves commonly observed in lakes or oceans, the properties of which derive from the gravitational forces upon the liquid. The velocity of the first kind of waves is proportional to the square root of the ratio of the surface tension (see Chap. 19) to the product of the density and wave length. The velocity of the second kind is proportional to the square root of the product of the acceleration of gravity g and the wave length. Dependence of velocity on wave length is referred to as *dispersion*, since waves of different wavelengths or frequencies, originating simultaneously at the one point, become dispersed or separated from one another. Volcanic activity resulting in major local disturbances of the ocean level gives rise to waves of many lengths; the longer ones move across the surface with great velocities, and the shorter ones arrive a distant point much later.

EXAMPLE. *Ocean waves.* As a more detailed illustration of the determination of the velocity of propagation of a wave by applying the conservation laws, let us consider the case of long waves on a water surface. If one observes the nature of the motion that takes place when such a wave is travelling along a surface, by charging the water with small specks or bubbles and looking at these through the transparent walls of a tank, one sees that these specks describe circles in planes perpendicular to the water surface and parallel to the direction in which the wave moves. The greatest circular amplitude is experienced by the particles near the surface, and the rotational frequency of the particles is the same as the frequency v of the wave. The direction of rotation relative to the passage of the wave is such that the particles move forward with the wave at the crests and backward at the troughs. This is illustrated in Fig. 6-11.

As long as energy resides in a moving wave form, the problem seems intractable. However, if a system of coordinates moving forward with the wave velocity c is chosen, then the wave pattern appears to be stationary. The water then appears to move backwards (i.e., in a direction opposite to that of the waves viewed by a stationary observer) with an average velocity c. Superimposed on this average backward motion of the water will be the circular motion mentioned above. Thus water at a crest will move back with a velocity $c - v$, and water in a trough will move back with velocity $c + v$, where v is the velocity around the circles. Clearly $v = 2\pi r v$, where the radius r of the circles is also the amplitude of the waves. The difference in height between crest and trough is $2r$; so the difference in gravitational energy of a small mass of liquid m at crest and trough is $2rgm$. If the energy of each mass of liquid remains unchanged during the passage of the wave, one may equate the sum of the kinetic and potential energies for the illustrative mass m at crest and trough:

$$\tfrac{1}{2}m(c + 2\pi r v)^2 - mgr = \tfrac{1}{2}m(c - 2\pi r v)^2 + mgr$$

or:
$$2\pi mcrv - mgr = -2\pi mcrv + mgr$$

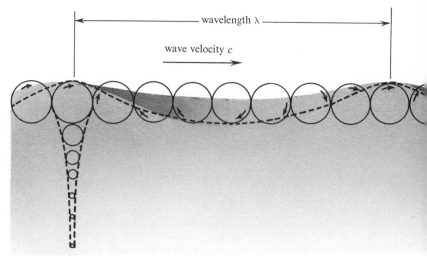

Cross-section of ocean wave travelling from left to right shows wave length as distance between successive crests. The time it takes two crests to pass a point is the wave period. Circles are orbits of water particles in the wave. At the surface their diameter equals the wave height. At a depth of half the wave length (left), orbital diameter is only 4 per cent of that at surface.

wavelength λ

wave velocity c

The same picture observed from a coordinate system in which wave pattern is stationary.

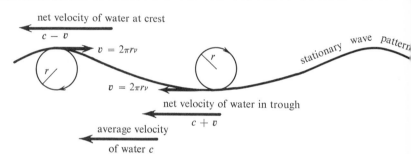

net velocity of water at crest

$c - v$

$v = 2\pi r \nu$

$v = 2\pi r \nu$

stationary wave pattern

net velocity of water in trough

$c + v$

average velocity

of water c

Figure 6-11   *Motion of water particles during passage of an ocean wave.*

and:

$$c = \frac{g}{2\pi\nu} = \frac{g\lambda}{2\pi c}$$

Thus the velocity of the wave c is equal to $(g\lambda/2\pi)^{1/2}$, as stated earlier.

6-5   *Standing waves*

In the cases of strings stretched between two supports, or of liquid surfaces of limited extent, the motion of the travelling waves reflected back and forth from the supports or boundaries gives rise to the phenomenon called *standing waves*. The combined effect of two similar waves travelling in opposite directions along the same stretched string is quite different from the effect of one wave by itself. The disturbance resulting from the sum of two oppositely travelling waves is shown in the supplementary section of this chapter to be:

$$y = A \sin 2\pi\nu \left(t + \frac{x}{c}\right) + A \sin 2\pi\nu \left(t - \frac{x}{c}\right)$$

$$= 2 A \sin (2\pi\nu t) \cos \left(2\pi \frac{x}{\lambda}\right)$$

This is no longer a function of the quantity $(t + x/c)$, and hence is not a travelling wave at all. The oscillations in t and x take place independently; at any one point along the string the oscillation takes place in time with the frequency ν and the amplitude $2A \cos (2\pi x/\lambda)$. As one proceeds along the string, points of zero amplitude (called *nodes*) are encountered, for which $2\pi x/\lambda = \pi/2$, $3\pi/2$, $5\pi/2$, etc., where $\cos (2\pi x/\lambda) = 0$. Between these lie *antinodes*, or points of maximum amplitude (namely $2A$), for which $2\pi x/\lambda = 0$, π, 2π, etc., where $\cos (2\pi x/\lambda) = 1$. This steady vibrational pattern with a periodic variation in amplitude along the string is said to be a standing wave pattern.

The formation of such a wave is illustrated in Fig. 6-12, where the dashed wave C represents the sum of the two oppositely directed waves A and B of equal amplitudes. It is seen that if initially the waves are in phase, then the net disturbance is a maximum; but with advancing time, and as the waves A and B move apart, they progressively get more and more out of phase until a time equal to one quarter of the period has elapsed, when the phase difference at all points is π and complete cancellation occurs. After another quarter period the disturbance is again a maximum, though oppositely directed to the original disturbance. Because symmetry is always maintained about the original points of maximum displacement, there can be no progression of the net wave C in either direction.

Standing waves are characteristic of the bowed strings of musical instruments. If the length of the string is $\lambda/2$, the frequency is the lowest that will produce a standing wave pattern, and the string is said to be vibrating at its *first harmonic* or *fundamental* frequency. Higher frequencies giving rise to 2, 3, 4, etc., half-wave oscillatory segments are said to be the second, third, fourth, etc. *harmonics*—also known respectively as the first, second, third, etc., *overtones*. These are shown in Fig. 6-13.

EXAMPLE. A violin string has a mass per unit length ρ of 1.162×10^{-3} kg. m.$^{-1}$, and a length l of 0.3333 m. If the tension F on the string is 100 Newtons, what is the frequency of the fundamental note? If, as is usual, the string is bowed at about one-eighth the length from one end, what higher harmonics are also excited in the string?

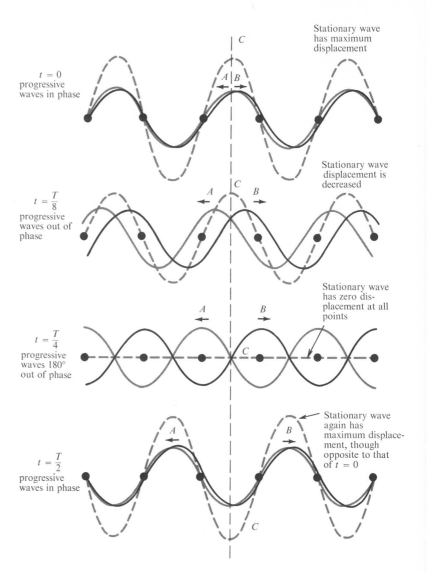

Figure 6-12 *Stationary wave C formed by the addition of two oppositely directed travelling waves A and B of equal amplitude. The heavy points are nodes, where the standing wave always has zero displacement.*

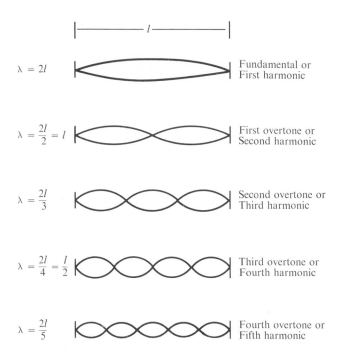

$\lambda = 2l$ — Fundamental or First harmonic

$\lambda = \dfrac{2l}{2} = l$ — First overtone or Second harmonic

$\lambda = \dfrac{2l}{3}$ — Second overtone or Third harmonic

$\lambda = \dfrac{2l}{4} = \dfrac{l}{2}$ — Third overtone or Fourth harmonic

$\lambda = \dfrac{2l}{5}$ — Fourth overtone or Fifth harmonic

Figure 6-13 *Standing waves of the first five harmonics for a stretched string.*

The velocity of a wave in a stretched string is, as noted in Sect. 6-3,

$$c = \sqrt{\frac{F}{\rho}} = \sqrt{\frac{100}{1.162 \; 10^{-3}}} = 293.2 \text{ m.sec.}^{-1}$$

The fundamental note (first harmonic) will have a wavelength $\lambda_1 = 2l$; the frequency ν_1 is given by the equation

$$\nu_1 = \frac{c}{\lambda_1} = \frac{c}{2l} = \frac{293.2}{0.6666} = 440 \text{ sec.}^{-1}$$

The higher harmonics correspond to wavelengths $\lambda = 2l/2$, $2l/3$, $2l/4$, etc., and have frequencies $\nu = 2\nu_1$, $3\nu_1$, $4\nu_1$, etc. Thus the higher harmonics have frequencies 880, 1320, 1760, 2200, and 2640 sec.$^{-1}$. The seventh, eighth and ninth harmonics require nodes or points of zero displacement roughly where the above string is bowed (i.e., excited); hence, these harmonics will be suppressed. In general, the upper harmonics will have less strength than the lower harmonics: so harmonics higher than the above will be neglected. Harmonics may be preferentially excited by appropriate fingering. For example, by lightly touching the string near its center, one may produce a node at this point; the first harmonic is damped, and the second harmonic is strongly excited.

The vibrating pattern of a bowed string will generally contain many harmonics. The relative strengths of the harmonics, both initial and sustained, as they are excited in the oscillating medium (string or air column) and amplified by a sounding board or resonating chamber, determine the characteristic *timbre*, or tone quality, of the voice and various orchestral instruments.

6-6 *Superposition of waves and interference*

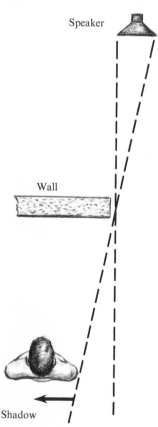

Figure 6-14 *A solid wall in front of a loud-speaker tends to cast a sound shadow if reflections from neighboring hard surfaces are not appreciable. The lower frequencies (longer wave lengths) exhibit more diffraction and are therefore enhanced in the shadow region.*

Speaker

Wall

Shadow

In the instances of waves of light and sound, and of other waves where the oscillations are too rapid to be followed by our sense of sight, it is not possible to recognize the actual crests and troughs of the progressive oscillatory motion. In such cases certain associated characteristics of wave motion enable us to identify the presence of travelling waves. One of these characteristics is the tendency of waves to spread out, not only from the source of the motion, but also from any irregularities in the medium through which they are passing. Discontinuities in the medium, such as foreign particles in the material through which they are passing, tend to scatter waves. This is evidenced by the scattering of light in a sunbeam by motes, and by the scattering of light in fogs and clouds. Boundaries—and particularly corners and irregularities —give rise to similar effects, with the result that waves tend to pass around corners and behind obstacles. This phenomenon is called *diffraction*. Only in those cases where the wavelength is very short in comparison with the linear dimensions of these irregularities do waves cast apparently sharp geometrical shadows (see Fig. 6-14). Diffraction effects are observed in the photograph of Plate 1.

These effects may be considered in terms of the superposition of two or more separate wave systems. A particularly simple instance is that in which the wave encounters a baffle or boundary in which there are two holes or slits which act on the far side as two separate sources of the waves. The superposition of the effects of these two waves is called *interference*. Consider the case of two dimensions only, as in that of a wave on a water surface. Fig. 6-15 indicates the geometry. The disturbance at a point to the right of the baffle is due to the sum of the effects of the two waves reaching it from S_1 and S_2. If the holes are of the same size, the amplitude A may be considered the same. The times (t's) in the wave function are the same, for the sources S_1 and S_2 are

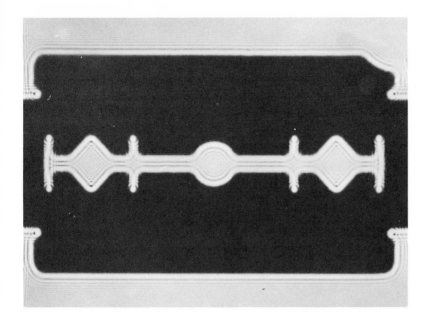

Plate 1 *Shadow of a razor blade, photographed with monochromatic light from a pinhole source. The edges are diffuse rather than sharp because some light has bent around them. Outside the edges strong interference patterns are observed. (From University Physics, by Francis Weston Sears and Mark W. Zemansky, Third Edition, Addison-Wesley, Reading, Mass., 1964.)*

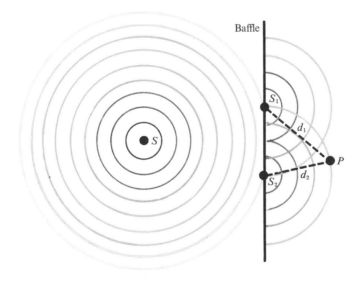

Figure 6-15 *Interference of waves from two sources.*

symmetrically disposed relative to S, and peaks and troughs of the waves leaving S_1 and S_2 occur at the same times. The distances travelled to the point P, namely d_1 and d_2, will in general be different from one another.

The disturbance at P, due to the two waves, is thus:

$$y = A \sin 2\pi \left(\nu t + \frac{d_1}{\lambda} \right) + A \sin 2\pi \left(\nu t + \frac{d_2}{\lambda} \right)$$

By the formula for the addition of circular functions given in the supplementary mathematical note to this chapter, this sum can be written more informatively as:

$$y = \left[2A \cos \frac{2\pi(d_1 - d_2)}{2\lambda} \right] \sin 2\pi \left[\nu t + \frac{(d_1 + d_2)}{2\lambda} \right]$$

The sine term of the product represents a periodic simple harmonic change in amplitude, with the time, at the frequency ν of the source. The amplitude of this oscillation is $2A$ times the cosine term, which varies in magnitude from 1 to 0, as $(d_1 - d_2)/\lambda$ changes from integral to half-integral values.

It is seen that maxima of intensity occur behind the baffle for points such that the difference of their distances from the holes S_1 and S_2 is some integral multiple of the wavelength λ. This is so, because the condition that the cosine be unity is: $d_1 - d_2 = n\lambda$, where n is any integer. The amplitude is zero for points such that $(d_1 - d_2)$ is an odd multiple of $\lambda/2$. For all other points where $(d_1 - d_2)$ does not satisfy one or the other of these conditions, there is some wave motion, but it is of a lesser amplitude than the maximum. This variation of intensity of oscillation over the area to the right of the baffle is called an *interference pattern*. Its presence is evidence of the wave-like nature of the phenomenon, and measurements of it can evidently yield values for the wavelength.

The above condition for an interference maximum to occur, namely that $d_1 - d_2 = n\lambda$, can readily be seen to follow if we consider the relative phases of the two waves. The condition describes the points where waves from S_1 and S_2 will be *in phase*, and hence will add to maximum amplitude. Similarly, at points where the paths d_1 and d_2, travelled by the two waves differ by an odd number of half-wavelengths, the waves will always be in *opposite phase*, and (for equal amplitudes) will always exactly cancel. When the phase difference between two waves is less than $\pi/2$, resulting in enhancement of the wave amplitude, the interference is said to be *constructive;* when the phase difference is greater than $\pi/2$, the interference is said to be *destructive.*

EXAMPLE. *The Diffraction Grating.* The phenomenon of interference may be applied to the measurement of wavelengths by means of a *diffraction grating.* This is a surface, either reflecting or transmitting, which is covered by a series of closely spaced parallel lines scratched upon it by a diamond point. The difficult technique of producing highly uniform gratings of many closely ruled lines was perfected by Henry A. Rowland, of Johns Hopkins University. If a plane wave of light is incident upon such a grating, each separate opening acts as a small window, or new source for a wavelet; the phase relation between them being determined by the time of arrival of the incident wave at the opening. Thus if Fig. 6-16 represents a plane normal to the direction of the grating rulings, and the direction of the incident light makes an angle α with the line of grating openings, then the phase of the light wave emitted from each as a result of the incident stimulus will lag behind that from the opening immediately to the left of it by $(d \cos \alpha)/\lambda$. If, at some angle of observation β, it is found that the intensity of the light emerging from the grating is large, this signifies that the light emerges from the openings and is propagated outward in constructive phase from neighboring openings; hence the total path difference between waves emerging from successive openings is λ, or some multiple of λ. This spatial difference is seen from Fig. 6-17 to be $d(\cos \alpha - \cos \beta)$ and, hence, for constructive interference:

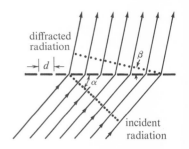

Figure 6-16 *Diffraction by a grating. The dotted lines are wave fronts perpendicular to the direction of propagation of the wave.*

$$n\lambda = d(\cos \alpha - \cos \beta)$$

The series of maxima corresponding to successive values of n are easily observed. And, from a knowledge of the spacing d and the angles α and β, the wave length λ can be determined.

Finally, an interesting phenomenon akin to interference takes place if there are two or more waves present of different frequencies, and if the velocities of propagation are frequency-dependent. It may be shown that any arbitrary wave shape may be made up of the sum of many simple harmonic wave components. So the following simple consideration of two such waves shows the general character of an arbitrary wave. The sum disturbance of two simple harmonic waves of two different frequencies and wavelengths, and of equal amplitude by the formula just used is:

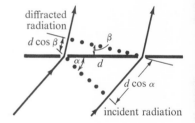

Figure 6-17 *Enlargement of Fig. 6-16. Along the incident wave front all the rays are in phase. However, along the diffracted wave front there is a path difference between neighboring rays of ($d \cos \alpha - d \cos \beta$).*

$$y = A \sin 2\pi(\nu_1 t + x/\lambda_1) + A \sin 2\pi(\nu_2 t + x/\lambda_2)$$

$$= 2A \cos 2\pi \left(\frac{\nu_1 - \nu_2}{2} t + \frac{1/\lambda_1 - 1/\lambda_2}{2} x \right)$$

$$\sin 2\pi \left(\frac{\nu_1 + \nu_2}{2} t + \frac{1/\lambda_1 + 1/\lambda_2}{2} x \right)$$

The nature of this expression is shown in Fig. 6-18; it is the product of two harmonic functions, the amplitude of the high frequency one of frequency $(\nu_1 + \nu_2)$ being modulated by the amplitude of the low frequency one of frequency $(\nu_1 - \nu_2)$. If the velocities of propagation are the same, then $\nu_1\lambda_1 = \nu_2\lambda_2 = c$, and the whole pattern travels unaltered in shape with this velocity. The radiation of the amplitude-modulated electromagnetic wave of radio broadcasting is of this nature.

Figure 6-18   *A travelling wave of two frequencies.*

If, however, the velocities are not the same, the high frequency and low frequency patterns move at different velocities. If ν_1 and ν_2 are not very different, the high frequency wave travels at the mean velocity; but the modulation pattern may travel at quite a different velocity, called the *group velocity*. The large-scale effect is characterized most obviously by this movement. This velocity is evidently $(\nu_1 - \nu_2)/(1/\lambda_1 - 1/\lambda_2) = d\nu/d(1/\lambda)$ if the quantities are small. In the instance of the water waves previously considered, $g/2\pi\nu = c = \nu\lambda$. Therefore $\nu = (g/2\pi)^{1/2} \cdot (1/\lambda)^{1/2}$ and hence $d\nu/d(1/\lambda) = \frac{1}{2}(g/2\pi)^{1/2}\lambda^{-1/2} = c/2$. Thus the group velocity is half the velocity of the high frequency waves composing the group. A water wave in general contains many different frequencies; it is these differences in velocity that cause the changing shape of a wave as it travels over the water's surface.

EXAMPLE. *Beat frequency.* One often can tune stringed instruments by listening to the *beat frequency* $(\nu_1 - \nu_2)$, which is very noticeable when two notes of slightly different frequencies ν_1 and ν_2 are simultaneously sounded. In Fig. 6-19, two displacement oscillations of equal amplitude A, one of frequency $\nu_1 = 5$ sec.$^{-1}$ and the other of $\nu_2 = 4$ sec.$^{-1}$, are displayed as a function of time. The heavy line is the displacement obtained by simply summing the displacements of both waves at every point in time. Initially $(t = 0)$ the oscillations are in phase; so they add constructively to produce amplitude $2A$. With increasing time the oscillations get more and more out of phase until, when $t = \frac{1}{2}$ sec. one oscillator has completed 2 oscillations and the other $2 + \frac{1}{2}$. The two oscillations are then $180°$ out of phase; hence, the sum of the displacements is zero. At $t = 1$ sec. the amplitude of the sum is again $2A$. Thus

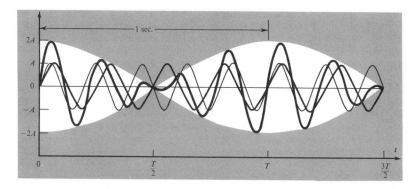

Figure 6-19 *The addition of two waves of frequencies 4 sec.$^{-1}$ and 5 sec.$^{-1}$ produces a beat frequency of 5 − 4 = 1 sec^{-1}.*

the frequency of occurrence of the maximum amplitude is 1 sec.$^{-1}$, or $(\nu_1 - \nu_2)$. At the same time the net displacement y oscillates with frequency $4 + \frac{1}{2}$ sec.$^{-1}$, or $(\nu_1 + \nu_2)/2$. These results agree with the formula derived by summing trigonometrically two sine waves, in spite of the fact that the beat frequency observed is $(\nu_1 - \nu_2)$, not $(\nu_1 - \nu_2)/2$. The two envelope curves that enclose the amplitude excursions have the frequency $(\nu_1 - \nu_2)/2$; but the maxima of each is heard by the ear, which thus appears to be aware of twice the envelope curve frequency. Thus if two notes of frequency 440 second^{-1} and 442 second^{-1} are sounded together, the envelope of the resultant wave form corresponds to a frequency of 1 second^{-1}. But the ear detects a waxing and waning (beating) of the sound, with intensity maxima occurring with frequency 2 second^{-1}, which is the so-called *beat frequency*. The frequencies discussed above are not to be confused with the so-called *sum* and *difference tones*, which are audible under suitable conditions. The latter are heard as true tones which, however, are produced by the nonlinear response of the ear.

Supplementary mathematical section   6-7

Rate of change of circular functions. The relationships between the sine and cosine functions and their rates of change may be deduced by the following geometrical argument. Considering first the triangle OPQ of Fig. 6-20, in which θ is defined as the angle between OP and OQ,

$$\sin \theta = \frac{PQ}{OP} \quad \text{and} \quad \cos \theta = \frac{OQ}{OP}$$

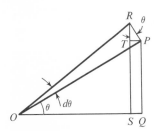

Figure 6-20 *θ is defined to be the angle between OP and OQ. dθ is then an infinitesimally small increase in θ, obtained by rotating OP to OR.*

Then, if θ is increased by an infinitesimally small quantity $d\theta$, by rotating OP to OR (i.e., $OP = OR$), it is seen from the triangle ORS that

$$\sin(\theta + d\theta) = \frac{RS}{OR} = \frac{PQ + RT}{OP} \quad \text{and} \quad \cos\theta = \frac{OS}{OR} = \frac{OQ - TP}{OP}$$

$$= \sin\theta + \frac{RT}{OP} \qquad\qquad\qquad = \cos\theta - \frac{TP}{OP}$$

Then, for the small angle $d\theta$, RP can be regarded as normal to OP. Also RS is normal to OS. Hence the angle between RP and RS will equal the angle between OP and OS. This angle is θ, and, from the triangle RTP,

$$RT = RP\cos\theta \quad \text{and} \quad TP = RP\sin\theta$$

Hence

$$\sin(\theta + d\theta) = \sin\theta + \cos\theta\,\frac{RP}{OP} \quad \text{and}$$

$$\cos(\theta + d\theta) = \cos\theta - \sin\theta\,\frac{RP}{OP}$$

where, for the small angle $d\theta$, RP may be approximated by the arc length, and hence $RP/OP = d\theta$. Hence, the angular rate of change of $\sin\theta$ is:

$$\frac{d(\sin\theta)}{d\theta} = \frac{\sin(\theta + d\theta) - \sin\theta}{d\theta} = \cos\theta$$

Similarly

$$\frac{d(\cos\theta)}{d\theta} = \frac{\cos(\theta + d\theta) - \cos\theta}{d\theta} = -\sin\theta$$

The expressions occurring in this chapter are of the form: $\sin b\theta$ and $\cos b\theta$, where b is some constant. These expressions may be handled in the following way:

$$\frac{d(\sin b\theta)}{d\theta} = \frac{d(b\theta)}{d\theta}\frac{d(\sin b\theta)}{d(b\theta)} = b\cos b\theta$$

$$\frac{d(\cos b\theta)}{d\theta} = \frac{d(b\theta)}{d\theta}\frac{d(\cos b\theta)}{d(b\theta)} = -b\sin b\theta$$

Addition of two circular functions. The addition of two circular functions is so frequently useful in the consideration of the effects of the super-position of two waves that the simple derivation is given here.

Considering the construction of Fig. 6-21, the line from the apex C, perpendicular to the side c, is equal to

$$b\sin A = a\sin B$$

Also

$$c = b\cos A + a\cos B$$

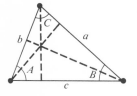

Figure 6-21 *Triangle with perpendiculars drawn from apices to opposite sides.*

Eliminating a from these two equations then yields:

$$b(\sin A \cos B + \sin B \cos A) = c \sin B$$

But considering the line from A perpendicular to a,

$$c \sin B = b \sin C$$

Since the sum $A + B + C = \pi$,

$$\sin (A + B) = \sin (\pi - C) = \sin C$$
$$= \frac{c \sin B}{b}$$
$$= \sin A \cos B + \sin B \cos A$$

Also, replacing B by $-B$,

$$\sin (A - B) = \sin A \cos (-B) + \sin (-B) \cos A$$
$$= \sin A \cos B - \sin B \cos A$$

Adding these two formulae,

$$\sin (A + B) + \sin (A - B) = 2 \sin A \cos B$$

A general formula for the sum of two sine functions may be obtained by writing $A + B = P$ and $A - B = Q$. Whence

$$A = \frac{P + Q}{2} \quad \text{and} \quad B = \frac{P - Q}{2}$$

Then

$$\sin P + \sin Q = 2 \sin \frac{P + Q}{2} \cos \frac{P - Q}{2}$$

Further reading:

Bascom, W., "Ocean Waves," *Scientific American*, vol. 201, No. 2, p. 74 (1959).

Scholes, P. A., *The Oxford Companion to Music*, "Articles on Acoustics and Timbre," 9th Edition (1955).

Problems

6-1 A ball bounces vertically up and down, making elastic collisions with the ground. Is this a good example of simple harmonic motion? Why?

6-2 An object of unknown mass is hung from a light spiral spring, and observed to extend it a distance of 0.1 m. If the system is set into oscillation, what will be the frequency?

6-3 If the period of a simple pendulum is to be 2 sec., what should be its length?

6-4 A chandelier consists of 8 lamps, each of mass 1 kg. and supported at a distance of $\frac{1}{2}$ m. from a central cable by a lightweight bracket. If the period of tortional oscillation is 10 sec., what is the value of k, the torsional constant of the cable?

6-5 An object oscillates simultaneously in both the x and y directions independently. If the amplitudes of the two motions are equal, sketch the path of the object when the two oscillations are in phase, and when the x motion leads the y motion by $\pi/2$, π and $3\pi/2$, assuming for each case that the periods of the two motions are identical. What would the path look like if the periods of the two motions were slightly different? How does the path change in each case if the y amplitude exceeds the x amplitude?

6-6 A radio station broadcasts at a wavelength of 10 m. What is the frequency of the radio waves?

6-7 The velocity of sound in air is about 340 m.sec.$^{-1}$. A sound reproducing system of high fidelity has a range of about 30 cycles per second to 30 kilocycles per second. What are the corresponding wave lengths of the sound waves?

6-8 All 3 dimensions of a room are 3 m. Why would this make a poor music room? What frequencies would be most distorted in natural strength in such a room?

6-9 A pure frequency note is played by 2 speakers, distant 2 m. apart. Along a line 3 m. in front of the speakers, the intensity is heard as a minimum immediately in front of each speaker, and there is only one maximum between these points. What is the frequency of the note?

6-10 An unstopped violin string, when sounded together with a note of 1000 cycles per second, produces a beat frequency of 2 beats per second. When the string is slightly shortened, the beat frequency decreases. What is the unstopped frequency of the string?

The propagation of light and the special theory of relativity

7

Wave nature of light 7-1

The light with which visual observations are made as well as that outside the narrow range of frequencies to which our eyes are sensitive displays the properties of wave motion. Isaac Newton showed that a parallel beam of light from the sun, passing through a glass prism, is dispersed through a range of angles (Fig. 7-1). On examining the light that has been refracted by the prism, one can see that the light bent through the greater angle is that which we call "violet"; the shades from blue through green, yellow, and orange to red are dispersed through lesser angles. On being passed through an oppositely oriented prism, all these shades recombine, and "white" light again emerges (Fig. 7-2). Thus, white light consists of components which separately determine our sense of color. The physiological reaction we experience as a result of the stimulus to the retina by light is still only imperfectly understood. Undoubtedly our visual sensations are basically determined by the frequencies associated with the energy that the lens focuses upon the sensitive nerve endings of the retina. But our perception of light does not in itself impute to it any wave-like quality.

The wave nature of light is most clearly brought out in the phenomena of diffraction and interference, which were referred to in the preceding

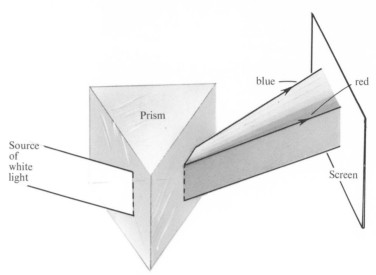

Figure 7-1 *Spectrum produced in dispersion of white light by a prism.*

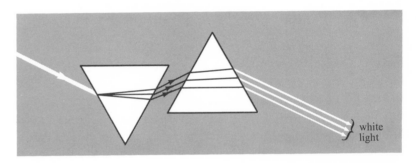

Figure 7-2 *Light of all wave lengths emerges in a parallel beam from the above combination of two identical prisms and produces white light.*

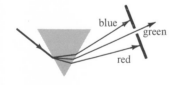

Figure 7-3 *Selection of monochromatic light by a prism and slit.*

chapter. If a narrow range of color of the light dispersed by a prism is permitted to pass through a small orifice (Fig. 7-3), diffraction effects which spread light around obstacles can be readily observed. And if the disposition of two subsequent slits is used as described in the earlier discussion of wave motion, an interference pattern in the chosen color is visible (Fig. 7-4). The light dispersed by the prism is called a *spectrum*, which simply means a spread in terms of frequency or wave length which determines color; the light permitted to pass, if a small diaphragm is interposed at the proper position to let one narrow region of color through, is said to be single-colored, or *monochromatic*. The virtue of

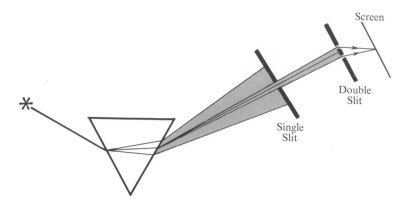

Figure 7-4 *Interference pattern from monochromatic light illuminating a double slit.*

performing interference experiments with monochromatic light is that only a narrow range of frequencies or wave lengths is included, and the effects are simpler and more easily understood.

An alternate to the two-orifice arrangement for producing an interference pattern, and one which is more generally useful in the construction of optical instruments, such as the interferometer, is to employ two reflecting surfaces to provide the two interfering beams. The colors displayed by light passing through soap bubbles, reflected from films of oil on a water surface, or those seen in many mineral specimens and in insect wings arise from the interference of certain portions light which have traversed greater distances in these media than have other portions. To be specific, let us consider a thin wedge of air contained between two plane glass surfaces, which are inclined at a slight angle to one another. This situation can readily be brought about by holding two rectangular pieces of plate glass in contact along one edge and separating them at the opposite edge by a thin strip of paper. Fig. 7-5 indicates a light beam incident upon such an arrangement, which can then be viewed at a slight angle from either side, since each surface transmits some of the light incident on it, and reflects the balance. The central portion of the beam passes through the wedge where the thickness of the air film is d. In consequence, the path difference between the waves (shown in the figure) that pass through the wedge at this point is $2d$. They will interfere constructively, producing maximum intensity if the two emerging waves combine in phase, crest to crest and trough to trough. Since the thickness of the wedge increases from top to bottom, viewed in a beam of light incident at approximately

Figure 7-5 *Interference produced by a light beam traversing the space between two reflecting surfaces. Part of the beam is directly transmitted and part experiences an internal reflection, thereby travelling an extra distance 2d.*

right angles to it, the wedge will appear to be crossed by dark and bright bands. The vertical distance between the center of two neighboring bright bands will be such that the difference in thickness of the wedge at the two heights is $\lambda/2$. Measurements of the wedge angle and observations of the dark and bright bands, called *interference fringes*, show that the wave length corresponding to violet light is of the order of 4×10^{-7} meters; that corresponding to red light is about 7×10^{-7} meters.

Light from a glowing body, such as the sun or an incandescent lamp filament, when dispersed by a prism, displays a continuous range of colors from the long-wave length red light to the short-wave length violet. The velocities with which all wave lengths traverse space are evidently the same; for when the heavenly bodies are eclipsed by one another, the light just before and after continues to be white, whereas it would evidently appear colored if there were an appreciable difference in velocity due to differences in wave length. It may be concluded from such experiments, and from others that can be performed on the earth's surface, that c, the velocity of light through space, is constant; hence, it may also be concluded that frequency is inversely proportional to wave length.

Interference and diffraction effects analogous to those which have been described can also be observed by nonvisual means. Thus, for instance, sensitive heat detectors may be used to explore interference patterns; electric currents may be induced in suitably disposed electrical circuits, when light of much longer wave length than light visible to the eye is used. The phenomena are thus clearly wave-like: we call the disturbance "light" when we can see it; *electromagnetic radiation* even when we cannot. The spectrum, which is the wave length or frequency spread associated with electromagnetic waves, is very great (Fig. 7-6). It extends from ordinary alternating current phenomena, through radio waves and light, to the very high frequencies characteristic of emissions from atomic nuclei. The techniques of experimental observation vary widely over this range. A few instances will be mentioned in subsequent discussions, though the observations throughout the entire range confirm the generic similarity among all wave lengths that

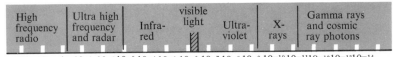

Wave length in meters of electromagnetic waves

Figure 7-6 *The electromagnetic spectrum.*

exhibit the properties called electromagnetic. In the long-wave length range, frequency is easily measured directly; in the intermediate range, both frequencies and wave lengths may be directly measured; and in the very short-wave length range, wave lengths only can be measured directly. All the evidence indicates, however, that the velocity of propagation of these waves in free space is the same throughout the entire known spectrum; hence, the frequency may always be inferred from the wave length, or vice versa, by recalling the relation between them: $\lambda\nu = c$.

Velocity of propagation of light   7-2

The velocity of propagation of electromagnetic waves was first measured astronomically. Öle Roemer, a Danish astronomer in the 1670's, in observing the passage of the moons of Jupiter behind this planet, found that eclipses appeared to occur relatively too soon when Jupiter was near the earth, and too late when it was far away. He correctly deduced that this was due to the time taken for the light that signalled the occultation of the moons to traverse the diameter of the earth's orbit (Fig. 7-7). The time difference he observed was about 1000 seconds, and as the diameter of the earth's orbit is about 186 million miles, or 3.0×10^{11} meters, the velocity of the light signal must be about 3×10^8 meters per second. This is very close to the best modern determination of this quantity.

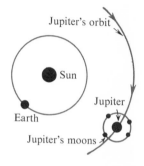

Figure 7-7 *Geometry of the earth and Jupiter and its moons.*

   The time it takes for light to traverse a carefully measured path along the surface of the earth can also be measured, and the velocity of propagation can be deduced. In these methods, a light beam is interrupted by a rapidly rotating toothed wheel or mirror, or by an electrical circuit, in order to furnish detectable discontinuities or modulation; the time taken for these successive segments of the light beam to traverse a precisely measured path is determined in terms of the period of interruption or modulation of the beam. Fizeau's method (Fig. 7-8), which was the earliest, is illustrative of them all. A light beam from a source is directed by an arrangement of lenses and mirrors over a path of several miles, and returns to an observer near the source. The outgoing and returning path each pass through the teeth of a slotted wheel which periodically occults and transmits the beam at a rate of $n\nu$ times per second, where n is the number of teeth and ν is the frequency of rotation of the wheel. If the time taken to traverse the path $2l$ is such that the pulse of light passed by one slot returns in time to be passed by the next slot, then the velocity of propagation is $2\,nl\,\nu$. Hence, if the speed of the

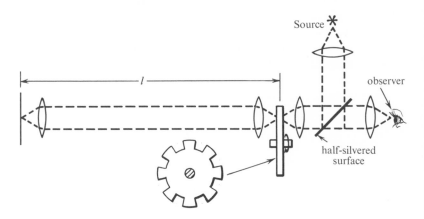

Figure 7-8 *Fizeau's method of measuring the velocity of light.*

wheel is increased to the frequency of rotation v, where maximum transmission is first observed, the velocity of propagation c is given by $2\,nl\,v$. By measurements such as this the velocity of light is found to be 299792.5 $\pm$ 0.2 km. sec.$^{-1}$. This very precise value is confirmed by other methods where precise measurements of frequency and wave length can both be made, and the velocity can be deduced from the product, since $c = \lambda v$.

The precision with which experiments such as Fizeau's can now be carried out by modern electronic techniques is striking. The most precise method of measuring great distances along the surface of the earth uses an instrument known as the geodimeter, which measures the time of transit t of a light signal over the path; from the relation $l = ct$, and the known velocity of light, the distance l may be determined with great accuracy.

7-3 *The Doppler effect*

So far in the discussion, the source of the wave motion being observed and the person or instrument making the observations have been considered to be at rest with respect to one another. If, however, the source of the waves moves through the medium while it oscillates and generates waves, or if the observer moves through the medium through which the waves are being propagated while making his observations, the results of his measurements may show evidence of such relative motions.

In particular, the frequency with which a wave pattern recurs for an observer will differ from the frequency emitted by the wave source, if there is any relative motion between them. This change in frequency, known as the *Doppler effect*, is produced by the motion of both the source and the observer separately in instances where the actual vibration of a material medium is evident, e.g., in the cases of waves on water surfaces or of sound passing through the air. If the source moves with a velocity u, it will traverse a distance Tu during the repetition period T of the oscillatory pattern; hence wave crests will be $(\lambda - Tu)$ apart in the direction of motion, and $(\lambda + Tu)$ in the opposite direction (Fig. 7-9). If the line of motion of the source is at an angle θ to the line

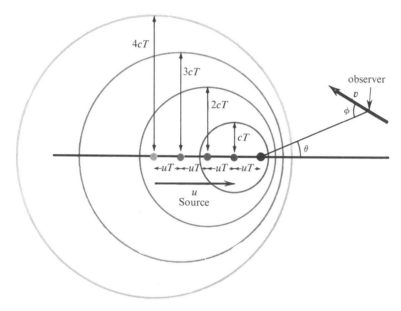

Figure 7-9 *Waves emitted from successive positions of a source moving with the velocity u.*

from the source to the observer, then the source will have a component of velocity $u \cos \theta$ in the direction of the observer; hence, the crests in this direction will be $(\lambda - Tu \cos \theta)$ apart. Similarly if the observer is also moving with a velocity v along a line making an angle ϕ with the line from the observer to the source, he will encounter successive crests or troughs with time intervals equal to the apparent wave length divided by his relative velocity with respect to the wave pattern, which is $(c + v \cos \phi)$. Hence the apparent frequency observed when source and observer are both in motion is:

$$\nu = \frac{c + v \cos \phi}{\lambda - Tu \cos \theta} = \frac{c(1 + v/c \cos \phi)}{\lambda(1 - u/c \cos \theta)} = \nu_0 \frac{1 + v/c \cos \phi}{1 - u/c \cos \theta}$$

where ν_0 is the source frequency. If θ and ϕ are $\pi/2$, there is no change in frequency to this approximation; if u and v are oppositely directed and the motion is along the line joining source and observer, the effect is greatest. As u and v enter the expression in different ways, we see from the above equation that in the case of a material medium, the apparent change in frequency depends upon both the relative motion of source and medium as well as upon the relative motion of observer and medium —not just upon the relative motion of source and observer. The most commonly encountered Doppler effect of this type occurs as a change heard in a sound's pitch when its source and listener are in motion.

EXAMPLE. The locomotive of a freight train has just completed a long U-bend of track. The caboose is just entering the U-bend, which is an exact semicircle. The fireman blows the locomotive whistle to warn a workman on the track ahead. If the whistle has a frequency of 400 cycles per second, and the speed of the train is 17 m.sec.$^{-1}$ (about 35 miles per hour), what frequency is heard by (a) the workman, (b) the fireman, (c) a brakeman in the caboose, and (d) a man in the center of the train? The velocity of sound in air is approximately 340 m.sec.$^{-1}$.

In Fig. 7-10, ν_0 is the source frequency, and ν_1, ν_2, ν_3, and ν_4 are the

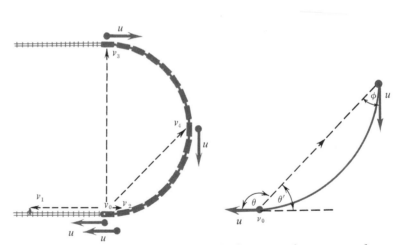

A locomotive whistle is heard by a workman on the track ahead, the fireman, the brakeman in the caboose, and a man in the center of the train. The frequencies heard depend on the motion of the source and of the observers.

The frequency of occurrence of waves travelling from source to observer is $\nu_0/(1 - u/c \cos \theta) = \nu_0/(1 + u/c \cos \theta')$. The frequency heard by the observer is $\nu_0(1 + u/c \cos \phi)/(1 + u/c \cos \theta')$, which is simply ν_0 if the angles θ' and ϕ are equal.

Figure 7-10   *The Doppler effect for sound waves.*

frequencies heard by the worker, fireman, brakeman and central man respectively. If u is the velocity of the train, and c the velocity of sound, then the frequency heard by the worker is:

$$\nu_1 = \nu_0/(1 - u/c) = 400/(1 - 17/340) = 400/0.95$$

$$\approx 421 \text{ cycles per second}$$

To reach the fireman, the sound must travel in a direction opposite to that of the source's motion; the fireman travels toward the source with the same velocity u as that with which the source recedes. Hence for the fireman, the frequency is:

$$\nu_2 = \nu_0(1 + u/c)/(1 + u/c) = \nu_0 = 400 \text{ cycles per second}$$

The motion of both the source and the observer are perpendicular to the line joining them in the case of the brakeman. Hence the correction terms both contain the cosine of 90°, which is zero. Therefore the frequency heard by the brakeman is:

$$\nu_3 = \nu_0 = 400 \text{ cycles per second}$$

In the case of the man in the center of the train, the source is approaching at an angle θ, or, as indicated in Fig. 7-10, the source is receding at an angle θ'. The observer is here approaching at an angle ϕ with the same velocity u; hence the frequency observed is:

$$\nu_4 = \nu_0(1 + u/c \cos \phi)/(1 + u/c \cos \theta')$$

Since θ' and ϕ are both equal to 45°, the observed frequency is ν_0, or 400 cycles per second. Note that at all points on the train not considered here, the angles θ' and ϕ are equal, and hence the observed frequency is equal to the source frequency ν_0.

The Michelson-Morley experiment 7-4

It has been seen that interference phenomena demonstrate the wave-like nature of light. It should be expected, therefore, that light would also exhibit a Doppler effect. In the foregoing analysis it was postulated that there were three participants in the phenomenon, namely: the source; the medium; and the observer. The relative motions between each pair of participants were observable. If the postulates were to be applicable to the wave motion of light, the formula derived for sound waves and surface waves which travel in material media should also be applicable to the propagation of light through free space, as well as through transparent materials. One should then be able to devise suitable experiments to determine u, v and c separately. One experiment of this type, that is readily performed by an observer having a source of light at rest with respect to himself on the surface of the earth, is to compare the apparent velocity of light in two mutually perpendicular directions. Inasmuch as the earth is rotating about its axis and also travelling in its orbit around the sun, one of the two mutually perpendicular directions may be chosen to lie more nearly along the line of motion than the other, at a particular time of observation. Hence the time taken for light to traverse equal distances along these two directions should be unequal. From such measurements the velocity of motion of the source and observer through space should be deducible. This is all on the assumption that the postulates regarding the propagation of waves through material media are applicable to the propagation of light through free space, and that it is sensible to speak of the motion of observers or light waves with respect to some absolute set of coordinates in space, just in the way one can speak of coordinates associated with material objects and material media.

The line of reasoning supporting such an experiment is as follows: light emitted from the source traverses the medium with the velocity c. The source moves through the medium with an assumed measurable velocity v. When it is at position A of Fig. 7-11, a light signal is emitted; this is reflected from each of two distant mirrors M_1 and M_2, which are adjusted to reflect the light back to the source after it has traversed two mutually perpendicular paths. During the time of the light's passage to the mirrors and back, the source will have moved to the new position B. If b is the separation of A and B, and the distance from the source to each mirror is l, then the path difference between the light reflected from the two mirrors is:

$$[2(l^2 + (b/2)^2)^{1/2}] - [(l + b/2) + (l - b/2)] = 2l[1 + (b/2l)^2]^{1/2} - 2l$$

If the velocity of light is much greater than that of the observer and his apparatus through space, the distance b is small compared to l, and the path difference is approximated by the first two terms in the expansion of the square root by the binomial theorem. Thus $[1 + (b/2l)^2]^{1/2}$ is approximately equal to $[1 + \frac{1}{2}(b/2l)^2]$, and hence the path difference is approximately: $b^2/4l$.

The time taken for the source and the observer to travel from A to B is b/v; this is the same time for the light wave or signal to travel the distance to each mirror and back, which is approximately $2l/c$. Equating

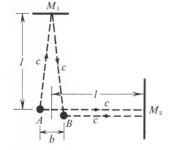

Figure 7-11   Comparison   of
two light paths from A to B.

these two quantities, $b/v = 2l/c$, or $b/2l = v/c$, the path difference for the two rays of light reaching B, which may be written ds, is:

$$ds = (v/c)^2 l$$

Since c is very large compared with v, ds is a very small quantity. But the known velocity of the earth is great enough for the effect to be measurable. A. A. Michelson and E. W. Morley set out to measure the path difference induced by the earth's motion through space in an historic experiment that yielded a most surprising result.

In this experiment, light from an intense source was focused by a lens to form a beam, which—on striking a partially silvered glass surface—was divided into two beams, one transmitted, the other reflected. Through the use of a system of mirrors, indicated schematically by M_1 and M_2 in Fig. 7-12, the beams traversed long paths in mutually perpendicular directions and returned to the partially silvered surface. There each beam was again partly reflected and partly transmitted; the combined portions emerging at right angles to the entering beam added together to produce an observable interference pattern. The entire apparatus was floated in a pool of mercury so that it could be rotated about a vertical axis to align one arm or the other with whatever velocity maximum the observations indicated. Any path difference induced by changing the direction of the path to M_1 and M_2 would be indicated by a shift in the interference pattern of the two recombined beams of light. If the path difference ds of the two beams were to change by $\lambda/2$, or half the wavelength of the monochromatic light used, then the relative phase of the two beams on recombination would change by π. Thus a bright field of view would change to a dark one; or, if the adjustment of the instrument produced a multifringe pattern, the pattern would shift by half the distance between fringes.

The actual result of the experiment was that no shift whatever was observed for any orientation of the instrument. Since a shift of $1/40$ fringe could easily have been detected, had it occurred, ds was always less than $\lambda/40$. Or, taking the wave length of green light as 5.5×10^{-7} m., ds was less than 1.4×10^{-8} meters. Taking l as about 10 meters, it is seen from the relation $ds = (v/c)^2 l$ that $(v/c)^2$ must be less than 1.4×10^{-9}. Thus v must be less than 3.7×10^{-5} times the velocity of light, or less than about 11,000 meters per second. The velocity of the surface of the earth near the equator is about 500 meters per second greater in the east-west direction than it is in the north-south direction, due to the earth's axial rotation; but this is evidently too little a difference to be detectable. However, the circulation of the earth about the sun corresponds to a velocity of 6×10^4 m.sec.$^{-1}$ This should have been detected by Michelson and Morley, and still more surely by subsequent

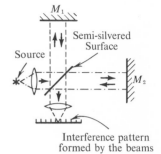

Interference pattern formed by the beams

Figure 7-12   *Schematic Michelson-Morley experiment.*

experiments of much greater precision. But no such evidence of the earth's velocity through space has been found. This was indeed a most surprising experimental result and a source of great debate in the scientific world. On the basis of Michelson's and Morley's results, we might be led to conclude that the earth is always at rest with respect to space; this conclusion is, of course, entirely at variance with the known motion of the earth.

7-5   *Einstein's interpretation of the Michelson-Morley results*

In 1905, Albert Einstein, who was then an examiner in the Swiss patent office, proposed a theory that not only brought Michelson's and Morley's results into accord with the general body of physical observations, but was also to have a far reaching effect on the future development of physical knowledge. Rather than try to force the Michelson-Morley results into the pattern of the old Galilean or Newtonian mechanics, Einstein made them a keystone of a new theory of relative motion. The theory rests on two basic postulates: the first is that an observer always measures the velocity of light to be the same in any direction, regardless of his apparent motion with respect to other bodies. As a corollary, it follows that all observers will arrive at the same value for the velocity of light; therefore absolute motion through space is unobservable, and hence a scientifically meaningless concept. The second basic postulate is that any two observers moving relative to one another with a constant velocity can agree completely on their data of observation and on the scientific theories or descriptions they can evolve from these data. This is in agreement with our observation that the physical laws apply equally well to all local and distant phenomena, although the earth at different times has different velocities relative to other celestial bodies. It should be mentioned that the centripetal acceleration of the earth in its orbit is small enough that the velocity at any time may be regarded as effectively constant to the accuracy that the theory has been tested.

The theory which was developed by Einstein and the major conclusions to which it leads were comparable in importance to the ideas of Galileo and Newton in the founding of mechanics. However, a number of years elapsed before Einstein's work was accorded general acceptance. A fundamental break with traditional thinking was required. Time could no longer be considered to occupy a unique position as the independent variable in the description of phenomena. The existence of an invariant velocity with which electromagnetic signals can be transmitted through space of necessity relates together the temporal and spatial variables that describe our observations. It will be seen later that an upper limit is imposed by the pattern of our universe upon any velocity that can be measured; the numerical value of this limit is the invariant velocity with which electromagnetic signals travel and is as basic a physical constant as the universal gravitational constant G. The fundamental relationship between space and time profoundly alters the forms of the expressions for the location of events which take place in what we must now call *space-time*. This concept (i.e., space-time) must be used by observers, in relative motion with respect to one another, who wish to compare their conclusions. An analysis of the detailed manipulation of meter sticks, clocks, and other instruments of measure brings out the meaning that must be attributed to the word similtaneity: namely, that it is a relative concept, dependent upon the relative motion of the observers determining it.

The *special theory of relativity* which emerged from Einstein's analysis of the experimental observations is so called because it is limited in its application to observers who are moving with a constant velocity relative to one another. The frames of reference, in terms of which such observers describe the results of their experiments, are called *inertial frames*, to bring out the limitation that relative accelerations are absent; hence inertial forces that would arise from accelerations or rotations and produce differential forces in the two frames do not exist. The consequences deduced from Einstein's theory have been repeatedly corroborated experimentally, and some of the most remarkable scientific advances of the century have been derived from it.

The Galilean transformation of coordinates   7-6

Before elaborating the consequences of Einstein's special theory of relativity as they relate to the laws of mechanics, it would be well to carefully consider the old ideas of relative motion between observers, and the transformation necessary to relate the measurements of one observer to those of another who is in relative motion with respect to him. These old ideas were the conceptions of Galileo and Newton; they remained unchallenged for more than 200 years. Indeed, they still form the basis for calculations where the velocities of relative motion are small in comparison to the velocity of light.

Consider the situation depicted in Fig. 7-13. A stationary observer at the point O measures the coordinates of some point as (x, y, z, t),

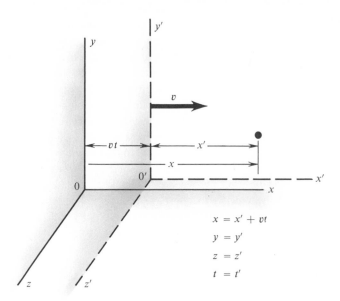

Figure 7-13   *Galilean transformation of coordinates.*

where t is the time of the observation. A second observer at O', the center of a coordinate system which is moving to the right (the positive x direction) with constant velocity v, measures the coordinates of the same point to be (x', y', z', t'). If the two systems coincide at the time $t = t' = 0$, then only at this time will the value of the x coordinate measured by the one observer equal the value of the x' coordinate measured by the other. At some later time t, their values will differ by the distance vt travelled by the observer with the primed coordinates. Of course the measurements of y, z and t by the stationary observer will always agree with those of y', z' and t' by the moving observer, since these are independent of any motion in the x direction. Thus the primed and unprimed coordinates of the Galilean system are related according to the following transformations:

$$x = x' + vt'$$

$$y = y'$$

$$z = z'$$

$$t = t'$$

If the observer with the primed coordinates likes to consider himself stationary, then he would see the unprimed system moving to the left with velocity v, or with velocity $-v$ in the x' direction. The appropriate transformations would then be:

$$x' = x - vt$$
$$y' = y$$
$$z' = z$$
$$t' = t$$

EXAMPLE. Consider the situation of a train which leaves a station, as it is observed by someone at the rear of the train and by someone else left behind on the platform (Fig. 7-14). Here the observer on the train is a moving observer with a coordinate system x', y', z' and t'; the stationary observer has a coordinate system x, y, z and t. If the train has a constant velocity v, if it left the station at time $t = t' = 0$, and if the locomotive is at a distance x' from the moving observer, then the distance of the locomotive from the stationary observer on the platform is $x = x' + vt$, where vt is the distance the train has moved.

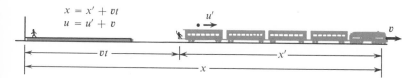

Figure 7-14 *Galilean transformations applied to a stationary observer and another on a moving train. The ball is thrown with velocity u' relative to the train whose velocity is v. The velocity of the ball relative to the stationary observer is $u = u' + v$.*

A ball thrown backward with a velocity of 20 miles per hour from the rear of a train moving forward at 70 miles per hour would have a resultant *forward* velocity of 50 miles per hour, measured by a stationary observer. If the ball were thrown forward, then its velocity relative to the stationary observer would be 90 miles per hour. The equation for velocity transformation is then:

$$u = u' + v$$

where u is a velocity measured by a stationary observer and u' is the velocity measured by an observer moving with velocity v with respect to the first.

In the intuitive approach to the ordering of events, which was at the basis of the mechanics of Galileo and Newton, spatial and temporal coordinates were quite unrelated to one another; it appeared sensible to conceive of absolute velocities and to arrive at the relative velocity of motion between two coordinate systems by adding algebraically the velocity of each relative to a third system of coordinates, which might be thought of as being absolutely at rest. This is seen (by the results of the Michelson-Morley experiment) to eventuate in a description which, at least when the velocity of light is in question, is at variance with observation. Thus the classical or so-called *Galilean transformation* from one system of coordinates to another moving relative to it is found to be wanting in general applicability, even if it has proven to be a very good approximation in cases where the velocities concerned are small in comparison with the velocity of light. The Galilean scheme must be included as an adequate approximation for low velocities in any more general theory that will also account for the phenomena encountered throughout the whole range of velocities up to and including that of light.

7-7 *The Lorentz transformation of coordinates*

One may start to enlarge the traditional picture of coordinate transformations on the basis proposed by Einstein, using the same simple figure to envision the relative motion of two observers—one at rest in the primed system of coordinates, and the other at rest in the unprimed system. Each is located at his respective origin, O' and O, and they agree that they are moving relatively to one another with the uniform velocity v along the x axis. The primed observer is moving to the right in the positive x direction viewed by the observer at O; the man at O is moving in the negative x' direction viewed by his counterpart at O'. Cogent arguments of symmetry and experimental evidence, advanced by Kennedy and Thorndyke, lead to the conclusion that the coordinates perpendicular to the direction of motion always remain independent of time; i.e., these coordinates are equal to their direct counterparts in the equations for the transformation of coordinates of special relativity: $y = y'$, $z = z'$. However, this is not true of x and x', and t and t'. These must mutually involve one another in a simple relationship. The relationship must involve only the first power of these variables, in order for the transformation to be concordant with the observable rectilinear propagation of light and with other established phenomena. Thus the relations between the coordinates must be of the forms:

$$x = \alpha x' + \beta t' \quad \text{and} \quad t = \gamma x' + \delta t'$$

where α, β, γ and δ are the four quantities relating the coordinates used by the two observers. These must be determined empirically.

Consider a point at the origin O' of the primed coordinate system in Fig. 7-15. In this system the point always has the displacement $x' = 0$.

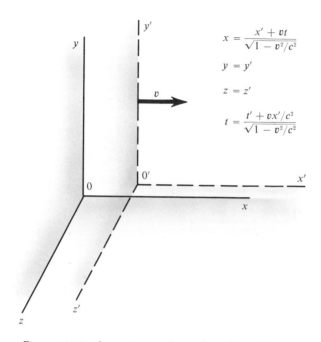

$$x = \frac{x' + vt}{\sqrt{1 - v^2/c^2}}$$

$$y = y'$$

$$z = z'$$

$$t = \frac{t' + vx'/c^2}{\sqrt{1 - v^2/c^2}}$$

Figure 7-15 *Lorentz transformation of coordinates.*

Therefore, for this point, $x = \beta t'$, and $t = \delta t'$. In the unprimed system, the point moves with the constant velocity $v = x/t = \beta/\delta$. Since v is a constant, this last relation holds at all times. Also, both observers observe a light impulse emitted from O and O', at the instant they are coincident, spread out at the same rate; the square of the radius of the spherical wave front would be written by the two observers as:

$$x^2 + y^2 + z^2 = c^2t^2 \qquad \text{and} \qquad x'^2 + y'^2 + z'^2 = c^2t'^2$$

the value of c being the same for each. Using the linear expressions for x, y, z, and t in terms of x', y', z', and t', the first equation may be transformed:

$$(\alpha^2 - c^2\gamma^2)x'^2 + y'^2 + z'^2 + 2(\alpha\beta - c^2\gamma\delta)x't' = c^2(\delta^2 - \beta^2/c^2)t'^2$$

This relation between x', y', z', and t' must be the same as the one already noted above. Hence the coefficients of corresponding terms in the two equations must be the same, and:

$$\alpha^2 - c^2\gamma^2 = 1$$

$$\alpha\beta - c^2\gamma\delta = 0$$

$$\delta^2 - \beta^2/c^2 = 1$$

Together with the previously determined relation $\beta/\delta = v$, these equations may be solved explicitly for the constants:

$$\alpha = \delta = \left(1 - \frac{v^2}{c^2}\right)^{-1/2}$$

$$\beta = v\left(1 - \frac{v^2}{c^2}\right)^{-1/2}$$

$$\gamma = \frac{v}{c^2}\left(1 - \frac{v^2}{c^2}\right)^{-1/2}$$

The equations relating the coordinates of the two observers are then:

$$y = y' \qquad\qquad y' = y$$

$$z = z' \qquad\qquad z' = z$$

$$x = \frac{x' + vt'}{\sqrt{1 - v^2/c^2}} \qquad x' = \frac{x - vt}{\sqrt{1 - v^2/c^2}}$$

$$t = \frac{t' + vx'/c^2}{\sqrt{1 - v^2/c^2}} \qquad t' = \frac{t - vx/c^2}{\sqrt{1 - v^2/c^2}}$$

These equations of transformation are known as the *Lorentz transformation equations*, after a distinguished physicist who arrived at them in the course of his studies of electromagnetic phenomena.

It has been shown that these equations are based upon the fact that any two observers, moving with respect to one another with the arbitrary velocity v, will each agree that the value of the velocity of light that he measures in his frame of reference is numerically the same as the value measured by the other observer in his frame of reference. These equations would be used by someone who makes observations, say, in terms of x', y', z', and t', to rewrite these observations in terms of x, y, z, and t, in order to compare his observations with those of another observer moving with respect to him with a velocity of $-v$. Or they would be used by the observer in the unprimed frame to rewrite his observations for comparison with those of the primed observer, moving relative to him with the velocity v. It is seen that if v is so small that it is negligible compared to c, then the equations revert to the simple Galilean equations of transformation given earlier. It is, of course, essential that they do so, for the simple addition of velocities is a well known feature of ordinary observations where relative velocities are small. Also it is seen that v can never exceed c; for if it were to do so, the term in parenthesis $(1 - v^2/c^2)$ would be negative, and its square root would therefore be physically meaningless. Thus c is the maximum velocity that can ever be observed; all other velocities actually encountered must be less than it.

Certain consequence of the   7-8
Lorentz transformation

The Lorentz transformation equations have certain very important implications in regard to the relationships between the kinematic quantities: distances; times; and velocities. If, for instance, an observer at rest in the unprimed system, say at O, wishes to measure an interval along the moving x' axis, he will dispose a measuring rod at rest with respect to himself along the x axis and then at the appropriate time, say t, simultaneously note the two positions x_1 and x_2 that he desires to measure. From the transformation equation for x' and x and t, the intervals are related by:

$$(x_2' - x_1') = \frac{x_2 - x_1}{\sqrt{1 - v^2/c^2}}$$

since the time of measurement t is the same for x_1 and x_2. If $(x_2' - x_1')$ is a distance l', and $(x_2 - x_1)$ is a distance l, then the distance l seen by the unprimed observer is shorter than the distance l' seen by the primed observer, since

$$l = l' \sqrt{1 - v^2/c^2}$$

Thus an observer with respect to whom an object is moving will measure a shorter length in the direction of motion than will an observer to whom the object appears stationary. This apparent shrinkage of length, measured parallel to the direction of motion, is called the *Fitzgerald contraction*. It is evidently very small for small values of the relative velocity v and escaped observation entirely prior to the theory of relativity.

Also, if each observer has a clock at rest with respect to himself, time intervals can be compared. If the clock of the primed observer at O' shows the values t_1' and t_2', the time interval appearing to the observer at O, moving with respect to it with the velocity v, is seen from the transformation equation for t and t' for $x' = 0$ to be:

$$(t_2 - t_1) = \frac{t_2' - t_1'}{\sqrt{1 - v^2/c^2}}$$

If $(t_2' - t_1')$ is a time interval T', and $(t_2 - t_1)$ is a time interval T, then the time interval T shown by the unprimed observer's clock is greater than the time interval T' shown by the primed observer's clock, since

$$T = \frac{T'}{\sqrt{1 - v^2/c^2}}$$

Thus when a clock moves with respect to an observer, it appears to him to slow down. The fact that time intervals measured in terms of moving clocks are greater than those measured by clocks at rest with respect to the observer is known as the *Fitzgerald time dilatation*. Again, this is a small effect that eluded observation prior to our knowledge of relativity.

EXAMPLE. Consider the observations of two men who set out in identical space vehicles, each 10 feet long, carrying identical measuring instruments. One of the ships passes the other at a uniform relative velocity of 1.8×10^8 m.sec.$^{-1}$ (about 110,000 miles per second). One of the men, who is of course stationary in his own system of coordinates, measures the length of his ship to be $l' = 10$ m. The man in the other ship travelling relative to the first ship with a velocity of $v = 1.8 \times 10^8$ meters per second, however, looks out and measures the length of the first ship to be:

$$l = l' \sqrt{1 - v^2/c^2} = 10 \sqrt{1 - \left(\frac{1.8 \times 10^8}{3 \times 10^8}\right)^2}$$
$$= 10\sqrt{1 - .36} = 8 \text{ meters}$$

He also observes that the measuring instruments in the first ship have contracted in the same proportion, so that a 10-cm. rule lying along the direction of relative motion has contracted to 8 cm. This, he imagines, would explain why the first observer cannot notice the contraction of his own ship. Similar arguments can be applied to the lenses of the first observer's eyes and camera, all of which contract in the direction of motion and hence distort the picture of his contracted ship, so that he believes it to be its original shape and length of 10 meters. The question is often asked: "Who is right; does the first ship contract or not?" But this question is meaningless, because whether or not the ship contracts depends on the relative velocity of the ship and the observer. It contracts to one observer and not to the other. Both are right and consistent in their own measurements; but they are not right if they attempt to equate these measurements with those made by someone in another coordinate system moving relative to their own. Of course the whole argument can be reversed, whereby the first observer measures the length of the second ship to be 8 m. whereas its occupant measures it to be 10 m. If this were not so, it would be possible to determine which ship was really moving; i.e. absolute motion with respect to space would be a meaningful concept. Similarly, each man observes that his own clocks remain accurate and his pulse rate normal, whereas the other's clocks and pulse rate appear to have slowed down to 80% of their normal rates.

EXAMPLE. *The appearance of rapidly moving objects.* It is interesting to consider the three-dimensional picture of an object as seen by an observer with respect to whom the object is moving. First assume that the object is a cube, at a considerable distance from the observer, so that light from all points of its surfaces is essentially parallel as it leaves in the direction of the observer. Also assume that the cube passes the observer with one face turned directly toward him. A stationary cube in such a position would have only one visible face. However, the motion in the above case allows the cube to move out of the way of light rays which would otherwise have been blocked from the observer's view, and thus the left side of the cube in Fig. 7-16 is also visible. Re-

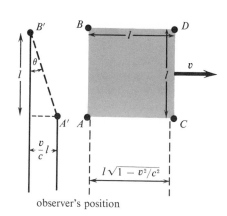

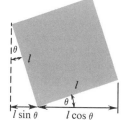

Light from the points A and B, which reaches the observer simultaneously, must have left these points when they were at A' and B' respectively. Thus the side AB of the cube is visible to the observer. The side AC appears to be contracted.

A stationary cube, when rotated through an angle θ, gives projected side lengths of $l \sin \theta$ and $l \cos \theta$.

Figure 7-16 *A rapidly moving cube appears to rotate as it moves past an observer.*

ferring to this figure, if light rays from the points A and B are to reach the observer simultaneously, then the light from B must have left the cube before the light from A. The difference in time of origin of these two light rays is apparently $t = l/c$; during this time interval the cube will have moved forward a distance $vt = lv/c$. Thus the side AB is visible to the observer, but appears to him to be in the position $A'B'$ with a projected length of lv/c. The side AC appears shortened (by the Lorentz contraction) to a value $l\sqrt{1 - v^2/c^2}$. In Fig. 7-16b, a stationary cube turned through an angle θ from an initial face-on attitude shows projected side lengths of $l\sin\theta$ and $l\cos\theta = l\sqrt{1 - \sin^2\theta}$. Thus the moving cube to a face-on observer appears to have been turned through an angle θ such that $\sin\theta = v/c$. Since the above argument can be applied to any measurements made parallel or perpendicular to the direction of relative motion, the argument is a general one, and the initial aspect of the object does not have to be face-on any more than the object has to be a cube. Any object, as it passes an observer with relative velocity v, will appear to him to be rotated from its stationary aspect by an angle θ such that $\sin\theta = v/c$.

EXAMPLE. *Generalization to a third observer who is also in motion along the same axis.* Suppose there is a third observer present, who—it seems to the primed observer—is moving with the velocity u in the x' direction. How rapidly will he appear to be moving with respect to the original unprimed observer? (Fig. 7-17)

The equations of transformation for the primed and doubly primed observers are:

$$y' = y''$$
$$z' = z''$$
$$x' = \frac{x'' + ut''}{\sqrt{1 - u^2/c^2}}$$
$$t' = \frac{t'' + ux''/c^2}{\sqrt{1 - u^2/c^2}}$$

and for the unprimed and primed observers:

$$y = y'$$
$$z = z'$$
$$x = \frac{x' + vt'}{\sqrt{1 - v^2/c^2}}$$
$$t = \frac{t' + vx'/c^2}{\sqrt{1 - v^2/c^2}}$$

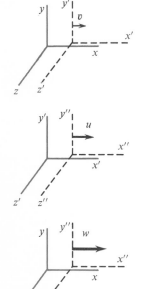

Figure 7-17   *Addition of velocities in special relativity.*

Of course $y = y' = y''$ and $z = z' = z''$. Also x' and t' can be eliminated between the four equations containing the radical, and the value of x/t for the origin of a double primed coordinate ($x'' = 0$), which is the velocity with which it is moving away from the observer at $x = 0$, can be found:

$$w = \frac{v + u}{1 + vu/c^2}$$

This may be written in an interesting way by dividing each side by c and subtracting 1 from each side:

$$\left(\frac{w}{c} - 1\right) = -\left[\frac{1 - v/c - u/c + vu/c^2}{1 + vu/c^2}\right]$$

$$= -\left[\frac{(1 - v/c)(1 - u/c)}{1 + vu/c^2}\right]$$

or:

$$\frac{w}{c} = \left[1 - \frac{(1 - v/c)(1 - u/c)}{1 + vu/c^2}\right]$$

In this form, it is easily seen that no matter how closely v and u may approach c, w/c is less than unity; or, in other words, w is always less than the maximum possible velocity c.

The Doppler effect for light   7-9

An interesting experiment, directly verifying relativistic kinematics, and demonstrating the nature of the Doppler effect to be expected in the case of light waves, has been performed by E. H. Ives and G. R. Stillwell. In this experiment, the wave length of a monochromatic component of the light observed from a discharge of electricity through a tube containing hydrogen gas was measured very precisely. Many of the atoms involved in the emission of this light were moving rapidly with respect to the apparatus. The apparent wave lengths of the light from both slowly and rapidly moving atoms could be compared; these differences in turn could be compared with the predictions based on the special theory of relativity.

The concept of this experiment is as follows. An atom of hydrogen, located say at O'—at rest in a coordinate system identified with x', y', z', and t' of Fig. 7-18—is moving with the velocity v away from the observer at O, at rest in the coordinate system x, y, z, and t. An event

Radiating atom at 0' observed at 0.

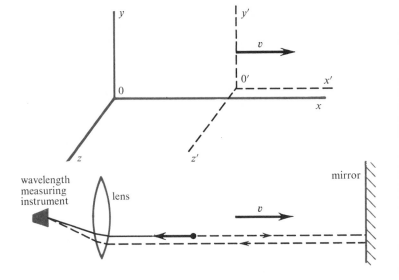

Light emitted in both the forward and backward directions by moving atoms is observed by a wave length-measuring instrument.

Figure 7-18 *Ives-Stillwell experiment for measuring the Doppler effect of light.*

at O' is described by the observer at O by the Lorentz equations where $x' = 0$, or:

$$x = \frac{vt'}{\sqrt{1 - v^2/c^2}} \qquad t = \frac{t'}{\sqrt{1 - v^2/c^2}}$$

A signal sent out at the time t, when the atom at O' is at the point x, arrives at O at the time $(t + x/c)$, or at the time

$$\frac{t'}{\sqrt{1 - v^2/c^2}} + \frac{vt'/c}{\sqrt{1 - v^2/c^2}} = \frac{t'(1 + v/c)}{\sqrt{1 - v^2/c^2}}$$

The next signal, sent out at the time $(t' + T')$, where T' is the source period, arrives at the time

$$\frac{(t' + T')(1 + v/c)}{\sqrt{1 - v^2/c^2}}$$

Thus the period of the waves as they arrive at O is

$$T = \frac{(t' + T')(1 + v/c)}{\sqrt{1 - v^2/c^2}} - \frac{t'(1 + v/c)}{\sqrt{1 - v^2/c^2}}$$

$$= \frac{T'(1 + v/c)}{\sqrt{1 - v^2/c^2}}$$

Or since $\qquad\qquad T = 1/\nu = \lambda/c$

where ν is the frequency and λ the wavelength of the waves, then

$$\lambda = \lambda' \frac{(1 + v/c)}{\sqrt{1 - v^2/c^2}}$$

If the atom emitting the light were approaching instead of receding with the velocity v, the expression for the apparent frequency or wavelength would be properly altered by changing the sign of v.

In the physical arrangement of the experiment, the light emitted by hydrogen atoms moving very rapidly in a hydrogen discharge tube was observed directly by an optical wave length-measuring instrument; also the light radiated in the opposite direction was reflected back from a mirror into the same instrument. Thus the velocity difference, reflected in the wave length difference, measured by the instrument was $2v$.

The wave length difference thus presented to the interferometer measuring the wave length separation was:

$$d\lambda = \frac{\lambda'[(1 + v/c) - (1 - v/c)]}{\sqrt{1 - v^2/c^2}} = \frac{\lambda'(2v/c)}{\sqrt{1 - v^2/c^2}}$$

Since the wave length emitted by such atoms at rest, i.e., λ', is known, the first order ratio v/c can be determined. It was found in this particular experiment to be about 6×10^{-3}.

The average value of the two wave lengths from atoms moving with the velocities $+v$ and $-v$ is not simply λ', but $\lambda'/\sqrt{1 - v^2/c^2}$, as can be seen by adding the values of λ' for $+v$ and $-v$ and dividing by 2. One would expect a difference between the average wave length for $+v$ and $-v$, and the wave length from an atom essentially at rest:

$$\frac{\lambda'}{\sqrt{1 - v^2/c^2}} - \lambda' \approx \lambda' \frac{v^2}{2c^2}$$

From the value of v/c given earlier, this difference should be about $18 \times 10^{-6}\lambda'$. This value was also confirmed by the results of the experiment. The reason that the average is not equal to the wave length as measured by an observer at rest, with respect to the emitting atom, is because of the Lorentz time dilatation, in accordance with which the time intervals between oscillations of the hydrogen atom appear to be different when observed by one who is at rest, or by one who is in motion with respect to the atom. Still more striking confirmation of the apparent slowing down of processes taking place in systems moving very rapidly with respect to an observer comes from measuring the apparent life-times of unstable nuclear particles travelling with velocities close to c where the difference in time scales becomes quite large.

Further reading:

BRONOWSKI, J., "The Clock Paradox," *Scientific American*, vol. 208, No. 2, p. 134 (1963).

COLEMAN, J., *Relativity and the Layman*, William Frederick Press Books (1954).

GARDNER, M., *Relativity for the Million*, Macmillan (1962).

McVITTIE, C. C., "Distance and Relativity," *Science*, vol. 127, No. 3297, p. 501 (1958).

MULLIGAN, J. F. and McDONALD, D. F., "Some Recent Determinations of the Velocity of Light," *American Journal of Physics*, vol. 25, No. 3, p. 180 (1957).

SHANKLAND, B. S., "The Michelson-Morley Experiment," *Scientific American*, vol. 211, No. 5, p. 107 (1964).

WEISSKOPF, V. F., "The Visual Appearance of Rapidly Moving Objects," *Physics Today*, vol. 13, No. 9, p. 24 (1960).

Problems

7-1 A whistle emits a note of frequency ν_0 as it is swung in a horizontal circle or radius r with constant angular velocity ω. Express the frequency heard as a function of time by three different observers, the first in the center of the circle, the second a great distance off in the same horizontal plane, and the third a height h vertically above the center of the circle.

7-2 A man bounces a ball on one spot of the rear platform of a train moving with constant velocity v along a straight track. Sketch the path of the ball as observed by someone at the side of the track. If the ball makes elastic collisions with the floor and bounces freely to a height h and back, what is the equation for the ball's path between bounces as seen by the above observer?

7-3 Why do airplanes generally land and take off against the wind? Express the *groundspeed* v_g in terms of the *airspeed* v_a and the wind velocity v_w in the case of a tail wind.

7-4 A rocket launching pad is 30 m. on each side. What would be the length of the diagonal measured from a rocket travelling parallel to one side with a constant velocity of 1.8×10^8 m.sec.$^{-1}$?

7-5 At what velocity does the longitudinal dimension of an object decrease to about 98 per cent of its stationary value?

7-6 Two space travellers, A and B, synchronize their accurate clocks and then leave the earth in opposite directions. After reaching constant velocities A notes that B's clock is running steadily 10 per cent too slow. What is the magnitude of A's velocity relative to B? What is the magnitude of B's velocity relative to A? Can B detect the "inaccuracy" in his clock? What observation would B make about A's clock? Do A and B agree on the distance between their rockets? Do they agree on the length of A's rocket?

7-7 A monochromatic light wave is observed to have frequency, wave length, and velocity values of 6×10^{14} sec.$^{-1}$, 5×10^{-7} m., and 3×10^8 m.sec.$^{-1}$ respectively. What values would be measured by a second observer travelling with respect to the first with a velocity $\frac{4}{5}$ that of light in the direction of motion of the light wave?

7-8 Two men fight a duel with pistols and fire simultaneously at one another from a distance of 10 m. according to a stationary observer. Which fires first, and by how many seconds according to an adjacent observer with a velocity component along the line of fire equal to $\frac{3}{5}$ of the velocity of light? Could such an observer see one of the duellists hit before firing his pistol?

7-9 A galaxy recedes from the earth with a velocity 90 per cent that of light. Another recedes from the earth in the opposite direction with a velocity 70 per cent that of light. What is the magnitude of their velocity relative to one another?

7-10 Apply the Lorentz transformation for time intervals to correct the source frequency in the Doppler equation for a source moving with velocity u towards a stationary observer; thus obtain the relativistic Doppler equation. Apply a similar correction to the observed frequency for an observer moving with velocity v towards a stationary source; thus obtain the relativistic Doppler equation for a moving observer. Be careful to use the correct transformations, according to whether the observer is stationary or moving. Show that for electromagnetic waves these two Doppler equations are of similar form. Combine the two equations (moving source and observer) and show that the observed frequency then depends only on the relative velocity w of the source and observer. Remember that w is not simply $u + v$.

7-11 The earth is approximately spherical with a radius R according to our measurements. What is its apparent shape to an observer in another galaxy moving with respect to us with a velocity 50 per cent of that of light? What dimensions does it appear to have for such an observer?

8 Implications of the special theory of relativity for mechanics and the more general theory of relativity

8-1 Implications of the Lorentz transformation for mechanics

It is quite clear from the Lorentz transformation equations that the relativistic description differs from the classical one in a very fundamental qualitative way. However, the quantitative difference, being of the order of v^2/c^2, amounts to only about one per cent, even for velocities in the very high range of one tenth the velocity of light itself. It might be thought, in consequence, that the practical effects of relativity would be of negligible importance. It is true that the velocities with which human beings travel relative to one another are such that the classical theory furnishes a very adequate description of everyday affairs, but the high energy particles produced with modern technology require the relativistic formulation for their description. Much more important, however, is the fundamentally different pattern of physical concepts that emerges as a result of relativistic thinking. The special theory, limited though it is to constant relative velocities, has enormously generalized, unified, and simplified the description of basic physical science. The direct effect of the theory, which is to have induced a symmetry between the kinematic variables of time and space that previously had not been in evidence, has implications for the dynamic quantity mass, and for the concepts of momentum and energy —which implications, within the framework of the conservation laws for these quantities, have led to much greater insight into the whole field of mechanics than had ever been gained before.

The conservation of momentum 8-2

In accordance with the basic philosophy of relativity, there are no specially favored coordinate systems; the laws of physical science must be of the same form for all observers who move at a constant velocity in relation to one another. The implications of this statement for the concept of momentum and its law of conservation may be illustrated by considering a simple collision problem from the points of view of two observers moving uniformly with respect to one another, both of whom are to conclude that momentum is conserved in the process they observe. The two small elastic masses that are considered to collide are compared on a balance with one another by both observers while they are stationary. They are found to be equal and of the value m_0. The observer in the primed coordinate system takes his mass, which may be thought of as a steel ball, and arranges to move with the velocity v with respect to the unprimed system along the common (x, x') axis (Fig. 8-1). This same observer is located out along the positive y' axis. He arranges to project his mass with the velocity $-u$, as he measures it in the primed system, down toward the origin. The observer in the unprimed system is located out along the negative y axis. He arranges to project his mass with a velocity u, measured in his unprimed system, toward the origin at just the right time to collide with the mass projected by the observer in the primed system. The two origins coincide at the instant of impact.

When the unprimed observer projects his mass m_0 upward, it is no longer at rest with respect to him, so he can't make a static measurement on it. Hence its apparent mass may change somewhat from m_0;

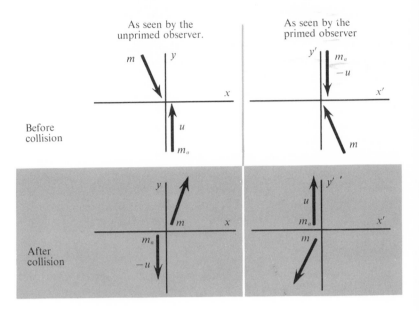

As seen by the
unprimed observer.

As seen by the
primed observer

Before
collision

After
collision

Figure 8-1 *Conservation of momentum at a collision.*

say, to m_a. He observes the primed observer's mass, called m, coming down and in from the left with an x velocity of v and an apparent y velocity not equal to $-u$. For, since $y = y'$ and $t = t'/\sqrt{1 - v^2/c^2}$ at $x' = 0$, the primed observer's velocity of projection is y'/t' or $-u$, and the unprimed observer finds the velocity to be:

$$y/t = (y'/t') \sqrt{1 - v^2/c^2} = -u \sqrt{1 - v^2/c^2}$$

After the collision he observes that m moves with a y velocity component $u \sqrt{1 - v^2/c^2}$, and m_a with the velocity $-u$. Thus he would express the conservation of momentum as:

$$2m_a u = 2m \sqrt{1 - v^2/c^2}\, u$$

The same conclusion would be reached by the primed observer. If u is small, the value of m_a must approach m_0. And the apparent mass being projected by the observer in relative motion with the velocity v must therefore be given by:

$$m_0 = m \sqrt{1 - v^2/c^2} \qquad \text{or} \qquad m = \frac{m_0}{\sqrt{1 - v^2/c^2}}$$

Thus a mass which appears to be m_0 in a static measurement must appear to have the greater value $m_0/\sqrt{1 - v^2/c^2}$ in dynamic experiments when it is moving with the velocity v, if the law of the conservation of momentum is to apply for both observers.

This is, of course, a very remarkable result from the point of view of classical mechanics, where masses are invariant quantities that do not appear to change at all in the range of velocities commonly observed in everyday experience. On the other hand, the result clearly does not contradict any experiment, for comparisons of mass are made by balances in static equilibrium, and the conservation of momentum is a law universally obeyed at all velocities and under all circumstances. The most striking verification of the apparent change of mass with velocity comes from the dynamic experiments performed with charged elementary particles that can be given velocities very close to that of light. These are found to obey the equations of relativistic dynamics, exhibiting apparent masses up to many times their rest masses.

The conservation of energy 8-3

Finally, concerning the implications of the ideas of special relativity for mechanics, the general law of conservation of energy should be examined with a view to determining what consequences, if any, arise if this law holds for all observers moving at constant relative velocities with respect to one another.

In the nonrelativistic case, where velocities are small compared with the velocity of light, the kinetic energy U_k of a free particle of mass m travelling with a velocity v is expressed in the form $\frac{1}{2}mv^2$, or equivalently $p^2/2m$, where p is the momentum mv of the particle. In the relativistic case of high velocities, it is found that this expression no longer denotes a conserved quantity, whether m is taken to be either the rest mass or the moving mass. If the concept of the conservation of energy is to be retained as valid, then some new formulation must be sought for the energy that does indeed represent a quantity that is conserved for all velocities, and which will reduce to the form $\frac{1}{2}mv^2$ for small values of the velocity v. Similarly, the new form of energy should be related to momentum by an equation that reduces to the form $p^2 = 2mU_k$ for small values of the velocity.

The momentum p may be expressed as a function of the masses only in the following manner:

$$p^2 = m^2v^2 = m^2c^2\,\frac{v^2}{c^2}$$

$$= m^2c^2\left[1 - \left(1 - \frac{v^2}{c^2}\right)\right]$$

$$= m^2c^2 - m^2\left(1 - \frac{v^2}{c^2}\right)c^2$$

$$= m^2c^2 - m_0^2c^2$$

$$= (m + m_0)(mc^2 - m_0c^2)$$

This expression relates momentum to kinetic energy: $(m + m_0)$ reduces to $2m_0$ for small velocities; similarly $(mc^2 - m_0c^2)$ reduces to $\frac{1}{2}mv^2$, as may easily be shown. Thus the quantity $(mc^2 - m_0c^2)$, may be thought of as the relativistic extension of the energy of motion, or the kinetic energy. This suggests a simplification and generalization of the energy concept quite concordant with all of our experimental evidence. For if $(mc^2 - m_0c^2)$ represents the energy difference between a moving mass and one at rest, then m_0c^2 may be thought of as a new form of energy; namely one associated simply with a mass at rest. The total energy of a mass in motion is then the sum of the rest energy plus the energy of motion which, for small ratios of v/c, is $\frac{1}{2}mv^2$.

Thus it is quite reasonable and consistent to define mc^2 as the total energy of a mass m. Since most of our observations and measurements have to do with the changing and exchanging of energy, the presence of the term m_0c^2 at zero velocity will not be evident unless mass is created or destroyed. This does not take place in ordinary processes, but the term is one that represents available energy in nuclear reactions in the course of which very great exchanges of energy—in the form of mass—take place. Thus in order that observers in relative motion with respect to one another may agree on the law of the conservation of energy, they must interpret as energy the product of mass and the square of the velocity of light. We may write:

$$U = mc^2$$

as the generalization of the expression for energy. This expression preserves the conservation law in accordance with the special theory of relativity. This very simple and remarkable result stems from the variation of mass with velocity, required for the conservation of momentum.

Momentum is, in a sense, a simpler and more easily perceived quantity than is energy; for, in having a direction associated with it, it is intimately related to the geometry of space and the immediate data of observation and experiment in the basic area of dynamics. The concept of energy has been seen to be equally useful in the description of mechanical or dynamical processes; but, not being a directed quantity, our intuitive appreciation of space and geometry contributes little to its perceptibility. Our senses, on the other hand, are directly aware of energy in the forms of light, heat, and sound. The protean nature of energy that pervades all areas of physical theory and manifests itself in different forms, depending upon the particular observations and measurements that are made, has been a major factor in the unification of physical science. Encountering it in many guises as the potential energy of gravitating bodies or elastically distorted bodies, as kinetic energy in the case of motion, as mass, and in a number of other forms to be mentioned later in these chapters, gives many occasions for incorporating energy as a connective theme in physical description, and accounts for its major significance in the theory of physical phenomena.

Its many-faceted ubiquity is also occasionally a cause of confusion which, however, is easily avoided if attention is constantly focused upon the actual observations or measurements through which the energy is evidenced. Thus in our now familiar illustration of the elastic collision between two bodies, the sum of the potential and kinetic energy remains constant. Were it convenient to make continuous measurements of the mass of the system, it likewise would remain constant. The energy stored in the form of elastic distortion of two colliding bodies at a possible instant of relative rest contributes as much to the mass of the combined system as does the preceding and subsequent motion. Similarly, in cases of physical systems too small to be observed by our eyes, or ears, or fingers, such as atoms and molecules and their constituents, changes in mass may be observed and confidently interpreted as equivalent to changes of energy. An imaginary surface may be thought of as enclosing some volume of space and its included matter; changes of the mass associated with this matter are experimentally found to be accounted for by the transport of material across the bounding surface, or by the passage of energy in some other form such as electromagnetic radiation from the enclosed matter through its enveloping surface. The concept of the conservation of energy lies at the root of the descriptions of physical phenomena that have been formulated by scientists to date, and no inconsistencies or discrepancies have arisen to lead us to question the logical adequacy of the resulting structure.

EXAMPLE. As a simple example of the above principles, consider the dynamics of a single electron—the lightest component of an atom. The rest mass m_0 of an electron is only about 9×10^{-31} kg. As a consequence of its small mass, only a moderate amount of energy is necessary to give the electron a velocity close to that of light. The rest energy of the electron is:

$$U_0 = m_0 c^2$$

$$= 9 \times 10^{-31} \times (3 \times 10^8)^2$$

$$= 8 \times 10^{-14} \text{ Joules}$$

For an energy ten times as great, the *effective* or *moving mass* of the electron will be ten times as great, since energy U is proportional to mass m. Thus:

$$U = mc^2 \qquad U_0 = m_0 c^2$$

and:

$$\frac{m}{m_0} = \frac{U}{U_0} = 10$$

But:

$$\frac{m}{m_0} = \frac{1}{\sqrt{1 - v^2/c^2}}$$

Therefore:

$$\left(1 - \frac{v^2}{c^2}\right) = \left(\frac{m_0}{m}\right)^2 = \left(\frac{U_0}{U}\right)^2$$

and:

$$\frac{v}{c} = \sqrt{1 - \left(\frac{U_0}{U}\right)^2} = \sqrt{1 - 10^{-2}} \approx 1 - \frac{1}{2} \times 10^{-2}$$

Thus:

$$v \approx 0.995c$$

In Fig. 8-2, the mass and velocity of an electron are shown as a function of energy. It can be seen how the nonrelativistic, or Newtonian estimates diverge from the correct values as the energy increases.

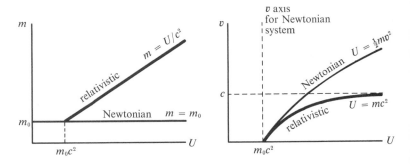

Figure 8-2   *Mass m and velocity v of an electron as a function of energy U according to the Newtonian and the relativistic equations.*

The Lorentz transformation equations described the way in which two observers, each equipped with instruments to measure intervals of time and distance and moving relatively to one another with a constant velocity, would intercompare their observations and find them concordant. Very similar transformation equations are implied by the mechanical conservation laws; indeed, the equations for the transformation of momentum and energy measurements are the same as the Lorentz equations if momenta components are substituted for the spatial coordinates, and energy divided by c^2 for the time.

This can be seen by recalling that the spherical wave front of a wave of light emitted by a small source is defined by setting the sum of the squares of the coordinates equal to c^2 times the square of the time interval between emission and measurement. In a dynamical problem, both c and the rest mass m_0 are agreed by each observer to be invariant; hence $m_0{}^2c^2$ is invariant during the course of any experiment, and may be written as

$$m_0{}^2c^2 = \frac{m_0{}^2c^2(1 - v^2/c^2)}{(1 - v^2/c^2)}$$

$$= \frac{m_0{}^2c^2}{1 - v^2/c^2} - \frac{m_0{}^2v^2}{1 - v^2/c^2}$$

$$= \frac{(mc^2)^2}{c^2} - (mv)^2$$

$$= \frac{U^2}{c^2} - (p_x{}^2 + p_y{}^2 + pz^2)$$

If this is compared with the equation for the spherical wave front of the light signal, we find that

$$0 = c^2t^2 - (x^2 + y^2 + z^2)$$

and recalling the argument for deriving the Lorentz equation, it is evident that ct and U/c, as well as x and p_x, y and p_y, and z and p_z play identical roles. In consequence

$$p_x = \frac{p_x' + vU'/c^2}{\sqrt{1 - v^2/c^2}}$$

$$U = \frac{U' + vp_x'}{\sqrt{1 - v^2/c^2}}$$

$$p_y = p_y' \qquad p_z = p_z'$$

EXAMPLE. Consider two particles each of rest mass m_0, which move toward one another with equal velocity v' and adhere to one another. The total momentum and energy would be described by the following equation:

$$p_x' = \frac{m_0v'}{\sqrt{1 - v'^2/c^2}} - \frac{m_0v'}{\sqrt{1 - v'^2/c^2}} = 0$$

$$U' = \frac{m_0c^2}{\sqrt{1 - v'^2/c^2}} + \frac{m_0c^2}{\sqrt{1 - v'^2/c^2}} = \frac{2m_0c^2}{\sqrt{1 - v'^2/c^2}}$$

Let us now consider an observer for whom the right hand mass is at rest; or, in other words, an observer moving to the left with a velocity v' (Fig. 8-3). For him the total momentum, which is all possessed by

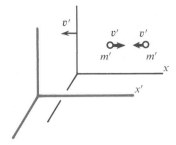

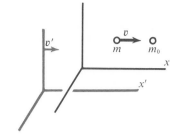

Event as seen by primed observer.

Same event as seen by unprimed observer, for whom right-hand mass is stationary.

Figure 8-3   *A collision event as seen by two observers moving relative to each other with constant velocity v'.*

the left hand particle, and the total energy would be written by the general formulae:

$$p_x = \frac{v'U'/c^2}{\sqrt{1 - v'^2/c^2}} \qquad U = \frac{U'}{\sqrt{1 - v'^2/c^2}}$$

From these equations the momentum of the left hand particle is given by:

$$p_x = \frac{v'}{c^2} U$$

8-4   *The general theory of relativity*

The special theory of relativity has made a remarkable contribution to our understanding of mechanical phenomena, and its ideological consequences have probably not yet been completely realized. However, it is evident that the limitation of the discussion to observers moving relative to one another with a uniform velocity is a very serious one, for it neglects the practical situations of relative acceleration and rotation. Increases or decreases in v, i.e., linear accelerations in the direction of motion, appear to present little difficulty; our observations agree with the statement that these are without effect upon the phenomena, except as they lead to increased or decreased values of the velocity used in expressions for the coordinates and those for mass, momentum, and energy. On the other hand, changes in the direction of the velocity, as in the case of a rotation, introduce very grave problems indeed. An instance of the type of difficulty encountered is the rotation of a large wheel about its axis. If the circumference is made up of A unit measuring rods, and each radial spoke by B such rods, the ratio of A to B while the wheel is at rest is 2π. When the wheel is rotating, the circumference is moving in its own direction. It, therefore, appears to an observer on the axis to be shortened, whereas the radial spokes, being normal to their direction of motion, not do not appear to be shortened. Hence, for an observer on the axis, the ratio of A to B would no longer be 2π; strange geometrical distortions would appear. In consequence, we see that the simple linear expressions we have been using heretofore are inadequate for this more complex situation. Of course, the expressions of the special theory of relativity must remain locally significant as an approximation to a more general theory, since these expressions have furnished results in such excellent agreement with local experiments.

A generalization of the special theory to also encompass gravitational phenomena, starting from the general principle of equivalence between gravitation and acceleration as they affect massive bodies, was proposed by Einstein. As we saw in earlier chapters, the kinetic energy and gravitational potential energy of a body both involve the same property: namely, mass. As an example, bodies of different masses are all accelerated toward the earth at its surface at the same rate g. The searching experiments of Eötvös, Dicke, and others that were referred to in earlier chapters have confirmed to a high degree of precision that, insofar as the properties of the material of the body are concerned, gravitational and centrifugal forces depend only upon the mass, and are independent of other characteristics such as shape, density, chemical constitution, etc. Thus inertial mass is indistinguishable experimentally from gravitational mass; hence, in a sense, the basic gravitational and dynamical phenomena must be essentially equivalent.

Proceeding from the principle of equivalence of acceleration and gravity, one can consider that each produces a *field*, or at every point in space gives evidence of itself. This evidence takes the form of distorting space in the sense that an infinitesimal clock or measuring rod shows certain rates or lengths characteristic of its location which differ from similar clocks and rods at other locations. In a local volume of space, sufficiently small that any distortion can be neglected, the square of an element of length, described in terms of Cartesian coordinates, by the Euclidean principle is:

$$(dS)^2 = (dx)^2 + (dy)^2 + (dz)^2$$

One may adopt the hypothesis that in the more general space distorted by gravitating masses this element of length depends in a more general way upon squares and cross products of the coordinate elements with certain coefficients varying with location which represent the local characteristics of the space caused by mass distributions throughout it.

Thus, the square of the element of length upon which the description of events depends might be written:

$$(dS)^2 = g_{11}dx_1{}^2 + g_{12}dx_1dx_2 + g_{13}dx_1dx_3 + g_{14}dx_1dx_4 +$$
$$g_{21}dx_2dx_1 + g_{22}dx_2{}^2 + g_{23}dx_2dx_3 + g_{24}dx_2dx_4 +$$
$$g_{31}dx_3dx_1 + g_{32}dx_3dx_2 + g_{33}dx_3{}^2 + g_{34}dx_3dx_4 +$$
$$g_{41}dx_4dx_1 + g_{42}dx_4dx_2 + g_{43}dx_4dx_3 + g_{44}dx_4{}^2$$

where x_4 stands for the time. The coefficients g are in general functions of the x's, and constitute the 16 components of what is called a *tensor*, describing the nature of space in the locality.

The problem of evolving a satisfactory general relativistic description is a matter of determining the proper values of this tensor to describe the observed properties of space. It is probable that this problem has not yet been completely and satisfactorily solved, although the complexity of the mathematics is such that it is not possible to arrive at an unambiguous answer, concerning the adequacy of the theory in its present form. Although there are no discordances between the predictions of the present formulation and observation, the theory certainly is limited in its application to gravitational and dynamic effects, and does not attempt to account for electrical or atomic phenomena. The tensor that describes the attributes of space depends not only on spatial coordinates, but also on the time; this dependence may cause distant regions to appear to move away from us. This is in accord with the astronomical observation that the light from all very distant stars appears to be shifted to lower frequencies, or toward the red end of the spectrum, as one would anticipate according to the Doppler effect from a receding source. Also according to the theory, space is not isotropic; i.e., the element of length at a point is not independent of its orientation. The consequence of anisotropy offers the possibility that the universe we live in is closed, in the sense that the surface of a sphere is closed (in the three ordinary dimensions). It would thus have no boundaries, but would return on itself. In an intuitive way, this would seem rather satisfactory, as it is easier to conceive of this kind of universe than of one which suddenly stops at some great distance from us. However, there is still no firm experimental evidence as to whether the red shift is due to the geometry of the universe, or to the Doppler effect of really receding sources; or whether the curvature of the universe necessarily results in its being open or closed. These questions are among the principle challenges of astronomical research today.

The extensive mathematical apparatus of the general theory of relativity is unnecessary as far as drawing certain conclusions from the equivalence between acceleration and gravitation is concerned. For instance, one would expect a beam of light to change direction or be bent in a gravitational field as would a mass projected along the same trajectory. And, indeed, a bending effect of a light path does appear to take place as one observes the light from stars passing near the limb of the sun. However, the precision with which this effect can now be measured is inadequate for a really critical test of the theory.

A second instance more precisely verifies the equality of the effects of gravitation and acceleration: i.e., measuring the wave length of light emitted by an atom in a gravitational field. Just as light appears to be of greater wave length for an atom in motion than for one at rest, it also appears to be of a greater wave length if the atom is in a field of acceleration or gravity than if it is not. This is readily seen if we consider the propagation of a light signal from an observer A to an observer B, who is presumed to be beneath the latter in a region of space where the acceleration of gravity is found by experiment to be g, (indicated in Fig. 8-4). In accordance with the general principle of equivalence between acceleration and gravitation, the effect must be the same as if there were no gravitational field present but instead the two observers are both accelerated upward at the rate-of-change-of-velocity g, retaining a constant separation. The time taken for the signal to pass from A to B, which are at rest with respect to one another and separated by the distance z, is $t = z/c$. Owing to the acceleration g, B changes his velocity upward during this time by the amount $v = gt$, or $v = gz/c$. The apparent proportional change in wave length, or the Doppler effect produced by this velocity, is (Sect. 7-9) to first order in the quantity v/c:

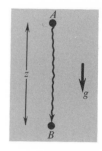

Figure 8-4 *Transmission of a light signal in a gravitational field.*

$$\frac{\lambda' - \lambda}{\lambda} = \frac{d\lambda}{\lambda} = \frac{-v}{c}$$

The Doppler effect observed by B at a position where the gravitational potential energy per unit mass is less by zg than at the source A is then:

$$\frac{d\lambda}{\lambda} = \frac{gz}{c^2}$$

Thus, in general, the Doppler effect for the radiation from an atom in a gravitational field would be expected to equal the difference in gravitational potential energy per unit mass (i.e., the *gravitational potential* between the position of the emitting atom and that of the observer) divided by c^2.

The fractional increase in wave length, which an observer would note, between the light from an atom at a distance r_1 from a spherical mass M, and an atom in his neighborhood, say, at the distance r_2 from the mass, would then be:

$$\frac{d\lambda}{\lambda} = \frac{GM}{c^2} \left(\frac{1}{r_1} - \frac{1}{r_2} \right)$$

Applying this result to the expected difference in light emitted, e.g., by a hydrogen atom at the sun's surface and a hydrogen atom at the distance of the earth, where we would conduct our observations, the fractional change is about 2×10^{-6}. A shift of this order is seen in the case of light from the limb of the solar disk, but the shift from the center of the sun's disk appears to be smaller. The reason for this is not well understood; hence, this evidence is not very conclusive. The shift to longer wave lengths in the case of light from stars of very high density is indeed greater than that from the sun, but the values of M and r for other stars are not sufficiently well known to fully substantiate the theory.

Recent advances in the precision of measuring small changes in wave length have been made in the case of high energy nuclear radiation under certain very favorable conditions. Using this technique, which allows detection of a fractional shift as small as 2.5×10^{-15}, observers have been able to detect variations in wave lengths that take place over certain relatively short vertical intervals at the surface of the earth and that are due to our local gravitational field. Such measurements, which were performed almost simultaneously by R. V. Pound and G. A. Rebka, Jr. at Harvard University and by T. E. Cranshaw and H. J. Hay and their associates at Harwell, England during the winter of 1959–1960, constitute our most direct and unambiguous verification of this phenomenon.

It is interesting to note that accurate measurement of radiation emitted from a close earth satellite provides a test for both the Doppler effect produced by the relative motion of the satellite and observer in accordance with the special theory of relativity, as well as the effect of the difference in their gravitational potential in accordance with the equivalence principle of the general theory. Consider, for simplicity, a circular orbit in which (cf. Chap. 5)

$$\frac{1}{2} mv^2 = \frac{GMm}{2r}$$

From the discussion of the Ives-Stillwell experiment earlier in Sect. 7-9, the average wave length from the approaching and receding satellite should differ from the wave length of the signal from a source at rest by $\lambda'(v^2/2c^2)$; or, in terms of the radius of the satellite's orbit, by $\lambda'(GM/c^2)\left(\frac{1}{2r}\right)$. Applying the general relativity formula given earlier to a satellite at a distance r from the center of the earth and an observer at the surface of the earth for which r_2 is R,

$$d\lambda = \lambda \frac{GM}{c^2}\left(\frac{1}{r} - \frac{1}{R}\right)$$

The special relativity change produces a shift to longer wave lengths (*red shift*); the general relativity change is negative, since R is less than r, and hence produces a shift to shorter wave lengths (*violet shift*). The two shifts will evidently be equal and opposite annulling one another when

$$\frac{1}{2r} = -\left(\frac{1}{r} - \frac{1}{R}\right) \qquad \text{or} \qquad r = \frac{3R}{2}$$

or when the satellite is at a height above the earth's surface equal to half the earth's radius. This is a height of about 2000 miles. The magnitude of the effect that must be measured in such an experiment is clearly of the order of (GM/Rc^2), which is about 7×10^{-10}. These wave length shifts are expected to be detectable whenever the experiment is performed, but the best techniques and most skillful observers will be required, since the fractional change is so small.

There is a third effect derivable from the general theory of relativity that does not come simply from the equivalence of acceleration and gravitation, but that requires full mathematical development of the theory for its proper comparison with observation. The theory predicts that the path of a planet or satellite about a sun will not be precisely a conic section, as is true in cases of Newtonian mechanics, but that the orbit, which is approximately an ellipse, will slowly rotate in the plane of its motion, so that the axes turn in space in the same sense as the satellite's rotation. For the planets in our solar system, this effect should be just sufficiently great to be observed in the case of Mercury, which passes closest to the sun. Observed and predicted values of this rotation of the planet's orbit (2×10^{-4} rad. per century) agree to within the accuracy of astronomical measurement. This single example of quantitative agreement between general theory and observation, while it is quite persuasive in itself, does not compel us to accept the theory as whole-heartedly as one would like to in a matter of such basic concern to our understanding of physical phenomena. This is particularly true, since any velocity-dependent force between gravitating masses, or any slight departure from the inverse square law of force, would likewise lead to other than simple elliptical orbits. But we have now approached the frontier of our knowledge in this field, and we must look to subsequent observation and experiment to further clarify our understanding.

Further reading:

DICKE, R. H., "Gravitation — An Enigma," *American Scientist*, vol. 47, No. 1, p. 25 (1959).

GINZBURG, V. L., "Artificial Satellites and the Theory of Relativity," *Scientific American*, vol. 200, No. 5, p. 149 (1959).

JAYNES, E. T., "Relativistic Clock Experiments," *American Journal of Physics*, vol. 26, No. 3, p. 197 (1958).

SCHIFF, L. I., "On Experimental Tests of the General Theory of Relativity," *American Journal of Physics*, vol. 28, No. 4, p. 340 (1960).

SCIAMA, D., "Inertia," *Scientific American*, vol. 196, No. 2, p. 99 (1957).

SCOTT, G. D., "On Solutions of the Clock Paradox," *American Journal of Physics*, vol. 27, No. 8, p. 580 (1959).

Problems

8-1   An electron of rest mass 9.11×10^{-31} kg. is accelerated to a velocity 60 per cent that of light. What mass does it then have? What would its mass be to someone moving with it?

8-2   An atomic particle is measured to have a velocity or 1.80×10^8 m.sec.$^{-1}$, and a momentum of 3.76×10^{-19} kg.m.sec.$^{-1}$. What is its rest mass?

8-3   A particle travelling with relativistic velocity v collides with a stationary particle of the same rest mass. The two particles move off together with velocity V. Express V as a function of v.

8-4   What is the mass equivalent of 9 J.?

8-5   What is the relativistic total energy of two stationary electrons (rest mass 9.11×10^{-31} kg. each)? What is the relativistic total energy of two electrons whose velocities are 80 per cent that of light?

8-6   A particle of mass 3.60×10^{-28} kg. is known to have a rest mass of 2.49×10^{-28} kg. How much energy is liberated when this particle is brought to rest?

8-7   Verify that $(mc^2 - m_0c^2)$ does in fact reduce to $\frac{1}{2}mv^2$ for values of v much less than c.

8-8   Our galaxy has a mass m. A distant galaxy is found to be receding from us with a velocity V and mass M. Taking the direction of recession as the positive direction, calculate the total momentum and energy of the bigalactic system. Use the relativistic transformations to calculate the equivalent quantities as measured by someone on the other galaxy. Check your results by transforming the masses and velocities and recalculating the total momentum and energy.

8-9   An elevator accelerates upwards at a rate of 0.21 g. What effect would this have on the period of a simple pendulum mounted in the elevator? What effect would it have on the period of a torsional pendulum mounted in the elevator?

Electricity 9

Introduction 9-1

The discussion of the preceding chapters has been concerned with the basic phenomena and the concepts derived from them having to do with the motion of material bodies under the influence of the forces they exert on one another at contact, or the gravitational forces between them when they are separated from one another. It will be seen later that the contact forces can be related to the forces exerted between atoms that are close together; hence they will not be further considered until the properties of atoms and their aggregates have been described. The nature of gravitational forces, or energies of interaction, has been described in Chaps. 5 and 7, to the extent that our present understanding enables us to do so. The universal law of gravitation represents an ultimate datum, in the sense that we do not yet have any deeper understanding of gravitational phenomena than the very statement of this law. The constant G, which characterizes gravitational force, is the numerical boundary of our knowledge of the gravitational structure of our universe. The relatively unalterable, intrinsic property of objects, which we call mass, enters both the dynamic conservation laws and the universal law of gravitation—resulting, for instance, in the equal acceleration of all bodies near the surface of the earth—in a way which appears to be quite fortuitous. This may seem strange, but we really have no further insight into the reason why inertial and gravitational mass appear to be the same, within the precision of our experiments. On the present state of our knowledge, this must be accepted as a pattern of our universe.

This chapter introduces the phenomena—and the concepts to which they have given rise—that are associated with a force between bodies which appears to have a fundamentally different genesis from that of gravitation. It is the only other cause of a mutual interaction energy, between bodies widely separated from one another, that has yet been identified by our experimental observations. Like the force of gravity, it can induce the motion of distant bodies; but, unlike that force, it is independent of the masses of the bodies concerned. This force may be evidenced in chemical action, in frictional processes, or in the manipulation of wires and magnets. Though there are a number of resemblances between these forces and those of gravity with respect to the laws of action, these new kinds of forces, being fundamentally independent of the masses of the interacting bodies, are clearly distinguishable from gravitational forces. They are designated generically: *electrical*; *magnetic*; or *electromagnetic* forces. These, together with the gravitational forces, constitute the only two categories of force capable of inducing the motion of material bodies on other than a molecular scale.

The forces of electrical origin differ from those of gravitational origin in the following respects. In the first place, electrical forces can be evinced and altered in magnitude by simple manipulations, whereas gravitational forces cannot: the property of mass upon which the latter depend is relatively immutable on the gross scale of laboratory experiments. Secondly, the electrical forces observed under simple static conditions can be either of an attractive or a repulsive nature. This contrasts with our experience of gravitating masses, where all of our observations to date indicate that the force between them is always attractive. Finally, electrical forces depend to a marked degree upon the presence of neighboring bodies, and upon any relative motion between the test objects and the observer. Gravitational forces, alternatively, appear to be quite independent of neighboring bodies, or of constant relative motion with respect to the observer—except as the equations of the special theory of relativity imply changes in apparent mass. Einstein's general theory of relativity predicts gravitational effects of this kind, but their magnitude would be very small.

9-2 *The electrostatic law of force*

The most elementary method of manifesting forces of an electrical nature under static conditions is the ancient one of rubbing two electrically unlike materials together. If a glass rod and a piece of fur are chosen as the test materials, it is found initially that they show no tendency either to attract or to repel one another. If they are rubbed smartly together and quickly separated, it is found that they tend to attract one another. A force not previously apparent has been made so by the process. Our description of the process says that the materials have become *electrified* or *charged*, and that the force of attraction arises in consequence. If the glass and fur are allowed to remain quiescently in contact, they return to their initial condition in which there was no force between them. If two glass rods are rubbed with fur, it is found that they tend to repel one another. If two pieces of fur are used, a force of repulsion becomes evident between these as well, and both attract both glass rods.

On the evidence of such simple experiments in *triboelectricity*, early experimenters were led to construct a qualitative description of electrification in terms of the separation of some quality or substance associated with the materials being rubbed together. *Electricity*, this quality or substance, may be regarded as two types, quite arbitrarily (but for the sake of a working convention) designated positive $(+)$ and negative $(-)$. Both types are considered to be initially present in equal amounts in each of the materials rubbed together, but during the rubbing process the properties of the materials cause one to retain an excess of positive and the other an excess of negative electricity. These two types of electricity, or *electric charge*, are of such a nature that charges of like sign tend to repel one another, and charges of unlike sign tend to attract one another. Electricity is neither created nor destroyed; the total algebraic sum of the charges present always remains the same. This has indeed proven to be precisely the case throughout all our experimental observations to date: the law of conservation of electric charge is as solid and as important a statement of the nature of physical phenomena as are the mechanical conservation laws of momentum, angular momentum, and energy. In the case of initially uncharged materials, the sum of the charges present is zero. The basic concepts involved in this description have proven to be an adequate foundation upon which our present precise and quantitative theory of electrical phenomena has been erected.

Also, on the evidence of simple electrical experiments, materials may be divided into two major categories: *insulators*, which tend to retain for some time, isolated upon their surfaces, the electric charges induced by frictional processes; and *conductors*, which readily share the charge with other objects in contact with them. In general, the latter class is comprised of the metals, which are substances with large tensile strengths, elastic rigidity, and shiny crystalline surfaces. Included in the former category are such materials as fibers, glasses, frangible crystals, and plastics.

The quantitative determination of the law of force between electric charges, which is the object of a scientific description, may be accomplished in several ways. Since the forces that are brought into existence are larger in practice than are those of gravity, the problems are less of delicacy of measurement than of understanding the electrical properties of the materials involved in the observations. Insulators are not actually perfect insulators, but rather tend to permit some flow of electricity through them and over their surfaces. High-precision measurements consequently involve considerable ingenuity in order for the experimenter to overcome confusing and misleading effects. However, in principle the procedures of measurement are very straightforward and easily understood.

Light balls of a conducting material, adjacent to one another and suspended from insulating fibers, provide convenient test objects for representative or demonstration experiments. When touched by an electrified body they partake—by conduction—of the electrification, and, gaining like charges, repel one another (as illustrated in Fig. 9-1). If two identical conductors, each supported by insulating columns in order to retain their charges, are brought into symmetrical contact with one another, the symmetry assures that the net charge will be shared equally. Evidently, procedures involving symmetrical objects provide a mechanism for subdividing a charge in a quantitative way, and hence charges in known proportion to one another can be placed on the test balls. One can vary the distance between the balls by adjusting the points of support of the insulating fibers; the magnitude of the force between them can be compared with the force of gravity acting upon their masses. Thus all of the necessary quantities can be measured in order to determine the dependence of the force between the charges upon magnitude and upon separation, which are found to be the only influential factors.

As a result of this series of manipulations, or one like it, we can readily establish that the force of attraction between unlike localized point

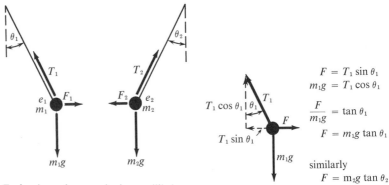

Each charged mass is in equilibrium under the action of three forces: a weight force mg, an electric force F, and a tension T in a string.

$$F = T_1 \sin \theta_1$$
$$m_1 g = T_1 \cos \theta_1$$

$$\frac{F}{m_1 g} = \tan \theta_1$$

$$F = m_1 g \tan \theta_1$$

similarly
$$F = m_2 g \tan \theta_2$$

Resolution of the tension into its vertical and horizontal components.

Figure 9-1 *Static configuration for verifying the law of force between electric charges.*

charges, or of repulsion between like charges, is proportional to the magnitude of each charge, inversely proportional to the square of the separation between them, and is operative along the line of centers of the charges. This is closely analogous to the law of gravitation. The force between charges can then evidently be written:

$$F \sim \frac{e_1 e_2}{r^2}$$

where the symbol $\sim$ indicates proportionality, e_1 and e_2 are the charges on the test objects, and r is the distance between them. A positive product, by convention, corresponds to repulsion, and a negative one to attraction. This is the opposite convention for the direction of the force from the convention in the case of gravitation, where repulsion is never encountered.

The above law, known as *Coulomb's law*, which has the same form as that of the law of gravitation, has been tested very accurately and has been found to hold with a high degree of precision. It was first discovered by Henry Cavendish, of Cambridge and London, a remarkable recluse who deduced all the qualitative and quantitative results of electrostatics by careful experimentation in the 1770's. But these results remained unknown in his notebooks until they were published by Maxwell a century later. Charles Coulomb, a French engineer, independently discovered and announced the law in the 1780's.

Rotating wheels and travelling belts, which conduct the electrification process much more efficiently than does simple rubbing, can be devised. Such devices can separate very large charges, and it is found that, eventually, tentacle-like streamers appear to develop from the electrified body; these result in a cataclysmic event accompanied by light and sound, called a *spark*. This is best described as the restoration of electrical equilibrium by the passage of an electric discharge through the air, between the body and its oppositely charged surroundings. On dry days moderate electrification of the human body causes the hairs to repel one another and to stand on end; small sparks pass from the fingers prior to contact with grounded metal objects such as door knobs. On warm, humid days, layers of moisture condense on the surfaces of insulators; this creates moderately conducting surfaces. The passage of large charges of electricity through the air also gives rise to meteorological phenomena, such as the flash of lightning and the accompanying roll of thunder. Lightning was recognized as an electrical phenomenon by Benjamin Franklin in 1752.

As Coulomb's law relates the quantity of charge to force and distance, the mechanical concepts that have been developed previously can be used to measure the quantity of any given electric charge. In Fig. 9-1 electric charge is measured in terms of the gravitational force on the mass of the suspended ball. Thus the practical unit of charge, called the *Coulomb* (C.), can be defined by the equation

$$F = K \frac{e_1 e_2}{r^2}$$

where F is in Newtons, r is in meters, e is in Coulombs, and the constant K has the value 8.9874×10^9 N.m.^{2}C.$^{-2}$. Thus a Coulomb is that charge which, if placed on each of two small conducting spheres 1 meter apart, will produce a force between them of 8.9874×10^9 N. Precision measurements of charge are not actually made by electrostatic techniques, but rather are made in terms of the velocity-dependent electrical forces that will be described in Chap. 10. However, reasonably precise electrostatic experiments can be performed by using large and small conducting shapes, such as spheres on insulating mounts or suspended from fine insulating fibers; the forces and the work necessary to change the configuration of charged conductors can be measured.

EXAMPLE. The analogy between Newton's law for gravitational attraction between two masses and Coulomb's law for electrical attraction between unlike charges suggests that the orbits of two charged particles in relative motion are of the type described for gravitating particles (Chap. 5). Actually, as will be seen in Chap. 10 in the case of electricity there are other forces that depend upon the velocity of the charges; forces that are absent or as yet undetected in the case of gravitation. But these forces are small for low velocities, and to a first approximation may be neglected. As a simple illustration, consider the case of a very light particle of mass m and charge $-e_1$, describing a circular orbit with velocity v about a very heavy central particle of charge $+e_2$. To a good approximation, the heavy particle may be considered fixed. The centripetal force on the light particle is provided by the Coulomb force of attraction between the two unlike charges. Hence:

$$\frac{mv^2}{r} = K \frac{e_1 e_2}{r^2}$$

which leads to:

$$r = \frac{Ke_1 e_2}{mv^2} = \frac{\frac{1}{2}Ke_1 e_2}{\frac{1}{2}mv^2} = \frac{\frac{1}{2}Ke_1 e_2}{U_k}$$

where U_k is the kinetic energy of the orbiting particle. Thus the radius of the circular orbit is directly proportional to each of the two charges and is inversely proportional to the kinetic energy of the orbiting particle. This is the basis for a very accurate method of determining the energy of charged atomic particles.

Just as it was in the case of gravity, the concept of a field is useful here. An electric field is a region of space in which a small test charge experiences a force. If the field is that produced by a point charge e, then the repulsive force on a unit test charge at a distance r is Ke/r^2, which is also the so-called electric *field strength* at this point. The unit for electric field strength is force per unit charge, or Newtons per Coulomb; the customary symbol is E.

Also analogous to the case of gravity is the emergence of the potential energy or stored capacity to do work as a concept of great importance and convenience in electrical calculations. In close analogy with the gravitational case, the potential energy of an electric charge e_1, at a distance r from a second charge e_2, is Ke_1e_2/r. No special name is commonly given to the unit of gravitational potential—i.e., the Joule per kilogram. In the electric case, however, the analogous quantity is a particularly useful one because of the ease with which the charge on a body can be increased or decreased; hence the unit of electric potential energy is given a special name. The difference in potential energy per unit charge, or more briefly the *potential*, between points in an electric field is commonly expressed in units of *Volts* (V.), where one Volt is one Joule per Coulomb. The unit of potential, the Volt, derives from the name of the Italian physicist, Allessandro Volta, who was an early experimenter in electricity. The symbol for electric potential is ϕ (phi). The difference in potential between two points, multiplied by the charge in Coulombs, moved from one point to the other, evidently yields the work done in Joules. Though the order of magnitude of electrostatic forces is such that measurements can be made conveniently with simple apparatus, the detailed interpretation of the experiments is made more difficult on account of the mobility of electric charge over conducting surfaces. If the separation between test conductors becomes sufficiently small to be comparable with the dimensions of the conductors themselves, the redistribution of charge over the surfaces of the conductors under the influence of the electric forces must be taken into account, and, except under very special geometrical conditions, this adds greatly to the practical complications.

Because of the scalar nature of energy, it is sometimes preferred to calculate the force on a charged particle by first calculating the potential energy. The force F on a charged particle and its potential energy U_p are related by the expression

$$F = -\frac{dU_p}{dx}$$

where x is the spatial vector in the direction of the force. Also, division of the force and the potential energy by the charge e on the particle yields the field strength E and the potential ϕ respectively. The above equation then becomes:

$$E = - \frac{d\phi}{dx}$$

or the electric field strength E in the x direction is equal to the spatial rate of *decrease* in that direction of the electric potential ϕ.

EXAMPLE. A principle commonly employed in the acceleration of charged atomic particles is to allow these particles to pass from one hollow metallic tube or other container to a similar one held at a different potential (See Fig. 9-2). If the charge on the particle is e, and the

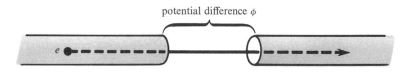

potential difference ϕ

Figure 9-2   *The kinetic energy gained by a charged particle in traversing a potential gap is equal to the electrical potential energy lost.*

potential drop across the gap between the tubes is ϕ, then the kinetic energy gained by the particle in traversing the gap is equal to the loss in electrical potential energy ϕe.

EXAMPLE. Three equal negative charges $-e$ form the points of an equilateral triangle. A particle of mass m and positive charge e_2 is constrained to move along a line perpendicular to the plane of the triangle and through its center, which is at a distance r from each of the negative charges, as shown in Fig. 9-3a. Calculate the natural frequency of vibration of this particle for small displacements from the equilibrium position.

For small displacements, the motion will presumably be simple harmonic, and therefore there is a known relation between the period and the force per unit displacement. Fig. 9-3b shows that a small displacement x, vertically "up" from the plane of the negative charges, will place the positive charge at a distance l from each of the negative

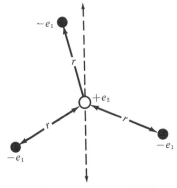

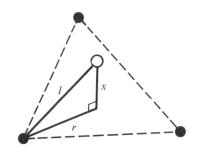

(a) A positively charged particle is constrained to a line through the center and perpendicular to the plane of an equilateral triangle whose points are formed by three equal negative charges.

(b) When the positive charge is displaced a distance x from the equilibrium position, then the distance between the positive charge and each of the negative charges is $l = \sqrt{r^2 + x^2}$.

Figure 9-3 *Simple harmonic motion of a particle subject to electrical forces.*

charges, where $l = \sqrt{r^2 + x^2}$. The total potential energy of the positive charge due to the three negative charges is then:

$$U_p = 3\left(-\frac{Ke_1e_2}{l}\right) = -3Ke_1e_2(r^2 + x^2)^{-1/2}$$

$$= \frac{-3Ke_1e_2}{r}\left(1 + \frac{x^2}{r^2}\right)^{-1/2}$$

For small displacements x, the fraction x^2/r^2 is much less than one, and hence the binomial expansion yields:

$$U_p \approx \frac{-3Ke_1e_2}{r}\left(1 - \frac{x^2}{2r^2}\right) = -\frac{3Ke_1e_2}{r} + \frac{3Ke_1e_2}{2r^3}x^2$$

The force on the positive particle is, from the consideration of symmetry, vertically "down," and given by:

$$F = -\frac{dU_p}{dx} = -\left[0 + \frac{3Ke_1e_2}{2r^3}2x\right] = -\frac{3Ke_1e_2}{r^3}x = -kx$$

where $k = 3Ke_1e_2/r^3$ is a constant, as is required for simple harmonic motion. Therefore, the period T of the motion is given by:

$$T = 2\pi\sqrt{\frac{m}{k}} = 2\pi\sqrt{\frac{mr^3}{3Ke_1e_2}}$$

EXAMPLE. *Deflection of a charged particle by an electric field.* Two parallel flat plates of separation s are connected to the two terminals of some source of constant potential difference ϕ. The space between the plates is evacuated and a particle of mass m and charge e enters parallel to the plates with a velocity v. What is the deflection of the particle, due to the electric field, in traversing the length l of the plates (Fig. 9-4)?

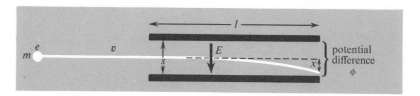

Figure 9-4 *A charged particle is deflected in the direction of a transverse electric field. The motion in the original direction is independent of the transverse motion.*

This example is exactly analogous to that of a projectile in a gravitational field. The motions parallel and perpendicular to the electric field are independent. The field is perpendicular to the plates, because this is obviously the direction of the maximum rate of potential change. The potential changes by an amount ϕ in a distance s; hence the field strength is:

$$E = \frac{\phi}{s}$$

The force is then Ee, and the acceleration is:

$$a = \frac{Ee}{m} = \frac{\phi e}{ms}$$

Hence the deflection perpendicular to the plates is:

$$x = \frac{1}{2} at^2 = \frac{\phi e t^2}{2ms}$$

where the time t taken to traverse the region is simply l/v. Thus the required expression for the deflection is:

$$x = \frac{\phi e l^2}{2msv^2}$$

9-4 *Conduction of electricity*

If work is done by oppositely charging two large conductors initially a large distance apart and then bringing them to a distance r apart, an amount of energy Ke^2/r is stored in the system, where e is the charge on each conductor. If these conductors are then connected by a long, thin metallic strip—for instance a fine copper wire—the electric charges of unlike sign will reunite by traversing the wire; the system will be electrically neutral and the stored energy will have disappeared from the electrical form without doing mechanical work or appearing as kinetic energy. It will be noted, however, that the wire has become hot; thus this is essentially a dissipative, or frictional process in which although conserved in the general sense, the energy has assumed the form called heat energy from which it can only be inefficiently returned to the electrical or mechanical form. If the amount of heat energy appearing is measured, by multiplying the temperature rise of the wire by the energy required to raise the temperature of this amount of copper through a unit temperature interval, the loss in stored energy is accounted for.

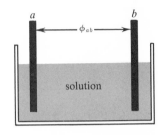

Figure 9-5   *Electrochemical cell or Galvanic cell.*

Experiments of this nature in the conduction of electricity are, however, more readily performed with charges that are separated in ways other than the mechanical one suggested above. For instance, the chemical processes that take place when two strips of unlike metal are placed in an acid or alkaline solution result in a difference of electric potential that appears between the exposed portions of the strips. Such an apparatus is known as a galvanic or *electrochemical* cell (Fig. 9-5); the difference in electric potential appearing is a function of the metals, the composition of the solution, and the temperature. Several of these cells connected in sequence constitutes an *electric battery*. A type of cell known as a *thermoelectric* junction (Fig. 9-6), which produces somewhat lower potential differences than the electrochemical cell, is formed if the junction of two metal strips is maintained at a different temperature from their remote ends.

The galvanic cell, if it is suitably prepared and maintained, provides a very constant and reproducible value of the potential difference between the open ends of the strips, and indeed furnishes a very convenient and satisfactory practical standard of potential difference. The potential difference produced by such a cell is of the order of one Volt. If the exposed terminals are connected by a wire, it is found that the wire gets hot. This phenomenon may be thought of as the conversion of chemical energy, at the expense of the differential dissolution of the electrodes, into electrical energy inducing or pumping a flow of electric charge through the wire and solution which eventually is dissipated in the form of heat. If ϕ is the potential difference maintained between the electrodes, and I is the rate of flow of electric charge through the wire, called the *electric current*, the rate at which the cell does external work is the product ϕI; this is the rate of dissipation of energy in the wire. If the process continues for a time t, the total heat Q generated in the wire is $\phi I t$. Thus if Q, ϕ, and t are measured, I can be determined. The units in

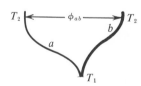

Figure 9-6   *Thermoelectric junction.*

which I appears, namely Joules per Volt per second are called *Amperes* (amp.) after the French physicist Andre Marie Ampere, whose research did so much to elucidate the mechanical forces between current-carrying conductors, which will be considered in the next chapter. The rate of change of energy, or generation of heat in this case, is termed the *power*. It is denoted by the symbol P, and its unit is called the *Watt* (W.), in honor of James Watt, who was associated with the development of the steam engine. The rate of generation of heat by the flow of electric current in the above instance is evidently $P = \phi I = Q/t$ Watts.

Ohm's Law. It is commonly found for such conductors of electricity as the common metals that the current I, or the rate at which charge passes into, out of, or along the conductor, is proportional to the potential difference between its ends. This is a property of a class of materials rather than a general law of nature. But as one looks into this further, the analogy between the passage of charge through a conductor and the flow of a liquid through a pipe becomes closer. The long thin pipe presents a greater resistance to the flow of liquid than does a short wide one. In the same way a short wide conductor of electricity passes more charge for the same potential difference between its ends than does a long thin conductor. Indeed it is found by experiment that to a very good approximation, the rate of passage of charge, or the current, is inversely proportional to the length l of the wire, and directly proportional to its cross sectional area A, as well as to the potential difference ϕ between the ends of the wire, and that the constant of proportionality between I and A/l is determined by the material of the wire. The constant of proportionality, which is dependent on the metal, is called the *resistivity*, symbol ρ (rho) (Fig. 9-7). The resistivity varies from about 2×10^{-8} for copper to about 2×10^{-7} for certain alloys of nickel and chromium. The unit is evidently the Volt-meter per Ampere. For a given piece of wire, ρ, l, and A are all constant, and may therefore be treated as the one constant R, called the *resistance* of the given piece of

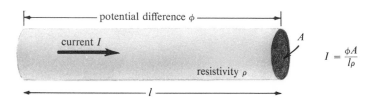

Figure 9-7 *The rate of flow of charge or the current through a conductor is directly proportional to the potential difference between its ends and the cross sectional area, and is inversely proportional to the length of the conductor and the resistivity of its material.*

wire. The unit of resistance is then the Volt per Ampere, or the *Ohm*. This linear relation between I and ϕ is known as *Ohm's law*, after the German physicist, Georg Ohm, who first announced it, even though it had previously been known to Cavendish. It is somewhat analogous to Hooke's law in mechanics in that it represents an excellent simple approximation of great general application to a wide variety of materials.

Thus the laws of flow of electric charge through metallic conductors and the rate at which heat is generated as a result are:

$$\phi = RI \qquad Q = I\phi t$$

where

$$R = \rho l / A$$

and

$$P = Q/t = I\phi = RI^2 = \phi^2/R$$

These are basic relationships in all practical electrical circuit theory and practice, and all of the quantities that appear, with the exception of ρ, refer to fundamental physical entities or concepts derived from dynamics —with the recognition of electric charge as the cause of the appearance of mechanical force. The quantity ρ, like the constant of elasticity in Hooke's law, is an empirical parameter which takes into account the property of a particular material. The new parameter, resistivity, enters as a consequence of the empirical proportionality observed by Ohm; the constant accompanying the introduction of the sign of equality does not represent the introduction of a basically new entity into our general description of physical phenomena as does the constant in Newton's law of gravitation or in Coulomb's law, but, like the elastic constant of mechanics, is simply a physical characteristic of a particular material.

EXAMPLE. *Power loss in a transmission line.* A transmission line is designed to carry 1 megaWatt of electrical power over a distance of 400,000 meters (approximately 250 miles). The source of power supplies a potential difference of 10 kiloVolts (kV.). Calculate the transmission losses, due to heating of the conductor, if the conductor of diameter 0.04 m. is made from material of resistivity 1.88×10^{-8} Ohm-meter. This corresponds approximately to a $1\frac{1}{2}$ inch diameter conductor of copper. (Fig. 9-8)

The potential drop along the length of the conductor is not known. However, the current I is readily calculated from the total power P, and the available potential ϕ:

$$I = \frac{P}{\phi} = \frac{10^6}{10^4} = 100 \text{ amp.}$$

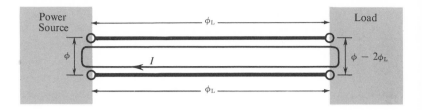

Figure 9-8 *Of the potential ϕ available from a power source, ϕ_L is dropped across each of the lines which carry the current to the load, thus leaving a potential drop of $\phi - 2\phi_L$ across the load. The current I, however, must be the same for every element of such a circuit.*

The power dissipated in a transmission line of resistance R, resistivity ρ, length l, and radius r is then:

$$P' = I^2R = \frac{I^2\rho l}{\pi r^2} = \frac{10^4 \times 1.88 \times 10^{-8} \times 4 \times 10^5}{3.14 \times 0.02 \times 0.02} = 6 \times 10^4 \text{ W}.$$

or 60 kW., which is 6% of the available 1 megaWatt. The total loss due to both the supply and return lines would, of course, be 12%. This figure may be uneconomically high, requiring that either a larger diameter conductor, or a higher potential at the source be used.

Problems

9-1 Two spherical bodies in space carry equal like charges distributed uniformly over their surfaces. If the mass of each body is 1 kg., what must the charges be for the gravitational and electrostatic forces to exactly annul one another?

9-2 A point charge of $+3$ C. and another of -3 C. are spaced 4 m. apart on a horizontal line. A point charge of -5 C. is placed midway between them. The charge of $+3$ C. is on the left. Find the force, the field strength, and the potential experienced by each charge and the total electrostatic potential energy of all three. Specify directions where appropriate.

9-3 Three point charges of $+5$ C. are placed at the corners of an equilateral triangle of side 3 m. What is the force, field strength, and potential experienced by each charge? Specify directions where appropriate.

9-4 A negative point charge $-e_1$ is equidistant from two positive point charges $+e_2$, which are a distance $2s$ apart. The negative charge is a distance x off the line joining the positive charges. Calculate the potential energy U of the negative charge as a function of e_1, e_2, s, and x. If the negative charge is released, but constrained to a plane of symmetry between the positive charges, it will oscillate about an equilibrium position. What is the condition that this oscillatory motion be approximately simple harmonic? What is then the period of the oscillation, if the negative charge is associated with a mass m?

9-5 A dipole consists of two equal unlike point charges, $+e$ and $-e$, rigidly connected by an insulating rod of length l. Such a dipole will tend to align itself along the direction of any external uniform electric field E, and if displaced from equilibrium will perform torsional oscillation about its equilibrium direction. Assuming that the mass of the dipole is concentrated in a mass m at each charge, calculate the natural frequency of oscillation for small displacements.

9-6 Charge placed on an isolated spherical conductor is always distributed uniformly over the exterior surface, as a result of the inverse square force of repulsion between like charges. What is the potential at the surface of a spherical conductor of radius r carrying a charge e? What is the *capacity* (ratio of charge to surface potential) of such an object?

9-7 There is no field inside a solid conductor once the charge distribution has reached equilibrium. Why? The solid conductor may be thought of as a hollow conductor surrounding a smaller solid conductor. The latter carries no charge, and in theory may be removed. What may be deduced about the field inside a hollow conductor? What may then be deduced about the potential inside a hollow conductor? It is interesting to note that the confinement of all charge to the outer surface of a solid conductor is dependent on the exponent in Coulomb's Law being exactly 2.

9-8 Two hollow concentric spherical conductors are insulated from one another. A charge $+e$ is placed on the inner one, and the outer one is connected to ground (an inexhaustible supply of charge at zero potential). When equilibrium has been reached, what will be the potential on the outer sphere? What charge will have collected on the outer sphere? What will be the potential on the inner sphere? Calculate the *capacity* of the system, defined as the ratio of the charge on the inner sphere to the potential difference between the two spheres.
Note: the results deduced in the previous problem may be needed to answer this one.

9-9 A 12 V. storage battery in a car is capable of supplying 50 amps of current for 1 hour. How much charge does it hold? If the car's two 54 Watt headlights and two 6 Watt taillights are all left on, how long will the battery take to discharge?

9-10

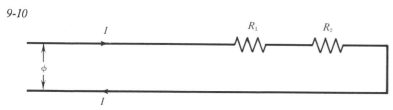

A source of potential difference ϕ supplies current I to a combination of two

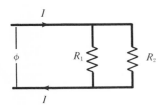

resistances R_1 and R_2, which are connected in *series*, as shown in the figure. State the current through R_1, the potential drop across R_1, the current through R_2, and the potential drop across R_2. Hence deduce the effective resistance R of two resistances connected in *series*.

9-11 A source of potential difference ϕ supplies current I to a combination of two resistances, R_1 and R_2, which are connected in *parallel*, as shown in the figure. State the potential drop across R_1, the current through R_1, the potential drop across R_2, and the current through R_2. Hence deduce the effective resistance R of two resistances connected in *parallel*.

Moving charges or electric currents 10

Experimental observation of a velocity-dependent force between moving charges or currents 10-1

If the two large oppositely charged conductors that were considered in the preceding chapter as being discharged through a wire connecting them were to be discharged by simultaneously making the connection between them through two long parallel wires quite close together, one would observe not only that the wires get hot, but also that they tend to pull together during the discharge process, i.e., there appears to be a force of attraction between the wires as a result of the passage of electric charge or the flow of electric current through them. The same phenomenon can, of course, be observed and measured more conveniently by employing the flow of current brought about by electrochemical cells or any other means. For very long parallel wires, the force of attraction per unit length is found to be directly proportional to the current flowing in each wire and inversely proportional to their separation.

An account of the motion of electric charge through a conductor such as a metal wire in terms of the atomic structure of the conducting material must be postponed until Chap. 20, but the preatomic description of the motion of electricity is quite adequate for our purpose here. The fundamental large-scale phenomena with which we are concerned could be accounted for by assuming that there are equal quantities of positive and negative electricity within the conductor to ensure over-all electrical neutrality, and that each type is capable of motion. The positive electricity would move in the direction of the field, the negative electricity in the opposite direction, and they would add algebraically to yield the total current. In fact, however, the positive charges in solid conductors are arranged in a regular and rigidly immobile space lattice, and the charges of the negative sign by our convention move relatively freely through this lattice under the influence of the electric field produced by the potential difference between the ends of the conductor.

The steady continuous flow of electricity must evidently take place in a conductor that is in the form of a closed contour or completed circuit, like the circulation of water in a continuous system of piping, for the flow of the mobile negative charge would quickly halt at a free end due to the large electrostatic forces that would immediately occur on the acquisition of a net positive charge by the conductor when the negative charge left it. The fundamentally closed nature of electrical circuits has many important physical implications; it also presents physical difficulties in demonstrating most simply the phenomena taking place in local portions of the circuit.

An electrical circuit in which the mobile negative charge circulates steadily, or oscillates periodically, represents only a quasi-equilibrium situation. It is not an equilibrium in which the energy remains constant in one form, or in which there is a free exchange of energy from one form to another. It is similar rather to dynamical motion in the presence of friction, for energy is continuously being dissipated in the form of heat as a result of the current flow. This energy must be furnished by the external source that supplies the driving potential or electromotive force for the circuit. The forces that are observed to move a rigid circuit or to alter the contours of a flexible one as a result of the establishment of electric currents in it or in neighboring circuits can—by various ingenious devices—be balanced by gravitational or electrostatic forces, or can be measured in terms of the rates of change of the momentum of bodies affected by them. These forces are found to be consistent with the concept that charges in relative motion exert forces on one another in addition to the electrostatic ones that they exert upon one another at rest. As was noted in the preceding chapter, the existence of velocity-dependent electric forces constitutes one of the principal qualitative differences between them and gravitational forces. Since electrical circuits are necessarily closed contours, and each portion of each circuit, or the moving electric charge in each portion, is presumed to exert a force on every other portion of each circuit as a result of the moving charges or currents, the geometry becomes complicated, and it is not easy to design experiments that elucidate the fundamental law of force describing the interaction of a particular infinitesimal current-carrying element and all of the rest of the elements making up the circuits.

The first understanding of the quantitative dependence of the forces between circuits carrying constant currents upon the geometry of these circuits was gained through an elegant and extensive series of experiments performed by Andre Marie Ampere early in the 19th Century. Some insight into these forces is gained by measuring the force of attraction between two wire frames, as shown in Fig. 10-1. Vertical segments conduct the current to the horizontal segments that can be varied relatively in orientation and separation; the lower frame is stationary and the upper frame is suspended from the arm of a balance for measuring the force. If the separation d is small compared with the length l of the horizontal segments, it is found that the force of attraction is directly proportional to the two currents I_1 and I_2 and to the length l, and inversely proportional to d for small separations. The force is also directly proportional to the cosine of the angle θ between the currents; there is maximum attraction when they are parallel, zero attraction when they are perpendicular, and a maximum repulsion when the currents are opposite, or antiparallel. If the upper frame is supported in such a way that it is free to rotate about the vertical, it is found that the flow of the electric currents exerts a torque upon the upper frame, proportional to the sine of the angle θ, which tends to set the upper frame so that the currents I_1 and I_2 are parallel.

The results of such an experiment, and of the many others that can be devised to elucidate the forces exerted between electric currents or moving charges, are consistent with the concept that each moving charge exerts a force on each other moving charge; or alternatively, that each element dl_1 of a circuit carrying a current I_1 exerts a force upon each other element dl_1 of the circuit, or of each element dl_2 of any other circuit carrying a current I_2. If the charges are not free to move about in space, but are constrained to remain within the boundaries of a conductor by the electrostatic forces between them and the oppositely charged lattice giving rigidity to the conductor, the forces on the mobile charges normal to the conductor's boundaries are, of course, transferred to and affect the conductor itself.

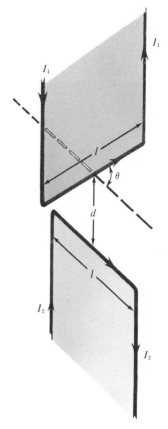

Figure 10-1 *Schematic experimental disposition for measuring the forces and torques between the current-carrying conductors.*

The velocity dependent force as a consequence of relativistic invariance   10-2

At first acquaintance, the velocity-dependent law of force between charges, deduced from experimental observations in the preceding section, might appear to be a new fundamental law of physics, independent of and of equal status with Coulomb's law of force between stationary charges. However, the following argument shows that the velocity-dependent force between moving charges is a direct consequence of the requirement that electrical laws be the same for all observers in inertial or unaccelerated frames of reference.

Consider the situation depicted in Fig. 10-2. An observer in a primed system of coordinates measures the electrostatic force of repulsion

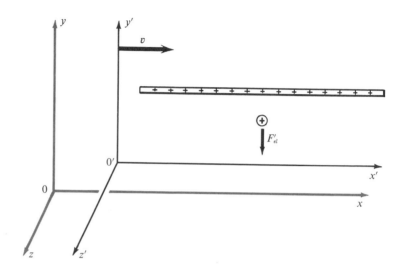

Figure 10-2 *A long uniformly charged wire and a point charge seen by two observers, one of whom is stationary with respect to the charges and the other of whom is moving with velocity v with respect to the first.*

between a small positive stationary charge and a very long array of positive charges distributed uniformly along a wire. The ends of the wire may be considered so far distant from the lone positive charge that they contribute little to the net repulsive force. It is obvious from the geometrical symmetry that the net electrostatic force of repulsion F'_{el} on the small charge will be in a direction perpendicular to the wire. It should also be obvious from Coulomb's law that this force will be proportional to the charge per unit length on the wire.

Next consider the same situation, viewed by an observer in an unprimed system of coordinates with respect to whom the lone charge and the long conductor are both moving with constant velocity v in a direction parallel to the wire. The force is also transverse to the direction of motion for such an observer. In Sect. 3 of Chap. 8 it was shown that a transverse momentum has the same value for both the moving and the stationary observers. A transverse force, defined as the time rate of change of the transverse momentum, will therefore transform inversely as the time, i.e.,

$$t = \frac{t'}{\sqrt{1 - v^2/c^2}}$$

and, therefore: $\qquad F = F' \sqrt{1 - v^2/c^2}$

where F is the transverse force detected by the observer for whom the charges are moving, and F' is the force detected by the observer for whom the charges are stationary. However, the unprimed observer, if he calculates the expected value of the electrostatic force in his system, will note that charges and transverse distances are unchanged by transformations whereas the long conductor must contract in the direction of motion, thus increasing its charge per unit length and hence the electrostatic force of repulsion. According to this argument, the electrostatic force for the unprimed observer should be:

$$F_{el} = \frac{F'_{el}}{\sqrt{1 - v^2/c^2}}$$

But for the stationary observer, F'_{el} is the only force present, and hence represents F' in the earlier equation. Therefore,

$$F = F' \sqrt{1 - \frac{v^2}{c^2}}$$

$$= F'_{el} \sqrt{1 - \frac{v^2}{c^2}}$$

$$= F_{el} \left(1 - \frac{v^2}{c^2}\right)$$

$$= F_{el} - F_{el} \frac{v^2}{c^2}$$

Thus the observer of the moving charges records a repulsive force that is less than the expected electrostatic force F_{el} by an amount $F_{el}v^2/c^2$. Such an observer might then conclude that there is an attractive force F_m equal to the above value arising from the motion of the charges. This force might conveniently be described as the *electrodynamic* force, in contrast to the *electrostatic* force. However, for historical reasons, the electrostatic and electrodynamic quantities are usually referred to as *electric* and *magnetic* respectively.

The electrostatic force of repulsion exerted on the lone charge e_1 by the charge e_2 contained in a small section of the wire immediately opposite is, by Coulomb's law,

$$F_{el} = K \frac{e_1 e_2}{r^2}$$

where r is the distance between the charges. Likewise the accompanying electrodynamic or magnetic force of attraction is

$$F_m = K \frac{v^2}{c^2} \frac{e_1 e_2}{r^2}$$

$$= \frac{K}{c^2} \frac{(e_1 v)(e_2 v)}{r^2}$$

When the force is expressed in this fashion, it may be anticipated that in the case of unequal velocities v_1 and v_2 of the two charges e_1 and e_2, the relation becomes

$$F_m = \frac{K}{c^2} \frac{(e_1 v_1)(e_2 v_2)}{r^2}$$

Thus the magnetic force between the charges is directly proportional to the products $e_1 v_1$ and $e_2 v_2$ and inversely proportional to the square of the separation r, the constant of proportionality being the electrostatic constant K divided by the square of the velocity of light. The above statement is not strictly true for two isolated charges because a finite time is required for transmission of the force via electromagnetic waves of velocity c; during this time the positions of the two charges change as discussed in Sect. 10-5. However, in most cases of interest the charge initiating the force is one of many in a closed circuit of fixed geometry, and no correction to the equation is necessary.

The expression for the magnetic force can be put into a more convenient form for the typical problem of determining the forces exerted upon one another by closed current-carrying circuits. If the moving charges are thought of as being channeled by the conductor, as in the flow of a liquid through a pipe, then e_1 will be the total mobile charge occupying each small length dl_1 of the conductor. Each charge e_1 will travel with the same velocity v_1. Therefore, in unit time each travels a distance v_1, and all charges in a distance v_1 will pass a given point in unit time, as illustrated in Fig. 10-3. But since a length dl_1 of conductor contains mobile charge e_1, then a length v_1 must contain an amount

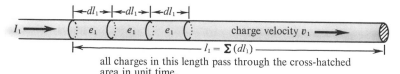

Figure 10-3   *A charge e_1 in every element of length dl_1 flowing with velocity v_1 along a conductor results in a current $I_1 = e_1v_1/dl_1$.*

of charge $(v_1/dl_1)e_1$. The current or amount of charge passing a given point in unit time is

$$I_1 = \frac{v_1}{dl_2} e_1$$

Similarly for a second conductor:

$$I_2 = \frac{v_2}{dl_1} e_2$$

Thus the force between two adjacent parallel short lengths dl_1 and dl_2 of conductors, carrying currents I_1 and I_2 respectively in the same direction, is

$$F = \frac{K}{c^2} \frac{(e_1v_1)(e_2v_2)}{r^2} = \frac{K}{c^2} \frac{(I_1\,dl_1)(I_2\,dl_2)}{r^2}$$

where the force is to be measured in Newtons, the currents in Amperes and the lengths in meters. There is no electrostatic term in the above expression because, although there is a flow of charge along a conductor, the presence of equal quantities of positive and negative charge leads to an overall electrical neutrality.

In a more general situation, owing to the vector nature of v_1 and v_2 or dl_1 and dl_2, the force also depends upon the angles between the two velocities, or current elements and the line joining them. Thus if r represents the vector between the current elements $I_1\,dl_1$ and $I_2\,dl_2$, and H represents a vector perpendicular to both $I_1\,dl_1$ and r, then the magnetic force on element $I_2\,dl_2$ is

$$F = \frac{K}{c^2} \frac{(I_1\,dl_1)(I_2\,dl_2)}{r^2} \sin\theta \sin\phi$$

where θ is the angle between $I_1\,dl_1$ and r and ϕ is the angle between H and $I_2\,dl_2$, as indicated in Fig. 10-4. The direction of such a force is perpendicular to both H and $I_2\,dl_2$. However, for the case of two long parallel current-carrying conductors, summation over the length of one

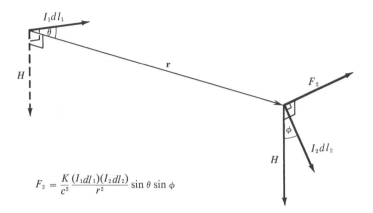

$$F_2 = \frac{K}{c^2} \frac{(I_1 dl_1)(I_2 dl_2)}{r^2} \sin\theta \sin\phi$$

Figure 10-4   The force F_2 on a current element $I_2 dl_2$ due to another current element $I_1 dl_1$ is perpendicular to both $I_2 dl_2$ and to H, where H is a vector perpendicular to both $I_1 dl_1$ and the radius vector r. Note that F_2 is, therefore, perpendicular to $I_2 dl_2$ and in the plane of $I_1 dl_1$ and r.

conductor greatly simplifies the expression for force, and for this geometry the force per unit length on either conductor is simply

$$F = \frac{K}{c^2} \frac{I_1 I_2}{d}$$

where I_1 and I_2 are the currents and d is the distance between the conductors. This agrees with the experimental results of Ampere, already referred to in Sect. 10-1.

10-3   *Analogy between the velocity-dependent law and the static laws; the magnetic potential*

It is seen that the velocity-dependent law is very similar in form to the static laws, force being proportional to the product of the entities to which the effect is attributable, and inversely proportional to the square of their separation. The constant K is the same constant that occurred in the electrostatic law, and c is the velocity of light. The occurrence of the ratio v/c shows that the forces due to relative motion are less in magnitude than the electrostatic forces between charges in a comparable geometry by the order of the product of the ratios of the charges' velocities to that of light. They are, however, of great practical importance in atomic phenomena and also in the large-scale conduction of electricity, because of the very large number of moving charges that can easily be made to traverse conductors in which equal quantities of positive and negative charges are present.

The value of the constant K/c^2 is exactly 10^{-7}. It is an exact constant because, as mentioned in the preceding chapter, the practical definition of quantity of electric charge is in terms of the velocity-dependent rather than the static electric force, and the definition enters at the point where the dependence of this force on the quantities in the expression $F = \dfrac{K}{c^2}\dfrac{I_1 I_2}{d}$ is formulated.

The magnetic force between parallel moving charges or current elements naturally gives rise to an energy of the form

$$U = -\frac{K}{c^2}\frac{(I_1\,dl_1)(I_2\,dl_2)}{r}$$

This quantity is inherently simpler than the force, since it does not depend upon the direction of the vector between the two interacting charges or elements. However, the vector nature of the velocities or elements is inevitably involved, so that if dl_1 is not in the same direction as dl_2, but is inclined at an angle θ to this direction, then the component of dl_1 in the direction of dl_2 must be used in calculating the magnetic energy. Thus, in general

$$U = -\frac{K}{c^2}\frac{(I_1\,dl_1\cos\theta)(I_2\,dl_2)}{r} = -\frac{K}{c^2}\frac{(I_1\,dl_1)(I_2\,dl_2)}{r}\cos\theta$$

as indicated in Fig. 10-5. Of course, the same result would have been reached by taking $dl_2\cos\theta$, the component of dl_2 in the direction of dl_1.

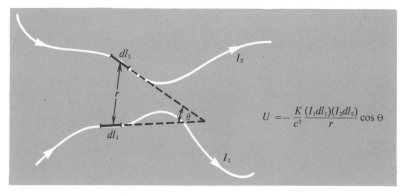

Figure 10-5 *The energy U of two current elements is proportional to the cosine of the angle between them.*

The forces on all current-carrying circuits and upon the complete rigid systems that, in sum, they constitute may be calculated from this expression for the potential energy. Likewise the force upon a moving charged particle in the presence of current-carrying circuits or other moving charged particles can be calculated. The derivation of the force in question proceeds, of course, by finding the difference in potential energy between two neighboring configurations; on dividing this by the change in displacement, the force is obtained. Or, if the motion involved is rotation, division by the angular displacement yields the torque. This is in accordance with the definition of work, or change in potential energy, as the product of the force and displacement, or torque and angular displacement.

EXAMPLE. The potential energy of two 0.01 m. lengths of conductors 0.5 m. apart is -8×10^{-11} J. The angle between the two current elements is 60°. If one conductor carries a current of 4 amps., what is the current in the other conductor?

Adopting the notation above, the potential energy is given as

$$U = -\frac{K}{c^2} \frac{(I_1 \, dl_1)(I_2 \, dl_2)}{r} \cos \theta$$

Therefore

$$I_2 = -\frac{c^2}{K} \frac{Ur}{(I_1 \, dl_1) \, dl_2 \cos \theta} = 10^7 \frac{8 \times 10^{-11} \times 0.5}{(4 \times 0.01) \, 0.01 \times 0.5} = 2 \text{ amps.}$$

In analogy to the gravitational potential Φ and the electric potential ϕ, a *magnetic potential A* may be defined as the potential energy per unit current element; only, in this case, account must be taken of the direction as well as the magnitude of current elements. Thus at distance r from a current element $I_1 dl_1$, the magnetic potential would be

$$A_1 = \frac{K}{c^2} \frac{I_1 \, dl_1}{r}$$

A second current element $I_2 \, dl_2$ at this distance, lying at angle θ to the first, would have a potential energy

$$U = -\frac{K}{c^2} \frac{(I_1 \, dl_1)(I_2 \, dl_2)}{r} \cos \theta$$
$$= -A_1(I_2 \, dl_2) \cos \theta$$

Thus A_1 is the magnitude of a vector in the direction of dl_1 as shown in Fig. 10-6; and θ, being the angle between the elements dl_1 and dl_2, is

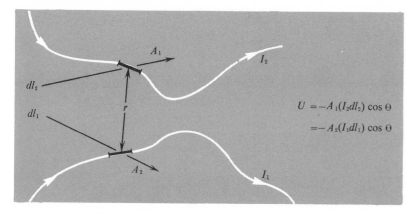

Figure 10-6 *The energy U of two current elements may be written in terms of one of the magnetic potentials. These are vectors in the directions of the current elements.*

also the angle between the magnetic potential A_1 and the second element dl_2.

The unit of magnetic potential is clearly the Joule per Ampere meter. Of course, the potential energy could also be written in terms of the potential A_2 produced by the second current element and experienced by the first:

$$U = - A_2(I_1\, dl_1) \cos \theta$$

The vector nature of the magnetic potential is a departure from the analogy with the static potentials which results from the vector nature of the element of current $I\, dl$ in contrast to the scalar nature of mass and charge. The magnetic potential at some point in the neighborhood of a current-carrying circuit is the vector sum of all the magnetic potentials produced at that point by the various elements of the circuit. This is in contrast to a mass distribution, or static charge distribution, where the potential at some point in the vicinity is simply an algebraic or scalar sum of the potentials due to the various masses or charges.

Finally, the force per unit current element, or a *Magnetic Field Strength H*, which results from any arbitrary configuration of electric circuits, could be defined in analogy with the gravitational and electric field strengths Γ and E. The precise nature of this magnetic field will be discussed in the following chapter.

EXAMPLE. What is the magnetic potential experienced by each of the current elements of the preceding example?

The potential experienced by the first current element at distance r from the second is:

$$A_2 = \frac{K}{c^2} \frac{I_2 \, dl_2}{r} = 10^{-7} \frac{2 \times 0.01}{0.5} = 4 \times 10^9 \text{ J. amp.}^{-1} \text{ m.}^{-1}$$

This is the magnitude of a vector in the direction of dl_2. The potential experienced by the second current element at distance r from the first is:

$$A_1 = \frac{K}{c^2} \frac{I_1 \, dl_1}{r} = 10^{-7} \frac{4 \times 0.01}{0.5} = 8 \times 10^{-9} \text{ J. amp.}^{-1} \text{ m.}^{-1}$$

This is the magnitude of a vector in the direction of dl_1.

10-4   Forces and torques on complete current-carrying circuits

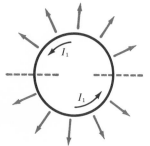

Figure 10-7   *Expansion into a circle of a current-carrying loop.*

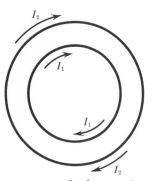

Figure 10-8   *Coplanar orientation of two current-carrying conductors.*

A circular current-carrying conductor is subject to a radial force of expansion, for it can be seen by symmetry and the opposite directions of the currents at the ends of a diameter that, under the influence of the forces between these halves, they tend to move apart. This produces the same effect as the centrifugal forces associated with masses traversing this circular circuit would produce. If a similar, but somewhat larger or smaller current-carrying concentric circle is suspended by a thread in the plane of the first, it will tend to take up a coplanar position with a similar sense of flow. This is the orientation of minimum potential energy, since it brings similarly directed current elements closest together, which is the natural tendency of the forces involved. These phenomena are illustrated in Fig. 10-7 and Fig. 10-8.

A quantitative determination of the forces between current-carrying circuits or electric charges in relative uniform motion that is of practical generality involves rather tedious geometrical calculations as well as judicious approximations, since circuits in which currents are continuously maintained must be complete. These circuits are usually of complex geometric shapes and must contain batteries or other sources that provide the energy represented by the configuration of currents relative to one another, as well as the constant dissipation of energy in the form of heat caused by the flow of the currents in the conductors. However, one can frequently dispose the circuits in question reasonably symmetrically with respect to one another in order to provide some simplification of the geometry and can also arrange to reduce the influence of the necessary but usually undesired wires connecting the principal parts of the circuits with the source of energy, such as an electrochemical cell, which maintains the constant currents.

The geometrical calculation is most conveniently performed in two steps. At some point in space, say that which is to be occupied by the element dl_2 carrying the current I_2, the calculation of adding together the vector elements $I_1 \, dl_1$ divided by the distance from each dl_1 to the point occupied by dl_2 is performed. This yields the vector A_1, the magnetic potential due to circuit 1. (Fig. 10-9).

$$A_1 = 10^{-7}I_1 \oint \frac{dl_1}{r} \cdot$$

The quantity K/c^2 accounts for the numerical factor 10^{-7}, the large letter S denotes the sum of all the little elements dl_1, and the small circle around it is a reminder that the sum must include the entire closed electric circuit in which current I_1 flows. If there are a number of current-carrying circuits present, they must all be taken into account to de-

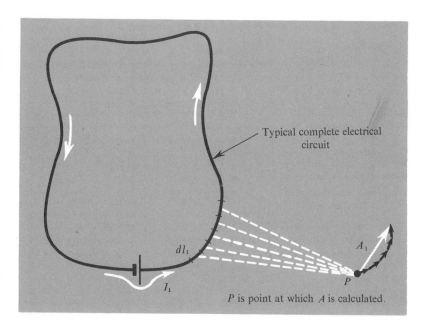

Figure 10-9 *Illustration of the geometrical process for calculating the magnetic potential due to a current-carrying circuit; five representative sequential infinitesimal elements are depicted. The potential A_1 produced by circuit 1 is the vector sum of all the potentials produced by each current element I_1dl_1.*

termine the energy of the element dl_2 carrying I_2 in their presence. The sum of all the vector potentials (including of course the rest of circuit 2) will simply be written A. To find the total energy, the value of A at each point of circuit 2 must be multiplied by $I_2\,dl_2$ and by the cosine of the angle between A and dl_2. Then these products must be added together for the complete circuit 2. Although this sounds very tedious and difficult, and in general it is, mathematical ingenuity has devised many shortcuts and simplifications; in principle, the process is very straightforward. The result for the total potential energy due to the two circuits is evidently the product of the two currents and a geometrical factor dependent upon their shapes and relative dispositions. Or,

$$U = I_1 I_2 L_{12}$$

where the geometrical factor L_{12} is called the *coefficient of mutual induction* between the circuits.

The foregoing discussion may seem unduly meticulous and detailed, but it can be put in better perspective by referring back to Ampere's law of force or energy content for the influence of two elementary current-carrying segments $I\,dl$, or moving charges ev on one another. What has been done in writing the energy for the complete circuits with which one must work practically in the form $U = I_1 I_2 L_{12}$ is to recognize that the two currents I_1 and I_2 are constant in their respective circuits and may be taken into consideration as constant multiplying factors in any resulting expression. The rest of the elements appearing in the expression are simply geometric ones which may be summed as indicated in the discussion to yield the geometrical quantity L_{12}.

In the case, for instance, of one circular loop suspended concentrically within another, L_{12} is a function of the angle θ between the planes of the loops, since this is the only geometric quantity that can vary. Thus the torque on the suspended loop, which is the ratio $-dU/d\theta$, is $-I_1 I_2 (dL_{12}/d\theta)$. If the rate of change of L_{12} with θ is known from the calculation, and the torque is measured, say by the amount by which the suspending fiber is twisted, I_2 may be determined if I_1 is known. This is a very convenient type of measurement for electrical currents, and is the basis not only for absolute measurements of current, but also of most practical current measuring devices as well.

EXAMPLE. Two adjacent current-carrying circuits have a potential energy of 0.01 J. What would the potential energy be if the currents were the same, but all the linear dimensions including the spacing were increased by a factor of two?

The potential energy may be written as

$$U = L_{12} I_1 I_2$$

where the mutual induction L_{12} is a sum of terms of the form $dl_1 \, dl_2/r$. Increasing all linear dimensions by a factor of two will increase these terms by a factor of $2 \times 2/2$, or a factor of two. Thus L_{12} will increase by a factor of two, and so will the potential energy U.

EXAMPLE. The current I_1 through a loop of wire is held constant at 3 amps. The current I_2 through another loop, suspended concentrically within the first, is held constant at 5 amps. The mutual induction L_{12} between the loops is $10^{-7} \cos \theta$ J. amp.$^{-2}$, where θ is the angle between the planes of the two loops. What torque must be provided by the suspension of the second loop in order to hold it perpendicular to the first loop?

The angular rate of change of $\cos \theta$ has been shown to be $-\sin \theta$. Hence the torque provided by the magnetic interaction between the loops is

$$ -\frac{dU}{d\theta} = -I_1 I_2 \frac{dL_{12}}{d\theta} = 3 \times 5 \times 10^{-7} \sin \theta $$

which, for $\theta = \pi/2$ radians or 90°, becomes 15×10^{-7} J. An equal but opposite torque must, therefore, be provided by the suspension.

Induction or the change in electric currents with time under the assumption of constant total available energy   10-5

The expression for the potential energy of two current-carrying circuits has another very important implication. If energy is to be conserved in general, aside from the steady drain of Joule or ohmic heating which is not here under consideration, a change in one of the currents in

$$ U = I_1 I_2 L_{12} $$

with L_{12} remaining constant, should induce a compensating change in the other current. Let us assume that the change in energy dU occurs in the time dt. Then the rate at which work is done, or energy is increased, is:

$$ \frac{dU}{dt} = I_1 \left(L_{12} \frac{dI_2}{dt} \right) + I_2 \left(L_{12} \frac{dI_1}{dt} \right) $$

The rate at which work is done in moving electric charges is the product of the charges, their velocities, and the electric field strength that opposes the motion. This is the same as the current times the electric potential opposing the current. Thus the quantity $L_{12}\, dI_2/dt$ is, in effect, the electric potential encountered by the current I_1 in traversing the complete circuit through which it flows as a result of the change in the current I_2 in circuit 2. Likewise $L_{12}\, dI_1/dt$ is the apparent electric potential induced in circuit 2 by the change of the current in circuit 1. These potentials induced in the circuits change the currents in them; or if no current previously existed, they induce one.

This effect of inducing currents in neighboring circuits, of course, does not exist if there is no change with the time. Conversely, the effect can obviously also be brought about if L_{12} changes with the time, as must occur also in the case of relative movement of the circuits because of the dependence of L_{12} on the spatial coordinates. Thus the electric potential induced in circuit 1 due to the motion of circuit 2 carrying a current I_2 would be $I_2\, dL_{12}/dt$. This effective generation of an apparently new type of electrical interaction or force, associated with the velocity-dependent interaction between electric charges, is actually a consequence of the law of conservation of energy applied to the motion of electric charges. It has very important practical effects in the genesis of electromagnetic waves, and in the generation of electric currents by the relative motion of other current-carrying conductors, e.g., in electromagnetic machinery.

Electromagnetic induction was first studied, and its description reduced to quantitative terms about a century ago by Michael Faraday in England and Joseph Henry in the United States. Their work laid the foundation for both the electrical and communications industries, as well as for the practical employment of electricity in all of its diverse aspects in modern industrial society.

10-6 *Electromagnetic waves*

The electrical forces that have been considered are essentially of three types: (1) those which are encountered in electrostatics, where the potential energy represented by two charges at rest is Ke_1e_2/r; (2) those which are encountered in the case of charges moving with constant velocities, where the potential energy of two current-carrying circuits is $I_1I_2L_{12}$; and (3) those which are dependent upon relative acceleration of charges, where the initiation of an electric current induces other currents in neighboring conductors which are proportional to the current change and to the geometric factor describing the disposition of the conductors and the changing current.

In Chap. 7 it was remarked that the phenomenon we call light is a wave-like phenomenon called electromagnetic because it can be identified with the changing motions of electric charges, and hence with the changes in the electric and magnetic potentials to which the changing motions of the charges give rise. Heinrich Hertz, a German physicist, and Oliver Lodge, an Englishman, at the end of the last century made the discovery that changing configurations of charges and currents gave rise to wave-like phenomena both along wires and through empty space, and that the properties of these waves—including the value of the velocity with which they were propagated—strongly suggested that they were generically the same as waves of visible light, though they were of much lower frequency and consequently of much longer wave length. Such waves have been extensively investigated in the intervening years, and the technology is now such that efficient methods of generation and detection exist for the broad spectrum of frequencies from the lowest that are practically useful which are many miles in wave length through the waves of radio, television, radar, and microwaves, right up to the long wave length end of the visible spectrum.

The relation of these waves to the electric and magnetic potentials discussed in this and the previous chapter is easily understood if account is taken of the time necessary for the propagation of a light signal from the configuration of charges whose motion is altered to the distant point at which the effect of this alteration is observed. Any change in the charge configuration at a time t' will not be observed at a distant point until a later time $t' + r/c$, where r is the distance from the charges to the observer, and c is the velocity of light. Or, conversely, if a detecting device indicates a small change in the electric current flowing through it at the time t as a result of the changing magnetic potential at that point, this change must have been caused by the generation of a small current at some other point at an earlier time $t - r/c$ if the separation between the generator and detector is r. In Chap. 6 it was pointed out that such a relation between phenomena observed at successively distant spatial intervals at correspondingly increasing time intervals constituted the phenomenon known as wave motion. Hence the occurrence of the magnetic potential A at a particular point a distance r from a current I, established in a short length dl of a conductor at the earlier time $t - r/c$, would be written:

$$A_{\text{time } t} = 10^{-7} \frac{I_{\text{time}(t - r/c)} dl}{r}$$

This represents a magnetic potential wave, which, in addition, decreases in amplitude as it spreads out due to the increasing value of r in the denominator.

10-7   Electrical phenomena as described by observers in relative motion

In Chaps. 7 and 8 the relationship of the observations made by persons in relative motion, subject to the constancy of the velocity of the most rapid signals they could send to one another and the conservation laws of energy and momentum upon which they could agree, were examined. The question should then be asked: "what would their conclusions be regarding the electrical phenomena which have been discussed in this and the preceding chapter, and could they agree upon any more general conservation laws relating to electricity, analogous to the mechanical laws of conservation of momentum and energy?"

This is a most useful question, for, as so frequently happens in the growth of science, the long and careful train of experimentation that elucidates a particular phenomenon, such as the work of Ampere in formulating the law of force between electric currents, is found to be a part of a larger structure of general theory and is capable of being stated in simpler and much more perceptive terms. In Sect. 10-2 it was concluded that if the quantity electric charge is invariant for fixed and moving observers, Ampere's law is an inevitable consequence of the theory of relativity.

Alternatively, given the correctness of the applicability of the special theory of relativity and the Lorentz transformation of space and time, it may be concluded that the electric charge e, like the velocity of light c and the rest mass m_0 or rest energy m_0c^2, is a quantity that remains invariant for observers in frames of reference moving with constant relative velocities. The electrostatic potential ϕ when multiplied by e, yielding the electrostatic energy, behaves just as does the mechanical energy $U = mc^2$ under transformations between observers. The magnetic potential A is a vector quantity which, again when multiplied by e, behaves just as does the vector quantity p in the transformation of mechanical quantities. Thus the formulae of Chap. 8 for transforming energy and momentum between observers can be used again to yield:

$$A_x = \frac{A'_x + \dfrac{v}{c^2}\phi'}{\sqrt{1 - v^2/c^2}}$$

$$\phi = \frac{\phi' + vA'_x}{\sqrt{1 - v^2/c^2}}$$

for transforming these electric and magnetic potentials between observers moving with respect to one another with the velocity v. Note that in certain frames of reference—those traveling relative to the primed system with velocity $v = -A'_x c^2/\phi'$ or $v = -\phi'/A'_x$—one or other, of the electric or magnetic potentials may disappear. Similar conclusions hold for the associated electric and magnetic fields.

Problems

10-1   The three long wires shown lie in the same plane. Each carries a current and hence produces a force on the other two. If the forces on the central wire are to cancel, what must be the magnitude and direction of the current in the right-hand wire?

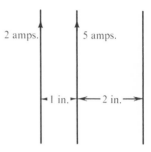

10-2   A rectangle of wire, 9 m. long and 0.6 m. wide, carries a current of 150 amps. What is the approximate force on each of the short sides?

10-3   An electron (charge $- 1.6 \times 10^{-19}$ C. and mass 9×10^{-31} kg.) travels with a velocity of 10^7 m.sec.$^{-1}$ parallel to a long conductor 10^{-3} m. away, which carries a current of 5 amps. in the same direction. What is the acceleration of the electron?

10-4   An electron has a velocity of 10^6 m.sec.$^{-1}$ inclined at an angle of $60°$ with respect to the direction of a circuit element 2 m. distant. The latter is 0.01 m. long and carries a current of 7 amps. What is the value of the magnetic potential due to the current element and experienced by the electron? What is the energy of the system?

10-5   Consider the current elements forming the ends of a long rectangular current loop. If one of these elements experiences a magnetic potential of magnitude A due to the other, what is the magnitude of the force experienced by each of the elements due to the other?

10-6   A right circular cone of base radius r and height h has a current I flowing around the perimeter of its base. What is the magnitude of the magnetic potential at its tip?

10-7   If a small current-carrying loop is placed in a large uniform magnetic field, the spatial rate of change of the magnetic potential is uniform, and hence the coefficient of mutual induction is independent of position. It is of course still a function of angle of orientation. Show that there is no net force on such a current-carrying loop.

10-8   Two coils, carrying currents I_1 and I_2 have a coefficient of mutual induction L. If the current in one of the coils is reversed, what is the charge in potential energy of the system?

10-9   (a) Two coils have a coefficient of mutual induction L_0. If the number of turns in one coil is increased by a factor of 2, and in the other by a factor of 3, what is the new value of the coefficient of mutual induction?
(b) A *transformer* consists of two independent but closely coupled loops of

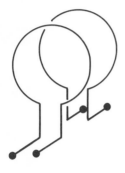

wire. The ends of one loop are connected to the two input terminals, and the ends of the other to the two output terminals. When a current is increased or decreased in the first, or primary loop, an opposing electric potential is induced around the primary loop, and hence across the input equal to that induced around the secondary loop, and hence across the output; i.e., the coefficient of self-induction is equal to the coefficient of mutual induction. The potential induced in the primary must be supplied to the system at the input. If the primary and secondary windings of the transformer had n_1 and n_2 turns respectively, what would be the ratio of input to output potential?

10-10 Transformers are frequently wound on iron cores to enhance the magnetic effects (see Sec. 11-1). Much power is dissipated in the heating of such a metallic core, unless it is subdivided into mutually insulated strips of small individual cross-section. How does this dissipation occur? The power losses become more serious as the frequency of alternation of the current increases, until iron is no longer useful at high radio frequencies? Why?

Magnetism; circulating and rotating electric charges

11

Equivalence between magnetized materials and circulating currents 11-1

Thales of Miletus, in the 6th Century, B.C., is credited with having known that amber, when rubbed, attracts and holds relatively light-weight objects by what we now call electrostatic forces, and also that the iron ore magnetite or loadstone found in his area possesses the property of attracting other lumps of magnetite or bits of iron. Magnetite was considered to be a very remarkable substance for this reason, and presumably it acquired its name from its source in the mountains of the ancient province of Magnesia in Asia Minor. Accounts of the earliest Chinese voyages through the southern islands, and west to the coast of Africa, describe the use of the compass needle for navigation during the first millenium A.D. The father of western knowledge of magnetism, however, was William Gilbert (1540–1603), a contemporary of Galileo and a strong supporter of the Copernican theory, who was Queen Elizabeth's personal physician. He performed many experiments with loadstones, magnetizing iron by heating it and working it in the earth's magnetic field. He observed that pieces of loadstone or magnetized iron retained their properties even when finely subdivided, and he demonstrated that a large sphere of magnetized iron exhibited the magnetic properties of the earth as far as he could determine with small test magnets; he concluded that the compass worked as it does because the earth is a great spherical magnet.

Basic knowledge of magnetism advanced little till the work of Michael Faraday and Joseph Henry, already referred to, and that of James Clerk-Maxwell a little over a century ago, though the details of the direction of the earth's magnetic field at the surface were measured and printed for the use of mariners much earlier. Gilbert's conclusion has been justified completely, and it is known that the magnetic field of the earth is principally due to the large central core of iron and nickel. It is modified to a certain extent by the materials in the crust, electric currents in this crust, and also by electric currents in the atmosphere.

For our purpose it is the connection between the properties of magnetic materials and those of electric currents that is of chief interest. Magnets move under the influence of neighboring electric currents as if they were themselves the seat of circulating currents. Small compass needles are most convenient devices for determining the magnitude and direction of the forces produced by currents in conductors. The accepted description of the magnetism of materials such as iron, cobalt, and nickel, and their alloys which display these properties particularly strongly, is that the atoms of these substances are characterized by an unbalanced circulating or rotating charge component, which—being relatively mobile and free to change its orientation—acts cooperatively with those of its properly disposed neighbors to enhance the effects of one another and give rise to the large magnetic phenomena observed.

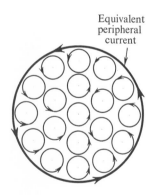

Equivalent peripheral current

Figure 11-1 *Equivalence of closely packed coplanar current whirls and a peripheral current.*

This is indeed the first phenomenon to be considered that may quite clearly be interpreted as implying some type of atomic structure, inasmuch as bulk current flow has been seen to involve the dissipation of electrical energy in the form of heat. Thus if magnetic effects are due to electrical circulations, then these must have a different source, and quite possibly may be identified with charges circulating unimpeded within the very small compass of a single atom, since no decrease of these currents takes place with time. A more complete description of this behavior in atomic terms will be postponed to a later chapter, but it is relatively easy to see from Fig. 11-1 that if a large number of contiguous elementary circulating currents, or current whirls, arrange themselves over a surface in such a way that the sense of rotation is the same for each, the net current flow or passage of charge within the configuration tends to vanish by reason of equal but oppositely directed motions, and the combined effect is essentially that of a current traversing the boundary of the aggregate in the same sense as that of the elementary components. The intra-atomic motion is resistanceless, and hence the effective circulating current at the boundary, unlike ordinary currents in conductors, is not accompanied by the generation of heat; any changes that take place with time are those that accompany changes in the orientation of the elementary components. Such changes may indeed be accompanied by the generation of heat due to action against retarding crystal forces, but in a steady state there is no Joule heating due to the intra-atomic currents. The magnetic materials are metals, and hence ordinary Amperean currents may be induced in them as well; in respect to these currents magnetic materials exhibit the same Joule heating as any other conductors.

The somewhat idealized picture that has been presented is subject, in practice, to many qualifications. These relate chiefly to the polycrystaline nature of the magnetic materials, the imperfections in these crystals resulting in a less well-ordered aggregate, and certain opposing or demagnetizing forces resulting from the geometry and disposition of the net effective current flow over the surfaces of the component crystals and macroscopic aggregates constituting the specimen of magnetic material. However, to a first approximation, a magnetized piece of iron, i.e., one in which this ordered orientation of the constituent atoms has been brought about, acts as if circulating currents traversed its surface. In some types of iron, which are relatively soft and malleable, the ordered configuration is retained only when real external Amperean currents flow in neighboring conductors giving rise to the forces that tend to produce the regular atomic alignment. In other hard specimens, in which the crystaline atomic forces produce more rigid constraints on the mobile current whirls, the ordered alignment, once brought about by external currents, is essentially frozen in, and permanent magnets are formed, which retain their properties after the external currents producing the configuration are removed.

Electromagnetic devices. Iron forms an essential element in most practical electromagnetic devices, either in the form of permanent magnets essentially providing permanent circulating currents, or in the form of soft iron in which the induced magnetic effect of atomic alignment supplements the applied Amperean currents. A cylindrical bar magnetized along its axis is ideally equivalent to a helix of wire closely wound over a cylindrical shell coincident with its surface. Magnetized iron forms bent back upon themselves, in the form of a torus with a disc removed, provide—within the resulting gap between the ends—a region where the effect of the opposite faces, called *poles*, is very strong. A small current-carrying coil in this region tends to set itself parallel to the pole surfaces in a way that makes the sense of current flow the same as that of the fictitious flow over the magnet surfaces adjacent to it. This is the basis of the galvanometer type of measuring instrument, in which

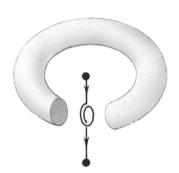

Figure 11-2   *Coil of wire sus-*
pended between the poles of a
torus.

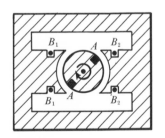

Figure 11-3   *Cross   section*
through a rotating electromag-
netic machine.

the rotation of a coil against the opposing torque of the suspending fiber from its position of rest normal to the pole surfaces is a measure of the strength of the current flowing in the coil (Fig. 11-2). Such an instrument must be calibrated empirically, by using known currents, since the effective strength of the magnet currents and their coefficient of mutual inductance with the coil are not generally amenable to calculation.

Somewhat similar configurations form the basis for the design of electromagnetic machinery. This is the generic designation for *dynamos*, which are devices to convert mechanical energy, generally derived from chemical or thermal forms, into electromagnetic energy, and for the *motors*, which are the complimentary devices for reconverting electromagnetic energy back into the mechanical form. These two types of machines are essentially the same in their structure, and provide for the continuous relative motion between current-carrying conductors necessary for the interconversion of mechanical and electrical energy, which must necessarily be rotational in nature. In order to make the most effective use of the properties of magnetic materials, the gaps necessary to permit relative rotational motion are made of minimum length, thus bringing the amperean currents in the conductors and the oriented current whirls in the magnetic materials into as close juxtaposition as possible. This maximizes the mutual energies and forces between them, since it will be recalled that the energy of interaction between two current elements is inversely proportional to their separation.

A cross section through such a machine is shown schematically in Fig. 11-3. The magnetic material, which is generally iron, is hatched in the diagram, and for mechanical strength part of it rotates with the representative current-carrying conductor shown in section as A. The stationary current-carrying conductor is indicated schematically in section at B_1 and B_2. When the central cylinder is rotated by an external torque derived from a water or steam turbine, the changing coefficient of induction between the conductors produces a current in the conductors which flows first in one sense and then in the other with each half rotation. The conductors are so interconnected that the resulting current is maximal, and sliding contacts may be employed at the terminals of the rotating conductor to reverse the external connections to it every half rotation, and thus to derive a unidirectional current, if this is desired. This apparatus is a generator of electric current, or a dynamo.

The current in the dynamo's conductors can then be led by wires to a similar machine at a distance where the current flow through the stationary and rotating coils provides a torque tending to rotate the central cylinder of iron and its imbedded conductor. The machine, when put to this use, is called a motor. The effective transmission of the energy derived from a prime mover through the medium of the dynamo, the transmission line, and the motor to rotational energy at the shaft of the latter constitutes our most practically useful development in the distribution and utilization of large amounts of power.

The circuital nature of the electrodynamic   11-2
potential and the magnetic field

It was indicated in the previous chapter that the magnetic potential A in the vicinity of a long current-carrying straight conductor is parallel to the conductor, and lies in the direction of the current (Fig. 11-4). In practice, all current-carrying circuits must be closed. For a current-carrying circular loop, as illustrated in Fig. 11-5, A is maximal in the vicinity of the conductor and is parallel to the direction of current in the nearest segment of the loop. It can be seen, from the symmetry of the geometry, that components of A in any other direction, due to other segments of the loop, must cancel out. Thus lines of constant potential (equipotentials) form circles that are coaxial with the current loop; the magnitude of the potential increases from zero at infinity to a maximum in the vicinity of the conductor, and decreases again to zero on the

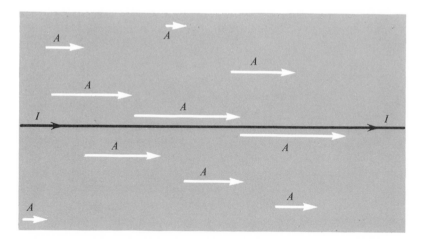

Figure 11-4   *The electrodynamic (magnetic) potential A in the vicinity of a long current-carrying straight conductor is everywhere parallel to the direction of current flow in the conductor.*

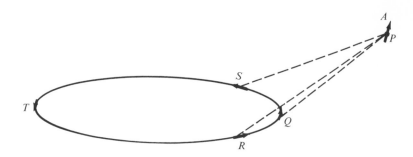

Figure 11-5 *At some point P in the vicinity of a current-carrying circular loop, the magnetic potential A has the direction of the current in the nearest segment Q of the loop. Other segments, such as R and S, contribute components of A both parallel and perpendicular to this, but the latter cancel out by symmetry. The net value of A is reduced by opposing contributions from the opposite side of the loop, e.g., segment T. But these are more distant and hence their contribution is weaker.*

axis of the loop where contributions from all segments of the loop must, again by the demands of symmetry, cancel (Fig. 11-6). The circular current loop is the most symmetrical circuit possible. However, for any closed current circuit, the electrodynamic potential A must be circuital; at distances large compared with the dimensions of the circuit, these closed lines of constant potential closely approximate the perfect circles generated by the current loop just considered.

A device that is used experimentally to explore the direction and magnitude of A is a small current-carrying loop, or a bar magnet that may be thought of as a permanently powered loop coincident with its periphery. This loop is mounted in gimbals, so that at any location in space it may set itself in the orientation determined by whatever electrodynamic potential is produced by all the currents in the conductors that influence it. This is a generalization of the tendency mentioned in Chap. 10 for concentric current-carrying loops to set themselves in the same plane, with parallel current elements of the same sense in close juxtaposition to one another. The direction of the magnetic field H is said to be the direction in which the north pole of the magnet would point, or the direction of the axis of the current loop, which direction is that in which a right hand screw would advance if it were rotated in the direction of the current flowing in the loop.

EXAMPLE. *The magnetic field of a straight conductor and of a coil.* Because the magnitude of the magnetic potential A decreases with distance from a straight current-carrying conductor, any current-carrying test loop of the type mentioned above will set itself so that the side nearest

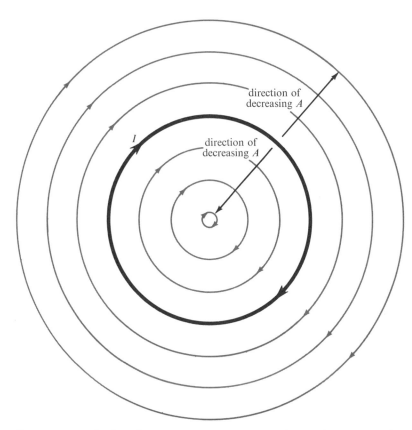

direction of
decreasing A

direction of
decreasing A

I

Figure 11-6 *Circles of constant magnetic potential A in the vicinity of a current-carrying loop.*

the straight conductor carries a current parallel, and in the same sense, to that in the straight conductor, as illustrated in Fig. 11-7. Since the magnetic field at any point is defined to have the direction of the axis of a test loop at that point, the lines of constant magnetic field strength H are circles about the conductor, as illustrated in Fig. 11-8. The direction of rotation of the field lines is that of a right hand screw advancing in the direction of the current. If a conductor is bent into the form of a loop, as in Fig. 11-9, the magnetic field inside the loop is that resulting from the constructive summation of the magnetic fields produced by all elements of the loop. Fig. 11-10 shows such a current loop, viewed side-on, and the distribution of its magnetic field. A coil is simply a series of loops, where magnetic fields add constructively; the resultant magnetic field distribution is shown in Fig. 11-11. Again, a bar magnet is effectively a current-carrying coil, and thus has a similar magnetic field distribution (Fig. 11-12).

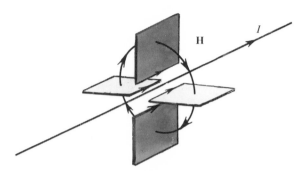

Figure 11-7 *A test current loop, free to turn in the vicinity of a straight current-carrying conductor, sets itself so that the side nearest the conductor carries current in the same sense and direction as the conductor. The magnetic field H is said to be perpendicular to the plane of the test loop, and hence circles the conductor.*

The magnitude of *H* may be defined, by analogy with the electric field strength *E*, as equal to the maximum spatial rate of change of the magnetic (electrodynamic) potential, i.e.,

$$H = \frac{dA}{dr} \qquad \text{by analogy with} \qquad E = -\frac{d\phi}{dr}$$

However, whereas the electric field *E* is opposite to the rate of change of the electric potential ϕ, the magnetic field *H* is perpendicular to both the direction of maximum rate of change of the magnetic potential *A* and to *A* itself. Thus, within a coil, the equipotentials *A* are azi-

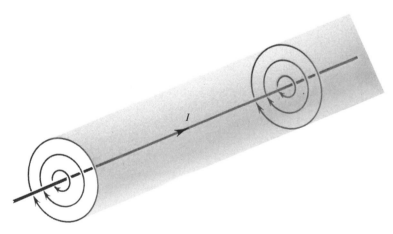

Figure 11-8 *Lines of constant magnetic field strength H in the region of a straight conductor.*

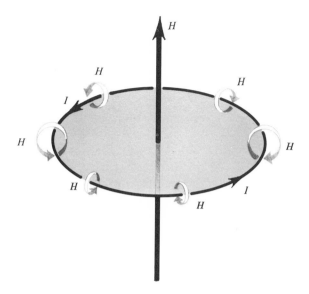

Figure 11-9 *Magnetic field lines through a current loop.*

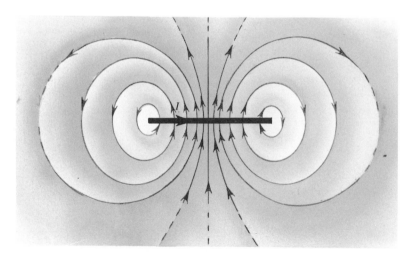

Figure 11-10 *A current loop, viewed side-on, showing the distribution of the magnetic field. The current direction shown is that in the near side of the loop.*

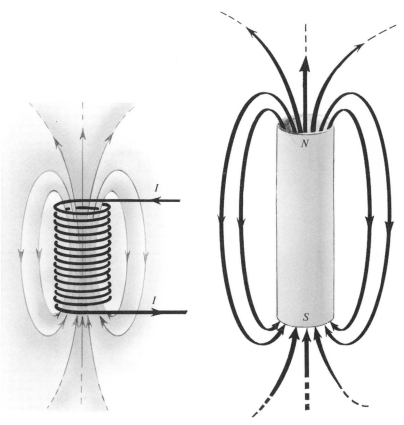

Figure 11-11 *Magnetic field distribution for a coil.*

Figure 11-12 *Magnetic field distribution for a bar magnet.*

muthal, and the directions of maximum change of A are radial, whereas the direction of the magnetic field H is axial.

11-3 *Motion and energies of charged particles in magnetic fields*

Again in direct analogy to the electric case, the force on a current-carrying element of conductor $I\,dl$ in a transverse magnetic field H is

$$F = HI\,dl$$

However, the direction of the force is seen from Fig. 11-13 to be perpendicular to both the field H and the current element $I\,dl$; the sense is that of the advancement of a right hand screw whose slot is rotated by the shortest possible arc from the direction of the current element to that of the magnetic field, as can also be seen from Fig. 11-13. A particle carrying a charge e and moving with a velocity v is equivalent to a current element, and hence is subject to the same force in a magnetic field:

$$F = Hev$$

In each case, if the magnetic field is not exactly transverse, then H is to be taken as the transverse component of the field.

EXAMPLE. *Cyclotron frequency.* A particle of charge e enters a transverse magnetic field of strength H. The particle has a momentum p. Find the radius of curvature r of its orbit in the field, and the angular velocity ω of its motion.

The force being a constant one and perpendicular to the motion, the trajectory must be a circle (Fig. 11-14) with the magnetic force supplying the necessary centripetal acceleration. If the velocity of the particle is v, then:

$$\frac{mv^2}{r} = Hev$$

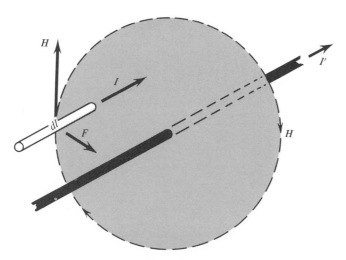

Figure 11-13   *The force F on a current element Idl in a transverse magnetic field H is perpendicular to both Idl and H.*

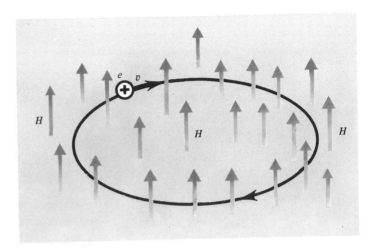

Figure 11-14 *Circular trajectory of a charged particle moving in a transverse magnetic field H.*

Figure 11-15 *Any motion of a charged particle in the direction of the magnetic field is unaffected by the field. Hence, in general, the trajectory will be a helix with the axis in the direction of the magnetic field H.*

Therefore:

$$r = \frac{mv}{He} = \frac{p}{He}$$

Note that because a magnetic field can only apply force normal to the motion of a charged particle, it can never change the magnitude of the particle's velocity. The angular velocity with which the particle describes the circle is

$$\omega = \frac{v}{r} = \frac{e}{m} H$$

Thus the frequency of rotation $\omega/2\pi$ is independent of the velocity or radius. This characteristic frequency determined by the magnetic field H and the ratio e/m is called the *cyclotron frequency*.

This is the only stable path for the motion of a charge e with a mass m moving with a velocity v in the plane x, y, perpendicular to the field H. Any velocity parallel to H is unaffected by H; hence, in general, the path in space is a helix with the axis in the direction of H as shown in Fig. 11-15. The angular velocity with which the circle is described is determined completely by the charge-to-mass ratio of the rotating particle and the value of the magnetic field in the neighborhood.

The three types of forces exerted upon an electric charge, due to other charges and their relative motions, may be written out explicitly in a form suitable for the solution of problems involving the motion of a free massive particle of charge e. The first is the electrostatic force per unit charge which has the components $-d\phi/dx$, $-d\phi/dy$, and $-d\phi/dz$, where ϕ is the sum $K\sum_i e_i/r_i$ for all other charges present at their various distances from e. The second is the force due to steady currents which is equal in magnitude to evH; in direction it is perpendicular to v, and in such a sense as to deflect a positive charge into a circular path in the opposite sense to that of A. The third force arises if the charges are being accelerated or the currents are changing with time, for it will be recalled from the discussion of induced currents that a force is then present, which is equal to $-dA/dt$. The sum of these three forces, in accordance with Newton's definition, equals the resulting rate at which the change in mechanical momentum of the mass carrying the charge occurs.

The motion of charged particles under the influence of a magnetic field, analogous to the presence of stationary charges in an electric field, gives rise to potential energy. The simplest configuration to treat is a rectangular current loop I in a plane perpendicular to the direction of a uniform magnetic field H, with the electrodynamic potential A parallel to the two sides of the loop (Fig. 11-16). If the potential has the value A_0 on one side of the loop of length l, then on the other side of the loop of breadth b the potential has the value $A_0 + (dA/dr)b$, where the spatial rate of change of A across the loop dA/dr is simply the magnetic field strength H. The potential energy of a current element $I\,dl$ in a region of antiparallel potential A is $AI\,dl$. Hence the potential energy of one side of the loop is A_0Il and the other side, carrying current in the opposite direction, has potential energy $-(A_0 + dA/dr\ b)Il$. The top and bottom of the loop contribute no potential energy, because they are perpendicular to the direction of A. Thus the total potential energy of the loop is:

$$U = A_0Il - \left[A_0 + \frac{dA}{dr}b\right]Il = -\frac{dA}{dr}bIl$$

$$= -HIa$$

where a is the area bl of the loop. Although deduced for a rectangular loop, the above relationship is of much wider application, since a current loop of any shape may be effectively replaced by an infinite number of infinitesimally small rectangular loops, each carrying the same current in the same sense of rotation and together making up the area of the single loop. This was demonstrated for circular current loops in Fig. 11-1. If the magnetic field H is not exactly perpendicular to the plane of the current loop, but is inclined to the perpendicular at an angle

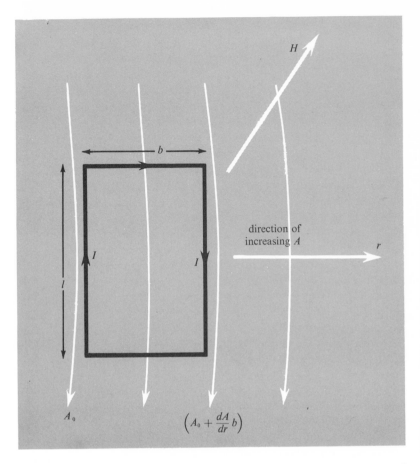

Figure 11-16   *A small rectangular test current loop with the equipotential lines A parallel to its two sides. For a uniform magnetic field, the equipotentials are equally spaced, since H = dA/dr is constant.*

θ, for instance, then the component of H perpendicular to the current loop is $H \cos \theta$ and the energy of the current loop is

$$U = -HIa \cos \theta$$

The torque tending to increase θ is then:

$$\mathbf{T} = -\frac{dU}{d\theta} = -HIa \sin \theta$$

i.e., there is a restoring torque $HIa \sin \theta$ tending to rotate the current loop into the plane perpendicular to H, with the current circulation in

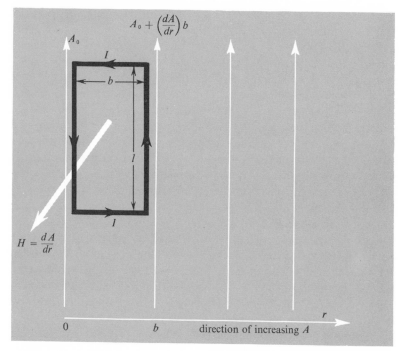

Figure 11-17 *Position of minimum potential energy of a current loop placed in a uniform magnetic field H. In the region of greatest magnetic potential A, the current I is in the same sense as A. A right-hand screw rotated in the sense of the current I would then advance in the direction of the magnetic field H.*

the rotational sense that would drive a right-hand screw in the direction of the magnetic field H (Fig. 11-17).

Spinning charges and magnetic moments   11-4

There remains only one other matter of general importance in the area of interaction of charged particles with one another: this relates to the conservation of angular momentum. If the charged particle is simply a structureless particle, there is no complication, and the complete description of it has already been given. Angular momentum is conserved, and if a charged particle is projected into a magnetic field and is deflected into a circular path, the angular momentum produced induces an equal and opposite angular momentum among the moving charges that give rise to the magnetic potential A, or the magnetic field H.

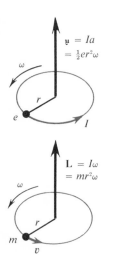

$$\mu = Ia$$
$$= \tfrac{1}{2}er^2\omega$$

$$L = I\omega$$
$$= mr^2\omega$$

Figure 11-18 *Magnetic moment* μ *and angular momentum* **L** *of a circulating or spinning charge.*

The case arises, however, in the properties of the elementary particles that constitute atomic systems, of the existence of an intrinsic angular momentum associated with a particle, just as if the particle were a small spinning top. Such particles and systems are observed to produce magnetic fields as already assumed in considering magnetic materials; since mass is associated with the charge, it is quite consistent to assume that an intrinsic angular momentum is associated with the rotating charged massive particle or system of particles. To picture the situation as a minute charged rotating sphere is being too particular, for it will later be seen that the properties observed do not always correspond exactly to this configuration. In addition to charge and mass, such atomic particles possess an intrinsic angular momentum, as would a spinning top, and also the property of a small circulating charge or current whirl called a *magnetic moment* (Fig. 11-18).

The magnetic moment μ of a small whirl of current or circulating charge is a vector defined in magnitude as the product of the current and the area enclosed by it, in the direction a right-handed screw would advance were it to rotate in the sense of the current. If this magnetic moment is placed in a magnetic field, it will tend to set itself in the direction associated with the magnetic field as mentioned earlier. Just as in the case of a spinning top of Sect. 4-3, however, if there is an intrinsic angular momentum *L* associated with the charge circulation, the vectors *L* and μ do not simply take up the direction of the magnetic field, but are found to precess or circulate about this direction maintaining a constant angular inclination to it. The torque that tends to set μ parallel to the vector *H* is equal to the product of the magnitudes μ and *H* times the sine of the angle between the vectors μ and *H* as was shown in the previous section.

If the vectors *L* and μ precess about *H* at such a rate that during the interval *dt* the vectors have moved through the angle *dθ* of Fig. 11-19, then the vector difference between two positions of the angular momentum vector *L* a time interval *dt* apart must be

$$dL = L \sin \phi \, d\theta$$
$$= L\omega' \sin \phi \, dt$$

or:
$$\frac{dL}{dt} = L\omega' \sin \phi$$

where ω' is the angular velocity of precession and ϕ is the angle between *L* or μ and *H*. Since this, by definition, is the torque which is $\mu H \sin \phi$, it is evident that

$$\omega' = \frac{\mu}{L} H$$

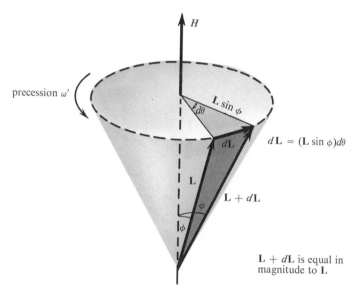

$$dL = (L \sin \phi)d\theta$$

$L + dL$ is equal in
magnitude to L

Figure 11-19 *Precession of* L *about H at the Larmor frequency* $\omega'/2\pi$.

Thus it is seen that the law of the conservation of angular momentum requires that a whirling or spinning charged mass forming what may be thought of as a rigid electric top shall precess or move about the axis of H in such a way that the angular momentum vector and the colinear magnetic moment vector shall rotate about the magnetic field vector H, remaining at a constant angular inclination to it.

The frequency of this precessional motion $\omega'/2\pi$ is called the *Larmor frequency*, named for Sir Joseph Larmor who pioneered in the theory of electrodynamics. From the earlier diagram (Fig. 11-18) the ratio of μ to L for a massive point charge is seen to be $e/2m$. Hence, in a specific case where the magnetic and mechanical moments may be thought of as arising from the circulation of a charged mass point in an orbit of area a, the angular velocity of precession is $eH/2m$. This is one-half the cyclotron frequency, which is the rate of description of a circular orbit by a charged particle in a magnetic field derived in Sect. 11-3. However, the precessional velocity ω', as given by the product of the field H and the ratio μ/L, is of much more general application than to the specific case just mentioned, and applies regardless of the particular distribution of charge and mass. The numerical value in the general cases may, of course, differ from $eH/2m$, but the nature of the precessional motion will still be the same. The experimental studies of the precessional frequencies exhibited by the elementary particles occurring in our universe has been one of the most fruitful avenues for the exploration of their natures, and for determining the angular momenta and magnetic moments associated with them.

11-5 *Summary of the concepts and laws of classical physics applicable to the atomic domain*

These first eleven chapters have been concerned with what is known as classical physics, which is the corpus of physical science which existed prior to the shift in the basic formulation of physical description to terms of the granular or atomic nature of matter. The concepts and laws that were evolved in the classical period necessarily form the groundwork for the specification of the atoms, their properties, and their components in terms of which our subsequent description will be presented.

The first requisite of physics was a system for specifying the positions of objects and the events in which they participate, in the most precise and convenient way, in terms of the variables of space and time. This requisite is conditioned by the symmetry requirement that all observers, whether stationary or moving relative to one another with constant velocities, shall agree upon the results of observations, and hence be satisfied with the same description of the physical phenomena observed. The fact that all observers agree that a particular velocity in our universe, namely the velocity of light, is the same introduces a relationship between spatial and temporal variables that places an upper limit on observable velocities.

The second concept was that of mass as a property of matter. With this idea in mind, it was possible to define the concepts of momentum and angular momentum and to relate them to our kinesthetic experience of force and torque through the definitions proposed by Newton, namely, that force is evidenced by and in suitable units equal to the rate at which momentum changes, and torque is equal to the rate at which angular momentum changes. The very useful concept of energy was also introduced, which is related to our immediate experience of work; and from this was derived the idea of power, which is defined as the rate at which work is done.

With these concepts well defined in terms of specific manipulations or procedures, experiment leads to the conclusion that there are three mechanical laws with which nature conforms, namely: the conservation of momentum; the conservation of angular momentum; and the conservation of energy.

In accordance with the general theory of gravitation, a property of mass was seen to be that it exerts a force of attraction on other masses in accordance with the universal law of gravitation. On the basis of this law and the associated computation of the gravitational potential energy between massive bodies of certain symmetrical or approximately symmetrical shapes, the motion of planets and satellites can be accounted for. Attempts to develop a more general theory of relativity upon the basis of the equivalence of gravitational fields and accelerations, and a representation of these in terms of the intrinsic properties of space, give promise of furnishing a more generalized description of the universe and of unifying the phenomena of mechanics and gravitation for observers moving arbitrarily in relation to one another.

The concept of electrification and electric charge was then introduced and reduced to quantitative terms by the experiments of Cavendish and Coulomb. The basic law of the conservation of charge assumed a comparable status with the mechanical conservation laws. The law of force between charges was seen to be of a closely analogous form to the law of gravitational attraction between masses. The velocity-dependent and acceleration-dependent electrical forces brought to light in quantitative form by the work of Ampere and Faraday have no parallel in the simple theory of the gravitational force between masses. But it was seen that, within the limitations of the restricted special theory of relativity electrostatic energy, $e\phi$ bears a close analogy to mechanical energy mc^2, and electromagnetic momentum eA bears a close analogy to mechanical momentum mv, in that these quantities transform in the same way for observers moving relative to one another with constant velocities.

Finally, it was seen that the magnetic properties of matter brought to light by observing the behavior of magnetic materials in the presence of Amperean currents bear a close relationship to an intrinsic angular momentum associated with matter. The ratio of the magnetic moment associated with an elemental material unit to the angular momentum, likewise associated with this unit, determines the characteristic frequency of precessional motion that is brought about in the presence of a magnetic field.

As a result of this survey of the phenomena of classical physics, quantitative procedural evidence capable of extension to observations of samples of matter from the very large to the excessively minute is educed. The parameters of mass and charge are evidenced through their involvement in the expressions for momentum and energy, and through the resulting motion of material objects in accordance with the conservation laws for these quantities. In a similar way the rotational motion of masses and charges is evidenced in terms of the dynamic quantities of angular momentum and magnetic moment, which react to mechanically or electromagnetically induced torques in accordance with the law of conservation of angular momentum. Masses and charges and the dynamic quantities of momentum, energy, angular momentum, and magnetic moment constitute the classical concepts that are most meaningfully extended to the description of atomic phenomena in subsequent chapters.

Further reading:

BITTER, FRANCIS, *Magnets, The Education of a Physicist*, Doubleday Anchor Books (1959).

BOZORTH, R. M., "Magnetic Materials," *Scientific American*, vol. 192, No. 1, p. 68 (1955).

PAKE, G. E., "Magnetic Resonance," *Scientific American*, vol. 199, No. 2, p. 58 (1958).

Problems

11-1   The coil suspension in a galvonometer type of measuring instrument is usually very delicate. Before moving the instrument, or subjecting it to any rough handling, the external leads to the coil should be connected together; i.e., the coil should be *short-circuited*. Why?

11-2   What would be the consequences of the laws of conservation of energy and angular momentum in the event that the system of a dynamo driving a motor were suddenly to be disturbed in each of the four possible ways: (i) the source of power rotating the dynamo ceases to supply energy to it, (ii) the electric circuit between them breaks open, (iii) the wires of this circuit come into electrical contact with one another, (iv) the load on the motor increases rapidly and stops the rotation?

11-3   Utilizing symmetry arguments, sketch the equipotential lines in the plane of a rectangular current loop.

11-4   (a) Sketch the distribution of the magnetic field for a bar magnet that has been bent into the form of a *U*.
(b) Do the same for a magnet in the form of a *C*, with the pole surfaces facing one another.

11-5   Sketch the equipotential lines in the plane of a long *U*-shaped current-carrying wire.

11-6 Can a magnetic field do any work on a charged particle? Why? Can it accelerate a charged particle? How?

11-7 Electrons that have a charge of 1.6×10^{-19} C. and a mass of 9×10^{-31} kg. are constrained by a magnetic field to circulate in a ring of radius 0.1 m. The field strength is 0.3 amp. m.$^{-1}$ (the amp. m.$^{-1}$ is the practical unit of field strength). What is the kinetic energy of the electrons?

11-8 A current of 3 amps. circulates through a circular coil of radius 0.1 m. and 7 turns. If the coil axis is parallel to the direction of an enclosing uniform magnetic field of strength 0.1 amp. m.$^{-1}$, what is the change in potential energy when the coil axis is rotated through π radians?

11-9 A small rectangular coil of n turns is free to turn about an axis through the centers of its two short sides of length d. Most of the coil's weight is concentrated in relatively massive side frames, each of mass m, attached to the long sides of length l. The coil carries a current I and is observed to oscillate with a period T for small displacements from equilibrium when the mounting axis is perpendicular to the direction of a surrounding magnetic field. What is the strength H of this magnetic field?

11-10 A Coulomb each of positive and negative charges are separated and held one above the other at some point on the equator. If the separation between the two charges is 2 m., what is the net magnetic moment produced as a result of the earth's rotation? Neglect any effect due to any flow of charges induced in neighboring bodies. If one of the charges could be removed to the north pole, what would the net magnetic moment be?

12 *The concept of atomicity and the determination of atomic masses*

12-1   *Evidence for the atomicity of matter*

Our concepts of continuity and atomicity first appeared in the course of the speculations of the Greek philosophers nearly 2,500 years ago. Continuity may be thought of as implying infinite divisibility, without ever encountering any change in nature, such as granularity. Atomicity represents the other possibility; namely, that at some stage in the refinement in the detail of our examination, an apparent smoothness gives place to a microscopic character or pattern of discrete entities such that any further divisibility that might be possible would drastically alter the nature of the substance under scrutiny. According to our present experimental evidence, time and space appear to have the property of continuity; whereas matter or mass does not appear to be indefinitely divisible. Leucippus, Democritus, and Epicurus, who were philosophers living during the first half-millenium before Christ, taught the atomic concept of matter though on the basis of inspired speculation rather than objective, scientific evidence.

Cogent arguments, based upon experimental procedures, for atomicity were not educed until about 200 years ago. Prior to that time the erroneous traditionalism of Aristotle and the classical philosophers, the narrowly technological interests of Arab alchemists such as Jabir ibn

Hayyan in the eighth century, and premature attempts at an alliance between chemistry and medicine by iatrochemists such as Paracelsus in the sixteenth century, all tended to misdirect natural inquiry; little of permanent value to an understanding of the structure of matter was contributed by these savants. It was a period in which undisciplined curiosity groped and floundered without the appropriate concepts in terms of which an adequate description of the results of observations could be couched. In the latter part of the eighteenth century, however, Joseph Black, a physician and Scottish professor of chemistry, and Henry Cavendish, the same eccentric recluse and genius whose electrical investigations anticipated those of Coulomb, took the first firm step toward the establishment of order in chemistry by the performance of quantitative experiments that demonstrated that the total mass of reacting substances remains unchanged. Very shortly thereafter, the great school of French chemistry led by Antoine Lavoisier clarified the nature of the chemical reactions of acids with metals and bases, and properly identified and distinguished between the common gaseous elements.

The most basic and direct large-scale observations supporting the conclusion of the atomicity of matter were those of these early chemists, establishing the definite proportions in which the chemical elements combine to yield homogeneous compounds. Thus hydrogen or carbon or iron will combine with oxygen, not in any arbitrary proportion, but only in a certain few invariable ratios in the several instances. The amount of the substance concerned is measured by its mass: for instance, the two gases oxygen and hydrogen commonly combine only in weights which bear the ratio of 8 to 1 respectively. If more of one gas or the other is present before the combining process is induced, as by an electric spark in the case of the formation of water from oxygen and hydrogen, the excess will remain uncombined at the conclusion. The resulting water in this instance can again be decomposed by passing an electric current through it; the constituent gases are recovered in the same proportions as they entered into the combination. It is very difficult to conceive of any mechanism, based upon the concept of continuity, that would not necessarily lack the possibility of unique fine-scale registration that could account for this general result.

Similarly, it is found that if carbon is burned in oxygen, either of two gases may be formed. In one the ratio of the weights of carbon and oxygen is 3 to 4; in the other, 3 to 8. If carbon is burned in hydrogen, its end-product gas shows a ratio of the weight of carbon to hydrogen of 3 to 1. The simplest description of any such constancy of simple ratios for the chemical combination of elements is in terms of a granular or atomic nature of materials in the light of which we can picture a 1 to 1, 1 to 2, 2 to 3, etc., matching of the fine-grained structure of the initial reacting substances to produce the final compounds which are themselves of a granular nature, the grains of which would, of course, be of differing complexities (Fig. 12-1). The finest subdivision of any

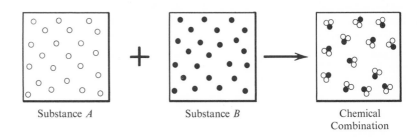

| Substance *A* | Substance *B* | Chemical Combination |

Figure 12-1 *Schematic illustration of the atomic implication of the law of definite proportions in a chemical combination.*

material is an aggregate of atoms called a *molecule*, representing within itself the same ratio of the masses of the constituents as does the macroscopic sample.

Upon the basis of such chemical evidence and the arbitrary assignment of a characteristic weight or mass to one element, chemists used the ratios to assign masses upon this arbitrary scale to all of the other 91 elements constituting the known stable chemical elements. Oxygen was initially chosen as the reference or standard element because of its readiness to combine with other elements, and hence the ease with which many direct comparisons can be made. More recently, for certain technical reasons, carbon has been officially designated as the standard element, and the arbitrary number 12, called its *atomic weight*, is assigned to it as being proportional to the mass of an atom of carbon. On this scale, the mass of an atom of oxygen is approximately 16, and that of an atom of the lightest known element—hydrogen—is approximately 1, or unity. Chemical measurements show that although the apparent atomic weight of an element is not in general integral, it is a characteristic parameter specifying the element which, to a large degree, is invariant in the course of chemical manipulations. This is not strictly true, for as will be seen later, the atoms of a single chemical species may occur with several quite separate and distinct characteristic masses. These different atomic weights for a single chemical element are called *isotopes*, and in certain chemical processes the rate of reaction is to some extent dependent on the mass; differential separation, for example, takes place with a resulting change in the average mass of the particular sample.

EXAMPLE. The law of simple ratios for the masses of the chemical elements that combine together to form homogeneous compounds leads to a simple concept of the bonding mechanism that holds atoms together in molecules. This will be discussed more fully in later chapters. One may think of a characteristic number of mechanisms of attachment or bonds possessed by each atomic type that, in a compound molecule, are shared pair-wise between atoms. The number of bonds an atom possesses is said to be its *valence*. Thus hydrogen is possessed of one bond and oxygen of two, so the water molecule would be depicted as follows:

$$H—O—H$$

In this two-dimensional charting of the associations of atoms in molecules, the direction in which the bond symbol (—) extends from the symbol for the atoms is not significant. The symbols can be disposed in any convenient way as long as the characteristic number of bonds terminate on each atom. Taking some of the more chemically abundant elements as examples, we find that the atom of hydrogen has 1 bond (H—), that of oxygen 2 bonds (O=), that of nitrogen 3 bonds (N≡), and that of carbon 4 bonds (C≡). Two-atom molecules would be written: H—H, O=O, N≡N, etc. As a convenient shorthand notation for writing the number of atoms in a molecule, subscripts are used. Thus the hydrogen and oxygen molecules are written H_2 and O_2 respectively, the water molecule is written H_2O, the ammonia molecule NH_3, etc.

In addition to this chemical evidence that led to the convincing arguments of John Dalton in 1803 for the atomicity of matter, there are a number of special phenomena that make the concept of atoms particularly apprehensible and compelling. One of these is the phenomenon of *Brownian motion*, which is the rapid, erratic, darting about of particles that may readily be seen by observing a suspension of fine particles in a fluid through a microscope, using very high magnification. The suspended particles move as if they were under the influence of the unequal buffeting of an ambient swarm of still smaller material particles in violent motion. Another instance is that of the fine spider webs of tracks that are left behind by high-energy particles after they have traversed a photographic emulsion or a region in which induced supersaturation causes a condensation of droplets upon the sensitive nuclei produced by such a disturbance. Again such particles, upon striking certain crystals of the type that possess the property of fluorescence, engender tiny local flashes of light, called scintillations. Such phenomena are the result of individual atomic events and provide striking evidence for the existence of sub-microscopic particles. Finally, the internal consistency of the description of all physical phenomena in terms of the atomic concept, which will form the subject matter of the succeeding chapters, provides the most complete and satisfying body of quantitative evidence for the atomic theory.

12-2 *Masses and dimensions of atoms*

The scientists who studied the properties of gases, from the time of Boyle in 1661 to that of Gay-Lussac in 1802, showed that the pressure exerted by a given quantity of a gas on the walls of its container is inversely proportional to the volume it occupies and directly proportional to the temperature on an appropriate scale. If the masses of the samples of the different elements in gaseous form are chosen to be equal to the molecular weights, the proportionality constant in the expression relating the measured pressure, volume, and temperature is the same for all gases. Thus the following simple expression for this relationship, known as the *perfect gas law*, provides an excellent approximate description of the properties of a gas:

$$P \sim \frac{T}{V} \qquad \text{or} \qquad VP = RT$$

The pressure is represented by P, the volume of a mass equal to the molecular weight by V, and the temperature on a suitably chosen scale by T. The numerical value of the constant R depends, of course, on the particular units chosen for the quantities appearing in the equation.

Thus since masses of gases in proportion to their molecular weights occupy equal volumes at the same pressure and temperature, it is evident that there must be the same number of molecules per unit volume for all gases under the same external conditions. This conclusion was reached by Avogadro in 1811, and is known as *Avogadro's law*. It is found from evidence of many types, including evidence gained from the study of chemical reactions, that in the gaseous form the atoms of most gases do not exist singly, but rather in combinations of two or three atoms closely associated together in a molecule. For instance, oxygen atoms have properties such that, in the gaseous form, two of these atoms are closely connected together in a molecule, and hence the actual elemental unit of oxygen gas, which determines its properties, is a pair of oxygen atoms. Since each of these has the atomic weight of 16, the molecular weight is 32. A mass of a gas which is equal in grams to its molecular weight is called a *mole*; a mass in kilograms equal to a molecular weight is called a *kilomole*. The number of molecules in a kilomole, or the number which all together weigh M kilograms, where M is the molecular weight, is said to be *Avogadro's number N*. Evidently if Avogadro's number is known, the mass of a molecule can be inferred: it is simply M/N. The mass of an atom can also be determined if it is known from chemical or other evidence how many atoms of the particular substance normally associate together to form a molecule.

Avogadro did not determine the numerical value of this universal constant N, but subsequent experiments have shown it to be 6.0225×10^{26} molecules per kilomole, with a precision of about one unit in the last decimal figure. The reciprocal of this quantity, which is 1.6604×10^{-27} kg. per unit atomic weight, is by definition $\frac{1}{12}$ of the mass of an atom of carbon. Thus, a carbon atom weighs 1.9925×10^{-26} kg. The precise comparisons of the combining masses of the chemical elements then give the ratios of the average masses of all elements relative to carbon, and the average mass of the atom of any element is immediately ascertainable. The mass of a hydrogen atom is about $\frac{1}{12}$ that of a carbon atom, namely, 1.66×10^{-27} kg.; that of an oxygen atom is $\frac{4}{3}$ the mass of a carbon atom, or 2.54×10^{-26} kg.; that of an average iron atom is 9.26×10^{-26} kg.; and that of the uranium atom, which is the heaviest permanent atomic constituent of our world, is 3.96×10^{-25} kg.

EXAMPLE. A thin-walled metal sphere having a volume of one cubic meter is suspended by a spring balance. When initially filled with air at the prevailing temperature and atmospheric pressure, it weighs 20.115 kg. When exacuated by an air pump, it is found to weigh exactly 20 kg. When filled successively with hydrogen, nitrogen, oxygen, and carbon dioxide at atmospheric pressure and with no change in temperature, the following weights are recorded:

Hydrogen	H_2	20.008 kg.
Nitrogen	N_2	20.112 kg.
Oxygen	O_2	20.128 kg.
Carbon dioxide	CO_2	20.176 kg.

The weight of the hydrogen is thus 8 g.; or, since hydrogen has two atoms in its molecule, this represents 4 moles of hydrogen. The volume of the sphere thus holds 4 moles of a gas at the prevailing temperature and pressure; hence the molecular weights of nitrogen, oxygen, and carbon dioxide are respectively $112/4 = 28$, $128/4 = 32$, and $176/4 = 44$. The atomic weight of nitrogen is then 14, of oxygen 16, and of carbon $(44 - 32) = 12$.

From the weight of the sphere when it is initially full of the atmospheric mixture of oxygen and nitrogen, it may be seen that air is composed of 25% oxygen and 75% nitrogen.

The mass of an atom or a combination of atoms forming a molecule is one of its most precise quantitative characteristics; its intrinsic angular momentum and magnetic moment, which will be considered in a later chapter, are equally well-defined. In addition, the molecule has certain more qualitative aspects; one of these is its size. The size of an atom or molecule is clearly less than the least dimension of any film or thread that can be produced of the substance; upper limits such as those deduced from soap films, less than one wave length of visible light in thickness, show atomic diameters to be less than 10^{-7} m., which is in reasonable accord with other simple observations. Another quality, symmetry, is related to the highly regular and characteristic shape of crystals formed by large aggregates of molecules. The remarkably precise reproduction of the angles between faces and edges for a particular material shows that the symmetry pattern of the association of the first few elementary atomic or molecular constituents reproduces itself in the large view, and determines to the last detail the symmetry and shape of the macroscopic crystal. The consistency of the experimental observations of the coherent scattering or diffraction of electromagnetic waves by the tiny spatial lattice structure represented by the regular pattern of placement of the contiguous atoms or molecules making up the crystal confirms the molecular structure of the crystal and sheds light upon the intermolecular forces holding the aggregate together.

12-3 *Quantitative determination of Avogadro's number and atomic masses*

The sequence of arguments involved in determining Avogadro's number by measuring the spacing of atoms in a crystal is an interesting one, which very directly brings out the basic procedures in the experimental program for measuring an atomic quantity in terms of fundamental macroscopic units.

(1) The first step is to measure accurately, in terms of the standard meter, the wave length of some convenient monochromatic light source. The spectra of gases, as will be discussed later, are composed of such monochromatic components representing very precisely determinable wave lengths. By selecting one of these as the source of illumination for an interferometer—such as that used by Michelson and Morley, except that it has one mirror that is movable—the number of cycles of change of illumination or the number of interference fringes passing across the field of view may be counted as the movable mirror is dis-

placed through a distance corresponding to the standard meter or some precisely determined fraction of it. Each illumination cycle corresponds to a mirror displacement of $\lambda/2$, and hence λ, the wave length of the monochromatic light, may be determined in terms of the standard meter.

(2) In principle this visible light could be used in the next stage to determine the atomic spacing, again by interference effects, but in practice its wave length is too long to be suitable, so that an intermediate experiment must be performed. In 1896 William Konrad Roentgen of Wurzburg, in studying the effects of the discharge of electricity through glass tubes from which the air had been partially evacuated, discovered that from the positive electrode emanated a form of radiation which induced fluorescence in certain minerals, and which was capable of passing through considerable thickness of materials opaque to ordinary light. This work had been stimulated by earlier experiments of A. Masson and J. P. Gassiot in Paris; Heinrich Geissler, a glass blower and apparatus maker of Tuebingen; and William Crookes, an English physicist who found that an electric current passed more readily through a partially evacuated tube than through air at atmospheric pressure, and that such passage was accompanied by a number of very colorful and intriguing phenomena such as glowing and pulsating regions within the tube and the fluorescence of its walls.

Roentgen correctly interpreted his experiments as indicating the generation of electromagnetic waves with too short a wave length to affect the retina of the eye. They were called *x-rays*, and were detectable by the fact that they rendered the air through which they passed a conductor of electricity and by their ability to affect a photographic plate. The most direct evidence of the wave nature of this radiation came from experiments by Max von Laue and his students at the University of Munich in 1912. They found that when a narrow beam of this emanation or radiation from the positive electrode of a discharge tube passed through a crystal, a pattern of intensity maxima, characteristic of interference effects, could be deduced from the dark spots which developed on the photographic plate behind the crystal. This phenomenon was confirmed and a variety of more elaborate experiments were performed by W. H. and W. L. Bragg in England. As a result, it became clear that the wave length of this radiation was comparable with the spacing of atoms in a crystal lattice, and that it provided a natural tool for the investigation of crystals by the characteristic interference effects of wave motion.

The method of comparing the wave length of visible light and X-rays is by means of a *diffraction grating*, which was described in Chap. 6. It was there shown that, for light incident on a grating at an angle α to the surface and emergent at angle α', the condition for an interference maximum is $n\lambda = d(\cos\alpha - \cos\alpha')$, where d is the grating spacing, λ is the wavelength of the light, and n is an integer. This is illustrated in Fig. 12-2.

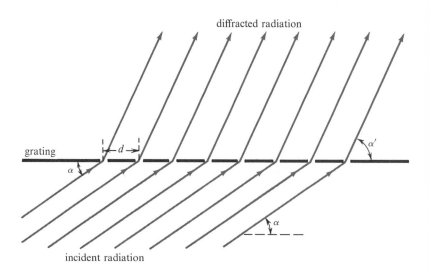

Figure 12-2   *Diffraction by a grating. α is the angle of incidence, and α' the angle of emergence of light waves. d is the spacing of the grating.*

Wave lengths of very different magnitude can evidently be compared by means of a grating, and careful angular measurements permit the quantitative determination of the wave length of a characteristic mono-chromatic x-ray beam in terms of the wave length of the visible light with a high degree of precision. Using the preceding technique, (1), to determine the wave length of a monochromatic beam of visible light, it is thus possible to determine the wave length of a suitably selected x-ray beam by this comparison process. The x-ray wave length range, being about a thousand times shorter than the visible range, presents values of λ that are smaller than the separation of atoms in a crystal, and hence diffraction patterns are evidenced when x-rays traverse the regular lattice structure of a crystal.

(3) The final step in the determination of Avogadro's number is then taken in the quantitative measurement of the pattern of interference of the x-ray waves scattered from the atomic crystal lattice as observed in the experiments of von Laue and Bragg. For simplicity, one may assume that the crystal used is one of cubic symmetry, where the axes

along which the atoms of the crystal lie are at right angles to one another, as are the Cartesian coordinate axes; the atoms are equally spaced along these axes. This is the case, for example, in a crystal of sodium chloride (common salt). The fact that this crystal is cubic and that the atoms of sodium and chlorine composing it alternate through the crystal is again a deduction from the nature of the interference pattern of the x-rays. The nature of the patterns gives the symmetry and the intensities of the maxima permit the deduction of the regular alternation.

The one-dimensional analysis of the grating interference pattern may be immediately extended to yield the pattern that should be expected from the three-dimensional grating or lattice which the crystal represents. If the direction of the incoming radiation makes the angles α, β, and γ with the three axes, and the direction in which the emergent radiation is observed makes the angles α', β', and γ' with these axes, the conditions for constructive interference producing the maximum intensity is given by the grating discussion extended to each of the three axes (Fig. 12-3):

$$n_1\lambda = d(\cos\alpha - \cos\alpha')$$

$$n_2\lambda = d(\cos\beta - \cos\beta')$$

$$n_3\lambda = d(\cos\gamma - \cos\gamma')$$

If these three equations are each divided by d, squared and added together, the following equation is obtained:

$$(n_1{}^2 + n_2{}^2 + n_3{}^2)(\lambda/d)^2$$
$$= (\cos\alpha - \cos\alpha')^2 + (\cos\beta - \cos\beta')^2 + (\cos\gamma - \cos\gamma')^2$$

$(\cos\alpha - \cos\alpha')^2$ is the square of the difference between x-components of unit vectors in the directions of the incident and emergent beams. And $(\cos\beta - \cos\beta')^2$ is the square of the y-component, and $(\cos\gamma - \cos\gamma')^2$ is the square of the z-component of the difference between the unit vectors in these directions. Thus the sum of these expressions is the square of the magnitude of the difference between unit vectors in the directions of the incident and emergent beams. From the simple geometry of the isosceles triangle, with the apex angle θ between unit vectors in the directions of these beams, the square of the length of the base is: $(2\sin\theta/2)^2$. Hence:

$$n\lambda = 2d\sin(\theta/2)$$

where

$$n = (n_1{}^2 + n_2{}^2 + n_3{}^2)^{1/2}$$

This equation relates d and λ through a measurement of θ and an identification of the various interference maxima with the possible values of n, made up of n_1, n_2, and n_3, each taking such integral values as 0, 1, 2, etc.; namely, $n = 1$, $\sqrt{2}$, $\sqrt{3}$, 2, etc. Hence if the atomic separation length d is determined by such an experiment, the relative atomic weights of the constituents and the mass of the crystal will determine the number of atoms in a mass equal to the molecular weight. The atom at each corner of the cube shown in Fig. 12-3 is shared by the eight cubes that meet at that corner. There being four sodium atoms and four chlorine atoms to every cube of volume d^3, the mass associated with such a volume is hence: $(M_{Na} + M_{Cl})/2$ where M_{Na} is the mass of a sodium atom and M_{Cl} that of a chlorine atom. Thus the mass of the crystal is given by:

$$M_{crystal} = \frac{V}{d^3} \frac{(M_{Na} + M_{Cl})}{2}$$

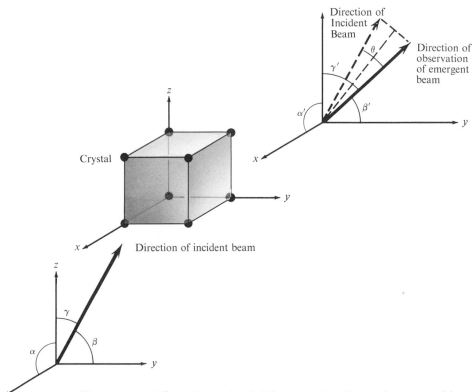

Figure 12-3 *Three-dimensional diffraction of radiation by a crystal lattice. The constructions at lower left and upper right show the angles that the incident and emergent beams make with the three axes of the crystal lattice and with each other.*

where V is the volume of the crystal. Since by definition Avogadro's number N is the number of molecules (NaCl) in a mass in kilograms equal to the molecular weight $\mathbf{M}$ then

$$N(M_{\mathrm{Na}} + M_{\mathrm{Cl}}) = \mathbf{M}_{(\mathrm{NaCl})}$$

and

$$N = \frac{\mathbf{M}_{(\mathrm{NaCl})}}{2M_{\mathrm{crystal}}} \frac{V}{d^3}$$

where M_{crystal} is the mass of the crystal in kilograms, and d and V are in any consistent units.

The order of magnitude of d is 10^{-10} m.; for the sodium chloride crystal in particular, it is found to be 2.814×10^{-10} cm. The molecular weight $\mathbf{M}_{(\mathrm{NaCl})}$ is 58.45, and the density, or mass of a cubic crystal of unit dimensions on each side, is 2.185×10^3 kg. m.$^{-3}$. Hence

$$N = \frac{58.45}{2 \times 2.185 \times 10^3} \frac{1}{(2.814 \times 10^{-10})^3}$$

$$= 6.022 \times 10^{26} \text{ atoms/kilogram atom, or molecules/kilomole}$$

This is Avogadro's number, or the number of atoms in 12 kg. of carbon, and approximately the number of atoms in 2 kg. of hydrogen, or 32 kg. of oxygen.

Problems

12-1 Chlorine and sodium each have a valence of 1. Magnesium has a valence of 2. What are the expected chemical formulae for sodium chloride and magnesium chloride?

12-2 If the smoke particles from a pipe are heavier than those from a cigarette, what difference would you expect in their Brownian motion, and why?

12-3 A container holds 0.0024 kg. of oxygen at atmospheric pressure and 20°C. When this gas is pumped out and replaced with nitrogen, also at atmospheric pressure and 20°C, what is the mass of nitrogen?

12-4 Two elements X and Y have atomic weights 16 and 32 respectively. A chemist measures the molecular weights of several compounds which he believes contain only these two elements. He finds these molecular weights to be: 48, 53, 64, 80, 96, 112, 150, and 176. He concludes that some of the molecules must contain other elements. Which molecular weights must belong to such *impure* molecules, and why?

12-5 The atomic weight of carbon is 12. The density of carbon is 1500 kg.m.$^{-3}$. How many atoms of carbon are there in 1 kilomole? How much volume does each occupy? What is the approximate diameter of a carbon atom?

12-6 An unknown element X forms five distinct molecular compounds with hydrogen. These are found to have molecular weights of 27.5, 53, 62.75, 74.5, and 121.5. The formation of 1 kilomole of each of these compounds requires respectively 3, 5, $4\frac{1}{2}$, 5, and 7 kilomoles of hydrogen. Remembering that hydrogen is diatomic, estimate the mass of element X in a kilomole of each compound, and hence make a reasonable prediction of the atomic weight of X. If possible, identify the element.

12-7 What is the mass in kilograms of an atom of neon (atomic weight 20)?

12-8 Nitrogen is diatomic and has an atomic weight of 14. How many molecules are there in 8.4 kg. of nitrogen?

12-9 The radius of the earth is about 6.4×10^6 m., and the average density of its material is 5.5×10^3 kg.m.$^{-3}$. Assuming the average molecular weight of its constituents to be about 50, calculate the approximate number of molecules that make up the earth. What is the approximate spacing between them?

12-10 Given the following data:
The oxygen molecule is diatomic.
The atomic weight of oxygen is 16.
The atomic weight of hydrogen is 1.
The mass of a hydrogen atom is 1.66×10^{-27} kg., or $\frac{1}{6} \times 10^{-26}$ kg.
The volume of one kilomole of oxygen is 16.2 m.^{3}, under the conditions of this experiment.

Using only the above data, find:
(a) The density of oxygen.
(b) Avogadro's number.
(c) The mass of an oxygen atom.
(d) The approximate distance between neighboring oxygen molecules.

The electrical properties of atoms and their constituents

13

Early experiments in the conduction of electricity through gases

The early experiments performed by Gassiot, Hertz, and Crookes on the discharge of electricity through rarified gases not only led Roentgen to the experimental discovery of X-rays, but they also stimulated many later investigators to undertake experiments of this type both for the purposes of studying the electrical properties of the atoms composing the gas and for perfecting the discharges themselves for practical uses such as illumination.

One of the most fruitful series of basic investigations was that carried on at Cambridge University under the direction of Joseph John Thomson. In order to bring about the state in which electricity would be conducted through a gas, potential differences typically of several thousand volts had to be maintained between two metallic electrodes in a glass tube from which most of the air had been removed by a pump. The highly varied and interesting phenomena accompanying the flow of electric current through the gas were systematically observed by the pioneers in this field (Fig. 13-1). The motion of small paddle wheels and suspended bodies indicated that in addition to the excitation of the

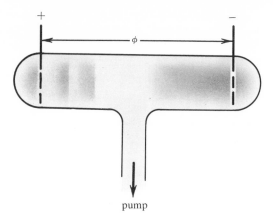

Figure 13-1 *Typical high-voltage gas discharge apparatus.*

gas to emit visible light, there was a flow of material particles within the discharge region. If holes were made in the electrodes, particles streamed through them; from the directions in which their paths were diverted under the influence of an electric or a magnetic field, it was shown that negatively charged particles streamed out through the hole in the positive electrode and positively charged particles through the hole in the negative electrode.

13-2 *Measurement of atomic charge-to-mass ratios*

In a series of experiments initiated by J. J. Thomson in 1907 and continued under his direction by F. W. Aston, the stream of particles emerging from a hole in the negative electrode was allowed to pass between two metal plates connected to a small battery of electric cells of considerably lower voltage than that maintaining the discharge. The electric field between the plates deflected the beam of particles showing that they were electrically charged, and the sense of deflection determined the sign of the charge. The designation *ion*, from the Greek word meaning to go or to migrate, was given to the charged particles carrying the current between the electrodes and observed to be streaming out behind them. If the potential difference across the battery of cells connected to the plates is ϕ, then the uniform electric field between them E, which is the force experienced by a unit charge, is equal to

ϕ/d, where d is the plate separation. This is readily seen, since the work done in moving a unit charge from one plate to the other against the force E over the distance d is, by definition, ϕ. The deflecting force on an ion of charge e is eE. Thus an ion moving parallel to the plates with a velocity v_x spends a time l/v_x in the region between the plates, if l is the length of the plates; during this time it is subject to a constant acceleration eE/m normal to its original path, where m is the mass of the ion. The velocity produced in the transverse or y direction is then the product of this constant acceleration and the duration of its application, i.e.,

$$v_y = \frac{eE}{m}\frac{l}{v_x} = \frac{e}{m}\frac{lE}{v_x}$$

If v_y is much smaller than v_x, then, to a good approximation, the ion emerges at an angle v_y/v_x to its initial path. By the above equation this ratio is equal to $(e/m)(lE/v_x^2)$. Thus if v_x is known, e/m—the ratio of the charge of the particle to its mass—can be determined in terms of the other known quantities (Fig. 13-2).

Unfortunately, v_x is found to have a range of values, since the ions originate throughout the entire region between the electrodes maintaining the discharge; hence another simultaneous measurement must be made if the necessity of a knowledge of v_x is to be obviated. In order to make this other measurement, a magnet was arranged so that its field H was parallel to the electric field E. As we have seen, this tends to deflect the ions out of the plane of the diagram illustrating the electric deflection, and along an arc of a circular path of radius r, where $r = (m/e)(v_x/H)$ (Fig. 13-3). Again, if the magnetic field H and the other

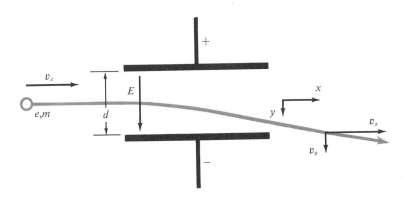

Figure 13-2 *Deflection of an ion in passing through an electric field at right angles to its path.*

quantities are such that the angular deflection is small, the angular deflection in the direction of the third or z axis is approximately l/r, or $(e/m)(lH/v_x)$.

Thus, in consequence of the two fields E and H traversed by the ions along the x axis, the ions suffer an angular deflection $(e/m)(lE/v_x^2)$ along y, and an angular deflection $(e/m)(lH/v_x)$ along z. If a fluorescent or photographic plate is placed normal to the x axis at a distance S from the deflecting region, the y and z components of the intersection of the paths of the deflected ions with this plate are:

$$y = S \frac{e}{m} \frac{lE}{v_x^2} \quad \text{and} \quad z = S \frac{e}{m} \frac{lH}{v_x}$$

and hence:

$$z^2 = S^2 \left(\frac{e}{m}\right)^2 \frac{l^2 H^2}{v_x^2} = \left(Sl \frac{e}{m} \frac{H^2}{E}\right) y$$

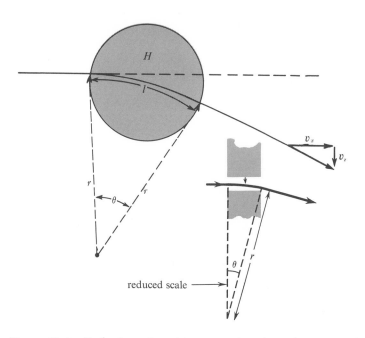

Figure 13-3 *Deflection of an ion on passing through a magnetic field at right angles to its path.*

The locus of the points of intersection of the ion paths with the plate is thus a parabola, for which the coefficient of the linear coordinate y (called the semi-latus rectum) is

$$S \frac{le}{m} \frac{H^2}{E}$$

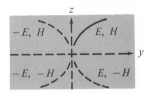

Figure 13-4 *An ion beam deflected by parallel electric and magnetic fields strikes a plate, which is perpendicular to the beam at some distance from the deflecting fields. The observed beam trace is part of a parabola that lies in a quadrant determined by the direction of each of the two fields.*

Reversing E and H separately provides the four complete branches of the two parabolas; they do not actually reach into the origin, for these coordinate values would correspond to a very great value of v_x (Fig. 13-4).

As all the quantities are known in the coefficient of y in the equation except e/m, this quantity can be determined by a measurement of the traces on the plate. When hydrogen is the residual gas in the discharge, two parabolas are seen: one of twice the displacement of the other. This is consistent with the interpretation of the presence of atomic and molecular hydrogen ions, for normal hydrogen gas is diatomic; i.e., each molecule consists of two closely associated atoms (Fig. 13-5). The two atoms composing a molecule can be separated by the forces in the discharge, so that some of the ions emerge as single atoms and others as molecules consisting of two atoms. The charge observed to be carried by the ions is positive, and the e/m ratio for the atomic beam is found to be about 0.9×10^8 C. per kg. When oxygen is the residual gas, again two principal parabolas are seen, with an e/m ratio of about $\frac{1}{16}$ that for the hydrogen parabolas, as would be expected from the atomic and molecular weights. In addition to these two, there are parabolas having e/m ratios of 16/17 and 16/18 relative to the original, which are much weaker than the strong atomic parabola indicating either a different charge or a different mass. Finally, there is often a weak parabola having an e/m ratio of twice that of the strongest parabola, corresponding to $\frac{1}{8}$ that of hydrogen, hence representing either twice the charge or half the mass of the main parabola.

A consistent explanation of these additional parabolas representing the positively charged particles or positive ions that populate a discharge emerges as a result of the many experiments of this type that can be performed under a variety of circumstances and employing different gases in the discharge tube. If the different values of the ratio e/m that occur for different gases are compared, it is found that the largest value occurs for one of the parabolas of hydrogen which has an e/m value of 0.96×10^8 C. per kg. The second hydrogen parabola has an e/m value of half the above figure, and, as has been noted above, can be ascribed to diatomic molecular ions that have twice the mass but the same charge as a single hydrogen ion. Because these are the only two strong hydrogen

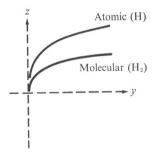

Figure 13-5 *Parabolas observed for a diatomic gas such as hydrogen.*

parabolas observed, it would seem that hydrogen never has more than a single charge of some unit amount, which is indicative that this is all of the negative charge that the neutral hydrogen atom can lose. The two strong oxygen parabolas, which have e/m values about $\frac{1}{16}$ those for the hydrogen parabolas, must then correspond to singly charged atoms and diatomic molecules of oxygen. The weak parabola sometimes observed for oxygen could represent a doubly charged oxygen atom. Thus the masses observed with the heavier gases may have single, double, or triple charges, etc., and are characteristic of the gas in the discharge. They represent the atoms as well as their combinations in diatomic molecules or still larger combinations, except for the so-called rare or noble gases, Helium, Neon, Argon, Krypton, and Xenon, which are always monatomic. The neighboring fainter parabolas that are separated from one another by only a few mass units, this unit being approximately equal to the mass of the hydrogen atom, indicate that the atoms of a chemical species are not all of the same mass. Such atoms of a single kind, as far as chemical properties are concerned, but with masses differing from one another by this mass unit are the isotopes of the element which were mentioned in Sect. 12-1. The masses of the isotopes, together with the abundance of each, lead to an average atomic weight or mass. The average atomic mass of a substance would be given by: $(M_1 f_1 + M_2 f_2 + \cdots)$, where the f's are the fraction of atoms of the substance having the corresponding mass.

The magnitude of the unit charge e possessed by a hydrogen atomic ion is readily deduced from the measured e/m value of 0.96×10^8 C. per kg., if m is taken to be the mass 1.66×10^{-27} kg. of the normal neutral hydrogen atom. These two values yield a value for e of 1.60×10^{-19} C.

The conclusions regarding the average value of e/m for ions are supported by other and quite different lines of investigation. In 1834, the great pioneer in electrical investigation, Michael Faraday, studied the phenomena accompanying the conduction of electricity through aqueous solutions of salts, and concluded that the mass of a dissolved substance plated out of the solution on an electrode as a result of the passage of a given quantity of electric charge through the solution is: (1) proportional to the charge that has passed; (2) proportional to the atomic weight of the substance; and (3) inversely proportional to the valence of the substance. The valence is equal to the number of atoms of hydrogen that would normally combine chemically with an atom of the substance. This is all seen to be consistent with the description of the electrical deposition of the components of a dissolved substance in terms of which each ion, in passing through the solution to reach an electrode, carries with it one, two, or three, etc., units of charge; the unit is constant for all elements, and the number of units depends upon the chemical properties as indicated by the valence. Quantitatively Faraday's observations agree quite well with the numerical values deduced by Thomson and Aston, for Faraday found that the passage of about 96,500 C. of electricity would deposit a mole of a univalent substance. Hence, if this charge is divided by the number of atoms in a mole, the universal indivisible unit of charge should be obtained. And indeed, 9.65×10^4 C. per mole divided by 6.02×10^{23} atoms per mole yields 1.60×10^{-19} C. per atom, which value agrees very well with the gas discharge conclusions.

The electron, its charge and its   13-3
charge-to-mass ratio

If the beam emerging through the hole in the positive electrode is analyzed in a way similar to that used for the beam associated with the negative electrode, it is found that there are some weak parabolas corresponding to negatively charged ions of the same species as found behind the negative electrode, but the main component is a single strong parabola with an e/m ratio of 1.76×10^{11} C. per kg. This is about 1800 times the value for the lightest positive ion, namely, that of hydrogen. Assuming the same unit charge, this would correspond to a particle 1800 times lighter than a hydrogen atom. This particle appears to be a common constituent of all atoms, for it is observed with the same e/m value for any gas used in the discharge; the heavier negative ions find a ready explanation if we regard them as resulting from the attachment of one of these light negative charges to a neutral gas atom. The universal negative charge component, much lighter than the rest of the atomic system of any chemical species, was given the name *electron* by Johnstone Stoney, who inferred its existence from experiments on electrolysis some 25 years before Thomson, in 1897, first isolated it and measured some of its properties by the technique just described.

A confirmatory experiment supporting the concept of atomicity and determining the magnitude of the naturally-occurring unit of charge was performed by Robert A. Millikan in 1909. He observed the motion of a small droplet of oil that could be balanced in the air between two horizontal plates a centimeter or so apart. The balance was produced by the downward force of gravity and the upward force exerted by an electric field between the plates upon the residual electrostatic charge given to the drop by frictional contact with the nozzle of the atomizer

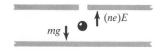

Figure 13-6 *Balanced electric and gravitational forces on a charged droplet.*

that formed it. Such a drop is observed to behave as if it gains and loses electric charge to the surrounding air in which a few free ions exist. Furthermore, it is found that these gains and losses do not take place continuously, but rather discontinuously in discrete units; in consequence the drop rises or falls under the influence of the electric field at a series of discrete rates as the charge varies. The equation for the balance of the electric and gravitational forces is: $(ne)E = mg$, where (ne) is the charge on the drop. To determine the mass m, the electric field may be removed and the drop permitted to fall under the influence of the force of gravity and the retarding viscous force of the air. The viscous force may be calculated with some accuracy in terms of the theory of the viscous drag on a sphere moving through a gas at the observed velocity. Equating this to the gravitational force when the velocity of fall is steady, one may effectively determine the unknown mass m of the drop. The experiment, indicated schematically in Fig. 13-6, not only confirms the discreteness of the charge changes, but also determines the quantitative value of the unit charge e. The numerical value found by this method agrees well with the one quoted earlier as having been derived from the other and quite different lines of investigation.

The conclusion that the electron is a universal constituent of all the atoms composing matter and is, in fact, the first to be discovered of the truly elementary particles out of which our universe is constructed is borne out by many other types of experimental results. The electron is recognized by the only two attributes which have so far been discussed, namely, its charge and its mass, or its charge and e/m ratio. It is found, for instance, that when a substance becomes very hot it not only emits light but, if an electric field is applied to it in the proper sense, an electric current will flow from it across an evacuated region. The proper sense is that in which the heated electrode is the negative in agreement with the identification of the liberated charge with the negatively charged electron of gas discharges, and, indeed, if the current drawn from the heated electrode through the evacuated region is confined to a narrow beam by a series of holes or slits and the beam is deflected by electric and magnetic fields, the characteristic value of e/m is found to account for the deflection observed (Fig. 13-7). Furthermore, the value of the velocity attained by the electrons, as determined, for instance, by the deflection type of experiments described earlier in this chapter, is found to be consistent with the law of conservation of energy applied to the conditions of this experiment; i.e., if ϕ is the potential difference between the heated electrode and the apparatus of slits, and stops defining the beam being deflected, it is found that the product $e\phi$ is equal to the quantity $\frac{1}{2}mv^2$, where e and m are the values of the electron's charge and mass respectively, and v is the velocity attained by the electron.

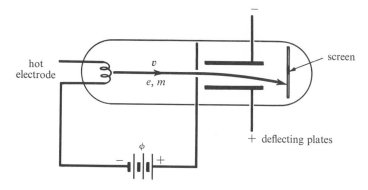

Figure 13-7 *Schematic depiction of the determination of the velocity and the ratio e/m for the electrons liberated from a heated electrode.*

Thus the electron behaves in the electric field just as a mass behaves in a gravitational field and gains the kinetic energy $\frac{1}{2}mv^2$ as a result of experiencing the potential energy decrease $e\phi$ in traversing the evacuated region forming the beam. Electrons can be liberated from the metal surface by strong illumination as well as by heating, and again prove to be the same particles as judged by their charge-to-mass ratio.

EXAMPLE. It was seen in Chap. 11 that the electromagnetic forces provide the centripetal acceleration for a particle of charge e and mass m pursuing a circular path with an angular velocity ω in a plane normal to a magnetic field H. The relationship between these quantities for this stable mode of motion is:

$$\omega = \frac{e}{m} H$$

This observation provides the basis for the measurement of e/m when ω and H are known. It is much easier to determine ω with a high accuracy than it is H, so that the comparison measurements of e/m for different atoms or molecules in the same magnetic field can be carried out very precisely by comparing their characteristic angular frequencies of rotation.

The schematic diagram shown in Fig. 13-8 indicates a region normal to a magnetic field H contained between two plates between which a sinusoidal electric field can be applied. If the region contains a gas at a low pressure in which ions are produced along a line parallel to H, lying centrally between the plates, the ions are subjected to the periodic force $eE_0 \sin \omega't$; if $\omega' = \omega$, the force will induce the ions to follow a

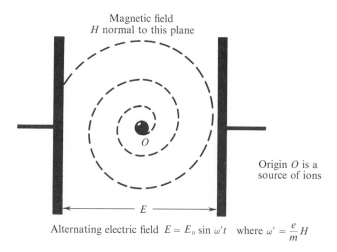

Figure 13-8 *Path of ions spiralling out from a source as a result of gaining energy synchronously from an alternating electric field in the presence of a magnetic field.*

spiral or expanding circular path, much as a pendulum's amplitude will increase when it is given small impulses in synchronism with its natural period. The ions gain energy by this process just as the pendulum would and, as $\frac{1}{2}mv^2 = \frac{1}{2}mr^2\omega^2$ increases for constant ω, the radius of the circular path r increases until the ions reach the plates or an electrode near them. Thus if ω' is varied until ions are recorded at large radii, this value of ω is proportional to the value of e/m for the ions present.

If light and heavy hydrogen (**D**) are present in both atomic and molecular forms, it is evident from the values of the atomic weights given in Table 23-1, that the frequencies at which ions are detected at the periphery are in the following ratios:

$$\frac{\omega_{H_2}}{\omega_H} = 2, \quad \frac{\omega_D}{\omega_H} = 2.01104, \quad \frac{\omega_{HD}}{\omega_H} = 3.01104, \quad \frac{\omega_{D_2}}{\omega_H} = 4.02208$$

13-4 *Electronic structure of atoms*

The continuing investigation of the phenomena presented by the discharge of electricity in gases has contributed very greatly to our knowledge both of the properties of electrons and the balance of the atomic systems of which they form a part. It provides as well highly precise measurements both of the quantitative presence of the isotopes of each element and of the numerical values of the masses of these isotopes. It has also led to particularly direct evidence concerning the energetics of the electronic structure of atoms.

In 1914, J. Franck and G. Hertz conducted an experiment in which the electrons from a glowing filament were accelerated by a potential ϕ applied to an open mesh grid surrounding the filament and then permitted to move at an approximately constant velocity under the influence of a small accelerating field provided by ϕ_1 of the figure (Fig. 13-9), through the low pressure gas occupying the tube, and finally to pass through another mesh grid, after which they were retarded to the velocity corresponding to the small potential ϕ_2 before they were measured as electric current reaching the surrounding plate. Frank and Hertz found that not all of the collisions between the electrons and the gas atoms were perfectly elastic, but that the electrons could lose energy to the intervening gas atoms or molecules. If this loss exceeded the energy $e\phi_2$, the electrons would not have enough energy at the end of their path to actually reach the plate; this was evidenced by a decrease in the current to it. The particularly interesting feature was that on studying the current to the plate as ϕ was increased, the energy losses were found not to occur until ϕ reached a critical value of a few volts. Below that value the collisions appeared to be elastic and no energy was lost by the electrons in passing through the gas. Above this critical value were other critical values of ϕ, characteristic of the gas in the tube, which were also identified as characteristic energy losses that occurred readily at electron-atom collisions. Between these energies the electrons appeared to

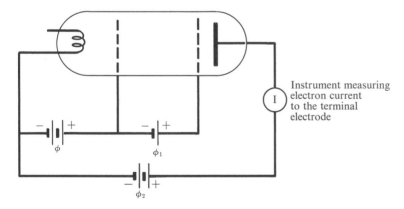

Figure 13-9 *Schematic illustration of the experiment measuring the critical potentials for electron energy loss in passing through a gas.*

sustain collisions relatively elastically with little or no loss of energy. These critical energy values found by Frank and Hertz were later identified with the energetic properties of the atomic systems composing the gas, through further studies of the light that such atoms are found to emit.

Experiments of this type—continued with many ingenious extensions and refinements by Professor J. T. Tate and his students at the University of Minnesota, and by Hagstrum, Coggeshall, and others at the Bell Telephone Laboratories—have added greatly to our understanding of atomic processes. It is found that not only are energy transfers likely between electrons and atoms only at certain critical electron energies, but that at somewhat higher critical energies additional electrons are apparently knocked from neutral atoms as a result of primary electron collisions. Positive ions as well as additional electrons appear, for instance, in mercury vapor when the impinging electrons have fallen through a potential difference of about 10 V. of energy, in neon at 21 V., in helium at 24 V., etc. At still higher energies, two electrons appear at collisions, at higher ones three, etc., except that atomic hydrogen never produces more than 1, helium never more than 2, etc. All the evidence indicates that these are the total numbers of electrons present in those atoms. The detailed studies of such collision processes between electrons and atoms and molecules have contributed greatly to our understanding of the energy structure of atomic and molecular systems, and have supplemented in an important way the more precise information that has come from an analysis of the radiation emitted from atoms, which will be considered later.

The masses of atoms and of their constituent or component parts are such very important quantities, both from the practical and theoretical points of view, that there have been very extensive programs of instrumental development based upon the techniques that have been here presented for the purposes of measuring isotopic abundances of all the chemical species and for obtaining precise values of the atomic masses associated with them. As a result of this program, there is now a very complete tabulation of all the different atomic masses associated with each chemical species of element, and the masses of many of these are known very precisely. This evidence, and that from the study of the radiation from atoms, clearly presents the relatively simple picture of an atom as consisting, first of all, of a massive portion, called the *nucleus*, which exhibits a well-defined mass and an integral number of positive electric charges in units of the electron charge. The number of units of charge, called the *atomic number*, determines the number of electrons associated with that particular nucleus to form the normal neutral atomic species, as well as the structure of this electron aggregate and its associated energy and angular momentum properties, which properties give rise to the chemical behavior of the element. The nucleus of a chemical element of atomic number Z may come in one or more varieties on a mass basis. The mass differences of these isotopes are of the order of a unit atomic mass, which is approximately that of a hydrogen atom, or more strictly $\frac{1}{12}$ that of the carbon atom, arbitrarily selected as the basis of atomic weights. The number of isotopes of a given element varies from one or two in the cases of the very light elements and most of the elements of odd atomic number, to ten or a dozen in the cases of heavy atoms of even atomic number. The relative abundances again vary from mere traces, in some instances, to approximately equal proportions in others. The values of certain atomic masses have been determined with very great precision in recent years; as instances, the accepted values for the two isotopes of hydrogen are found to be:

$$H_1 \text{ (hydrogen) } (Z = 1)M_1 = 1.001842 \ (\pm 3 \text{ parts per } 10^6)$$

$$H_2 \text{ (or } D_2) \text{ (deuterium) } (Z = 1)M_2 = 2.014744 \ (\pm 2 \text{ parts per } 10^6)$$

As will be seen in later discussions, this precision is highly significant because, through the mass-energy relationship, these mass values determine the energetic properties of the nucleus.

Electrical phenomena in gases   13-5

The early studies of the phenomena associated with the passage of electric current through gases were conducted by scientists of great insight who were able to arrive at far-reaching qualitative conclusions about the electrical properties of atomic systems with which the preceding discussion has been concerned. It is also evident from their work that the conduction of electricity through gases follows a very different mechanism from the conduction of electricity through a metal. In the latter case, a rigid spatial lattice of atomic centers is so closely packed that certain of the more loosely held electrons are shared between many atoms, and move quite freely amongst them under the influence of an electric field established by a potential difference maintained between the ends of the conductor. In the case of a gas, the spacing between the atoms is much greater—evidently more than ten times as great— indeed, since the densities of gases at ordinary pressures are about 1/1000 the density of solids. Moreover, the atoms of a gas are not rigidly held in position, but are themselves free to move because they fall under the influence of applied fields on their residual positive charge when an electron has been removed from their structure. Thus electricity is conducted through a gas both by the motion of positive ions in the direction of an applied electric field, as well as by the motions of the negatively charged electrons in the opposite direction.

At low potential differences between the electrodes, and consequently low current densities through the gas, the current consists of the motion of those electrons that are induced to leave the positive electrode by heating or illumination. At somewhat higher potential differences between the electrodes, the electrons, in passing through the gas, gain sufficient energy to liberate other electrons from atoms with which they collide, thus adding new carriers to the stream and increasing the current. Even at these low current densities, however, it is evident that Ohm's law as it applies to metals would not be expected to hold, because of the regenerative phenomena of the addition of new carriers with the increase in the driving electric field. At still higher potential differences between the electrodes, the electrons liberated at collisions themselves liberate others, and a cataclysmic enhancement of the current takes place. This is accompanied by the emission of light from the atoms in the discharge as a result of the readjustment of their surrounding electrons, which, on absorbing some of the mobile electrons' energy, are disturbed from their normal configurations. The phenomena at high current densities vary markedly with the pressure and the nature of the gas and, because of the large charge densities, the electric field is no longer uniform between the electrodes, but exhibits well-differentiated regions wherein the fields and charge densities have widely different values.

The study of the passage of electric charges through gases has not only been a major source of knowledge about the electrical components of atoms and their structure, but has contributed very important techniques for general scientific investigation, and also useful devices with applications in many specific fields. Such discharges have a major role as non-ohmic elements in electric circuits, where they are used for the interconversion of alternating and direct currents, for the limiting of currents to certain maximum values, as indicating devices, and in many other ways. The major application of such discharges, however, is in the generation of light for special purposes. The wide employment of discharge tubes for general-purpose illumination is a particularly efficient way of converting electrical energy into visibly radiant energy because of the properties of the free atoms in the discharge, which emit light with little accompanying loss of energy in the form of heat. Also light of particular wave lengths or frequencies, characteristic of the atomic structures in the discharge, may be very conveniently obtained in this way. Within recent years techniques have been developed to store for very brief periods of time relatively large quantities of energy in the constituent atomic structures and to trigger their sudden release, thus giving rise to beams of light of vastly greater energy and coherence than had ever been available before. These devices, which are called *Lasers*, an acronym for "light amplification by the stimulated emission of radiation," are opening up great possibilities for the investigation of properties of matter, improving the precision of measurement, optical-electric control, and the transmission of signals over great distances that would be useful for rocket ship communication.

EXAMPLE. The principle underlying the high efficiency of conversion of electrical energy into radiant energy or light in a gas discharge is brought out by considering a simplified picture of the process taking place during the collision of an electron with an atom in such a discharge. In a simple elastic collision between an electron of mass m and an atom of mass M, the velocity imparted to the atom is $2m/(m + M)$ times the electron's velocity. Using this ratio of the velocity of the atom after the collision to that of the electron before the collision, the ratio of the kinetic energy of the atom to the initial kinetic energy of the electron is $4Mm/(M + m)^2$. If the mass of the atom is 10^4 times that of the electron, the energy acquired by the atom is 4×10^{-4} that of the electron. If, however, the collision is inelastic and nearly the total energy of the electron can be converted to excitation of the atom, the conversion of electrical energy into atomic radiation is greatly enhanced.

Further reading:

CHAWLOW, A. L., "Optical Masers," *Scientific American*, vol. 204, No. 6, p. 52 (1961); vol. 209, No. 1, p. 34 (1963).

NIER, A. O. C., "The Mass Spectrometer," *Scientific American*, vol. 188, No. 3, p. 68 (1953).

NIER, A. O. C., "New Unified Scale for Atomic Masses and Weights," *The American Physics Teacher*, vol. 1, No. 1, p. 11 (1963).

Problems

13-1 A beam of electrons (mass m and charge e) is accelerated through a potential difference ϕ, and then passes through a region of electric field E and magnetic field H. If the two fields and the electron velocity are all mutually perpendicular, what value of the magnetic field strength H will exactly cancel the effects of the electric field E, and hence produce zero deflection of the electron beam?

13-2 A stream of particles, each having the same mass m and carrying the same charge e, drift horizontally with different velocities through a region in which they experience small deflections by a horizontal transverse electric field E and a vertical gravitational field Γ. The particles finally strike a transverse plate. What pattern do their centers of impact form on the plate?

13-3 What is the e/m ratio of a doubly charged atom of neon (atomic mass 20.0)?

13-4 In an experiment of the Millikan type, the following values are obtained for the charges measured on oil drops: $(-4.8, -3.4, -6.9, -3.1, -6.6, -5.2, -5.3, -3.7, -6.6) \times 10^{-19}$ C. What value for the electronic charge e would you estimate from these results?

13-5 Silver may be electroplated on to a clean copper surface by immersing a silver bar and the copper article in a solution of some silver salt and passing a current between these two electrodes. Silver ions from the salt solution plate out on the article and are replaced by ions from the bar. Should the article be connected to the positive or negative terminal of the supply? How many kilograms of silver are deposited in 10 hrs. by a current of 5 amps.? The silver ions carry a single charge and have an atomic mass number of 108.

13-6

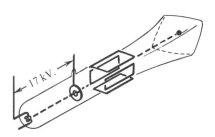

A television tube accelerates electrons with an applied potential difference of 17 kV. (1 kV. = 1000 V.). The electron beam is deflected in the horizontal and the vertical directions by two 8 cm. long pairs of current-carrying coils, each pair straddling the tube. What magnetic field strength must each pair of coils be capable of producing to swing the electron beam spot over a screen 20 in. square, 10 in. away from the deflecting coils?

13-7 What is the approximate mass in kilograms and the charge in Coulombs on the nucleus of a fluorine atom ($A = 19$, $Z = 9$)?

13-8 What are the velocities of the following particles after acceleration over a potential gap of 20 kV.: electrons, hydrogen atomic ions, deuterium atomic ions, singly charged hydrogen molecular ions, doubly charged hydrogen molecular ions, singly charged oxygen atomic ions?

13-9 It has been found that the binding energy B with which two atoms of hydrogen are held together in a molecule is equal to the energy an electron would gain in falling through a potential of about 4.78 V. By the principle of equivalence of mass and energy, the decrease in mass of a hydrogen molecule over the sum of the masses of two hydrogen atoms is then:

$$m_{H_2} - 2m_H = \Delta m = \frac{B}{c^2}$$

The fractional change in mass of a hydrogen atom upon being incorporated by a molecule is thus:

$$\frac{\Delta m}{m} = \frac{B}{mc^2}$$

Calculate this quantity and show that it is less than one hundredth as great as the order of magnitude of the errors involved in measuring atomic masses by present techniques as implied by the expression for the masses of hydrogen and deuterium in the text.

13-10 An element has an average atomic weight of 39.10. It has two isotopes of atomic weights 38.96 and 40.96. Calculate the per cent abundance of each isotope.

14 The interaction of radiant energy and electrons; the extension of the concept of wave motion to the atomic domain

14-1 The conservation of energy in the emission and absorption of radiation by electrons

The wave nature of the propagation phenomena associated with electromagnetic waves and their unique velocity of propagation have already been considered. All the evidence throughout their broad frequency or wave length spectrum indicates that the production and absorption of such waves, including visible phenomena, are associated with emission or acquisition respectively of energy by an electron or a system of electrons composing the structure of an atom or a group of atoms. Radio waves are generated by the induction of electric currents in systems of conductors, and they are detected by the amplification of the minute currents induced in conductors sutiably tuned to resonance. The wave length region above about 10^{-4} m. is now becoming tractable to techniques of this nature through advances in solid-state technology. However, thermal excitation of the electrons in solids by intense heating and the bombardment of atomic systems in the gaseous or solid state by electrons from filaments or gas discharges produce electromagnetic waves in infrared, visible, ultraviolet, and X-ray regions, which exhibit all of the characteristics in regard to propagation that are familiar in the case of long-wave length electromagnetic radiation.

Although it was obvious from the heating effect of the radiation from a flame or glowing solid that energy was transported by radiation, little was known about the energetics of the emission and absorption process until 1900, when the study of the characteristics of the radiation emitted by incandescent bodies led Max Planck of the University of Berlin to the conclusion that there is a unique linear relationship between the energy unit associated with radiation and the frequency of the radiation. At the time, this was a surprising and unexpected result, but it was confirmed in numerous ways by experiments with radiation and electrons, both in association with atoms in the gaseous state and in solids. One of the most direct and unambiguous experiments was that first performed by P. Lenard, who showed that electrons emitted from a metal plate upon which light is permitted to shine possess greater kinetic energy, the higher the frequency of the incident light.

Such an experiment is indicated very schematically in Fig. 14-1. If light of a given frequency or wave length is permitted to strike a metal plate in an evacuated glass container, and the potential of another plate, shielded from the light, is increased negatively, the small electron current initially detected is reduced to zero at some definite value of this potential, e.g., ϕ. If this value of ϕ at which the electrons are prevented from reaching the collecting plate is recorded for a series of frequencies of the incident light ν, it is found that there is a linear functional relation between ϕ and ν, as shown in Fig. 14-2. Unless the frequency of the light exceeds some value ν_0, no electron current at all is observed.

These phenomena are what would be anticipated if energy were not continuously transported by radiation, but if it were present in discrete units, and the size of these units or *quanta* were proportional to the frequency of the radiation. Thus an electron within the metal, but near the surface, could absorb such a quantum of energy, thereby acquiring kinetic energy; if this is greater than some minimum value, say $e\phi_0$, where ϕ_0 is an effective electrostatic potential holding the electron in the metal, the electron can emerge and traverse the evacuated space

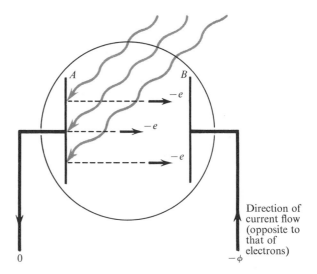

Figure 14-1 *Light incident on a surface A causes electrons to be emitted. The energy of these electrons is measured by application of a retarding electric field between plate A and a collecting plate B.*

to the collector. If a retarding potential ϕ is applied, the electron is prevented from surmounting this energetic barrier if its residual kinetic energy is less than $e\phi$. In the form of an equation representing the condition of photoelectric current cut off,

$$h\nu = e\phi_0 + e\phi$$

where h is the constant of proportionality between the energy of a quantum and its associated frequency ν. The linear relation between ϕ and ν permits an evaluation of the magnitude of h, since the value of e is known. The constant h is known as Planck's constant, and it is found to have the value of 6.6256×10^{-34} J. sec. The quantity $e\phi_0$ is a property of the material known as the work function. The residual kinetic energy $\frac{1}{2}mv^2$ possessed by the electron as it leaves the surface is, of course, equal to the work $e\phi$ required to bring it to rest or, according to the above equation,

$$\tfrac{1}{2}mv^2 = h\nu - e\phi_0$$

i.e., the kinetic energy of the ejected electron is equal to the energy of the quantum less the work function $e\phi_0$.

The nature of the interaction of radiation and electrons, in terms of the finite and specific quanta of energy carried by the former, strongly suggests discreteness or granularity as a property of radiation, much as elementary particles are a property of massive matter. This is evi-

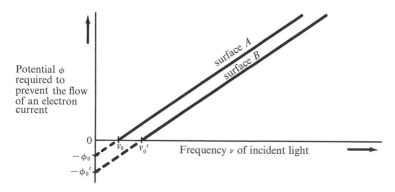

Figure 14-2 *The electric potential required to prevent the flow of an electron current from one electrode to the other is a linear function of the frequency of the incident light. Surfaces of different materials have different threshold frequencies v_0 and "work functions" $e\phi_0$.*

denced in emission, absorption, and scattering phenomena. This particle nature, analogous to the atomicity of matter, indicates the propriety of giving a name to the unit of radiation. This unit is called the *photon*. The extensive body of evidence that has been obtained in the course of physical experimentation and research since Planck's initial observations in 1900 confirms both the adequacy of this description and its fruitfulness in unifying and extending our understanding of basic physical phenomena.

The transfer of energy from the form of radiation to that of the kinetic energy of an electron in the photoelectric effect justifies the association of the concept of energy with that of the photon. This is confirmed by the discreteness characterizing the absorption of radiation by the electrons composing an atomic system, as will be described in later chapters. The converse of this effect is the emission of radiation by electrons as they change their energy configurations in atomic systems. Also, the converse of the gain of kinetic energy by an electron upon the absorption of a photon's energy is the emission of a photon of radiant energy by an electron that is decelerated by passage through matter or by an electric field opposing its motion.

The nature of the event in which the electron emits a photon of radiant energy determines the photon's energy; the frequency v associated with the photon is then equal to the energy divided by the constant h. This frequency determines the effective wave length displayed by the photon while it is being propagated from its point of origin to its point of absorption through the relation: $\lambda v = c$. The wave length in turn determines the dimensions of any interference pattern to which it may give rise. The analogy with the spreading wave observed on a surface of water, after it is disturbed e.g., by dropping in a stone, is somewhat misleading when it is applied to the emission of a photon by an electron. The wavelike nature of the propagation phenomenon is about the only similarity. The energy of the falling stone carried away by the water wave is determined rather by the amplitude of the wave than by its frequency, and it spreads and dissipates itself with time over the surface. The photon emission by an electron, and its subsequent absorption by another, represents two sequential events separated in time by r/c, where r is the separation of the emitting and absorbing electron. A wavelike nature is characteristic of the process because we find that the probability of a given electron absorbing the energy $h\nu$ is proportional to the intensity of the interference pattern in its neighborhood as produced by a wave of length $\lambda = c/\nu$, emanating from the emitting electron and under the particular geometric conditions of the event being observed.

EXAMPLE. Light of wave length 3×10^{-7} m. illuminates a clean surface of aluminum that has a work function of 3.0 electron Volts (e.V.). What is the maximum energy electron that can thereby be emitted from the surface?

The frequency ν of the light is c/λ, where λ is the wavelength and c the velocity of light, 3×10^8 m. per sec. The energy of each photon is therefore $h\nu$ or hc/λ, where Planck's constant h has the value 6.6×10^{-34} J. sec. The work done in removing an electron from the surface is $e\phi_0$, where e is the electronic charge 1.6×10^{-19} C., and $e\phi_0$ is the work function. Consequently the maximum energy an electron can have is:

$$U = \frac{hc}{\lambda} - e\phi_0$$

$$= \frac{6.6 \times 10^{-34} \times 3 \times 10^8}{3 \times 10^{-7}} - 1.6 \times 10^{-19} \times 3$$

$$= 6.6 \times 10^{-19} - 4.8 \times 10^{-19}$$

$$= 1.8 \times 10^{-19} \text{ J.}$$

$$= \frac{1.8 \times 10^{-19}}{1.6 \times 10^{-19}} = 1.1 \text{ e.V.}$$

In calculations involving atomic particles, a convenient unit of energy is the electron Volt, which is equal to 1.6×10^{-19} J.

EXAMPLE. As an illustration of the dual particle-wave nature of light, consider the formation of an interference pattern by light traversing two closely spaced narrow slits in a baffle, as illustrated in Fig. 14-3. Both the source of light and the screen on which the interference pattern is observed are well removed from the baffle so that the rays entering either slit may be considered parallel, and so may the rays emanating from either slit and travelling to some given point on the screen. As was shown in Sec. 6-6 of Chap. 6, lines of maximum illumination are observed on the screen at points such that the distances d_1 and d_2 to either slit differ by an integral number of wave lengths λ of the light. As might be expected from the corpuscular nature of light, if the intensity of the light source is weak enough so that the time of arrival of individual photons is experimentally detectable, then this is indeed observed by a detector such as the photosensitive apparatus of Lenard, as shown in Fig. 14-4. If this apparatus is placed immediately in front of the screen, each photon is found to have the energy $h\nu$ or hc/λ. If the detector is moved across the screen, the rate of arrival of photons is found to be maximal at those points where the maximum intensity is observed in the interference pattern, and minimal at the points of minimum intensity. The formation of the maxima and minima is explicable in terms of the constructive or destructive interference of waves emanating simultaneously from the two slits. Such a pattern would

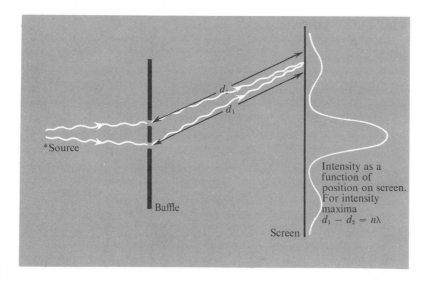

Figure 14-3 *Formation of an interference pattern by light waves traversing two slits in a baffle.*

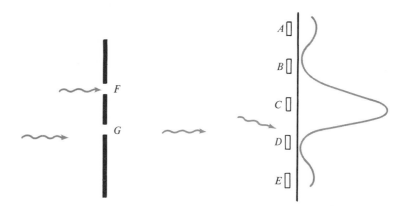

Figure 14-4 *By placing photon detectors in front of the screen, one finds that the interference maxima at A, C, and E correspond to a maximum rate of arrival of photons at those positions. Photons always arrive intact at one point on the screen, and detectors at F and G will show that photons arrive intact at one slit or the other.*

not be expected if the photons behave as classical particles, well separated in time and space and traversing either one slit or the other. Their particle nature may be readily tested by the use of several detectors. Not only is it found that individual photons reach the screen intact— i.e., an individual photon contributes to only one point in the interference pattern—but, by placing a detector at each slit, it is observed that photons pass through one slit or the other, but never through both simultaneously. What is more, if one slit is covered with a detector and the other is left uncovered, then the characteristic double slit interference pattern disappears, as of course it must; although according to the corpuscular measurements noted above the photons appearing at the covered slit were separate and unrelated in time to those at the open slit, and therefore, if their behavior is classical, they should not have been able to interfere with the latter. Thus it is found that light travels from the source to the screen in the form of photons, and the probability in a given time of observing a photon at any point on the screen is proportional to the intensity of the interference pattern in that neighborhood. It is necessary then to regard the photon as inseparable from its wave field, which guides it in its path and is responsible for any interference or other effects of a wave nature. Further elucidation of the nonclassical behavior of these "particles" requires a greater understanding of the localizability of a photon and what this implies. The subject will be taken up again in Sec. 14-3.

Conservation of momentum and angular momentum in the interaction between electrons and photons

The above concept of the photon as a particle suggests that the other two basic mechanical quantities that were conserved during mechanical events, namely, momentum and angular momentum, may be identifiable properties of the photon as well, and may be found to be conserved in emission and absorption processes. The inelastic scattering of radiation by electrons that are relatively free of attachment to heavy atomic systems very clearly exhibits the photon's momentum. In such an interaction, first established quantitatively by A. H. Compton in 1922, both momentum and energy are shared between the electron and photon during the process, and the sum of each is conserved or remains constant. X-rays are more suitable than visible light or radio waves for such experiments, since their frequency is higher and their energy and momentum are greater. Hence the residual forces exerted by neighboring atomic systems on the electrons participating in the process are of lesser importance and can, to a first approximation, be ignored. If the diffraction pattern of a beam of x-ray photons is examined as a function of angle of deviation, it is found that in addition to elastically scattered photons with wave lengths the same as that of the incident beam, there is also a component of longer wave length or lower frequency; the wave length becomes longer, or the frequency becomes lower, as the angle of deviation of this scattered component increases. Or if a beam of monochromatic x-rays is sent through a photographic emulsion, one may observe the tracks defining the trajectories of electrons that have suffered collisions with photons. One may also detect the scattered photons as radiation of altered frequency or wave length that have deviated in angle from the initial beam, as indicated in Fig. 14-5.

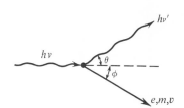

Figure 14-5 *Compton scattering of a photon by a free electron. Energy and momentum are conserved in such an event.*

The energy of a colliding photon is $h\nu$ and, since it travels with the velocity c, its effective momentum should be its effective mass times c. Since a basic property of photons is that they are always in motion with the unique velocity c, the concept of a rest mass is without application, but the relativistic description of energy as mc^2 is undoubtedly applicable. Thus since mc^2, where m is an effective mass, is equivalent to $h\nu$, the momentum mc may be written as $h\nu/c$ or h/λ. The energy $h\nu$ may thus be written as hc/λ. Application of the principle of conservation of momentum in both the forward and transverse directions and the principle of conservation of energy yields three independent equations involving the wave lengths of both incident and scattered photons, the velocity of the scattered electron, and the angles at which the photon and the electron scatter. The mass of the moving electron can be expressed, of course, in terms of its velocity and its rest mass. Since there are three equations, any two of the unknown quantities can be eliminated. Thus if momentum is to be conserved in the transverse direction, the transverse momentum of the scattered electron must be equal and opposite to the transverse momentum of the scattered photon, there having been no transverse momentum before the collision occurred. Referring to the figure:

$$mv \sin \phi = \frac{h}{\lambda'} \sin \theta$$

The forward momentum of the scattered electron must equal the difference in forward momenta of the incident and scattered photons:

$$mv \cos \phi = \frac{h}{\lambda} - \frac{h}{\lambda'} \cos \theta$$

If these two equations are squared and then added, it is seen that

$$m^2v^2(\sin^2 \phi + \cos^2 \phi) = h^2 \left[\frac{1}{\lambda'^2} (\sin^2 \theta + \cos^2 \theta) + \frac{1}{\lambda^2} - \frac{2}{\lambda\lambda'} \cos \theta \right]$$

which, because the sum of the squares of the sine and cosine of any angle is 1, reduces to;

$$m^2v^2 = h^2 \left[\frac{1}{\lambda'^2} + \frac{1}{\lambda^2} - \frac{2}{\lambda\lambda'} \cos \theta \right]$$

thus eliminating ϕ.

The energy of the scattered electron must equal the original total energy (including the rest energy m_0c^2 of the electron) less the energy of the scattered photon:

$$mc^2 = m_0c^2 + \frac{hc}{\lambda} - \frac{hc}{\lambda'}$$

Dividing through by the common factor c, and then squaring both sides:

$$m^2c^2 = m_0^2c^2 + h^2 \left[\frac{1}{\lambda^2} + \frac{1}{\lambda'^2} - \frac{2}{\lambda\lambda'} \right] + 2m_0ch \left(\frac{1}{\lambda} - \frac{1}{\lambda'} \right)$$

Subtraction of the previous equation for m^2v^2 then gives:

$$m^2(c^2 - v^2) = m_0^2c^2 - \frac{2h^2}{\lambda\lambda'} (1 - \cos \theta) + 2m_0ch \left(\frac{1}{\lambda} - \frac{1}{\lambda'} \right)$$

On application of the transformation

$$m = \frac{m_0}{\sqrt{1 - v^2/c^2}} = \frac{m_0c}{\sqrt{c^2 - v^2}}$$

the left side of the above equation is found to equal $m_0^2c^2$, and consequently the equation simplifies to

$$\frac{h(1 - \cos\theta)}{\lambda\lambda'} = m_0c\left(\frac{1}{\lambda} - \frac{1}{\lambda'}\right) = m_0c\left(\frac{\lambda' - \lambda}{\lambda\lambda'}\right)$$

or:

$$\lambda' - \lambda = \frac{h}{m_0c}(1 - \cos\theta)$$

Thus, as a result of an inelastic scattering process, there should be a wave length change in the scattered radiation varying from $2h/m_0c$ for backward scattering to zero for forward scattering, if momentum and energy are to be conserved. This is accurately borne out by the experimental observations. The quantity h/m_0c, which has the value 2.42621×10^{-12} m. for the electron, is called the *Compton wave length*, λ_c.

EXAMPLE. X-rays of wavelength 1.0×10^{-11} m. are incident on free stationary electrons. What is the wavelength of the x-rays that are scattered directly backwards? What is the energy gained by the scattered electrons in this case?

The scattering angle θ is here π, or $180°$, for which $\cos\theta$ has the value -1. Consequently the increase in x-ray wave length is

$$\lambda' - \lambda = \frac{2h}{m_0c} = 2 \times 2.4 \times 10^{-12} = 0.48 \times 10^{-11} \text{ m.}$$

The backward scattered rays therefore have a wave length

$$\lambda' = 1.48 \times 10^{-11} \approx 1.5 \times 10^{-11} \text{ m.}$$

The incident and scattered waves have respective frequencies:

$$\nu = \frac{c}{\lambda} = \frac{3.0 \times 10^8}{1.0 \times 10^{-11}} = 3.0 \times 10^{19} \text{ sec.}^{-1}$$

$$\nu' = \frac{c}{\lambda'} = \frac{3.0 \times 10^8}{1.5 \times 10^{-11}} = 2.0 \times 10^{19} \text{ sec.}^{-1}$$

Therefore, the incident and scattered photons have respective energies:

$$h\nu = 6.6 \times 10^{-34} \times 3.0 \times 10^{19} = 2.0 \times 10^{-14} \text{ J.}$$
$$h\nu' = 6.6 \times 10^{-34} \times 2.0 \times 10^{19} = 1.3 \times 10^{-14} \text{ J.}$$

The scattered electron must therefore receive the difference in energy:

$$U = h\nu - h\nu' = 0.7 \times 10^{-14} \text{ J.}$$
$$= \frac{0.7 \times 10^{-14}}{1.6 \times 10^{-19}} \approx 4 \times 10^4 \text{ e.V.} = 40 \text{ keV.}$$

It appears also that the concept of motion that is rotational in nature, deriving from our large scale experience, can be usefully projected into the realm of the elementary events taking place between photons and electrons. The law of conservation of angular momentum introduces nothing new in the preceding analysis of the Compton scattering process, dealing as it does with dimensionless entities colliding at a point. For, under these circumstances, the conservation of angular momentum is a trivial consequence of the conservation of momentum. However, a number of lines of experimental evidence lead us to the conclusion that a photon is endowed with an inherent quantity of angular momentum as well as the linear momentum which the Compton scattering process has shown it to possess.

A beam of light incident upon an absorbing surface exerts a pressure which is equal to the rate at which photon momentum is changed by absorption at the surface. Thus the pressure is equal to $n(h\nu/c)$, where n is the number of photons of frequency ν incident upon a unit surface per second. The surface absorbing the photons could also be disposed in a way that would render it sensitive to any torque produced upon absorption of the photons. Our observations are consistent with the hypothesis that the angular momentum vector of a photon is directed either parallel or anti-parallel to its direction of motion. But the absorbing surface would, in general, exhibit no tendency to rotate, because on the average the photons incident upon it carry as much angular momentum in one sense as in the other. However, there are certain transparent substances, such as quartz, in which the atoms and their surrounding electronic structures are so disposed as to introduce effectively a difference in the velocity of propagation of the photons having these two senses of angular momentum. By means of such materials, one can essentially produce a beam of photons containing predominantly those with one sense of angular momentum only. Such a beam is said to be right or left circularly polarized, depending on whether the photon angular momentum is parallel or anti-parallel to its trajectory. A circularly polarized beam, on being absorbed by a blackened surface, would transmit angular momentum as well as linear momentum to it, or (as shown in Fig. 14-6) the beam of photons with angular momentum predominantly in one sense could be sent through, say, a suspended disk of properly cut and oriented quartz, whose thickness creates the apparent effect of reversing the sense of the angular momentum of the photons. In this case the torque on such a disk would evidently be twice that carried by each photon traversing it; but, as the photons would not be stopped or absorbed, there would be no change in linear momentum or force exerted on the disk in the direction of travel of the photons.

The effect described is small for beams of light of ordinary intensity,

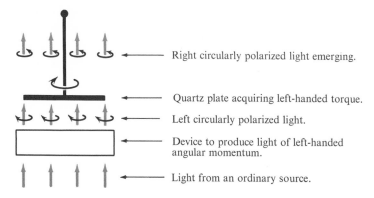

Figure 14-6   *Schematic experiment demonstrating the angular momentum carried by photons.*

and the precision of such experiments is less than that of those to be described in a later chapter, which measure the angular momentum balance at the emission or absorption of photons by individual atomic systems. Precise angular momentum balance experiments lead to the conclusion that with each photon is associated an angular momentum equal to $h/2\pi$.

In summary of the preceding discussion, the photon may be thought to possess the following properties, by which it may be experimentally recognized and identified:

1. It possesses the energy $h\nu$.
2. It possesses the momentum $h\nu/c = h/\lambda$.
3. It possesses the angular momentum $h/2\pi$.
4. It is constantly in motion with the velocity c.
5. It possesses no rest mass or electric charge.

The spatial location of a photon and the   14-3
principle of indeterminacy

A photon possesses nothing like shape, individual markings or identity, but it is created or absorbed in radiation processes involving charged massive particles such as electrons. Its trajectory during the process of transmission may be thought of as guided by a wave field. The number of photons passing per second, or the intensity of the beam of radiation, may be calculated by the technique for determining the interference pattern of waves. For this reason, the photon cannot be localized in space, and the precision of knowledge of its spatial location along its trajectory is of the order of the wave length λ. Thus, the inherent error or uncertainty in locating it along its path, say δx, is of the order of λ. The product of the precision of knowledge of position δx and of momentum δp is thus of the order of magnitude of Planck's constant h. Similarly, one cannot ideally determine the frequency ν in a time less than about one period of oscillation; so $\delta \nu \delta t$ is of the order of unity, and the product of the uncertainties in determining a photon's energy δU in a time δt is given, because of its fundamental wave nature, by Planck's constant h also. This principle of "uncertainty" or "indeterminacy" was recognized by Werner Heisenberg, a German physicist, who first stated it in 1927. The limit to the accuracy with which a photon's spatial or temporal coordinates and corresponding dynamic coordinates may be simultaneously determined may seem surprising in the basic processes of an "exact" science. However, the wavelike properties of photons were known long before their corpuscular properties were discovered. Wave phenomena have inherent extension in both space and time and, hence, an associated corpuscle cannot be truly infinitesimal. Thus it should be remembered that the classical concept of a particle such as a photon as a mass point with a precise location and momentum is not strictly applicable.

EXAMPLE. Returning to the discussion of the double slit interference pattern for light, it has been shown (Fig. 14-3) that the successive intensity maxima in the interference patterns correspond to successive values of the integer, n, in the formula:

$$n\lambda = d \sin \theta$$

If the slit is very narrow, the intensities of these maxima decrease rapidly with increasing n, the majority of the photons leave the slits at angles θ, such that n is not greater than 1. Consequently, as a rough approximation that implies the uncertainty in the value of θ, it is possible to write:

$$d \sin \theta \approx \lambda$$

where the symbol $\approx$ is to be read as "is of the order of."

Treating the photons strictly as particles, their deflection at a slit must be interpreted as the acquisition of a transverse component of momentum (the total momentum, including that transmitted to the slit, must, of course, remain constant). From Fig. 14-7 it is seen that the transverse momentum acquired is $p \sin \theta$, where p is the initial momen-

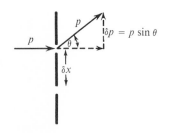

Figure 14-7 *Photons are scattered (diffracted) as they pass through a slit, and thereby receive an unknown component δp of transverse momentum.*

tum in the forward direction and θ is the angle of deflection. Thus under the conditions for which an interference pattern is observed, the photons may pass through either slit; hence their transverse spatial coordinate at this time is known only to an accuracy δx, equal to the slit spacing d. As they traverse a slit they are scattered through an unknown angle θ, and thereby acquire a small component of transverse momentum $\delta p = p \sin \theta$. The product of these two uncertainties is then found to be:

$$\delta x \delta p = dp \sin \theta \approx \lambda p$$
$$\approx h$$

The wave-like aspect of material particles, 14-4
and the defining properties of the electron

At this stage of the discussion, the electron would appear to be a totally different type of particle from the photon with no elements of resemblance at all, except that they participate together in the processes of emission and absorption of radiation. But in 1927, C. J. Davisson and L. H. Germer of the Bell Telephone Laboratories, who were investigating the scattering of electrons from the surface of a crystal of nickel, observed a pattern of scattered intensity for the electrons that bore some resemblance to the interference pattern observed in the scattering of x-ray photons from a crystal lattice. This was a very surprising result at the time, but was confirmed by a number of other investigators, and indeed interference patterns characteristic of a wave were observed when a beam of electrons was directed upon a ruled grating, such as that used for the diffraction of light. That the pattern was due to electrons rather than to photons was clearly demonstrated by the fact that the pattern as a whole was displaced in the presence of a magnetic field by just the amount that would be calculated from the values of H and e/m for electrons. The value of the apparent wave length of the electrons, as deduced from the dimensions of the interference pattern and the crystal lattice spacing, was found to be equal to $h/\sqrt{2e\phi m}$, where ϕ was the value of the electric potential accelerating the electrons forming the beam. Since $e\phi$ is equal to their kinetic energy $\frac{1}{2}mv^2$, the apparent wavelength is seen to be h/mv. This is formally precisely the same as for photons where it was also seen that the wave length is equal to the constant h divided by the momentum.

Shortly thereafter, experiments were performed with positive ions, neutral atoms, and molecules, which again showed the interference patterns characteristic of waves for the scattering of atomic masses of all types from regularly spaced lattice or grating structures. The wave length in all cases corresponded to the quotient of Planck's constant h and the momentum of the particles. The wavelike character of particles much larger than atoms would not be expected to be discernable because the momentum cannot be made small enough in comparison to h for the quotient h/mv to be measurable by available diffraction structures. For instance, a dust particle one tenth of a millimeter on a side, with the velocity characteristic of thermal equilibrium at ordinary temperatures, would have an associated wave length of about 10^{-19} m., which is much smaller than any regularly spaced diffracting structures that we know.

The discovery of the wave properties associated with massive particles produced a basic reorientation in the thinking of scientists about the elemental constituents of our universe. It suggested, in particular, a much closer analogy between matter and radiation, or between electrons and photons, than had previously been thought to exist. The wave-like properties are, of course, in no way contradictory to the particle-like properties of localizability in space and the relationship between mass and velocity and the expressions for momentum and energy. The wave-like properties are simply supplementary to the particle-like properties. The analogy between the electron and the photon can be seen to be very close indeed. Our first acquaintance with the electron led to the concept of it as a particle with a characteristic rest mass m_0 which could move with a variable velocity, leading to expressions for the dynamic quantities momentum, mv, and energy mc^2. Our first acquaintance with the photon led to the concept of it as a wave with a characteristic velocity c, a variable frequency ν, and wavelength λ related to c through the expression $\lambda\nu = c$. The dynamic quantities momentum and energy were found to be equally applicable to the photon and were $h\nu/c = h/\lambda$, and $h\nu$, respectively. With the discovery of the wave nature of particles, such as an electron, the dynamic analogy between the electron and photon becomes complete; one may consider that, for both the electron and the photon, the expressions appearing on both sides of the equation $mv = h/\lambda$ may be thought of as the quantity "momentum."

In the year 1926, just before the experiments of Davisson and Germer, the French physicist Louis de Broglie published his speculation upon the possibility that the photon might not be unique in possessing both particle and wave properties, and that this dual nature is a unifying characteristic of all forms of matter and radiation. He suggested that a characteristic wave length should be associated with a moving electron through the equation $\lambda_b = h/mv$. This is seen to be the conclusion to which the experiments of Davisson and Germer subsequently led. It can be seen that λ_b relates to the Compton wave length $\lambda_c = h/m_0 c$ by expressing the effective mass m in terms of the rest mass m_0 and the velocity of the electron v:

$$\lambda_b = \frac{h(1 - v^2/c^2)^{1/2}}{m_0 v}$$

$$= \lambda_c (c^2/v^2 - 1)^{1/2}$$

From the analogy between the expressions for the energy mc^2 of a particle, such as an electron, possessing a rest mass, and $h\nu$ for a photon having a constant velocity c, one may use the expression for momentum $mv = h/\lambda$ to write formally:

$$mc^2 = \frac{hc^2}{\lambda v} = \frac{h\nu'}{vv'/c^2}$$

Here v'/ν' has been written for λ in accordance with the expression for the velocity of a wave in terms of the wave length and frequency $v' = \lambda \nu'$. The velocity v' may be thought of as the phase velocity of waves whose velocity varies with frequency or wave length in such a way that the resulting group velocity is c^2/v' (see Sec. 6-6). If this group velocity is identified with the velocity v of the electron, then the denominator in the above equation is unity. The frequency ν' may be thought of as the frequency which, when multiplied by h, yields the energy of the electron mc^2.

EXAMPLE. The electron microscope. The analogy between the wave properties of a material particle and an electromagnetic quantum, or photon, is put to direct application in an instrument known as an electron microscope. It was shown in Chap. 6 that, whereas light rays normally appear to cast sharp shadows of an object, if the shadow or image of a small object is examined, the edges appear indistinct, as though some light had bent around the object. This *diffraction* of light waves places an ultimate limit on the resolution of a microscope, where the object or detail studied is comparable in size to the wave length of the light used to study it. Thus the best optical microscope, when used with blue light of wave length 4×10^{-6} m., is just able to resolve two lines of spacing 2×10^{-6} m. When used with ultraviolet light of wave length 2×10^{-6} m. and a photographic plate in place of the eye, the same microscope has a resolution of 1×10^{-6} m. However, an electron of only 100 keV. energy (equivalent to 1.6×10^{-14} J.) has a momentum

$$p = \sqrt{2mU}$$

where U is the energy; hence it has a wave length:

$$\lambda = \frac{h}{p} = \frac{h}{\sqrt{2mU}} = \frac{6.6 \times 10^{-34}}{\sqrt{2 \times 9 \times 10^{-31} \times 1.6 \times 10^{-14}}}$$

$$= \frac{6.6 \times 10^{-34}}{1.7 \times 10^{-22}} = 4 \times 10^{-12} \text{ m.}$$

Since electrons are deflected by electric and magnetic fields, it is possible to focus an electron beam by such fields in much the same way as a beam of light or photons is focussed by an optical lens. With such an electron beam the ultimate resolution obtainable is about 2×10^{-12} m., an improvement over the optical instrument by a factor of 10^6. Although this limit has not yet been attained, because electromagnetic lenses cannot yet be made with the precision of their optical counterparts, electron microscopes have achieved resolutions of less than 2×10^{-9} m. Of course, the magnitude of the ultimate limit could be further reduced by the use of higher energy electrons or heavier atomic particles.

EXAMPLE. As an example of the principle of indeterminacy as it affects measurements made on a material particle, consider the situation in which the position and momentum of an electron are to be measured by observing its position at two known times and noting how far the electron moved in the given time interval. In order to observe an object, it is necessary for the observer to interact with the object in some way. Thus, if in this imaginary experiment (*gedanken* experiment) the electron is observed with a microscope, a photon will be seen to bounce off the electron. This Compton event will then transfer momentum to the electron. A small uncertainty in determining the electron's position at any time requires the use of a short wave length, and, therefore, a high frequency and a high energy photon that will transfer a large amount of momentum on collision with the electron. If the aperture of the microscope is reduced to better define the photon's path, and hence to better determine the momentum transferred in the Compton event, the laws of optics predict that the resolution of the microscope will become correspondingly worse. Thus the product of the uncertainties in position and momentum is always constant; the value of this constant can be shown to be approxmately the value of Planck's constant.

The fact that photons exhibit intrinsic angular momentum, and that they are emitted or generated as well as absorbed by interaction with electrons, is strongly presumptive evidence that electrons possess intrinsic angular momentum as well. In fact, anticipating other lines of evidence from the electronic structure of atoms, which will be considered in a later chapter, electrons are found to have associated with them an intrinsic angular momentum or spin which is equal in magnitude to one-half of that carried by photons. Thus an electron possesses the angular momentum $h/4\pi$; a reversal in sense of an electron's angular momentum vector, e.g., from being in the direction $+x$ to being in the direction $-x$, would constitute a change in its angular momentum contribution to a system of which it and a photon were components by $h/2\pi$, which is just the amount that a photon generated at such an event would possess.

As an electron possesses both angular momentum and electric charge, by analogy with large scale circulating currents or rotating charged bodies, it should be expected to exhibit a magnetic moment. On the other hand, since no charge is thought to be associated with the photon, it would not be expected to do so. This is indeed found to be the case; but, if an electron is assumed to have its charge and mass distributed in like manner, then the simple considerations educed in the discussion of magnetism, which would lead to a ratio of the magnetic moment to the angular momentum of $e/2m$, do not yield the result that is observed experimentally. The ratio of these two intrinsic properties of the electron is found to be about twice the simple classical value. The hypothesis that an electron possesses an intrinsic angular momentum, or spin, and a magnetic moment was first advanced by G. H. Uhlenbeck and S. A. Goudsmit in 1925 to account for the structure of the characteristic spectra emitted by atoms (Chap. 15). The quantitative explanation of the electron's magnetic moment had, however, to await the relativistic

Table 14-1 *Recapitulation of the properties of photons and electrons*

	Photon	Electron
Energy, U	$h\nu$	mc^2
Momentum, p	$h\nu/c = h\lambda$	$mv = h\lambda_b$
Intrinsic Angular Momentum	$h/2\Pi$	$h/4\Pi$
Rest Mass	—	m_0
Electric Charge	0	$-e$
Magnetic Moment	0	$eh/4\Pi m_0$ (approximately)

$$m = m_0(1 - v^2/c^2)^{-\frac{1}{2}} \qquad \lambda_b = \lambda_c(c^2/v^2 - 1)^{\frac{1}{2}}$$

formulation of the quantum theory of electrons ten years later by P. A. M. Dirac, and its detailed refinement by J. Schwinger another fifteen years after that. The value of the electron's magnetic moment thus calculated is in agreement with the experimentally observed value to an accuracy of one part in a million.

The properties of photons and electrons are summarized in Table 14-1.

Further reading:

ALLEN P. J., "A Radiation Torque Experiment," *American Journal of Physics*, Vol. 34, No. 12, p. 1185 (1966).

GAMOW, G., "The Principle of Uncertainty," *Scientific American*, vol. 198, No. 1, p. 51 (1958).

GORDY, W., "The Shortest Radio Waves," *Scientific American*, vol. 196, No. 5, p. 46 (1957).

SCHROEDINGER, E., "What is Matter?" *Scientific American*, vol. 189, No. 3, p. 52 (1953).

Problems

14-1 What energy (in Joules) do the photons have in a light beam of wave length 2.5×10^{-12} m.? Express this energy in M.e.V. (million electron Volts)? What is the mass equivalent of this energy in kilograms? How many electron masses is this?

14-2 Light of frequency 10^{16} sec.$^{-1}$ falls on a metal surface, and electrons of maximum energy 37 e.V. are emitted. What is the value of the work function for the metal?

14-3 Show from the requirements of conservation of energy and momentum at a photon-electron collision that it is not possible for a photon to give up all its energy at a collision with a free electron.

14-4 A very intense beam of light falling on a blackened surface raises the temperature at a rate corresponding to the arrival of 10 J. of energy per second (10 Watts). If the wave length of the light is 5×10^{-7} m., how many photons arrive per second?

14-5 Show that the force exerted on the surface by an intense beam such as that in the previous problem is less than the weight of a 0.1 mm. radius drop of water (density 10^3 kg.m.$^{-3}$).

14-6 What mass would an object have to have in order that the product of the uncertainties in its velocity and position be approximately 10^{-4} m.^{2}sec.$^{-1}$?

14-7 A particle of known mass m has an unknown velocity v. A time interval δt is utilized in determining the particle's energy $U = \frac{1}{2}mv^2$. Apply the uncertainty relationship between momentum and position to derive a second relationship ($\delta U \, \delta t \sim h$) between energy and time.

14-8   Discuss the classical *law of causation*, according to which the state of an isolated system at some time $t = 0$ will completely determine its state at all future time. Is a deterministic philosophy still possible in light of the ideas discussed in this chapter?

14-9   Use the relativistic equation relating the total energy U to the momentum p and rest mass m_0 of a particle to estimate the total energy of an electron of wave length 4×10^{-12} m.

14-10   It is possible to specify an *helicity* (clockwise or anticlockwise spin in the direction of motion) for a particular photon, independent of any reference frame. Why is this not possible for an electron?

15 Radiation from atomic systems and the one electron atom

15-1 Electronic structure of atoms

The experimental evidence that has been presented so far leads to the description of an atom of a chemical element as consisting of a massive portion or nucleus, which carries a positive electric charge, and which has associated with it a number of electrons that just neutralize its nuclear charge by virtue of the negative charge that each electron carries. In magnitude, atomic masses are found to have a discrete set of values that are almost integral multiples of the mass of the lightest atom, which is that of hydrogen. However, the masses of heavier atoms are not precisely multiples of hydrogen atom masses, but are somewhat less than such multiples. In consequence of the equivalence between mass and energy, we could interpret the difference between the measured mass of an atom and the nearest integral multiple of the mass of a hydrogen atom as the binding energy of this number of hydrogen atoms, if we were to assume that they could, in some way, be induced to compress together and—losing this binding energy—remain compacted as a new nucleus. As will be seen later, this is not exactly our present description of nuclei, since it would imply that the electric charge carried by any nucleus should also be proportional to its mass, and that this charge-to-mass ratio for any nucleus would be the same as for that of hydrogen. This is not found to be the case. The charge-to-mass ratio for stable nuclei is found to decrease with increasing atomic mass, and, consequently, there must be some other component in nuclei that permits lesser charge-to-mass ratios than the one for hydrogen. However, the general picture of compacting simple nuclear building blocks to form more massive nuclei is found to be correct. The nearest integer to the quotient of the mass of an atom and the mass of a hydrogen atom is a useful atomic parameter called the *mass number A.*

Although the chemical species of elements can be placed in order of increasing average mass, an atom of a given chemical type may occur with a range of mass numbers, as we saw in Chap. 13. In the case, for instance, of the chemical element arsenic, there is but one stable mass number in nature, namely 75, whereas for the gaseous element xenon there are nine mass numbers, or isotopes, varying from 124 to 136. The characteristic of an atomic species that can be uniquely associated with its chemical identification and properties is not the mass number, but the number of electrons that constitute its atomic structure. Since atoms in their normal state are electrically neutral, this number is equal to the positive charge that is carried by the nucleus measured in units of the electron charge. Thus the positive nuclear charge occurs in precise multiples of the magnitude of the electronic charge, and the number of charges carried by the nucleus in terms of this unit is the *atomic number,* usually written as Z. It ranges continuously throughout the sequence of the elements from 1 for hydrogen, to 92 for uranium.

Since atoms are normally electrically neutral, it is reasonable to picture an atom as consisting of the massive positively charged nucleus surrounded in some as yet undefined way by an aggregate of electrons equal in number to Z, so that the nuclear charge Ze is exactly counterbalanced by the charge of the associated electronic structure, $-Ze$ (see Fig. 15-1). The evidence from many studies, such as those of the energy losses experienced by electrons in passing through rarefied gases, the characteristic electronic energies at which additional electrons are liberated from atomic systems subject to electron impact, and the emission and absorption of photons by atomic systems strongly suggests that there is a characteristic energetic or ergodic pattern that is exhibited by such a structure or assemblage of electrons clustered about a massive, positively charged atomic nucleus.

The forces between the nucleus and the electrons, and between the electrons themselves, are certainly at least partially of an electrical nature; hence the energy of binding of the structure is certainly, in part, of the form Ze^2/r and $-e^2/r$. However, it may be shown quite generally that electrostatic and electromagnetic forces alone cannot account for stable configurations of charges either at rest or in motion.

Figure 15-1 *An atom consists of a massive nucleus of charge $+Ze$ surrounded by Z electrons, each of charge $-e$. The individual electrons are localizable only to the confines of the atom.*

There must, quite evidently, be some other consideration that leads to a satisfactory account of the stable configurations of these charged particles. This is, of course, without reference to the basic question as to why particles with unlike charges do not simply coalesce. The continuing existence of particles carrying unlike charges in proximity to one another must be accepted as a fact which, it will be seen later (Chap. 24), can be described in terms of conservation laws for certain classes of elementary particles. There are indeed pairs of charged particles, one of which is of a transient nature, which are compatible with one another for coalescence and self-annihilation, but electrons and atomic nuclei are not such compatible pairs.

The consideration that led to a consistent theory of the behavior of electrons in an atomic structure had its genesis in our recognition of the wavelike nature of electrons, which was introduced in the preceding chapter. Before proceeding to develop the consequences of this, it is first necessary to familiarize ourselves with the experimental evidence for the observed ergodic structure and also with the evidence concerning the spatial localization of the massive positively charged nucleus about which the electronic structure is disposed.

15-2   *Radiation from atoms*

Our most precise knowledge of the energetic properties of atomic systems has been obtained from a study of the electromagnetic radiations or photons that are found to be emitted or absorbed by atoms when the electronic structure characterizing them changes from one state to another, under the influence of appropriate excitation. The radiation from a solid body heated to incandenscence, when it is dispersed in frequency or wave length by a prism or diffraction grating, displays a continuous spectrum, or distribution of energy extending from the far infrared through the visible region out into the ultraviolet. If the intensity, or energy carried by the photons per unit time, is measured as a function of the wave length, it is found to have a maximum value that depends in magnitude and position along the wave length scale upon the temperature of the glowing solid source. The relation between the temperature T on the Kelvin scale, for which water freezes at 273°, and the wave length λ_m, at which the maximum occurs, is independent of the atoms composing the solid source, and is given by:

$$\lambda_m T = 2.8978 \times 10^{-3}$$

in units of meters times degrees Kelvin.

Under the conditions obtaining in a solid body, the atoms are packed so closely together that the electronic structures may be considered to overlap, and the unique energetic pattern of an isolated atom characteristic of the material of the solid is lost. On the other hand, if a substance is dispersed tenuously throughout such a large volume that each atom may be considered to be relatively isolated and uninfluenced by its neighbors, at least for times of the order of that involved in the process of emitting a photon with a wave length in the region of the spectrum near the visible, the radiation is found to consist of a large number of monochromatic components. Gases or vapors at pressures somewhat below that of the normal atmosphere satisfy this condition, as was mentioned in Chap. 13. As will be brought out in Chap. 18, the velocities of the atoms of a gas at ordinary temperatures are such that the times between collisions are much greater than that necessary for the accurate determination of the energy of a wave of the length characteristic of the region of the spectrum concerned. The necessary time is determined by the condition derived in the preceding chapter, namely, that $\delta U \, \delta t$ is of the order of magnitude of h. The pattern of discrete components of the spectrum observed from a gas that is stimulated to emit radiation, for instance by the passage of an electric current through it, is found to be uniquely characteristic of the atoms of the particular chemical element of the gas with certain finer features that are characteristic of the several isotopes present. The spectrum pattern of discrete frequencies in general is enormously complex, and the frequencies present and their intensities follow no simple or immediately obvious rule. Fig. 15-2 shows the characteristic spectra of some common gaseous elements.

Many regularities in the frequency pattern among groups of these monochromatic components, which are called lines because of their form in most optical instruments, were recognized by early investigators long before the time of Planck's work, which was described in the preceding chapter, and hence long before any recognition of the linear relationship between the frequency of the radiation and the energy of the photon associated with it. The early investigators of these phenomena sought to analyse the characteristic frequencies emitted by suitably stimulated gas atoms or molecules in terms of harmonic relations such as those commonly encountered in acoustic oscillating systems, where frequencies of 2, 3, 4, etc., times the fundamental frequency are observed (Sec. 6-5). This search was unsuccessful, but the first step in the right direction was taken by J. J. Balmer in 1885 when he observed the existence of a series of lines in the hydrogen spectrum that could be represented in terms of wave length by the series:

$$\frac{1}{\lambda} = R \left(\frac{1}{n_1{}^2} - \frac{1}{n_2{}^2} \right)$$

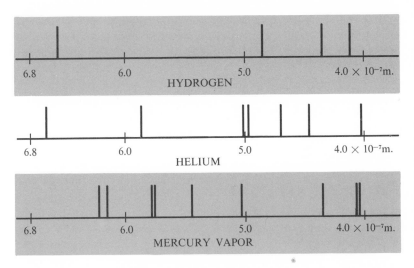

Figure 15-2 *Wavelengths of the line spectra emitted by hydrogen, helium, and mercury vapor in the visible region. The scale is one of wave length.*

or, in terms of frequency:

$$\nu = Rc\left(\frac{1}{n_1{}^2} - \frac{1}{n_2{}^2}\right)$$

where R is a constant, n_1 is equal to 2, and n_2 takes successively the values 3, 4, 5, 6, etc. T. Lyman, F. Paschen, and others discovered additional series relations of the above form for $n_1 = 1$, 3, 4, etc., thus presenting a picture of a large group of frequencies proportional in value to $1/n_1{}^2 - 1/n_2{}^2$, where n_1 and n_2 take small integral values.

This kind of relationship between the frequency and the series of integers strongly suggested that the separate terms in the formula represent characteristics of the electron system before and after the emission process; it was found by W. Ritz that this idea was a very fruitful one, and that the frequency patterns in spectra in general could be represented by differences among what were called *term values*, namely, a series of frequencies characteristic of the atom, the cross differences between which yield the observed frequencies of emission (Fig. 15-3). These terms in atoms other than hydrogen do not fit as simple a formula as that of Balmer, but the general principle of observed frequencies being the difference between characteristic frequencies of the atom proved to be of great generality and use.

In the period between 1914 and 1917, Niels Bohr of Copenhagen and Ernest Rutherford of Manchester, who was to succeed Joseph

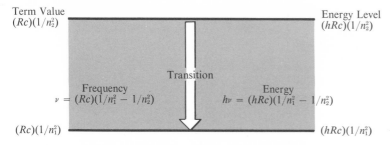

Figure 15-3 *Schematic representation of term values and energy levels and of the transition of the atomic structure between them leading to the emission of light of frequency v and photon energy hv.*

John Thomson at Cambridge, advanced the description of atomic phenomena in several very important ways. In the first place, on the basis of Planck's concept of quanta of radiation or photons, Bohr proposed that the terms introduced by Ritz were in effect atomic energy levels or characteristic stable or quasi-stable energy values, and that the radiation of a photon of frequency v corresponded to the change of an atom from the energy state U_2 to the energy state U_1, i.e.,

$$h v = U_2 - U_1$$

as depicted in Fig. 15-3. In the case of hydrogen, to accord with the series of terms observed, the energy levels must be given by:

$$U = hR/n^2$$

where n takes the values 1, 2, 3, 4, etc.

The nuclear atomic concept 15-3

Ernest Rutherford and his colleagues at Cambridge in the course of investigating radioactive phenomena, which will be discussed in a later chapter, established the basic geometry of atomic structures. One of the radioactive processes is that in which a massive positively charged atomic particle, known to be the nucleus of the second lightest atom, helium, is projected from the disintegrating atom with a high velocity corresponding to some millions of electron Volts of energy. The way in which these helium nuclei are scattered from atoms of other substances was studied, and it was found that their trajectories were conic sections. The trajectories followed by these scattered particles are not closed ellipses as in the cases of planetary orbits, but, since the total energy is large and positive, the paths resemble those of comets in being open hyperbolas (Fig. 15-4). At the extremities of these hyperbolas the scattered particle is moving freely and, neglecting the recoil of the much heavier scattering nucleus, with the same velocity at the beginning as at the end, but with a deviation in angle between the final and initial path. From this it may be inferred that the law of force between the impinging particle and the deflecting nucleus is that of the inverse square electrostatic repulsion of the charges $2e$ of helium and, say, that of $13e$ for a scattering aluminum nucleus for which $Z = 13$. The electron structure surrounding the nucleus is inconsequential in these scattering events because the electrons are relatively so light that they are swept aside and, as was seen in the earlier consideration of collision processes (Sec. 4-3), very little energy is exchanged between colliding particles when there is a great disparity in their masses.

The order of magnitude of the dimensions of atomic nuclei may be determined by a study of such collision processes between them. The helium nucleus emitted by Polonium in decaying into lead has a measured energy of 5.3×10^6 e.V. The equation giving the distance of closest approach for a head-on collision between such a particle and an aluminum nucleus, neglecting to a first approximation the recoil of the aluminum nucleus, is that found by equating the kinetic energy of the incident particle and the electrostatic energy of closest approach of point charges $2e$ and $13e$, or:

$$U = \frac{K Z_1 Z_2 e^2}{r}$$

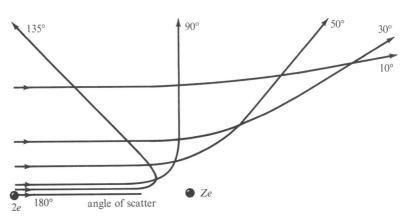

Figure 15-4 *Representative hyperbolic trajectories of a particle scattered by an inverse square law of force (neglecting recoil).*

or:

$$(5.3 \times 10^6) \times (1.6 \times 10^{-19}) = 8.99 \times 10^9 \frac{2 \times 13 \times (1.6 \times 10^{-19})^2}{r}$$

from which the distance of closest approach r is found to be 7×10^{-15} m.

Since Rutherford's early experiments on the scattering of alpha particles from thin metallic films showed that the observed scattering represented conformity with this law of force for all of the scattering collisions, the massive positively charged atomic centers must behave as point charges down to these minute dimensions. Since the spacing of atoms in crystals has been seen to be of the order of 5×10^{-10} m., the positively charged massive atomic cores must be smaller than this at least by the factor of 10^5, or 100,000. In consequence, the picture inevitably emerges of a very small massive positive core or nucleus at the center of an electronic structure marked by distinguishing energetic properties that extend out 10^5 times the dimensions of the nucleus to a distance of the order of 10^{-10} m. It is not surprising that the dimensions of the nucleus are small, for this accords with the relationship between mass or momentum and wave length, brought out in the preceding chapter, where it was seen that the wave length associated with an atomic mass is inversely proportional to this mass. Since a nuclear mass is of the order of 10^4 times that of an electron, it would be expected to exhibit dimensions very like those indicated by Rutherford's experiments.

The early attempts to account for the nature of the electron structure and, in particular, to provide a quantitative description of its energetic properties pictured an electron cloud centered upon the small massive nucleus—like a vapor cloud some meters in extent with a buck shot at its center. Such conceptual attempts were inadequate, but tantalizing, in that they were somewhat speciously successful. The crux of the difficulty was that these efforts were made prior to the experimental observation of the wavelike nature of the electron, and quite naturally the concept of the electron as a small massive negatively charged sphere pervaded the thinking, and the dynamic and electric properties that such an object would have were extrapolated directly from large-scale experience. However, given the knowledge that the motion of an electron must be described, like that of a photon, as a wave phenomenon, it is quite clear that over distances comparable with its wave length the electron is not localizable in the ordinary sense. Thus an entirely different type of behavior would be expected than for the extension into indefinitely minute dimensions of the concept of a massive charged particle. It is obvious that the length of a wave associated with an electron's motion, if calculated from the energy it would acquire on being permitted to move to within atomic dimensions of a positively charged nucleus, would be of the order of these dimensions themselves. Letting the kinetic energy $\frac{1}{2}mv^2$ equal that gained by the disappearance of the potential energy, when the separation of the charges is reduced to r, namely KZe^2/r, and eliminating v by using the expression for the wave length $mv = h/\lambda$,

$$\frac{KZe^2}{r} = \tfrac{1}{2}mv^2 = \frac{(mv)^2}{2m} = \frac{h^2}{2m\lambda^2}$$

and hence:

$$\lambda = \frac{h}{e}\sqrt{\frac{r}{2mKZ}}$$

which for $Z = 10$ and $r = 10^{-10}$ m. yields a value for λ of 10^{-10} m. Since Z, in practice, always lies between 1 and 100, the above value of Z cannot introduce an error much greater than a factor of 3 in the value of λ. Thus λ and r are found to be essentially the same for values of r of 10^{-10} m., which we have earlier seen to be the order of magnitude of the dimensions of an atom. Thus it is essential to take the wavelike properties of the electron into account in the construction of any theory of atomic structure.

EXAMPLE. It was noted in the text that as one looks at the sequence of known atomic species from hydrogen, which is the lightest, up to lead, which is one of the heaviest, the atomic number does not increase as rapidly as the mass number, i.e., the ratio of net positive nuclear charge to nuclear mass decreases. One might investigate the hypothesis that heavier nuclei have increasing numbers of negatively charged electrons actually incorporated in their nuclei in order to account for this fact. A strong argument against this hypothesis is a consequence of the small size of the nucleus implying the very short electron wave length that could be accommodated within it, and the very large consequent energy of an electron so constrained by nuclear boundaries.

It will be recalled from the discussion of the relativistic expression for energy and momentum that

$$(mc)^2 - (mv)^2 = (m_0c)^2$$

Using the relation between the momentum and wave length of a particle $mv = h/\lambda$, the expression for its energy $U = mc^2$ in terms of its rest energy $U_0 = m_0c^2$ becomes:

$$U^2 - U_0^2 = \left(\frac{hc}{\lambda}\right)^2$$

or:

$$\left(\frac{U}{U_0}\right)^2 = 1 + \left(\frac{\lambda_c}{\lambda}\right)^2$$

where $\lambda_c = (h/m_0c)$ is the Compton wave length 2.426×10^{-12} m. If the electron with the wave length λ is in an electronic structure external to a nucleus with linear dimensions of the order 4×10^{-10} m., λ can be of this magnitude itself; inserting this number for λ in the above expression yields an energy $(U - U_0)$ of about 20 e.V., which is in the range of the binding energies of electrons in atomic structures. Using nuclear dimensions of, say, 4×10^{-15} m., $U \approx U_0\lambda_c/\lambda$, with $U_0 = 5.12 \times 10^5$ e.V. it is seen that: $U = 3.1 \times 10^8$ e.V. This is far greater than nuclear binding energies, as will be seen in Chap. 23. Thus, from this point of view, it is inconsistent to postulate the presence of electrons in nuclei, and the true explanation of the excess of mass number over atomic number must be postponed until a later chapter.

The theory of hydrogen as the prototype 15-4
of the one-electron atom

Our present theory, which describes very successfully—both in comprehensiveness and in detail—the electronic structure of atoms and the interaction of these through the emission and absorption of photons, is based upon the properties of electrons and photons educed in the preceding chapter. The extensive experience that classical physicists had had in describing the phenomena of wave motion under conditions closely parallel to those appropriate for describing electron waves in atomic structures was drawn on to provide rapid progress, once the fundamental properties of the electron were understood. This theory, which will not be presented in detail because of its highly mathematical nature, encompasses all types of atomic and molecular systems together with their interaction with photons. Being based fundamentally upon the wave nature of the photon and the electron, a function that describes the electron wave amplitude in much the same way as that describing the photon or any other wave motion is introduced. The intensity of the electronic presence, or alternatively stated, the probability of observing an electron in a particular small volume of time and space, is proportional to the square of the amplitude of this function, just as is the intensity in an interference pattern produced by a light wave. As in all other parts of the general consistent theory of physical phenomena, the conservation laws of energy, momentum, and angular momentum are the basic postulates, and the observations are concordant with them.

A greatly simplified and somewhat schematic approach to the description of a single electron as the structure surrounding a nucleus gives some elementary insight into the situation, and also yields quantitative values for the observable energy states and frequencies of the light that would be emitted as a result of transitions between these states. The hydrogen atom, consisting of the electrically neutral system of a nucleus and one circumambient electron is the simplest system, but the analysis is the same for an ion having a charge Ze on its nucleus and one electron charge $-e$ associated with it. Consider that the electron is in a stable state at an average distance r from the nucleus, and that it has associated with it an angular velocity and momentum so that it forms a standing wave system in this circular orbit, i.e., the wave function describing the electron joins up and is single-valued. Were this not the case, the wave would interfere destructively with itself and ultimately cancel itself out. The condition for this is that the circumference of the circle of radius r is equal to an integral number of wave lengths. If there are n waves about the circumference

$$n\lambda = 2\pi r$$

or as

$$\lambda = h/mv \quad \text{and} \quad v = r\omega$$

$$\lambda = h/mr\omega$$

and

$$nh = 2\pi mr^2\omega$$

Figure 15-5 *An electron as a standing wave about a nucleus.*

This condition clearly associates an angular momentum with the standing wave pattern of the accompanying figure (Fig. 15-5). If we write the angular momentum as L:

$$L = (mv)r = mr^2\omega = \frac{nh}{2\pi}$$

we see that this is equal to a multiple of $h/2\pi$. The rotation of a mass m with this angular momentum at the radius r, implies the existence of a centripetal force $m\omega^2 r$. This may be postulated to arise from the electrostatic attraction between the electron and nucleus. Adopting this hypothesis:

$$m\omega^2 r = K\frac{Ze^2}{r^2}$$

and eliminating ω with the expression for the angular momentum yields:

$$r = \frac{n^2 h^2}{4\pi^2 mKZe^2}$$

Thus the condition for the static standing wave configuration implies that there are certain radial zones about the nucleus which are determined by the integral values of n, and which are suitable for preferred electron occupancy.

The sum of the energy of motion and the electrostatic energy of the charges then yields the following:

$$U = -K\frac{Ze^2}{r} + \frac{1}{2}mv^2$$

$$= -K\frac{Ze^2}{r} + \frac{1}{2}mr^2\omega^2$$

$$= -\frac{2\pi^2K^2Z^2e^4m}{n^2h^2}$$

Thus the stable energy states are given by a constant divided by the square of an integer n, which can take any value from 1, through 2, 3, etc.

The form of this expression is correct to represent the series of monochromatic spectrum components that have been seen to comprise the spectrum of the hydrogen atom, and, in consequence, it is in very satisfactory qualitative agreement as a pattern of energy levels or states. Thus if a transition occurs between two permissible energy states, say n_2 and n_1 of the electrons, then the energy radiated will be the difference in the two energies:

$$U = -\frac{2\pi^2K^2Z^2e^4m}{n_2^2h^2} + \frac{2\pi^2K^2Z^2e^4m}{n_1^2h^2} = \frac{2\pi^2K^2Z^2e^4m}{h^2}\left(\frac{1}{n_1^2} - \frac{1}{n_2^2}\right)$$

and consequently the frequency radiated will be:

$$\nu = \frac{U}{h} = \frac{2\pi^2K^2Z^2e^4m}{h^3}\left(\frac{1}{n_1^2} - \frac{1}{n_2^2}\right)$$

or in terms of the wave length λ the expression may be written:

$$\frac{1}{\lambda} = \frac{\nu}{c} = \frac{2\pi^2K^2Z^2e^4m}{ch^3}\left(\frac{1}{n_1^2} - \frac{1}{n^2}\right) = RZ^2\left(\frac{1}{n_1^2} - \frac{1}{n_2^2}\right)$$

where $R = 2\pi^2K^2e^4m/ch^3$ is known as the Rydberg constant. Furthermore, the quantitative agreement between the observed wave lengths and the value of the constant in the equation gives convincing evidence that the concepts employed are appropriate to the problem. For hydrogen, $Z = 1$, and

$$\frac{1}{\lambda} = R\left(\frac{1}{n_1^2} - \frac{1}{n^2}\right)$$

From the known values of K, e, m, c and h, $R = 10,973,731$ per meter, with an accuracy of about three parts in ten million.

The nature of the quantitative comparison with experiment can be seen from the following tabulations of the first eight members of the Balmer series for hydrogen:

$$\frac{1}{\lambda} = R\left(\frac{1}{2^2} - \frac{1}{n^2}\right)$$

n	λ	$1/\lambda$	$(\frac{1}{2}^2 - 1/n^2)$	$R = [\lambda(\frac{1}{2}^2 - 1/n^2]^{-1}$
3	6.56280×10^{-7}m.	1523301	0.138889	10,967,775
4	4.86138	2056457	0.187500	10,967,775
5	4.34051	2303231	0.210000	10,967,775
6	4.10178	2437282	0.222222	10,967,775
7	3.97011	2518110	0.229592	10,967,775
8	3.88909	2570571	0.234395	10,967,775
9	3.83543	2606537	0.237654	10,967,775
10	3.79793	2632264	0.240000	10,967,775

The quotient is not exactly the same as the Rydberg constant given earlier, which is accounted for by the fact that in the simplified picture that has been presented, the motion of the nucleus of the atom has been neglected. The schematic depiction of the electron as a circumferential wave in Fig. 15-5 should be supplemented by an analogous small concentric circle representing the nuclear motion; the common center being the center of mass of the system. Thus both electron and nucleus must be considered to rotate about the center of mass of the two particles, and as seen in Sec. 5-4, this decreases the effective mass by just the amount necessary to account for the discrepancy.

The qualitative and quantitative agreement is not only excellent for hydrogen, but also for ionized helium, i.e., the helium atom, for which Z is 2, lacking one of its normal electron complement making it hydrogen-like as far as the electron structure is concerned. From the preceding analysis, it can be seen that the energy levels and frequencies for ionized helium should all be greater than those for hydrogen by a factor of 4, and this is found to be the case. Again, for doubly ionized lithium, for which Z equals 3, the pattern of emitted radiation is similar to that for hydrogen; all the energy magnitudes, however, are 9 times greater.

15-5 The fine structure of the energy levels of the hydrogen atom

It is seen from the table of wave lengths of the spectrum lines constituting the Balmer series of hydrogen that each of these lines is monochromatic, or of a single frequency, to quite a high degree of precision.

This, of course, reflects the fact that the energy states, or energy levels between which the transitions giving rise to the emission of photons occur, must also be sharply defined and single-valued to the same precision. Figure 15-6 indicates schematically as horizontal lines the energy levels corresponding to the values of $1/n^2$. The total energy, being one of permanent binding, is negative; $(\frac{1}{1})^2$ represents the largest negative value, $(\frac{1}{2})^2$ the next, and so on up through its higher levels, which become closer and closer together. The vertical lines indicate the photon-emitting transitions between levels; hence the spectrum lines in the several series. The transitions terminating on the $n = 2$ level represent the Balmer series, whose wave lengths were listed previously.

However, if one of these apparently single levels is examined more minutely by studying the wave lengths of the photons emitted by the atom, using optical or electronic methods of very high precision, the existence of a very interesting structure of the energy level is brought to light. As an example of the nature of this substructure, one of the gross energy levels, that for $n = 2$, is shown on a greatly enlarged scale in Fig. 15-7, and the magnitudes of the separation of the components of this level are given in terms of U/hc or $1/\lambda$, using the units of the number of wave lengths per meter.

It will be recalled from the discussion of planetary orbits that for a given energy of an orbit, various angular momenta are possible, the largest value corresponding to a circular orbit with the greatest area,

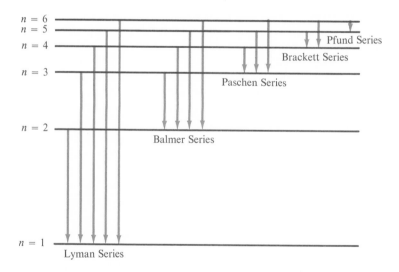

Figure 15-6 *Major features of the energy levels of a hydrogen-like atom.*

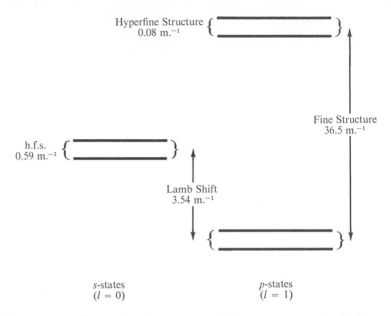

Figure 15-7 *Energy levels structure of the state n = 2 of a hydrogen atom. The energy spacings (not drawn to scale) are given in reciprocal wave length units, m⁻¹.*

and decreasing values being associated with the same major axis length but a shorter minor axis length (Sec. 5-4). A generically similar situation may be imagined to pertain in the quantum description, but both the total energy and angular momentum are *quantized*, by which we mean that they occur in discrete amounts. The energy values for a hydrogen atom are given by hRc/n^2, where n is an integer. The angular momenta can be written $l(h/2\pi)$, where l is an integer, and, as there is classically an upper limit for the angular momentum consistent with a given energy, so in the quantum theory the integer l is limited to the values 0, 1, 2, etc. up to a maximum which is set by $n - 1$. Note that the circular orbit would correspond to $l = n$ as discussed in the previous section, but this is not in fact permitted.

Thus, for the level $n = 2$ shown in the diagram, there are two possible values for the angular momentum, namely, $0(h/2\pi)$ and $1(h/2\pi)$, which are customarily designated as "*s*-states" $l = 0$ and "*p*-states" $l = 1$ respectively.

The major separation of these components of this level is 36.5 in reciprocal wave length units, which is about 4×10^{-7} of the separation between the levels for $n = 1$ and $n = 2$. Thus the entire pattern of Fig. 15-7, if reduced to the scale of Fig. 15-6, would fall well within the breadth of the printed line representing $n = 2$ on that diagram. This small difference in energy arises through the interaction of the magnetic moment associated with the angular momentum $h/2\pi$ of the p-state, and the magnetic moment associated with the intrinsic angular momentum or spin, which is an inherent property of the electron as mentioned in the preceding chapter. In the case of an s-state, the angular momentum is zero, and hence there is no energy of interaction with the intrinsic electronic magnetic moment. The nature of the interaction of these two tiny magnetic moments—the one associated with the angular momentum of the electron about the nucleus and the other associated with its inherent spin—is again found experimentally to be quantized in the sense that total angular momentum of an electron in an atom can only have values which are equal to the algebraic sum of or difference between the orbital and intrinsic angular momenta. As seen in Sec. 14-5, the intrinsic angular momentum of the electron is $h/4\pi$. Hence the total angular momentum of a p-state can be $h/2\pi \pm h/4\pi$, which leads to the two values $\frac{1}{2}(h/2\pi)$ and $\frac{3}{2}(h/2\pi)$. The directions of the magnetic moments being aligned with the angular momenta can then be in these two possible relative directions, and may be thought of as small vectors either parallel or antiparallel to one another, as shown in Fig. 15-8. The energy difference between these two configurations is the circumstance that gives rise to the separation of 36.5 m.$^{-1}$ represented in Fig. 15-7.

From the diagram, another energy difference identified as hyperfine structure (h.f.s.) is indicated. This is only about 0.2% of the fine structure energy difference, and it has been found to be identifiable with the energy of interaction between the small intrinsic magnetic moment found to be associated with the atomic nucleus and the magnetic field produced by the electron structure. Again, the laws of atomic and nuclear processes are such that only two relative orientations are possible; hence, the two energy levels.

Finally, there is an energy difference labeled "Lamb Shift," for Willis Lamb, at one time of Columbia University, who first discovered and identified it. The levels on the right of Fig. 15-7 have an angular momentum of one unit of $h/2\pi$ associated with them, but those on the left have no angular momentum at all. The latter configuration may be thought of as essentially a more static and centrally symmetric distribution of the electron or its probability of location about the nucleus. In such a situation the nucleus and the electron are effectively in the closest possible proximity permitted by the laws of atomic structure; the energy is most sensitive to any small relative displacement. The hypothetical absorption or emission of a photon with the consequent reaction on the electron momentum would have a greater effect upon

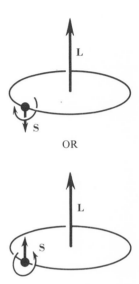

Figure 15-8 *The electron in an energy state with finite orbital angular momentum has two permissible orientations of its spin angular momentum* **S** *(spin-up or spin-down) with respect to its orbital angular momentum* **L**.

its interaction energy with the nucleus in the lowest s-state than in its lowest p-state. The Lamb Shift represents just this energy difference between the virtual emission or absorption processes in these two states.

The difference in energy between the two possible orientations of the direction of the spin and magnetic moment of the hydrogen nucleus, relative to the intrinsic spin and magnetic moment of the electron, in the state for which $n = 1$ and—of necessity—the orbital angular momentum measured by l is zero, corresponds to a wave number of 4.76 m.$^{-1}$, or a wave length of 21 cm. This hydrogen absorption line is observed by astronomers in the "radio-astronomy" range for the radiation reaching us from outer space, since space is sparsely populated by hydrogen atoms in this lowest energy state. This energy which is that necessary to reverse the relative orientation of the electron and hydrogen nucleus, is one which is predominantly abstracted from the radiation reaching us from the radiant sources at a great distance.

Further reading:

LILLEY, A. E., "The Absorption of Radio Waves in Space," *Scientific American*, vol. 197, No. 1, p. 48 (1957).

Problems

15-1 The electron in a particular hydrogen atom is known to be in the second excited state, i.e., two energy levels above the lowest state. Draw an energy level diagram and indicate on the diagram all the possible frequencies of light waves that may be emitted as the electron returns to its ground state; determine the numerical ratio of these frequencies.

15-2 An astronomer claims that a distant galaxy is composed of atomic particles whose mass and charge are one tenth those of their equivalents here in our galaxy. Of course, the fundamental constants G, K, h, c, etc., are the same for both galaxies. What effect would these fundamental changes have on atomic sizes and electron localizability?

15-3 If the radius of the lowest Bohr orbit for an electron were 0.5×10^{-10} m., what would be the momentum of the electron?

15-4 Some particles of mass m are shut up in a box of length l. Considering only their motion in one direction, they will bounce elastically back and forth between two opposite faces of the box. *Quantise* the system by demanding that each particle exist as a standing wave.
(a) What are the permissible energy states of the particles?
(b) What frequencies can be radiated by the system?
(c) What frequencies can be absorbed by the system?

(d) What wave lengths can be radiated by the system?

HINTS: The standing waves must have nodes at the reflecting walls. Unlike the hydrogen atom, there is no potential energy term to consider.

15-5 Examine the quantum equation for the orbital angular momentum of a circular orbit in the Bohr (simple) model of the hydrogen atom. In the light of the uncertainty principle, show that it is unreasonable to expect that we could ever observe an electron in such a well-defined orbit.

15-6 Compare the quantized energy equations for the particle in a box and the hydrogen atom. Discuss the significance of the different ways the principal quantum number n enters, and the sign ($+$ or $-$) of the energy.

15-7 The energy of a hydrogen atom in which the electron is in a state or orbit labelled by the integer n can be written:

$$U = -13.6 \left(\frac{1}{n^2}\right) \text{e.V.}$$

(a) How much energy does it take to completely remove the electron from the atom (to ionize the atom), if the electron is in its lowest state?

(b) How much energy does it take if the electron is in its highest state?

15-8 The extent of the Balmer series of hydrogen along a wave length or frequency scale is very nearly the same as the window of human visibility of the electromagnetic wave spectrum. Show that the first few lines of the series $n_1 = 3$, and the latter ones of the series $n_1 = 4$ for singly ionized helium, lie in the visible region.

15-9 When quantum mechanical calculations were first introduced into physics, the *correspondence principle* was found to be very useful. This principle insists that the predictions of quantum physics should be identical to those of classical physics in those situations where classical physics has been shown to apply. This should be the situation for the Bohr atom, when the radius of the orbit is very large and no longer of normal atomic dimensions, i.e., when n is very large. Classical theory predicts that the electron will radiate energy with a frequency equal to the frequency of rotation in its orbit. Show that for very large n this is approximately equal to the frequency emitted by an electron in a Bohr atom when its quantum number n decreases to a value $n - 1$.

15-10 The helium nucleus has no angular momentum or magnetic moment. What effect should this have on the emission and absorption spectra of the helium atom?

16 Polyelectronic atoms and molecules

16-1 The interaction of electrons in atomic systems

The success of the wave theory of matter, or quantum mechanics as it is also called, based upon the pioneering imaginative work of Erwin Schrodinger, Max Born, Werner Heisenberg, Wolfgang Pauli, and P. A. M. Dirac has been very great. It can be said to provide a complete and adequate ideological structure for the description of the interaction of electrons with one another and with photons, whether these electrons are isolated or whether they comprise the aggregate forming an atomic or molecular system. The application of the theory extends well beyond the low-energy phenomena concerned with atomic and molecular interactions, but a discussion of the high-energy implications will be postponed till later chapters. Detailed calculations involving several electrons in the same atomic system present complications that have deterred scientists from carrying them out except in a few cases of special interest, but with the general availability of high-speed computers, there are few such problems beyond the range of our abilities if the time and expense involved in their solutions are justified.

The general features of the interaction of electrons in atomic systems that derive from the basic classical theory of the earlier discussion are quite simple to state, and their qualitative consequences are readily deduced. The forces of greatest magnitude are those arising from the electrostatic interaction of electrons; magnetic forces are of less account, as can readily be seen from the expression for the energy given in the discussion of electrical phenomena. The electrostatic energy of two charges e, a distance r apart, is Ke^2/r, where K is about 9×10^9 in our units. The electromagnetic energy of two current elements likewise involves the geometrical factor $1/r$, but there is also the numerical factor of the square of the ratio of the velocity of the charges to the velocity of light. Except for very large values of v this ratio is small, as is borne out by the relative magnitude of the fine structure separation to the principal term separation discussed in the preceding chapter. In addition to these forces, it was also seen that the wave nature of the elementary particles constituting atomic systems or, equivalently stated, the quantum conditions that determine the symmetrical framework of an atomic structure lead to stability and the correct quantitative description of simple atoms consisting of a nucleus and a single electron. Still further, quantum effects evidence themselves when more than one electron is part of an atomic system and the inherent properties of elementary particles with which these effects are associated again are novel and not familiar to us from observations on large-scale samples of matter.

Professor W. Pauli of Zurich recognized in 1925 the existence of a hitherto unknown attribute of electrons, which may be stated in the form of the fundamental physical principle that no two electrons may be described in precisely the same way in terms of mass, charge, position, time, and direction of orientation of intrinsic spin; or, if they are members of the same atomic system, no two electrons may be characterized by precisely the same specifications in terms of the parameters designating the energy and angular momentum. This statement, which is called the *exclusion principle*, appears to be closely related to the basic identity or complete lack of distinguishability—even in imagination, let alone by experimental observation—that pertains to the permanent particles of which our universe is composed. As an instance, given that the masses, charges, intrinsic angular momenta (spins), and magnetic moments are identical for all electrons, two electrons that are in close spatial proximity at any instant must be distinguishable by the different relative orientation of the vectors representing their spins or those representing their intrinsic magnetic moments.

A consequence of the quantum theory of electrons, analogous to the limitation on the orientation of an electron's spin s relative to the orientation of its orbital angular momentum vector **L** of Sect. 5-5, is that these spin vectors can not take up an arbitrary orientation with respect to the residual magnetic field always present in the neighborhood of matter or the field produced by a neighboring electron. They are limited to orientations that are either parallel or antiparallel to the direction distinguished by the local field. More precisely, they may be thought of as precessing about this direction, as seen in an earlier chapter, but the steady net component along the local field during the precession can take only the two discrete values of $\pm h/4\pi$.

Within the electronic structure of an atom, the effect of the exclusion principle is to tend to pair electrons with oppositely oriented spins in the normal electronic configuration of lowest electrostatic energy. This will be seen in Sect. 16-3. The energy associated with this pairing tendency is not to be confused with the magnetic energy of interaction between the moments of the two electrons or their interaction with orbital motion, for these magnetic effects are so small that they influence only the finer details of the ergodic structure of the electrons surrounding a nucleus.

EXAMPLE. The very small contributions to the total energy of the electron configuration of an atom or a combination of atoms in a molecule or crystal that is made by the magnetic energy of interaction of the electronic magnetic moments was indicated by the discussion of the fine structure of the hydrogen spectrum in Sect. 15-5. There it was seen that the reversal of the direction of the intrinsic spin and magnetic moment of the electron relative to the orbital angular momentum about the nucleus changed the total energy of the electron-proton structure constituting a hydrogen atom only by about 1 part in 10^8. The reversal of the direction of the proton's angular momentum and magnetic moment relative to the orbital angular momentum of the electron accounting for the hyperfine energy structure was seen to be only $0.08/36.5$, or about 2.2×10^{-3} as important energetically as the reversal of the electron's magnetic moment.

From the discussion in Sect. 11-4, it will be recalled that the ratio of the magnetic moment to the angular momentum of a spinning mass and charge should be proportional to the ratio of the charge e to the mass m. The intrinsic spin or angular momentum of the proton is the same as that of the electron, and because of its greater mass, the proton's magnetic moment would be expected to be of the order of a thousandth that of the electron. Experimentally this order of magnitude is verified, but the numerical value is about three times as great as this simple argument would suggest.

Again in Sect. 15-5 it was stated that for the hydrogen atom in the lowest energy state, for which there is no orbital angular momentum, the electron may be thought of as centrally surrounding the proton, as in Fig. 16-1, and an amount of energy equal to 4.76 m^{-1} or about 6×10^{-6} e.V. could be absorbed from radiation impinging upon it, causing a reversal of the direction of the proton's magnetic moment relative to that of the electron. From these considerations it would be expected that two electrons in close spatial association with one another would have a lower energy with their angular momentum and magnetic moment vectors aligned than opposed by about 10^3 times the proton-electron mutual energy, namely about 6×10^{-3} e.V. This is smaller by the order of 10^3 than the binding energies of molecules that are furnished by electron pairing (Sect. 16-4) and hence clearly not the significant contributor to electron bonding.

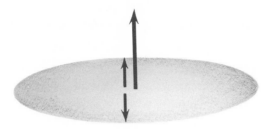

Figure 16-1 *Schematic depiction of the mag-netic moment vectors for the electron and for the two possible orientations of the proton in a hydrogen atom in its lowest state of n = 1 and l = 0.*

The effects produced by an external 16-2
magnetic field

The study of the radiation emitted by atomic systems in the presence of an externally applied magnetic field has been very useful in clarifying the relationship between the energy levels of electronic systems. The changes in wave length or frequency of the emitted radiation brought about by the magnetic field is known as the *Zeeman effect,* and it of course reflects the changes in energy of the initial and final levels, the transitions between which give rise to the radiation. In the case of a hydrogen-like atom in the absence of the applied field, the magnetic interaction between the magnetic moment produced by the orbital angular momentum of the electron and the magnetic moment associated with the spin results in the doubling of each level corresponding to the two possible spin orientations relative to the orbital angular momentum.

It was shown in the preceding chapter that the orbital motion of the electron is characterized by an angular momentum $L = lh/2\pi$, where l may take the values $0, 1, 2, \ldots$ etc., up to the maximum value of $n - 1$. It will be recalled from Sect. 11-4, that a circulating charge e of mass m_0 and angular momentum L has a magnetic moment associated with it which is equal to

$$\mu = \frac{1}{2}\frac{e}{m_0}L = l\frac{eh}{4\pi m_0}$$

The quantity $(eh/4\pi m_0)$ is the unit of atomic magnetic moment and is given the designation *Bohr Magneton.* When a magnetic field H is applied, the magnetic moment μ tends to precess about the direction of the field as indicated in Fig. 16-2, with angular velocity

$$\omega' = \frac{\mu}{L} H = \frac{eH}{2m_0}$$

The laws of quantum mechanics specify that the orbital angular momentum **L** must align itself with respect to the field so that its component in that direction is quantised in units of $h/2\pi$, i.e., the component of the orbital angular momentum in the direction of the field can only be $m_l(h/2\pi)$, where m_l can have any integral value between $-l$ and $+l$. Consequently the component of the orbital magnetic moment in the direction of the field is $m_l(eh/4\pi m_0)$. Likewise, the electron spin tends to precess about the field with a magnetic moment component $\pm (eh/4\pi m_0)$, according to whether the spin is up (parallel to the field) or down (antiparallel). However, since the ratio of magnetic moment to angular momentum μ/L is $(eh/4\pi m_0)/(h/4\pi)$ or e/m_0, which is twice the value for the orbital ratio, the rate of precession for the spin magnetic moment is twice that for the orbital magnetic moment. Thus the different precessional rates tend to disrupt the normal interaction between spin and orbital motion in the absence of an applied magnetic field.

This normal relationship between these local atomic motions is but slightly perturbed for very small applied fields, and the atom exhibits an average moment little different from that in the absence of the field;

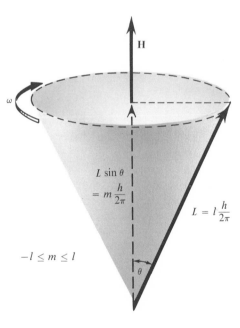

Figure 16-2   *The angular momentum vector L precesses about the direction of an applied magnetic field H. L is quantized and the angle between L and H must be such that the component of L in the direction of H is also quantized.*

but for large external fields, the energy of interaction of the circulatory and spin moments with the field is so much greater than the energy of interaction with each other that each proceeds to precess independently and at its characteristic rate about the field. The effective magnetic moment then takes all values from $(l + 1)$ to $-(l + 1)$ in units of $eh/4\pi m_0$. However, because of the fact that the photon can take but one unit of angular momentum from an atomic system when it is emitted at a radiative process, the transitions between these many states when l is large are limited to those for which l does not change by more than one unit. Thus l may increase or decrease by a unit, or remain unchanged, and the resulting modification in the observed spectrum is that each previously single spectrum line becomes triple. In more complex atomic systems of several electrons, the behavior is similar in principle, but the details of the motion and resultant change in photon emission becomes much more involved.

Enumeration of the electrons in a polyelectronic atom 16-3

The possible electron configurations in polyelectronic atoms may be considered in the light of the foregoing considerations. It is simple to list the possible values of the parameters specifying an electron within an atomic structure beginning with the simplest and proceeding to the most complex under the general methods of specification that have been indicated. The gross energy is specified by the principal quantum number. It can take integral values:

$$n = 1, 2, 3, 4, \ldots \ldots \ldots \ldots$$

The angular momentum quantum number, sometimes called the *orbital quantum number*, can take the values up to $n - 1$ for a given energy:

$$l = 0, 1, 2, \ldots \ldots \ldots \ldots (n - 1)$$

The orientation of the angular momentum vector, sometimes called the *magnetic quantum number*, because it is proportional to the component of the oribtal magnetic moment aligned with a local magnetic field, may be:

$$m_l = -l, -(l - 1), -(l - 2), \ldots \ldots 0 \ldots (l - 1), l$$

The component of the electron spin m_s may be $+\frac{1}{2}$ or $-\frac{1}{2}$, again in units of $h/2\pi$.

According to the Pauli principle, only one electron in a given atomic system may be specified by exactly the same combination of all these parameters. The following tabular ordering beginning with the smallest n of unity and working on up through successive integers indicates the permitted combinations of specifications that are possible using these parameters, which are concordant with the Pauli principle. The resulting sequential order in this nomenclature represents the lowest energy states or the actually observed normal states of the electrons in the first eighteen atoms of the chemical table (Fig. 16-3). The complex dependence of the energy upon the angular momenta of the component electrons and their orientations introduces irregularities in the ordering beyond this point. Our limited mathematical abilities preclude our carrying out the detailed calculations that would be necessary in order to determine the numerical values of the energy states of structures composed of an arbitrary number of electrons. Our knowledge of these is largely empirical, and comes from the analysis of the frequencies observed in the emission and absorption of photons by these atoms in a gas or vapor.

In Table 16-1 the electron configuration is written in a form of shorthand employing expressions such as (as^α), (bp^β), (cd^γ), etc. Here a stands for the value of the principal quantum number, i.e., the n-value of the s- electrons for which the angular momentum is zero; b stands for the same quantity for the p-electrons, which have unit angular momentum; etc. The exponents α, β, γ, etc. indicate the number of the electrons of the given type that are present.

This method of listing in increasing complexity of electronic structure is another way of portraying the familiar periodic table of chemistry that was first constructed in outline by the Russian chemist D. I. Mendeleev towards the end of the last century. With helium, all possible electrons of the $(1s)$ type, namely, 2, are present, and the $(1s)$ shell is said to be closed. With beryllium the 4 electrons occupying the $(1s)$ and $(2s)$ shells are present, and with neon the $6(2p)$ electrons, which are all of that type that can be accommodated are present, and the $n = 2$ shell of s and p electrons is closed. On referring to the table, we see that the closing of a shell of any type of electron s, p, d, etc. presents a configuration of zero total angular momentum, for the sums of both m_l and m_s are zero at those positions in the atomic sequence. The chemical properties, depending as they do primarily upon the configurations occupied by the most loosely bound electrons, tend to recur with the periodicity of shell closings. Single $(1s)$, $(2s)$, $(3s)$, etc., electrons beyond a closed shell tend to present similar chemical or combining properties, which fact accounts for the generic similarity among the alkali metals lithium, sodium, potassium, rubidium, and cesium. Likewise, the gase-

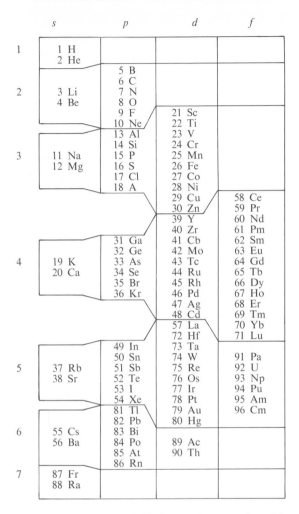

Figure 16-3 *Atomic sequence folded into the periodic table of the elements. In the "d" and "f" columns the lowest energy structure is often represented by a shifting of the outer electrons to lower angular moments and a higher ordinal quantum number.*

ous elements helium, neon, argon, krypton, and xenon closing s or p shells are particularly inert chemically and do not form strong molecular combinations.

As the nuclear charge, or atomic number Z mounts along the sequence, the innermost electrons of low n are bound with greater and

Table 16-1 Normal electron structures of the first eighteen elements

added electrons n l m_l m_s		configuration	chemical element
1 0 0 $\frac{1}{2}$	1 electron	$1s$	Hydrogen
0 $-\frac{1}{2}$	2 electrons	$1s^2$	Helium
2 0 0 $\frac{1}{2}$	3 $''$	$1s^2.\,2s$	Lithium
0 $-\frac{1}{2}$	4 $''$	$1s^2.\,2s^2$	Beryllium
2 1 1 $\frac{1}{2}$	5 $''$	$1s^2.\,2s^2.\,2p$	Boron
1 $-\frac{1}{2}$	6 $''$	$''$ $''$ $2p^2$	Carbon
0 $\frac{1}{2}$	7 $''$	$''$ $''$ $2p^3$	Nitrogen
0 $-\frac{1}{2}$	8 $''$	$''$ $''$ $2p^4$	Oxygen
-1 $\frac{1}{2}$	9 $''$	$''$ $''$ $2p^5$	Flourine
-1 $-\frac{1}{2}$	10 $''$	$''$ $''$ $2p^6$	Neon
3 0 0 $\frac{1}{2}$	11 $''$	$''$ $''$ $''$ $3s$	Sodium
$-\frac{1}{2}$	12 $''$	$''$ $''$ $''$ $3s^2$	Magnesium
3 1 1 $\frac{1}{2}$	13 $''$	$''$ $''$ $''$ $''$ $3p$	Aluminum
1 $-\frac{1}{2}$	14 $''$	$''$ $''$ $''$ $''$ $3p^2$	Silicon
0 $\frac{1}{2}$	15 $''$	$''$ $''$ $''$ $''$ $3p^3$	Phosphorus
0 $-\frac{1}{2}$	16 $''$	$''$ $''$ $''$ $''$ $3p^4$	Sulfur
-1 $\frac{1}{2}$	17 $''$	$''$ $''$ $''$ $''$ $3p^5$	Chlorine
-1 $-\frac{1}{2}$	18 $''$	$''$ $''$ $''$ $''$ $3p^6$	Argon

greater energies. From the formula for the energy of the one-electron, or hydrogenic atom, it would be anticipated qualitatively that the binding energy of these electrons would increase in proportion to Z^2. This is found to be the case, and the very high energy characteristic x-ray photons that heavy atoms may be stimulated to emit correspond to the removal of one of these electrons and subsequent settling down of the configuration by filling the vacancy thus created from among more loosely bound electrons. The lowest hydrogen state, or ground state, corresponds, as has been seen in Chap. 15, to a frequency of cR, or 3.29×10^{15} sec.$^{-1}$, or an energy of hcR, which is 2.14×10^{-18} J. The energy in electron Volts is this quantity divided by e, or 13.6 e.V. For instance, the most tightly bound electron for an element such as zinc ($Z = 30$) should have an energy of about 900×13, or 12,000 e.V.

An electron impinging upon a zinc atom would have to fall through a potential difference of about 12,000 V. to remove such a tightly bound electron, and its return to this position in the zinc electronic structure would result in the emission of an x-ray photon of this energy.

EXAMPLE. It is, of course, clear from the wave nature of the electrons composing the outer electronic structure of atoms that the boundary of an atom is not a sharp one. However, a rough measure of atomic dimensions may be derived from the preceding considerations in the text. The separations between the centers of atoms held together by electronic structure forces in molecules and crystals can be determined by diffraction experiments. Contrary to what might, at first thought, be assumed, the heavier atoms with larger and more complex electronic structure do not have much greater dimensions than the lighter simpler atoms such as hydrogen and helium. The expression in Sect. 15-4 for the radius of a circular orbit of a single electron provides the dependence in such a case of r on n and Z in terms of certain constants. On inserting the values of these constants the orbit radius is found to be

$$r = 0.5 \times 10^{-10} \frac{n^2}{Z} \text{ m.}$$

The radius of the hydrogen atom in its lowest energy state, for which case $n = Z = 1$, is thus 0.5×10^{-10} m. The binding energy is hcR/e in electron Volts, which is seen to be about 13.6 e.V.

The simple calculation for a one-electron atom can not be expected to be applicable with any precision to atoms with many electrons. Even so, the order-of-magnitude comparisons are of interest. The lowest energy states ($n = 1$) have the smallest radius, and their energies are least interfered with by more distant electrons. Their energies are found to be quite strictly proportional to Z^2, as the simple theory of Chap. 15 predicts. Also the energies of the next higher states (n = 2) are given quite satisfactorily if the shielding effect of the two inner electrons ($n = 1$) is allowed for. Thus, if maximum shielding were assumed, the presence of the two ($n = 1$) electrons inside the orbit of the ($n = 2$) electrons would reduce the effective central charge from $+Ze$ to $+(Z - 2)e$. Even the sizes of the heavier atoms are given in order-of-magnitude by the simple one-electron expression for r, if reasonable values are used for n and Z. In Table 16-2 the diameter of the outermost orbit is calculated for the alkali metal elements, each of which has one electron in its outermost orbit. The calculation is made for the two extreme assumptions—no shielding, for which the diameter is $n/Z^2 \times 10^{-10}$ m. and maximum shielding, for which the same formula holds, but with an effective Z equal to 1. The measured crystal spacings are seen to lie between these two extreme values.

Table 16-2 *Calculated and measured values of atomic dimensions for the alkali metal elements*

element	Z	n	no shielding	maximum shielding	crystal spacing
Lithium	3	2	1.33	4	3.51×10^{-10} meters
Sodium	11	3	0.82	9	4.29
Potassium	19	4	0.84	16	5.34
Rubidium	37	5	0.68	25	5.71
Caesium	55	6	0.66	36	6.08

16-4 *Combinations of atoms forming molecules*

The outermost electrons are largely shielded by the inner ones from the electrostatic attraction of the nucleus, so they find themselves in an electric field like one that would be produced by a charge of the order of one electronic unit at a distance corresponding to about an atomic diameter, which is of the order of 10^{-10} m. Upon inserting these values in the equation for the electrostatic energy, the order of magnitude of from 1 to 10 e.V. is obtained; this is the order of the binding energy experienced by these electrons. Hence, the energy liberated in chemical reactions, such as the burning of fuels, depends little upon the atomic weight of the participating elements or the chemical nature of the fuel. The energy liberated or absorbed in a chemical reaction is determined to the first order by the number of molecules of the substances reacting together, the constant of proportionality being much the same for all reactants. Table 16-3 gives the values of the thermal energy liberated when the substances listed are burned or combined with oxygen to the extent that occurs in ordinary processes. Taking the mean atomic weight to be about 10, the number of Joules per kilomole varies from 10^8 to 5×10^8, and the electron Volt equivalent per atom is this quantity divided by Ne, which is approximately 10^8, confirming that the energy of chemical combination lies in the region of 1 to 5 e.V. per atom.

Table 16-3

substance	Joules per kilogram
Alcohol	2.70×10^7
Gasoline	4.83
Kerosene	4.60
Butter	3.86
Charcoal	3.40
Pine Wood	1.85
Sulfur	1.01

The atoms of the chemical elements enter into combinations with other atoms of the same and different chemical species to form polyatomic aggregates varying in complexity from the two hydrogen atoms that associate together to form the hydrogen molecule, through other types of homogeneous and heterogeneous di- and tri-atomic molecules, up to the long complex chains, spirals, and rings of many hundreds or thousands of atoms constituting the chemical substances found in living organisms. Crystals, in a sense, are also giant molecules representing as they do ordered aggregates of atoms. However, there is no natural limit to the size of a crystal, whereas even the giant molecules of biochemistry do not exceed microscopic size.

The chemical properties of molecules are, of course, different from the characteristics of the constituent atoms, but they are determined by these characteristics in the sense that the electron structure of the molecule is the aggregate of the electron structures of the atoms composing it, modified to the extent that these electron structures influence one another. The magnitude of this mutual influence is, in energy terms, of the same order of magnitude as that of the binding of the outer electrons. In fact, the nature of the molecular bond is the sharing of outer electrons by the atomic systems. In the diatomic hydrogen molecule, the two electrons are shared between the two nuclei. This case is simple enough to yield to approximate calculation and reasonably good energy values can be computed from first principles. Under the electrostatic forces of the two pairs of like charges, the two electrons tend to take up a central position between the nuclei with their spins oppositely oriented (↑ ↓) in accordance with the exclusion principle for electrons tending to occupy the same space (Fig. 16-4). This type of electron bond is the common characteristic of molecular aggregation. Sometimes the result-

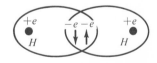

Figure 16-4 *Symmetrical hydrogen molecule H_2 (schematic) showing sharing of oppositely oriented electron pair.*

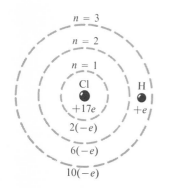

$n = 3$

$n = 2$

$n = 1$

Cl   H

$+17e$ $+e$

$2(-e)$

$6(-e)$

$10(-e)$

Figure 16-5 *Schematic hydrogen chloride molecule HCl.*

ant electron structure is very unequally shared between the nuclei, as in hydrochloric acid (HCl), where the structure obviously centers on the chlorine atom (Fig. 16-5), and sometimes two electrons from each atom are shared quite symmetrically as in the case of the molecule formed by divalent oxygen.

The electromagnetic radiation from molecules again is similar to that from atoms, and as the energy levels of the outer electrons are of the same order of magnitude, the photons lie in the same frequency range. But the greater complexity of the molecular systems leads to a much more extensive and complex line structure in the spectrum of molecules. There are also somewhat lower frequencies present, and these can readily and unambiguously be associated with the vibratory or rotational motion of the atomic nuclei and their closely associated inner electron shells within the looser elastic matrix of the outer shared electrons. The harmonic vibrations of the nuclei about their natural positions of equilibrium whithin the structure evidently occur under the action of forces similar to those holding the electron structure itself together. Therefore, the constant k, which is the force per unit displacement for oscillatory motion discussed in Sect. 6-2, must have similar values in the two cases. Thus, since the frequency ν of vibratory motion in each case is related to k by the formula

$$\nu = \frac{1}{2\pi}\sqrt{\frac{k}{m}}$$

it is seen that the ratio of the spectrum frequencies for nuclear vibrational motion to that for electronic motion would be expected to be $(m/M)^{1/2}$, which is approximately 10^{-2}; this is born out by experiment.

Again, if the center of charge and center of mass of a molecule are not coincident, end-over-end rotation of the molecule should give the impression of an alternating charge dipole and photons should be emitted. Assuming that the system possesses but a few units of angular momentum in terms of $h/2\pi$, the angular momentum $Ma^2\omega_n$ of the molecule is of the same order of magnitude as $ma^2\omega_e$ of the electron structures, where the linear dimensions a are the same for the nuclear and electronic separations. Thus, for rotational spectra, the frequencies should be less than the electronic spectrum frequencies by the factor m/M, or about 10^{-4}, which is again found to be the case.

The study of molecular spectra has led to a very complete understanding of the nature of the disposition of the nuclei and central shells within the outer binding electronic structure of the molecule. This electronic structure may be thought of crudely as represented by a gel in which are embedded the massive nuclei. The gel is resistant to distor-

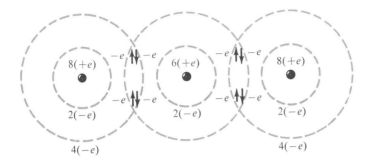

Figure 16-6 *Linear carbon dioxide molecule in which two pairs of electrons are shared between the carbon and oxygen atom.*

tions of extension or compression and bending or twisting shears; after a displacement, oscillations result and photons may be emitted if there is an associated periodic electric field. The symmetries of the molecular structure are very high, and the details of this as well as of the quantitative separation and force parameters may be deduced from the analysis of the emitted spectra. In diatomic molecules the nuclei, of course, lie on a single line; in triatomic atoms they may also do so, as in the doubly bonded CO_2 (Fig. 16-6). But, alternatively, they may form a triangle, as in H_2O, in which instance the opening angle is about 105° (Fig. 16-7). Four-atom molecules have a very wide possibility of symmetries open to them; in the case of the ammonia molecule NH_3, the shape is that of a symmetrical pyramid with the nitrogen atom at the apex. This can pop back and forth through the triangle formed by the hydrogens, and the frequency of the radiation emitted due to this motion is easily identifiable.

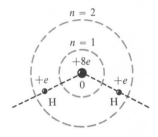

Figure 16-7 *Triangular water molecule, H_2O.*

Further reading:

GAMOW, G., "The Exclusion Principle," *Scientific American*, vol. 201, No. 1, p. 74 (1959).

GORDY, W., "The Shortest Radio Waves," *Scientific American*, vol. 196, No. 5, p. 46 (1957).

KAMPER, R. A., "Paramagnetic Resonance," *American Journal of Physics*, vol. 28, No. 3, p. 249 (1960).

LAX, B., "Cyclotron Resonance," *Science*, Vol. 134, No. 3487, p. 1333 (1961).

Problems

16-1 What are the restrictions, if any, on the amount by which the magnetic quantum number m_l may change during the emission or absorption of a photon by an atomic electron?

16-2 An electron flips over from spin-up to spin-down. What is the resultant change in angular momentum? What could prevent this from happening to some atomic electrons?

16-3 How many electrons in a single atom can have the principle quantum number $n = 4$? List the values of l, s, m_l and m_s for each. If possible, deduce a general formula for the total number of electrons that can have the same principle quantum number n.

16-4 The elements cesium and barium are next to each other in the periodic table, occupying the first and second columns. Explain, using the theory of atomic structure, whether you would expect these elements to combine chemically with one another readily to form a compound.

16-5 What is the net angular momentum (orbital plus spin) of the electron structure in a sodium atom in its ground or unexcited state?

16-6 What would be the consequences if the Pauli exclusion principle did not apply to atomic electrons?

16-7 Write down the electronic configurations for titanium ($Z = 22$) and praseodymium ($Z = 59$), using the notation employed in the text. Caution: praseodymium has no electron in the $5d$ shell.

16-8 (a) What is the change in energy for the transition $n = 4$ to $n = 3$ of an electron in a doubly ionized atom of lithium?
(b) If the orbital angular momentum was a maximum both before and after the above transition, and if the direction of this angular momentum remained the same, what was the change in angular momentum? Assume no change of spin for the transition.
(c) If the orbital angular momentum was a minimum both before and after the transition, what was the change in angular momentum, again assuming no change of spin?

16-9 A molecule of lithium chloride (LiCl) undergoes vibratory motion whose energy may be expressed roughly as $U = 200x^2$, where x is the amplitude of vibration of the lithium nucleus of mass number 7. The chlorine nucleus of mass number 37 may be treated as essentially fixed for the accuracy required. Show that the natural frequency of vibration is approximately 3×10^{13} sec.$^{-1}$.

16-10 The energies of vibratory motion in a diatomic molecule are given by the formula $U = (n + \frac{1}{2})h\nu_0$, where n is an integer and ν_0 is the frequency of vibration. Taking the result from the previous problem, calculate the separation between energy levels for this vibratory motion of a LiCl molecule. Express the answer in Joules and also in e.V. What is the *zero point* energy (minimum possible energy) associated with this type of motion? What is the amplitude of vibration for the zero point energy?

Equilibrium conditions characterizing large aggregates of atoms and molecules

17

Energy exchange and the interaction energy between atoms and molecules 17-1

In the preceding chapters the basic concepts that evolved in the study of mechanical and electrical phenomena were supplemented by the quantum phenomena displayed by electrons, and employed to formulate a theory of the matter composing our universe in terms of the atoms of the chemical species and the combination of these atoms into molecules. The interaction of single electrons and aggregates of electrons in atomic structures with photons, whereby an exchange of energy through the medium of radiation is brought about between electrons and between atomic systems, has also been described. The discussion has been limited, however, to what is thought of in physics as the region of low energy interactions comprising the transitions between the energy states of the electronic structures of atoms and molecules. The photons concerned are those in the spectrum described in Chap. 7, having wave lengths greater than about 10^{-11} m., or energies less than a few hundred thousand electron Volts. The high energy phenomena involving atomic nuclei and the larger-scale interchange of energy between mass and radiation will be considered in later chapters dealing with nuclear phenomena.

In addition to the molecular bonds that hold atoms together in small molecular aggregates and in crystals with energies in the 1 to 10 e.V. range, there are still smaller energies of interaction which tend to form films of gas atoms and moisture on surfaces of solids, and to draw together gas atoms and molecules so that they do not behave as if they were quite independent entities that would collide and separate like billiard balls with no energy of association. These smaller forces between atoms and molecules represent energies of association in the region of 1 e.V. or less, and result in the ephemeral, evanescent, loose, and constantly shifting bonds between atoms in vapors and in thin adsorbed films. These also account for the departures from the simple laws of gaseous behavior, called the perfect gas laws, which are based upon the assumption of no energy of association between the gas molecules occupying some confining volume.

The properties of matter consisting of atoms and molecules held together in the tenuous gaseous state by the walls of a container, as well as in the closer packing together that is self-maintaining and characterizes liquids and solids, are to a considerable extent conditioned by the energy content or heat energy that is shared and continuously interchanged between the constituent molecules in the quasi-steady state known as thermal equilibrium. One may classify the forms this energy may take in terms of individual and cooperative atomic and molecular processes: (1) energy of excitation of the electronic structure of certain atoms and molecules of the population leading to a more energetic configuration than the lowest ground states of these structures, and representing the temporary storage in this way of from 1 to 10 e.V. per atom from the ambient energy reservoir; (2) energy of vibration of the nuclei of the atoms composing molecular structures, or liquid or crystalline aggregates, about their positions of equilibrium under the influence of the elastic forces arising from electric, magnetic, and electron bonding forces; (3) energy of rotation of molecules; (4) energy of permanent association or transient propinquity of atoms and molecules, representing their tendency to adhere together; (5) kinetic energy of translation of the atoms or molecules of a gas between collisions with their neighbors; (6) energy in the form of photons transporting quanta of radiant energy between atomic systems. At very high temperatures, where the ionization of atoms may result from thermal collisions, energy may also reside in the ion-electron separation and the kinetic energy of translation of these charged fragments. The total energy present in all of these forms remains constant, in accordance with the principle of the conservation of energy for any completely closed and isolated system of particles or sample of matter; but by the emission and adsorption of photons and by the collisions of massive particles energy is constantly being exchanged between the constituent atoms and molecules and between the several forms in terms of which the state of the system is described. If the isolation of a sample is not complete, which it never actually is in practice of course, the system gains and loses energy to some extent from and to its surroundings in the above ways as well.

Elementary statistical considerations bearing on the distribution of energy among a group of interacting particles 17-2

The detailed description of such a complex situation as is presented by the exchange of energy among these several forms within a macroscopic sample of matter containing, say, 2.7×10^{19} molecules, as in a cubic centimeter of air under normal conditions of temperature and pressure, is clearly much too formidable to contemplate under any circumstances. However, statistical methods may be employed to yield very complete and precise results within their inherent limitations. The mortality tables upon which life insurance rates are based do not tell how long an individual of a given age will live, but they do give an adequate answer to the question of how many people of a large population of known character will die per year within each age interval. Similarly, one can proceed to construct a statistical theory upon very reasonable *a priori* grounds that will predict with a high degree of reliability how many molecules will possess a given amount of energy, and in what form it is most likely to be present under specified conditions for a large assembly of molecules.

The development of a statistical theory of large aggregates of molecules was shown to be possible by the pioneering work of Professor Josiah Willard Gibbs of Yale University, who was probably the outstanding American scientist of the nineteenth century. The procedure is briefly as follows: one considers the various forms of energy as exhibited by molecular motion as constituting a sequence of closely spaced energy levels or intervals within which are comprised all of the states of motion of which the constituent molecules of the system are capable. The number of types of motion contributing to the energy levels of the system in the neighborhood of, say, the energy u_j may be quite different from the number in the neighborhood of, say, the energy u_l, owing to the contribution of many types of motion in a high energy region, but very few, possibly only slow translational kinetic energy, in the low energy region. However, such matters may be determined from molecular theory and a weighting or level density factor provided so that, let us say, the density of energy levels due to all forms of motion in the neighborhood of u_j is g_j. Then the question to be determined is: what is the most probable distribution of the N molecules constituting the sample of matter under consideration over the energy level pattern as determined by molecular properties and under the condition of a constant total energy content of the system? A unique answer to this question exists, and one may proceed to determine the number of molecules, n_j with energy u_j as a function of the assumed parameters; one may also show that the probability of observing any departure from this most probable distribution is so small that it is completely negligible if one is dealing with very large populations, i.e., if all the n_j's are large. If this condition is fulfilled, the solution is almost certain to be applicable and to provide a precise description of the situation.

The theory of probability is one of the most interesting examples of the interplay of induction and deduction, but only the simplest concepts will be required for the present discussion. If a good coin is flipped or spun, it is found that in any one instance it is as likely to come to rest lying face up as face down. Using 1 to denote certainty, the probability of getting a head is then $\frac{1}{2}$, as is likewise the probability of getting a tail. On the basis of this observation, the *a priori* probability of a series of independent events is the product of the probability of each separately, and hence the probability of any specific sequence of heads and tails of N members is $(\frac{1}{2})^N$. However, the question is more often asked: what is the probability of throwing n_1 heads and n_2 tails in N throws where $N = n_1 + n_2$? This is a different matter, for if the precise order is not of concern, a number of the different sequences will correspond to the requisite division of N into n_1 heads and n_2 tails. The answer to this question comes immediately from a consideration of the binomial expansion given in the final section of Chap. 1. Let a and b be any two fractions representing probabilities whose sum is unity [in the case of a good coin ($a = b = \frac{1}{2}$)], thus the expansion

$$(a + b)^N = a^N + Na^{N-1}b + \frac{N(N-1)}{2!} a^{N-2}b^2 \cdots \cdots$$

$$+ \frac{N!}{(N-n_1)!n_1!} a^{(N-n_1)}b^{n_1} \cdots \cdots \cdots \cdots + b^N$$

represents unity on each side, and the coefficient of $a^{n_1}b^{n_2}$, where $(N = n_1 + n_2)$ represents the number of different products of a taken n_1 times and b taken n_2 times in the multiplication; hence $N!/(n_1!n_2!)$ represents the number of different sequences of $n_1 a$'s (heads) and $n_2 b$'s (tails) in the total assembly of sequences. Hence this is the weighting factor for $(\frac{1}{2})^N$, which should be applied to the particular total numbers of heads and tails stipulated, and $(N!/n_1!n_2!)(\frac{1}{2})^N$ is the probability that, in N throws, exactly n_1 heads and n_2 tails are observed. The binomial coefficients increase from 1 to a maximum in the middle of the series where $n_1 = n_2$ if N is even, or where they differ from one another by one unit if N is odd. Hence the most probable assembly or sequence is that for which heads and tails are present in nearly equal numbers.

EXAMPLE. The probability of throwing n_1 heads and n_2 tails in $N = n_1 + n_2$ throws of a coin is $N!/(n_1!n_2!)(\frac{1}{2})^N$. The product of the factorials in the denominator is smallest when $n_1 = n_2 = N/2$, and the probability of throwing exactly half heads and half tails is then:

$$P_0 = \frac{N!}{\left(\dfrac{N}{2!}\right)^2} \left(\frac{1}{2}\right)^N$$

The probability of throwing one more head and one fewer tail is:

$$P_1 = \frac{N!}{\left(\dfrac{N}{2}+1\right)!\left(\dfrac{N}{2}-1\right)!} \left(\frac{1}{2}\right)^N = P_0 \frac{\left(\dfrac{N}{2}\right)}{\left(\dfrac{N}{2}+1\right)}$$

The probability of throwing two more heads and two fewer tails is:

$$P_2 = \frac{N!}{\left(\dfrac{N}{2}+2\right)!\left(\dfrac{N}{2}-2\right)!} \left(\frac{1}{2}\right)^N = P_0 \frac{\dfrac{N}{2}\left(\dfrac{N}{2}-1\right)}{\left(\dfrac{N}{2}+1\right)\left(\dfrac{N}{2}+2\right)}$$

For small values of N these probabilities and their ratios to the most probable outcome are readily calculated. For instance, if subscripts are written for the number of heads and tails in 10 throws:

$P_{55} = 0.246$, $P_{64} = P_{46} = 0.205$, $P_{73} = P_{37} = 0.117$, $P_{82} = P_{28} = 0.044$

$P_{91} = P_{19} = 0.010$, $P_{100} = P_{010} = 0.001$

the total of all of these add to unity, as they must. If N is very large compared to unity, the binomial expansions of the expressions within parentheses in the expression for P_1 and P_2 in the preceding paragraph yield $P_1 = P_0(1 - 2/N)$, and $P_2 = P_0(1 - 8/N)$ to a first approximation. Thus, if 100 throws are made, the chance of finding one more or less head or tail is 98 per cent of the probability of finding equal numbers, and the chance of finding two more or less heads or tails is about 92 per cent.

It is easy to extend this line of thought to, for instance, the throw of a die that comes to rest with one of its six faces uppermost. Each face from 1 to 6 is equally likely to be on top at any throw, and any particular sequence of N throws has a probability of $(\frac{1}{6})^N$. However, as in the case of the coin, the probability of given numbers of each digit from 1 to 6, regardless of order of occurrence in the sequence of throws, is the product of $(\frac{1}{6})^N$ and the coefficient of the appropriate term in the expansion of $(a_1 + a_2 + a_3 + a_4 + a_5 + a_6)^N$. Or, by simple analogy with the binomial coefficient, the probability of n_1 1's, n_2 2's, n_3 3's, etc. in N throws is:

$$\frac{N!}{n_1! n_2! n_2! n_3! n_4! n_5! n_6!} \left(\frac{1}{6}\right)^N$$

It is readily seen by inspection that the denominator is least, and hence the probability of occurrence is greatest, when each of the n's is the same, i.e , when each of the faces turns up an equal number of times. The relative probability of a departure from this most probable situation is found by taking the ratio of the probability of the departure from the situation of equal n's, as for example increased n_3 by 1 and decreased n_4 by 1.

Neglecting for the moment the possible difference in likelihood of a particle's occupancy of one energy level or another in the physical problem with which we are dealing, the principal difference between that and the throws of a die is that the total energy of the system of particles must remain constant when the most probable distribution is being determined, Fig. 17-1 represents six particles distributed over energy levels with energy values $u_0 = 0$, $u_1 = 1$, and $u_2 = 2$. In the first instance of the figure, the total energy U is zero; hence all must be in the lowest energy state. In the second $U = 1$, and hence 1 particle can be in the state $u_1 = 1$. When $U = 2$, there are two possibilities as shown: the one on the left is the more probable for this energy, since $(n_0! \cdot n_1!)^{-1} = \frac{1}{48}$; whereas $(n_0! \cdot n_1! \cdot n_2!)^{-1}$ for the other is $1/120$, since 0! and 1! are both equal to 1. For $U = 3$ and $U = 4$, the most probable situations are shown at the left, which may be verified by moving one particle energy

Total Energy

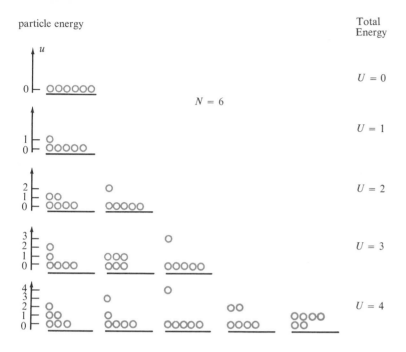

Figure 17-1 *Distribution of six particles in energy for various low total energies.*

particle up one level and another down one to keep the total energy constant and calculating the resulting probabilities. This simple example may be pursued to higher energies, but the above discussion indicates the basic considerations that are involved.

It is evident from this example that at least for small total energies the particles tend to present a pattern in which most of them are in the lowest energy state, and decreasing numbers occupy the higher levels. Figure 17-2 represents an extension of this example to 28 particles with three values of the total energy, namely $U = 40$, $U = 56$, and $U = 66$. The fact that these represent the most probable situations may be verified again by the simultaneous moving of one particle up and another down an equal number of energy intervals, as suggested by the arrows in the lowest diagram. The pattern of each is again roughly triangular, changing from a triangle of large base and small altitude to one of small base and large altitude as the total energy shared by the particles increases.

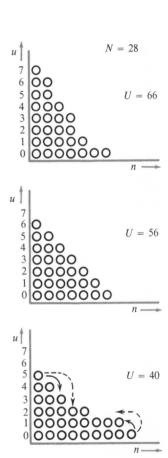

Figure 17-2 *Most probable distribution of 28 particles in energy for these arbitrary values of the total shared energy.*

17-3 The law for the distribution of a very large number of particles over an extended system of energy levels which in general have different probabilities of occupancy

For the moment, the matter of the variation of the probability of occupancy by a particle of the different energy levels may be neglected, though of course it increases very rapidly as one goes up in the energy scale, as was pointed out at the beginning of the preceding section. Our attention will first be focused on the possibility of finding a technique that can handle the maximizing of the probability of observing the occupancy distribution pattern of a series of equally weighted energy levels by such a large number of particles that the method of the preceding section would be much too laborious to be feasible. The way to approach this problem is suggested by a law of large numbers, known as Stirling's formula, which states that the logarithm of $n!$ to the natural base, $\epsilon = 2.781828$, can be written simply in terms of n itself. The formula is: $\ln (n!) = n \ln (n) - n$, where ln means the logarithm to the natural base ϵ. Table 17-1 indicates the degree of precision of the formula as n increases in magnitude.

Table 17-1

n	$\ln(n!)$	$n \ln(n) - n$	ratio of columns 2 & 3
5	4.787	3.045	.63
10	15.104	13.026	.86
20	42.335	39.914	.94
40	110.350	107.552	.97
100	363.90	360.52	.99

The probability that is to be maximized is given evidently by

$$P = \frac{N!}{n_1! n_2! \cdots n_j! \cdots}$$

where there are as many n's in the denominator as there are energy levels, and all the n's may be assumed to be large. The condition under which the largest value of P is to be found is that the total energy shared among the particles, U, which is the sum of all the quantities $n_1 u_1, n_2 u_2 \ldots n_j u_j \ldots$, is to be constant. Since the numerical value of P that represents its maximum is of course uniquely represented by its logarithm, one can equally well seek the answer to the question of maximizing P by determining the distribution of the n_j's over the u_j's whereby the logarithm of P is the greatest. Applying Stirling's formula to P, and recalling that the logarithm of a product is the sum of the logarithms of the factors, the result is:

$$\ln(P) = [N \ln(N) - N] - [n_1 \ln(n_1) - n_1]$$
$$- [n_2 \ln(n_2) - n_2] - [n_3 \ln(n_3) - n_3] \ldots \ldots \ldots \ldots \ldots \text{etc.}$$

It is shown in a supplementary section to this chapter that $\ln(P)$ is greatest when the n_j's are distributed among the energy levels, u_j, according to the function:

$$n_j = A\epsilon^{bu_j}$$

where the constant b is determined by the total energy shared among the particles, and the constant A additionally depends upon the total number of particles. The constant b is inherently negative; so ϵ^{bu_j} is the reciprocal of a quantity that increases exponentially with increasing u_j. So the occupancy of the energy levels decreases rapidly as one goes to higher energy levels, as suggested by the examples of small numbers of particles in the preceding section.

Figure 17-3 illustrates the nature of the most probable distribution pattern for three different values of the negative parameter b, as given by the function $n_j = A\epsilon^{bu_j}$. These inverse exponential curves resemble the distributions of the simple examples given earlier, and the tendency to occupy higher energy levels as the total energy increases is again indicated by the behavior of these curves; for b is an inverse measure of the total shared energy, and b_1 is greater than b_2, which is in turn greater than b_3. In the earlier simple examples, departures from the most probable situation were not unlikely enough to be negligible, but as the total number of particles dealt with increases, the probability of observing any considerable fractional departure from the most likely situation represented by the inverse exponential function becomes so remote that the exponential curve may be taken as almost certainly representing the result of any instantaneous detailed observation of the system. As will be seen in the subsequent chapter, the constant b may be related to the concept of temperature. The present discussion provides the atomic basis for the understanding of large-scale phenomena

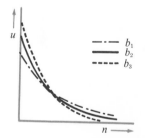

Figure 17-3 *Variation in the shape of the exponential distribution curve for three values of the parameter b. b_1 is more negative than b_2, which is in turn more negative than b_3.*

having to do with the behavior of gases, liquids, and solids under various conditions of density, pressure, and temperature.

Finally, it will be recalled that at the beginning of this section it was stated that the possible effect of the inequality of the number of different forms of energy exemplifications, such as translation, rotation, vibration, electronic excitation, etc. at the different u_j levels, would for the moment be neglected. This variation in the probability of occupancy of the various energy levels is of course a very material consideration, particularly for elementary particles obeying the Pauli exclusion principle. For in accordance with this principle, it is forbidden that any two particles may be specified as to their position, momentum, and energy in precisely the same way. Thus the occupancy of low energy levels within a restricted spatial geometry may be so limited that many of these levels are filled completely, entirely distorting the exponential distribution law at low total energy contents. Again, since the number of participating forms of energy exemplification increases rapidly with increasing energy level, as pointed out in the first section of this chapter, a greater weighting factor should be accorded a particle's occupancy of higher energy levels in assessing the most probable distribution. This consideration may also be taken into account in a more detailed analysis, and the upper portion of the distribution curve is modified by the inclusion of such a weighting factor g_j in the constant A of that discussion. Thus the distribution function well above those energy levels low enough to be effected by the limitations of the Pauli principle is finally given as

$$n_j = Ag_j\epsilon^{bu_j}$$

Figure 17-4 illustrates schematically a distribution of particles in energy including the effects of the weighting factors of the several energy levels on a population of particles obeying the Pauli principle. The thermal properties of such a distribution are, of course, different than those for the simple exponential distribution. Observations on large samples of matter, as in the case of the determination of specific heats, verify the correctness of the fundamental atomic hypotheses that led to the inclusion of the Pauli principle and the weighting factor g_j.

17-4 Supplementary section: derivation of the inverse exponential distribution law

In the preceding section, it was shown that the natural logarithm of the probability of observing a pattern of energy distribution among an

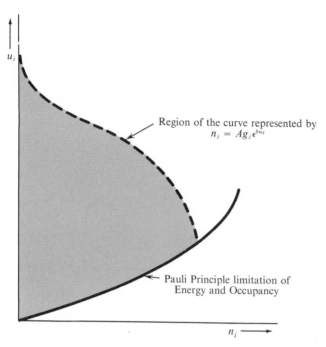

Figure 17-4 *Modified distribution law for unequally weighted energy levels and particles obeying the Pauli Principle.*

assembly of particles with equal *a priori* probability of occupancy by a particle of any given energy level may then be written:

$$\ln(P) = N \ln(N) - N - \sum_j [n_j \ln(n_j) - n_j]$$

where $\sum_j$ is written for the sum over the energy levels. Since $\sum n_j = N$, this may be simplified to:

$$\ln(P) = N \ln(N) - \sum n_j \ln(n_j)$$

It is desired to determine the values of n_j that will make $\ln(P)$ greatest, subject to the conditions that:

$$\sum n_j = N, \quad \text{and} \quad \sum n_j u_j = U$$

where N is the total number of particles, and U is the total energy shared among them.

The function $\ln(P)$ of the variables n_j is greatest at the values of n_j such that either an increase or decrease of any of these will result (to a first approximation) in no change in $\ln(P)$, and (to a second approximation) in a decrease in $\ln(P)$. The rate of change of $\ln(x)$ with x is shown at the end of this section to be equal to $1/x$. Thus:

$$\frac{d[\ln(n)]}{dn} = \frac{1}{n}$$

Hence:
$$d[\ln(P)] = -\sum_j [\ln(n_j) + 1] \, dn_j$$

and, as N and U are constants:

$$\sum_j dn_j = 0 \quad \text{and} \quad \sum_j u_j \, dn_j = 0$$

The simplest way of inserting the two conditions, namely that N and U are constant in the variation of the n_j's limiting two of these variations, is to multiply the variation in N by a constant a, and the variation in U by another constant b, and add them to the variation in $\ln(P)$, thus adding two terms, each of which is zero. One may then require that the variation in $\ln(P)$ in this form be zero, with the assurance that each n_j is now quite independent of the others, through the constants that are included for this purpose. Thus absorbing the units appearing in the variation of $\ln(P)$ in the constant a:

$$d[\ln(P)] = \sum[-\ln(n_j) + a - 1 + bu_j] \, dn_j = 0$$

If this equation is to be satisfied for arbitrary changes dn_j, the coefficient of each dn_j must be zero, which condition may be written:

$$-\ln(n_j) + a - 1 + bu_j = 0$$

or:
$$n_j = \epsilon^{a-1+bu_j} = \epsilon^{a-1}\epsilon^{bu_j} = A\epsilon^{bu_j}$$

where A is a constant equal to ϵ^{a-1}. This is the form of distribution that appeared in the preceding section for the most probable distribution.

Having succeeded above in finding the most probable distribution of the particles over the energy states in statistical equilibrium, we can see that it is of interest finally to ascertain how likely it is that this most probable state will indeed be found, if a detailed instantaneous observation of all the particles in the energy state, say u_j, is made. In other words: how likely would it be that some fractional departure, say dn_j/n_j, would be found in the number of particles occupying the state u_j?

The rate at which the logarithm of the probability, namely $\ln(P)$, changes is, of course, zero at the most probable distribution; it was from this consideration that the distribution law was derived. But a little way from the maximum, the probability will be less, and in order to find what it is for a small departure from the maximum condition, the rate at which the coefficient of dn_j changes with n_j in the expression for $d(\ln P)$ must be found. Recalling that this coefficient is

$$\ln(n_j) + a - 1 + bu_j$$

its rate of change with n_j is $1/n_j$.

Figure 17-5 displays the region of the curve $\ln(P)$ where it drops from $\ln(P_{max})$ for a small change dn_j in n_j. The quantity x of the diagram, which is $\ln(P_{max}) - \ln(P)$, is evidently a decrease of n_j times $(1 - \cos d\theta)$, which for the small angle $d\theta$ is $(\frac{1}{2})(d\theta)^2$. Hence

$$\ln(P) = \ln(P_{max}) - \frac{1}{2}\left(\frac{dn_j}{n_j}\right)^2 n_j$$

or:

$$P = P_{max}\epsilon^{-1/2(dn_j/n_j)^2 n_j}$$

Hence, for large values of n_j, e.g. a million particles, the probability of observing a per cent departure in dn_j/n_j is ϵ^{-50}, which is a very small quantity indeed, and evidently decreases rapidly when still larger numbers are taken for n_j.

Note: In Chap. 1 it was mentioned that ϵ, the natural base of logarithms, provided a particularly convenient base. This fact is illustrated in the derivation of the rate of change of the logarithmic or exponential function of a variable. Assume an arbitrary base a such that:

$$x = a^y \quad \text{or} \quad y = \log_a x$$

and that the small increments to each of the two variables x and y are written dx and dy. Using the log form of the relationship, then

$$y = \log_a x$$

and:

$$y + dy = \log_a (x + dx)$$

Then

$$dy = \log_a (x + dx) - \log_a x$$

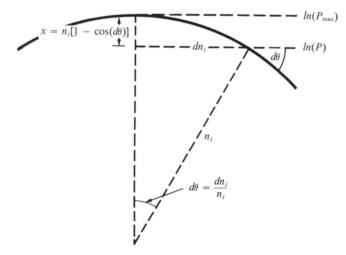

Figure 17-5   *Illustration of the geometry near the maximum of the curve of $\ln(P)$ as a function of n_j.*

Since the subtraction of logarithms yields the logarithm of the quotient of the arguments:

$$dy = \log_a\left(1 + \frac{dx}{x}\right)$$

The ratio of dy to dx is then:

$$\frac{dy}{dx} = \frac{1}{dx}\log_a\left(1 + \frac{dx}{x}\right) = \log_a\left(1 + \frac{dx}{x}\right)^{1/dx}$$

If the logarithm on the right is divided by x at the same time its argument is raised to the power x, it is unchanged, hence:

$$\frac{dy}{dx} = \frac{1}{x}\log_a\left(1 + \frac{dx}{x}\right)^{x/dx}$$

But in Chap. 1 it was shown that the binomial expansion of $(1 + 1/n)^n$ for very large n approaches the number ϵ. As dx becomes small, as for an infinitesimal increment in x, the argument of $\log_a$ becomes the number ϵ; so if ϵ is chosen as the base the logarithm becomes unity, and

$$\frac{dy}{dx} = \frac{d\ln(x)}{dx} = \frac{1}{x}$$

Thus the rate of change of the natural logarithm of x is the reciprocal of x. The rate of change of the exponential function $x = \epsilon^y$ is then dx/dy which from the above result is x, i.e.,

$$\frac{d\epsilon^y}{dy} = \epsilon^y$$

Problems

17-1 A good coin is thrown six times. What are the probabilities of turning up 6 heads, 3 heads followed by 3 tails, 3 heads and 3 tails in any combination, 4 heads and 2 tails in any combination?

17-2 Three good coins are thrown together. What is the probability that all the faces turned up are identical? What is the probability of all being identical if one coin is bad (identical on both sides)?

17-3 A good die is thrown three times. What is the probability of a 1, 2, and 3 turning up in that order? What is the probability of their turning up in any order?

17-4 Three good dice are thrown together. What is the probability of a 1, 2, and 3 turning up? What is the probability of the face values totaling 6?

Given that the total face value is 6, what is the probability that the individual face values are 1, 2, and 3?

17-5 A man searches for a fly that moves randomly about a room of height 10 ft. and area 100 ft.^{2} What is the probability that at any given time the fly is within a foot (either way) of eye level? What is the probability that at any given time the fly is within a foot (in any direction) of the center of the room?

17-6 Bullets are fired in random directions in the vicinity of a target. Plot the relative number of hits per inch as a function of the horizontal distance from the center of the target. Plot the relative number of hits per inch as a function of the radial distance from the center of the target. Plot the same two distributions for the case of a marksman who aims at the center of the target to the best of his ability.

17-7 37 particles are distributed among energy levels ranging upwards from 0 M.e.V. in steps of 1 M.e.V. There is no restriction on the occupancy of any level, but the total energy of the system is 79 M.e.V. Show that the most probable distribution is 11, 8, 5, 4, 3, 2, 2, 1, and 1 particles in the levels of energy 0, 1, 2, 3, 4, 5, 6, 7, and 8 M.e.V. respectively.

17-8 Show that the distribution of energies in the previous problem is in approximate agreement with the exponential distribution formula: $n_j = A\epsilon^{bu_j}$. Find the approximate value of A, and then an approximate simple value for b. (Hint: $n_j = A/\epsilon$ when $u_j = -1/b$). Test the formula by calculating n_j for $u_j = 0, 2, 4, 6,$ and 8 M.e.V. ($\epsilon \approx 2.7$ and $\epsilon^{2/3} \approx 2$).

17-9 What significance does the area under the energy distribution curve have? How will it behave as a function of the total energy of the system?

17-10 The distribution of energy among a large number of electrons in solid matter is sometimes likened to that among gas molecules. However, when the total energy content of a gas is increased, the energy of all the molecules tends to increase; whereas for the case of electrons, most of the excess energy is taken up by those electrons which previously had the highest energies. Explain the difference in behavior of the molecular gas and the so-called *electron gas*.

18 *The relation of the concepts of heat and temperature to the expression for statistical equilibrium*

18-1 *The determination of the constants introduced in the statistical description of an assembly of molecules in terms of the number of particles concerned and the temperature*

Before proceeding to consider applications of the statistical description of aggregates of particles developed in the preceding chapter, it is necessary to identify the constants A and b in terms of physically measurable quantities. It will be recalled that these parameters entered the description in consequence of two conditions that were imposed. The first was that the number of particles making up the systems under consideration was to be constant. The second was that the system was considered to be isolated from its surroundings, as if it were enclosed by some membrane or surface, which was impermeable to energy so that in the equilibrium condition no energy could come to it or leave it; in consequence of the conservation of energy, the total energy content was then constant.

The argument employed in deriving the distribution law:

$$n_j = Ag_j\epsilon^{bu_j}$$

was very general indeed, and consequently, its range of applicability is very wide. There was no limitation on the physical systems between which the energy is shared, and thus the law describes all statistical aggregates whether they are composed of atoms, molecules, or still larger bodies made up of many individual atoms and molecules; and it includes all states of matter: gaseous, liquid, and solid. Due regard must, of course, be paid to those exceptional situations noted in the derivation, where certain of the numbers involved may not be large compared to unity. Consequently, some of the approximations made must be reconsidered in order to obtain detailed concordance between the description and the experimental observations when such situations are involved.

A very simple application, however, may be chosen to determine the two constants A and b that occur in the distribution law. Such an instance entails a highly rarified gas confined to the interior of a rectangular box. Assume that the box contains N atoms of mass m, which move back and forth between collisions with the walls. Consider first of all the component of the velocity along the x axis of an atom in the gas, and the force that its elastic reflexion from the walls perpendicular to the x axis exerts upon these walls (Fig. 18-1). If v_x is the component of its velocity along the x axis, the atom moves back and forth between the walls perpendicular to the x axis colliding with the wall at one end $v_x/2l_x$ times per second. Each time the x component of the velocity is reversed, the change of momentum is $2mv_x$. From the definition of force as rate of change of momentum, this atom transferring the momentum $2mv_x$, $v_x/2l_x$ times a second, exerts an average force on the end of the box equal to mv_x^2/l_x. Pressure is defined as the force per unit area, so the average pressure exerted by this atom on the end of the box is $mv_x^2/l_xl_yl_z$, or mv_x^2/V, where V is the volume of the box. If one then considers all the N atoms present within a range of velocities v_x the total pressure exerted on the end surfaces will be the sum of mv_x^2/V for them all, which can also be written as N times the average of this quantity for each. As m and V are common to them all, the average of v_x^2 alone must be taken; and, if this is indicated by a bar over the quantity, and P is written for the pressure, the result is:

$$PV = Nm\overline{v_x^2}$$

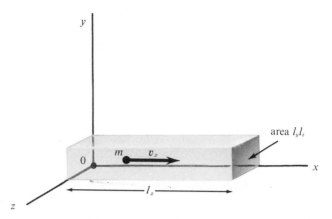

Figure 18-1 *Schematic view of the motion of a gas mole-cule along one axis of a box.*

Of course, precisely the same argument could be used for the y and z components of the velocities of the atoms leading to exactly the same equation with v_y or v_z replacing v_x. This equation can also be written in terms of the magnitude of the vector velocities of the atoms instead of their components, through the relation $v^2 = v_x{}^2 + v_y{}^2 + v_z{}^2$. The average of v^2 is then the sum of the average of the squared component velocities, and PV is then also equal to $\frac{1}{3}Nm\overline{v^2}$.

Inasmuch as the statistical distribution law is an expression for the number of atoms in any assembly like the one here being considered, which have energies corresponding to the energy levels u_j, it should be possible to use it to calculate the average value of the kinetic energy associated with the x component of the velocity $\frac{1}{2}m\overline{v_x{}^2}$ for the atoms in the gas, and to compare the result with the one just given. This is not difficult to do; the algebra involved is explained in a supplementary section to this chapter. If one does use the distribution law to calculate the average value of the kinetic energy applicable to the system being considered, it is found that the average of $\frac{1}{2}mv_x{}^2$ is equal to $-\frac{1}{2}b$, in terms of the parameter b in the expression for n_j. Thus, comparing these results, it is seen that $b = -N/PV$ in this case.

It is possible, however, to use this example in a very much more significant way to provide a precise definition of the very useful concept called *temperature*. We say that a sample of matter that feels hot when we touch it is at a higher temperature than a sample of matter that we say feels cold. This, however, is a very subjective and qualitative reaction, and one commonly uses a thermometer consisting of a reservoir of mercury with an extension into a thin glass tube to measure more quantitatively this property of the matter under consideration. This device, which depends for its action on the relative changes in volume of the mercury and its constricting glass envelope with the changing external circumstance to which we give the designation temperature, is a relatively crude empirical device that does not relate the concept of temperature to the mechanical quantities in terms of which physical theory has been developed.

Much greater insight comes from using a thermometer that employs a tenuous gas instead of mercury as the expansible substance. The work of the early chemists Boyle, Charles, and Gay-Lussac, referred to in Chap. 12, established that the product of the pressure and volume of a tenuous gas was closely proportional to a parameter that corresponded with the sensation to which the designation T had been given. Thus the product PV can be written as approximately equal to a constant times the temperature T; indeed, this constant is found to be universal, i.e., it is the same for all gases, provided that the samples of gases compared have masses proportional to their molecular weights— which means that each sample contains equal numbers of molecules. This law is thus of the same form as the equation relating the product PV to the average kinetic energy derived in a preceding paragraph. The so-called perfect gas law, which states that the product of the pressure and the volume of a mass of a gas equal to its molecular weight is a constant times the temperature, is only an approximate one because of the small residual forces between molecules that vary somewhat from one molecular type to another. The identification of the quantity PV/N for an ideal gas, or in other words one for which PV/N is exactly equal to a constant times the temperature T, provides a much more satisfactory and precise definition of the temperature as being proportional to the mean kinetic energy of a particle in a given assembly in statistical equilibrium. If the constant of proportionality is written as k, the temperature of an aggregate of matter is defined as

$$\tfrac{1}{2}m\overline{v_x^2} = \tfrac{1}{2}kT$$

and $-1/b$ of the distribution law is then identified with $m\overline{v_x^2}$ or kT.

Of course, the perfect gas law, with which most gases conform approximately at temperatures much higher than that at which they condense to liquids or solids, is then:

$$PV = NkT$$

If the sample of gas is such that its mass in kilograms is equal to its molecular weight, then N is Avogadro's number, and Nk is called the gas constant per kilomole. The constant k may then be thought of as the gas constant per molecule, and is called *Boltzmann's constant*, in recognition of the pioneering work of this Austrian physicist in the statistical theory of matter. Experimentally it is found that the numerical value of PV/T for a quantity of gas whose mass is equal to its molecular weight in kilograms is 8314.3 J. per degree Kelvin (or per degree centigrade) per kilomole. This is the gas constant per kilomole. If one divides this by the number of molecules in a sample of gas whose mass in kilograms is equal to its molecular weight, namely Avogadro's number 6.02252×10^{26} molecules per kilomole, one finds that the gas constant per molecule, or Boltzmann's constant k, is equal to 1.38054×10^{-23} J. per degree per molecule.

The constant A is related to the total number of particles by the condition that the sum of all n_j's is equal to N. This, in general, involves a calculation for each specific type of assembly, and though these calculations often become tedious, they rarely present any serious difficulties. Since the result of such a calculation is of particular rather than general interest, and since our discussion is concerned more with broad principles rather than with specific instances, the evaluation of A will not be considered further. The explicit expression for A in terms of N is given for a particular instance in the supplementary section to this chapter. It will be seen in the several instances of the application of the distribution law that are considered later that the precise value of the constant A is rarely of importance; most of the phenomena of interest require only ratios of the numbers of particles in various energy states, rather than the absolute numbers of these for their description.

18-2 *Thermodynamics*

The statistical distribution law, in terms of the temperature as a parameter, is an expression of very great generality that applies to assemblies of objects of every degree of size and complexity, from elementary atomic particles to macroscopic objects. The concept of temperature as it describes the state of the assembly, which was initially suggested by the special instance of the gas law, comes to have a much more general connotation when it is identified as a linear measure of the average kinetic energy of any of the entities in an assembly of bodies in thermal equilibrium. Though the statistical distribution law strictly describes an equilibrium condition only, it may—with suitable precautions—be used to account for processes involving the transfer of energy and slow changes with time. These changes may be thought of as taking place sufficiently slowly so that the states of the system in transition constitute a series of equilibrium states merging gradually into one another from the initial to the final state.

Of course, the argument is not limited to states of kinetic energy of translation, but encompasses energy states of all sorts, such as potential energy of both gravitational and electrical natures, as well as vibration, rotation, and the quantum energy of electron structures. The exponential form of the law permits each of these forms of energy to be considered separately if this is desired, and the distribution among each of them is, in general, the same as that among all of them together, with due regard to the fact that the density of available levels on the energy scale, which is represented by the form of g_j, varies for the different forms of energy.

One of the most interesting and far-reaching consequences of the statistical theory of aggregates of atoms and molecules relates to the nature of the energy exchange, whereby men commonly derive useful work from the energy stored in chemical or nuclear form. It was seen in the discussion of mechanics that in frictional processes mechanical energy is converted into what was called "heat energy," and in reactors nuclear energy will be seen to be converted into "heat energy." This is simply another way of saying that energy, initially in some other form, becomes available for sharing and interchanging among the individual constituents of the statistical assembly of atoms or molecules making up some sample of matter. When this occurs, the total energy distributed changes from some initial value, say U_1 for the assembly at the temperature T_1, to some new and greater value U_2 at the higher temperature T_2; the total number of particles or systems in the assembly, of course, remains the same. The difference between the initial and final states is that in the final state the higher energy levels become more heavily populated than they are in the initial state, at the expense of the lower energy levels.

It is not possible to reconvert the mechanical energy dissipated by friction or chemical or nuclear energy released in furnaces or reactors completely back into mechanical form, once the energy has been shared by such an assembly, i.e., once it has been converted into "heat." Some of it, however, may be reconverted; the form of the distribution law determines this fraction. The device for reconverting a part of the shared energy in an assembly of molecules, or "heat energy," into a useful mechanical form is called a *heat engine*. It may take any of a wide variety of special forms, but in essence it involves some substance, like a gas, that is composed of atoms or molecules among which energy is shared in equilibrium according to the distribution law that has been derived.

Consider that the engine of Fig. 18-2 is initially in contact with some large part of its environment for which the distribution is determined by the temperature T, and that this temperature remains practically unaltered as a result of any change in the engine because its environment is very much larger than the engine or because in some way, of no concern for the present purpose, energy is supplied to it and the temperature is kept at a constant value. Connected to the engine is some device that can do mechanical work or store energy in a potential form which may be called, for generality, a *machine*. Now assume that the engine is permitted to alter slowly its initial state, i.e., the quantitative description of the position of all of its parts which determine the n_j's, so slowly indeed that the equilibrium state represented by the distribution law of n_j particles in each level u_j may be considered to be always fulfilled. To make the image concrete, one may think of a piston being retracted from a cylinder containing a gas with its walls maintained at the temperature T, and the movement of the piston doing work or storing mechanical energy in the machine. As a result, distributed energy from the environment, say dQ, has been transformed into the distributed energy of the engine, say dU, and into some mechanical work, say dW, accomplished by the machine. By the law of the conservation of energy:

$$dQ = dU + dW$$

However, the quantitative exchange of energy between the engine and its environment is not so arbitrary as it would seem to be from this equation, if one deals entirely with equilibrium processes to which the energy distribution function applies. This may be seen by examining the change in distributed energy in the engine that occurs on moving the piston, thus tending to disturb the distribution of the molecules within the engine over the energy levels u_j. The change in U is then given by:

$$dU = d(\textstyle\sum_j g_j u_j \epsilon^{-u_j/kT})$$

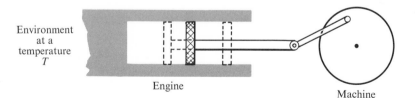

Environment at a temperature T

Engine

Machine

Figure 18-2 *Schematic thermal engine.*

But, if both sides of this equation are divided by T, and x_j is written for the quantity u_j/kT, the equation becomes

$$\frac{dU}{T} = \sum_j kd(g_j x_j \epsilon^{-x_j})$$

The sum of the changes in the terms in parentheses, however, depends only upon the change in the value in parentheses $g_j x_j \epsilon^{-x_j}$ at the two extremes of this quantity (see Sect. 2-5): at each of the extremes of this quantity $g_j x_j \epsilon^{-x_j}$ the value is nearly zero. For at one extreme x_j is very small and at the other, when x_j is large, the exponent ϵ^{-x_j} is very small. Thus the quantity dU/T, which is called the change in *entropy*, is zero during an exchange of energy between the environment and the substance constituting the engine, if the change occurs through a series of states of thermal equilibrium.

Assume then that the heat engine is first in contact with some hot source of energy at the temperature T_2, and an amount of energy dQ_2 is absorbed, as would be the case for an environment of steam well above the boiling point of water. Then it is cooled to the temperature T_1 by placing it in contact with water somewhat above its freezing point. The amounts of heat energy first absorbed and then discharged, dQ_2 and dQ_1, would be related to one another by $dQ_2/T_2 = dQ_1/T_1$. If the state of the engine is the same before and after the exchange, representing one cycle in a continuing process such as the to and fro motion of the piston in the example, the work done by it dW must equal the difference between dQ_2 and dQ_1. Hence:

$$dW = dQ_2 - dQ_1 = \frac{T_2 - T_1}{T_2} dQ_2$$

The efficiency of the engine, defined as the work done per unit energy intake at T_2 is evidently:

$$\frac{T_2 - T_1}{T_2}$$

This is clearly the maximum fraction of the distributed energy in the heat source assembly that can ever be converted into useful work by an engine that operates through a series of equilibrium states where the distribution law is continuously obeyed. Such an engine is reversible, and can transfer heat energy to or from the mechanical form. It is more efficient than any other, for if heat energy is permitted to be transferred simply by e.g., conduction from the hot environment to the cold one, no mechanical work is done at all; to the extent that this takes place, energy in the distributed form is lost completely and the efficiency is lowered by that amount.

This expression for the efficiency of an ideally perfect heat engine explains why one always strives for higher working temperatures in heat engines, for as $T_2 - T_1$ increases, the efficiency mounts. T_1 is effectively set by the temperature of the engine's surroundings at, say, normal room temperature, which on the absolute gas scale is about 300° K. In the early days of steam, the upper temperature was limited by that at which cast and wrought iron loses its tensile strength to about 500° K., giving a maximum efficiency of less than 40 per cent; in practice, the efficiency was much lower. Modern high temperature steels permit a working temperature of yellow heat in the neighborhood of 1200° K., raising the maximum efficiency to about 75 per cent, though this figure is, of course, not practically achieved.

EXAMPLE. Most of the naturally occurring fuels are made up of hydrogen and carbon in varying proportions. In the fossil fuels the complex organic molecules of living matter have been broken down into simple hydrocarbons containing two hydrogen atoms per carbon atom along a chain (Sect. 20-1). The "burning" of a fuel is the chemical combination of its constituent atoms with the oxygen of the atmosphere which, when the reaction goes to completion, yields as its final products water (H_2O) and carbon dioxide (CO_2). The oxidation of one kilogram of carbon provides 3.4×10^7 J. of energy, and of one kilogram of hydrogen 14×10^7 J. Thus as the carbon atom weighs 12 times that of hydrogen, the number of Joules provided by the burning of a fuel in which the molecule contains twice as many hydrogen as carbon atoms would be:

$$\frac{14 \times 2 + 3.4 \times 12}{14} \times 10^7 = 4.9 \times 10^7 \text{ J. per kg.}$$

This is approximately the amount of energy per unit mass liberated on the burning of coal, petroleum and its products, or natural gas.

The simple burning of fuels, of course, does not produce useful mechanical work. The intervention of some type of heat engine is essential, i.e., an engine designed to yield the maximum efficiency for its purpose within the fundamental thermodynamic efficiency limit. The internal combustion engine burns petroleum products under high pressure, which increases the upper temperature limit at which the oxidation takes place. The upper temperature T_2 may be of the order of 2500° K., and the exhaust temperature 1000° K., leading to a theoretical maximum ratio of mechanical work to energy liberated during the burning of the fuel of 2500 − 1000/2500 = 60 per cent. The process is, of course, not one of continuous thermal equilibrium; energy is lost through heat conduction and friction so that the actual obtainable efficiency of such an engine is of the order of one half the theoretical value, or 30 percent.

An important consideration in thermal phenomena is that the molecular constituents of any sample of matter, to which energy is added, rise through its characteristic structure of energy levels, which is determined by the physical parameters as a result of this addition of energy, and occupy the succession of energy levels quite independently of one another, and without regard to whether they are energies corresponding to translation, rotation, vibration, or electron excitation. The density on an energy scale of these levels as given by the weighting factor g_j increases markedly at higher energies. As the temperature rises and the swarm of molecules is elevated so that larger numbers enter the range of increasing level density, the rate of increase of internal energy with temperature rises rapidly. This ratio (the rate of change of internal energy with temperature) is called the *specific heat* of the molecule or of the substance. For a monatomic substance below the region where electronic excitation is important, i.e., where the temperature is not high enough to produce states of electronic excitation, the only energy states are those of translation. As it has been seen that the average kinetic energy associated with the velocity along each of the three axes is $\frac{1}{2}kT$, the total internal energy of translation for the N molecules of a kilomole is $(3/2)NkT$, or $(3/2)RT$, and the rate of change of this energy with T is $3R/2$. This is the constant specific heat per kilomole of such gases as helium, neon, or argon.

The polyatomic gases that can have energy of rotation and vibration show an increasing specific heat with temperature up to many times the value of R at very high temperatures. Thus the temperature does not need to increase by nearly as much with respect to internal energy content for such gases when a considerable number of the molecules begin to participate extensively in rotational and internal vibratory motion. Electronic excitation, except in rare cases, is unimportant below an average internal energy per molecule of the order of one electron volt, or a temperature corresponding—through the equation $kT = eV$—to 12,000° K. or more. The energy states of a crystalline structure, in which the individual atoms are held in place by elastic bonds with their neighbors, arise from the elastic vibratory motion of the molecules about their positions of equilibrium. The average kinetic energy of vibration of each molecule separately, which represents the highest frequency and maximum energy, is $(3/2)kT$, as is the case for the kinetic energy of translation of a gas molecule. The average potential energy is of like amount, so the specific heat of a crystal at high temperatures approaches the value of $3k$ per molecule, or $3R$ per kilomole.

18-4   *Other consequences of the distribution law*

The fact that all of the constituent particles, atoms, molecules, and larger aggregates participate equally in the energy reservoir characterized by the temperature is known as the *equipartition law*. Its consequences are of great practical importance and are evident in many ways. Experimental observations of a wide variety permit the direct verification of the distribution of molecular translational velocities, e.g., the observation of the width of spectrum lines emitted by gases at various temperatures provides a direct confirmation. In Chap. 8 it was seen that there is a first order Doppler effect for the light emitted by an atom with a velocity v_x along the line of sight that shifts the apparent frequency or wave length in proportion to v_x/c. Figure 18-3 is a plot of the distribution function $n_{vx} = A\epsilon^{-mv_x^2/2kT}$ in terms of the fraction of the atoms or molecules with line-of-sight velocities of the various values given by the abscissas. This curve should then reflect the energy distribution with frequency, or the shape of a spectrum line, since the ordinate should be proportional to the logarithm of the number of atoms contributing to this frequency and the abscissa should be proportional to the change in the frequency. It is, of course, symmetrical about $v_x = 0$ for negative values of v_x. The curve agrees with observation for the spectrum lines emitted by gases at low pressures; the variation in line width with $T^{1/2}$, which is proportional to the mean velocity, is the same variation that is observed.

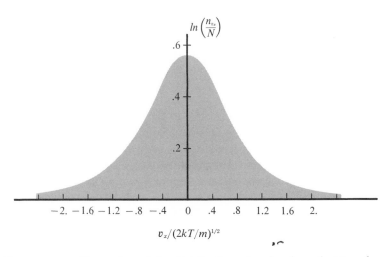

Figure 18-3   *Illustration of the distribution of molecular velocities along any one coordinate axis in statistical equilibrium.*

The equipartition law applies to large bodies that are in thermal equilibrium with their surroundings as well as to atoms and molecules. Since the average kinetic energy associated with motion along any arbitrary coordinate direction is the same for any particle participating in the distribution, a particle large enough to be seen in a microscope should exhibit this motion, and the average velocity should be in the ratio $(m/M)^{1/2}$ to that of a molecule, where M is the mass of the large particle and m the mass of a molecule. This ratio is verified by experiment. Much larger systems, e.g., a mirror suspended on a fine fiber, exhibit the equipartition of energy as well. Such a mirror, if observed through a high precision instrument, exhibits erratic angular oscillation of just the expected amount. If the restoring torque of the fiber is f N. m. per radian, the energy associated with torsion through an angle θ is $\frac{1}{2}f\theta^2$; by the equipartition law, this is $\frac{1}{2}kT$ on the average; the square root of the mean square value of the angular displacement of the mirror should be $(kT/f)^{1/2}$, which is found to be the case. From these examples it is evident that the fluctuating displacement of objects under the influence of thermal energy partition is an important limit to the precision of measurement, and that there is great advantage in working at the lowest possible ambient temperature if high-precision measurement is to be achieved.

EXAMPLE. A sensitive galvanometer, consisting of a coil of wire suspended in a constant magnetic field as mentioned in Sec. 11-1, carries a small mirror that reflects a bright spot of light on a transparent scale at the distance of 1 m. With no current flowing in the galvanometer coil, and with the apparatus at room temperature of 20°C. or 293°K., the erratic movement of the spot along the scale is observed at regular time intervals. It is found that the average value of the square of the displacements is equal to 0.9 cm² or 9×10^{-5} radian². From the expression for the energy stored in a small rotation $d\theta$ against the torque f per unit displacement (Sec. 6-2):

$$\tfrac{1}{2}f(d\theta)^2 = \tfrac{1}{2}kT$$

the torque f per unit angular displacement of the coil is 4.5×10^{-17} N.m.

An electric current of 10^{-9} Amp. sent through the galvanometer coil is found to displace the average position of the spot on the scale by 2.2 cm. or 2.2×10^{-2} radians. Since the square root of the mean square thermal displacement is 9.45×10^{-3} radians, the precision with which the current of 10^{-9} Amp. can readily be measured in a short time is of the order of the ratio of 9.45 to 22, or about 40 per cent. If the galvanometer is placed in a container the walls of which are cooled by liquid nitrogen, the random motion of the coil would be reduced by a factor equal to the ratio of the square root of the temperature of liquid nitrogen, which is 78°K., to the square root of 293°K. This ratio is 0.52. Thus the precision with which a small current could be measured in a short time by this instrument would be increased by a factor of about 2 as a result of lowering its temperature by this amount.

The distribution of density, or the number of molecules per unit volume in the earth's atmosphere, is another instance of the application of the statistical distribution law. The energy levels u_j in this case arise from the gravitational energy of a molecule in the earth's gravitational field. If the atmosphere were isothermal, i.e., if the temperature were the same at all heights, the distribution of molecules with height should be

$$n_h = A\epsilon^{-mgh/kT}$$

since gravitational energy immediately above the surface of the earth is given by mgh. However, the temperature is found to decrease by about 50° to 100° over the first 20 to 25 km., and then to increase again at greater heights. This alters the atmospheric density from that of an isothermal atmosphere; but the general nature of exponential decrease of density with height is observed in limited atmospheric strata.

EXAMPLE. Since the potential energy of a molecule in the earth's gravitational field depends upon the mass of the molecule, it would be expected that the ratio of oxygen to nitrogen in the atmosphere would vary with height above the surface of the earth. The extent of this variation should be given by

$$n'_O = n_O\epsilon^{-m_Ogh/kT}$$

and

$$n'_N = n_N\epsilon^{-m_Ngh/kT}$$

where the primes yield the number of molecules at the height h in terms of the unprimed n's, which represent the numbers at the surface of the earth where $h = 0$. Assuming the atmosphere to be all at the same temperature, which may be taken as 0°C., or 273°K., and that relative concentrations of the two gases are to be compared at the surface and the height of 1 km.:

$$\frac{n'_O}{n'_N} = \frac{n_O}{n_N}\epsilon^{-(m_O-m_N)gh/kT}$$

Inserting numerical values of m, g, h, k, and T, the ratio of the concentration at the two heights is found to be $\epsilon^{-1.75\times10^{-2}}$, which is approximately 0.98, or a change in the concentration ratios over this height of about 2 per cent. This is very much too small to be measurable under practical circumstances.

The equipartition law also determines the nature of the atmosphere of the sun and the planets. In Chap. 5 it was seen that if an object at a distance R from a spherical gravitating mass M has a radial velocity in excess of $(2GM/R)^{1/2}$, it will escape entirely from the neighborhood of M. Thus, if the equipartition law is applied to the vertical velocity of a molecule of mass m, namely $\frac{1}{2}kT = \frac{1}{2}m\overline{v^2}$, it is seen that, if kT/m is greater than $2GM/R$, many of the molecules will escape. If M is very large, as in the case of the sun, even light molecules such as hydrogen can be retained in spite of the high temperatures. For a given M and R it is easier to retain heavy molecules. For this reason the earth's atmosphere has a much higher ratio of oxygen and nitrogen to hydrogen than the ratio found in the average normal constitution of the universe. A body such as the moon experiences high temperatures where the sun shines on it, and being of small M, almost all gas molecules can leave its surface, it has practically no atmosphere at all.

Finally, the statistical distribution law can be applied to the ephemeral photon as well as to the permanent atomic system as a constituent of a large assembly. The first approach to the quantum theory of radiation was made by Max Planck as a result of his studies on the radiation density within an enclosure. The basic considerations upon which a statistical theory of photons is formulated are somewhat different than the considerations for atoms or electrons, for instance, photons are absorbed and re-emitted; therefore they are not present in a constant number. Also, they are not governed by the exclusion principle, and more than one photon in an assembly can have the same energy specifications. These modifications produce less change in the distribution law than might be expected. The form of the expression for the number of photons with wave lengths in the neighborhood of λ in an enclosure at a temperature T is:

$$\frac{8\pi hc}{5} \frac{1}{\epsilon^x - 1}$$

where

$$x = \frac{hc}{kT\lambda}$$

And when ϵ^x is large compared to unity, it is seen that this distribution law closely approaches the simple exponential one with hc/λ or $h\nu$ taking the place of u_j. The maximum value of the distribution curve occurs for $\lambda T = 0.29$, in centimeters times degrees absolute. Thus, at ordinary temperatures (300°K.) the largest number of photons, or the maximum of the distribution curve, occurs at about a thousandth of a centimeter.

18-5 Supplementary section on the gas thermometer

The importance of the gas thermometer in the interpretation of temperature and in establishing the empirical absolute scale of temperature warrants a brief description of the principles of this device for those who are unfamiliar with it. If one takes a sample of gas of known mass, and hence containing a known number of molecules, and confines it in an apparatus that is maintained as a whole in intimate thermal contact with a mixture of ice and water, we say that the system is in a state of equilibrium at a constant temperature: namely, that characterized by the melting of ice. The volume occupied by the molecules may be altered, e.g., by the displacement of a piston in a cylinder, and the consequent variation of its pressure measured. The numerical value of the product of the pressure (say in Newtons per square meter) and the volume (say in cubic meters) per molecule is found to be a constant, if the pressure is not permitted to become too high and thermal contact with the mixture of ice and water is maintained. If the same experiment is now performed with the apparatus in thermal contact with boiling water, or with the steam that is evolved, the quantity PV/N is again found to be constant, but its numerical value is different. If, as in the centigrade scale of temperature, the number 0° is associated with the ice point for which the pressure and volume are P_i, V_i and the number 100° is associated with the steam point for which the pressure and volume are P_s, V_s, the quantity PV/N may be displayed on a diagram as in Fig. 18-4 for which the other coordinate is the centigrade scale. The straight line passing through these two experimental points intersects the axis of $PV/N = 0$ at the temperature coordinate $- 273.16$°C.

This gas sample constitutes a thermometer, its readings being the values PV/N. The zero of this scale is uniquely defined by the linear projection from the ice and steam points indicated above. The units of the scale chosen to be the same as those of the centigrade system are, of course, quite arbitrary, as are, for instance, our units of length, time, or mass. The temperature scale so defined with the ice point at 273.16° is called the *absolute* or *Kelvin* scale of temperature. The rising importance of the low temperature region in both theory and applica-

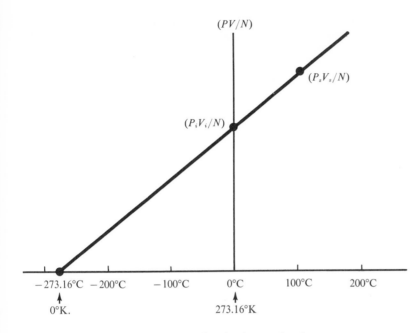

(PV/N)

(P_sV_s/N)

(P_iV_i/N)

−273.16°C −200°C   −100°C   0°C   100°C   200°C

0°K.   273.16°K

Figure 18-4   *Definition of the absolute scale of temperature.*

tion has emphasized the inconvenience of having the experimental error in defining the absolute temperature scale attach to the zero point as it does in the above definition. In consequence, in 1954 it was decided to define the triple point of water (approximately the freezing point) as being exactly 273.16°K., and the small experimental uncertainties then attach to the measurement of other points on the temperature scale. There is some analogy between this method of definition and the method of the quantitative definitions of force and work. These quantities were defined in terms of the previously determined units of length, mass and time, but were shown to be in qualitative concordance with our muscular sensations. In much the same way, temperature is defined in general agreement with our sensory perceptions of hot and cold.

Supplementary mathematical section   18-6

As was stated earlier in this chapter, the average value of the kinetic energy of the particles sharing energy among one another in an assembly described by the distribution law can be calculated relatively simply. As an instance that leads to the general result, the motion along one

Cartesian axis may be considered. By definition, the average value of a quantity is the sum of the products of that quantity times the number of particles possessing this particular value of the quantity over the whole assembly divided by the total number of particles. The number of particles with a velocity in the interval dv_x in the neighborhood of v_x is, in accordance with the distribution law:

$$A\epsilon^{b(\frac{1}{2}mv_x{}^2)}\,dv_x$$

If this is multiplied by the energy corresponding to v_x, namely $\frac{1}{2}mv_x{}^2$, summed over all values of v_x from large negative through zero to large positive values, and divided by the sum of the number of particles, the result is

$$(\tfrac{1}{2}mv_x{}^2)_{\text{average}} = \frac{\sum A(\frac{1}{2}mv_x{}^2)\epsilon^{b(\frac{1}{2}mv_x{}^2)}\,dv_x}{\sum A\epsilon^{b(\frac{1}{2}mv_x{}^2)}\,dv_x}$$

Now it is useful to look at the rate at which the particular function $v_x\epsilon^{b(\frac{1}{2}mv_x{}^2)}$ changes with v_x. This can be done by the usual method of replacing v_x by $v_x + dv_x$, and observing the change produced, or by any of the rules that may be remembered for special functions. The result is:

$$d(v_x\epsilon^{b(\frac{1}{2}mv_x{}^2)}) = (\epsilon^{b(\frac{1}{2}mv_x{}^2)} + bmv_x{}^2\epsilon^{b(\frac{1}{2}mv_x{}^2)})\,dv_x$$

Since b, as will be seen later, is inherently negative, the quantity $v_x\epsilon^{\frac{1}{2}bmv_x{}^2}$ is very small for very large values of v_x either positive or negative because of the very large negative value of the exponential factor. Assuming that these extreme values are so small as to be negligible, the sum of the increment $d(v_x\epsilon^{\frac{1}{2}bmv_x{}^2})$ for all values of v_x from one extreme to the other may be neglected, or set equal to zero. This is a consequence of the general equality between the area under the curve representing the rate of change of a function over a given range of the variable and the difference in values of the function at the end points of the range, as was seen in the supplementary section of Chap. 2. Hence:

$$\sum(\epsilon^{\frac{1}{2}bmv_x{}^2} + bmv_x{}^2\epsilon^{\frac{1}{2}bmv_x{}^2})\,dv_x$$

is also zero, or:

$$\sum bmv_x{}^2\epsilon^{\frac{1}{2}bmv_x{}^2}\,dv_x = -\sum \epsilon^{\frac{1}{2}bmv_x{}^2}\,dv_x$$

The left hand term closely resembles the sum in the numerator of the fraction yielding the average value of $\frac{1}{2}mv_x{}^2$; indeed, on comparing these expressions, it is seen that:

$$(\tfrac{1}{2}mv_x{}^2)_{\text{average}} = \frac{-\sum (A/2b)\epsilon^{\frac{1}{2}bmv_x{}^2}\,dv_x}{\sum A\epsilon^{\frac{1}{2}bmv_x{}^2}\,dv_x}$$

$$= -\frac{1}{2b}$$

This agrees with the result used in Sec. 18-1. It is seen that the evaluation of the sum $\sum A\epsilon^{\frac{1}{2}bmv_x^2} dv_x$ is unnecessary in order to determine b. This sum equal to the total number of particles N can readily be evaluated, but to do so a greater familiarity with the calculus is necessary than the one here assumed. The result when the sum is carried out is that A equals $(-2bm/\pi)^{1/2}N$. This result is interesting, but much less generally significant than the determination of b in terms of the temperature. The ratios of the numbers of particles in various energy intervals is practically important, but the absolute numbers are rarely required.

Further reading:

DUWEZ, P., "High Temperatures: Materials," *Scientific American*, vol. 191, No. 3, p. 98 (1954).

DYSON, J., "What is Heat?" *Scientific American*, vol. 191, No. 3, p. 58 (1954).

SUMMERFIELD, N., "High Temperatures: Propulsion," *Scientific American*, vol. 191, No. 3, p. 120 (1954).

Problems

18-1 The conditions within a heavy atomic nucleus are sometimes compared to those of a contained gas, and the term *nuclear temperature* is used. The constituents of nuclear matter have energies that may be conveniently measured in M.e.V. What temperature in degrees absolute corresponds to 1 M.e.V.?

18-2 kT has the units of energy. As T was defined in our consideration of the ideal gas, precisely what energy is T a measure of? What does this imply about the motion of every molecule in the gas at zero degrees absolute?

18-3 What is the average translational kinetic energy of air molecules at 27°C.? What is the average (root mean square) velocity ($\sqrt{\overline{v^2}}$.) of the oxygen molecules? What is the average of this quantity for the nitrogen molecules?

18-4 Consider two ideal gases confined to separate but equal volumes at the same temperature. One of the gases is composed of particles of mass m and the other of mass M. Both gases contain the same number of particles. M is greater than m. In which gas is the pressure greatest? In which gas is the average kinetic energy per particle greatest? In which gas is the average particle velocity greatest?

18-5 Show that the mean square amplitude of a pendulum oscillating in equilibrium with an ambient molecular atmosphere at a temperature T is given by $\overline{\theta^2} = \dfrac{kT}{mgl}$, where m is the mass of the pendulum bob, l is the length of the pendulum, and g is the acceleration of gravity. Assuming the following values: $m = 10^{-7}$ kilograms, $l = 10^{-3}$ meters, $T = 300°$A., calculate $\sqrt{\overline{\theta^2}}$.

18-6 (a) Explain why evaporation from the surface of a liquid cools the body of the liquid.

(b) Explain why, when a hot object and a cold object are placed in contact, heat flows from the hot object to the cold object until both are at the same temperature. Why shouldn't heat flow away from the cold object to make it even colder?

18-7 Assuming that the atmosphere is composed mostly of diatomic nitrogen molecules ($A \approx 14$), and that the air temperature is a uniform 27°C., calculate the difference in height between two points if the ratio of the pressure at these two points is 2.7.

18-8 When the terminals of a very sensitive voltmeter are connected to the ends of a carbon resistance, small voltage fluctuations may be observed. What is the origin of these fluctuations?

18-9 If the ratio of oxygen to hydrogen in the earth's atmosphere at sea level is 1000 to 1, what would it be at 17 km. above the earth's surface, on the basis of the exponential distribution law and constant atmospheric temperature of 300°A.?

18-10 How would you expect the behaviour of gases to depart from the ideal gas law, i.e., would the departure occur for low or high temperatures, and what form would the departure take?

The fluid state of matter 19

The states of matter 19-1

The state of aggregation of the atoms of a particular sample of matter is determined by the internal energy that is available for sharing amongst these atoms. The state that presents itself when there is the least energy available, or in other words, when the sample is at the lowest temperature or coldest, is the *solid state*. The electronic structures about each atom are then in their lowest levels, and the kinetic energy of motion of the atoms is least. This generally also represents an association of all of the atoms closely keyed together into a regular, rigid, three-dimensional lattice structure in which there is a minimum of oscillatory motion of each atomic center about its lowest energy equilibrium position. The resultant crystal structure is typical of the solid state, which is one that we recognize as resisting, through its internal forces, any external forces we may apply which tend to compress or in any way distort the regular geometric form that is assumed.

If the energy content of this assembly of atoms is increased; e.g., by heating the crystal, the number of atoms in high-energy states is enhanced at the expense of those in low energy states, as was seen in Chap. 17. The lowest energy states of the assembly of atoms constituting the crystal are those associated with the outer electron structures of the atoms, which bind them together in the regular crystalline array. Of these states, those that represent close, tight binding are of lower energy than those in which the atoms are more widely separated and loosely bound. Hence, when the crystal is heated, the bonds holding the atoms rigidly in the lattice structure are the first to be loosened. The atoms then tend to move a little farther apart. This causes the crystal as a whole to expand. If further energy is added by continued heating, the atoms eventually cease to occupy the regular, permanent spacing pattern of a solid, and migrate about among one another, remaining fairly close together, but less so than they would be in the crystalline state. This configuration is called the *liquid state*. It is characterized by a considerable resistance to compression because the atoms are still close together and under the influence of their mutual attraction. Liquids, however, offer little resistance to a change of shape or distortion because of the considerable mobility of the individual molecules composing the aggregate.

A further increase in internal energy raises the average energy of the particles to such an extent that the tendency to cluster closely together is largely overcome and the separate atoms, or the tightly bound atoms in small molecules, move about throughout the confining space quite freely, each having only a very slight energetic influence upon the others. This is the *gaseous state*, which is fluid and distortable, as is the liquid state, but which is quite compressible as well, since the gas atoms expand to fill any container, and on the average are relatively widely separated.

The above are the states of matter that are commonly encountered on the earth. The divisions between them are by no means sharp. The amount of vapor in equilibrium with the liquid form of a substance depends upon the temperature, pressure, and volume. At a critical combination of pressure, volume and temperature, the bounding surface, or *meniscus*, separating the liquid and vapor phases of a substance disappears and the two states of the substance become indistinguishable. Also viscous liquids grade continuously through plastics and glasses to crystalline solids. The particular temperature range characterizing the earth's surface provides the balance of these states that characterizes our environment. If the temperature were to vary only 50°C. one way or the other, life as we know it would be impossible. If the temperature of the earth's surface were to drop about 200°C, almost all of the permanent gases of the atmosphere would liquify or solidify, and if it were to rise by 100°C, almost all of the liquids would vaporize.

Under a few special conditions on the earth, such as conditions in nuclear explosions and in the plasmas currently being investigated to bring about nuclear fusion, transient equilibrium conditions are brought about that correspond to very much higher temperatures. Also, in the sun and other stars there are quasi-equilibria that correspond to many millions of degrees centrigrade. Here the energy of the assembly is so great that molecular bonds are no longer effective, nor are the binding energies between atomic nuclei and electrons great enough to hold these particles together. The particles constituting the assembly are then electrons and stripped atomic nuclei. As will be described in a later chapter, these conditions cause a distribution of matter among atomic nuclei of various types that differs markedly from that characterisitc of either our particular earthly environment or of the universe as a whole. We are far from any detailed understanding of the behavior of assemblies of matter under such extreme conditions of high internal energy density.

The gaseous state 19-2

The gaseous state is distinguished by both fluidity and compressibility, and the gross mechanical phenomena exhibited by the swarm of molecules constituting a gas can be described in terms of the few simple experimental parameters that characterize these two quantities. For steady flows or changes in the bounding surfaces that do not alter the volume and that take place at rates very much less than the average molecular velocities, the compressibility feature is of little quantitative importance, and one need only regard the fluidity feature. Gas flow under these conditions is said to be *stream line* flow, from the fact that the phenomena may be quite successfully described in terms of hypothetically isolated small constituent volumes, which in the course of the flow follow smoothly curving lines, distorting isovoluminally somewhat in the course of their translation along these lines to conform to variations in the contours of the confining boundaries. These lines may be seen and photographed if smoke or other light suspended particles are injected, and the paths of these tiny particles are followed in the course of their flow.

A real gas transfers momentum to the bounding surfaces, which may be the walls of flexible ducts, the blades of turbines, or the wings of airplanes; in accordance with the mechanical laws, the forces on these surfaces are equal to the sums of the rates at which the gas momentum changes over the areas. The molecules of the gas striking a bounding surface exert a force perpendicular to the area equal to the sum of the gas pressure over the area. If there is a streaming of the gas along the surface, the impinging molecules exert a net force on the surface in the direction of flow or a viscous drag on the surface. The viscous force may be thought of as arising from a gradient of the gas velocity from zero at the boundary to some constant rate of flow at the outer edge of a transition layer of gas under laminar shear, as indicated in Fig. 19-1. The coefficient of viscosity, generally written μ, is by definition the tangential force per unit area exerted on the boundary per unit spatial rate of change of the velocity of flow as one moves away from the surface into the gas.

The description of the interaction of a fluid and its boundaries in

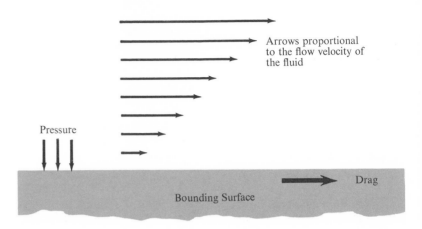

Figure 19-1 *Schematic depiction of the movement of a fluid parallel to a bounding surface.*

terms of streamline or laminar flow is adequate for many purposes, so long as the momentum being transported by the fluid is not too much greater than the tangential momentum transmitted to the bounding surfaces through the viscous mechanism just described. The momentum transported per unit time per unit area by a fluid of density ρ flowing with a velocity v is ρv times v, or ρv^2. This is half the pressure that would be exerted upon an area normal to the flow if the flow were to be reversed by striking a surface. Thus the ratio of the rate of forward momentum transfer by a fluid flowing parallel to a surface to the dragging force experienced by a bounding surface is $(\rho v^2)/(\mu v/l)$; this dimensionless quantity $\rho vl/\mu$ is known as *Reynold's number* (Fig. 19-2). The

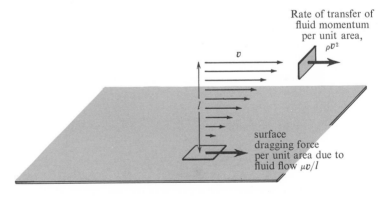

Figure 19-2 *Momentum transfer per unit time per unit area by a moving fluid. Reynold's number* $= (\rho v^2)/(\mu v/l) = \rho vl/\mu.$

magnitude of the Reynold's number for a particular physical situation determines whether the flow is actually of the assumed steady stream-lined form or not. For low Reynold's numbers (low densities and velocities, small dimensions and large viscosities) the viscous forces predominate, whereas for large Reynold's numbers (high densities and velocities, large dimensions and low viscosities) inertial effects completely dominate the viscous effects. For very large Reynold's numbers, 1,000 to 10,000, the boundary layer tends to become very unstable, and vortices and turbulence develop which completely change the character of the flow and the reaction of the fluid on the boundary. The lift of an airplane wing may drop to very low values under such circumstances. One way of postponing the onset of this unstable turbulent condition is to arrange to continuously suck in the boundary layer through holes or slots in the wings, thus preventing its growth and the ensuing detrimental effects.

EXAMPLE. In the course of the motion of extended bodies, such as fluids and solids, the loss of energy from the mechanical form is generally so appreciable that it severely limits the application of the conservation of energy in the mechanical form for the solution of practical problems. However, the idealized case of the absence of viscosity or turbulence is often a useful approximation of actual cases. In this case an element of volume follows a tube defined by stream lines, and the conservation of energy principle yields an equation known as *Bernoulli's equation*, which is easily derived. Consider an element of fluid (Fig. 19-3) which flows through a tubular volume bounded by stream lines from a region where the pressure is P_1 to one where the pressure is P_2, and let the cross sectional areas at these termini be A_1 and A_2, the heights be h_1 and h_2, the velocities v_1 and v_2, and the density of the entering fluid be ρ_1 and that leaving be ρ_2. The rate at which the mass of fluid crosses the area A_1 is $\rho_1 A_1 v_1$ (analogous to the relation between a current element and a moving charge of Sec. 10-2). The rate at which work is done by the pressure at the entrance to the tube plus the rate of increase of gravitational potential energy there, plus the rate of increase of the kinetic energy of motion there equals the sum of these quantities emerging at the exit, or

$$(P_1 A_1)v_1 + (\rho_1 A_1 v_1)gh_1 + \tfrac{1}{2}(\rho_1 A_1 v_1)v_1^2$$
$$= (P_2 A_2)v_2 + (\rho_2 A_2 v_2)gh_2 + \tfrac{1}{2}(\rho_2 A_2 v_2)v_2^2$$

Since the same mass enters and issues per unit time, $\rho_1 A_1 v_1 = \rho_2 A_2 v_2$, and

$$\frac{P_1}{\rho_1} + h_1 g + \frac{1}{2} v_1^2 = \frac{P_2}{\rho_2} + h_2 g + \frac{1}{2} v_2^2$$

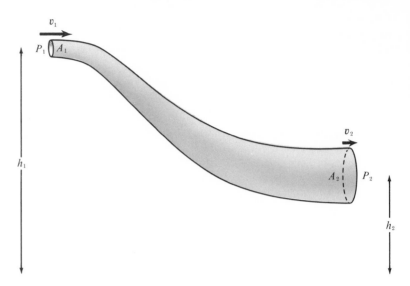

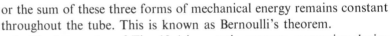

Figure 19-3 *Streamline flow of fluid entering area A_1 that is bounded by given stream lines remains within the "tube" bounded by these lines until it emerges at area A_2.*

or the sum of these three forms of mechanical energy remains constant throughout the tube. This is known as Bernoulli's theorem.

1. The barometer of Fig. 19-4 is a static pressure measuring device in which a tube, closed at one end, is filled with liquid and inverted in a container of a similar liquid. The level of the liquid in the tube falls to such a point that the forces on the liquid are in equilibrium and the velocities are zero. At the upper surface P_1 is zero, and at the lower surface P_2 is equal to the atmospheric pressure P. If $h_1 - h_2 = h$, then:

$$hg\rho = P$$

if ρ is constant. Thus the height of the upper level above the lower is a measure of the atmospheric pressure upon the latter surface.

2. If a vessel presenting an open liquid surface is rotated about a vertical axis, the surface takes the form indicated in Fig. 19-5. The pressure on the surface is nearly uniform, disregarding the variation of atmospheric pressure with height. Thus:

$$hg + \tfrac{1}{2}v^2 = k$$

where k is some constant. Or, since $v = r\omega$:

$$(k - hg) = \tfrac{1}{2}\omega^2 r^2$$

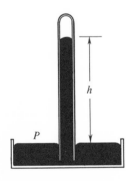

Figure 19-4 *A barometer. The pressure at the top of the column is zero. At the bottom the pressure is atmospheric.*

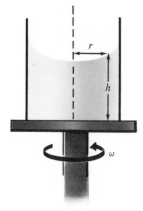

Figure 19-5 *The top surface of a rotating liq-*
uid takes a parabolic shape. A point r distance
from the axis of rotation has a velocity v = rω,
where ω is the angular velocity. h is the height
of the point above some horizontal plane such
as the base of a beaker.

The linear relationship between h and r^2 is the characteristic of a parabola or a parabolic bowl shape created for the surface of the rotating liquid.

3. If water is led from a reservoir under pressure P_1 to a nozzle in a volume to which air has access, the device acts like a pump drawing air in at the opening O (see Fig. 19-6). From Bernoulli's equation:

$$P_0 + \tfrac{1}{2}\rho_1 v_1{}^2 = \text{constant}$$

or if ρ is constant, as for water:

$$P_1 - P_2 = \tfrac{1}{2}\rho(v_2{}^2 - v_1{}^2)$$

and if the pipe and nozzle areas are in the ratio n:

$$P_1 - P_2 = \tfrac{1}{2}\rho v_1{}^2(n^2 - 1)$$

and P_2 is less than P_1 by this quantity, drawing air in at the opening O if P_2 is less than atmospheric pressure.

EXAMPLE. When viscous forces dissipate energy from the mechanical form, even though the streamline nature of the flow persists, or at higher velocities when turbulence sets in and mechanical energy is

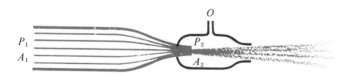

Figure 19-6 *A jet pump. A reduction in pressure of the jet*
draws air in at the orifice O.

eventually lost by the dissipation of the eddies, Bernoulli's theorem no longer applies, and precise calculations become difficult or impossible. In these cases a helpful guide for finding empirical relationships to describe observed forces and motions is that these must be independent of the units chosen for mass M, length L, and time T. This must be so, since these units are basically arbitrary and the same phenomena will be observed whether mass is measured in terms of pounds or kilograms, or length in terms of feet or meters.

As an example, consider a solid object such as a ball falling through a real fluid at a constant rate (Fig. 19-7). If the mass and velocity of the ball remain constant, there can be no net force on it, and hence the drag exerted by the fluid must equal the force drawing the ball downward. This drag is caused by the relevant physical properties of the fluid, which may be listed as:

1. The radius r of the fluid cavity occupied by the ball of dimensions. L.

2. Velocity of relative motion of the fluid and the ball v of dimensions L/T.

3. Density ρ of the fluid of dimensions M/L^3.

4. Viscosity μ of the fluid of dimensions force per unit area per rate of change of velocity with distance, or:

$$(F/L^2)/[(L/T)/L]$$

As the dimensions of F are (ML/T^2), those of μ are M/LT. Thus, if the retarding force is to involve these quantities, each quantity raised to some power, the force must be given dimensionally as

$$F = \frac{ML}{T^2} = k(L)^a \left(\frac{L}{T}\right)^b \left(\frac{M}{L^3}\right)^c \left(\frac{M}{LT}\right)^d$$

where k is a dimensionless constant. For M and L to occur to the first power on the right, and T to the minus second power:

$$c + d = 1$$
$$a + b - 3c - d = 1$$
$$-b - d = -2$$

These three conditions will not determine the four exponents in the general case, but if the velocity is small, so that higher powers of it may be neglected, $b = 1$, and it is then seen that $a = d = 1$ and $c = 0$, or:

$$F_{\text{drag}} = k_1(L)(L/T)(M/LT)$$

This gives the retarding force due to viscous drag, which depends on the first power of the dimension of the ball, on the first power of the

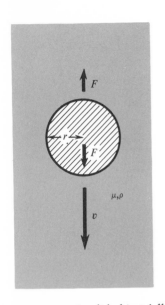

Figure 19-7 *A solid object falling through a fluid attains a terminal velocity when the downward force on it is balanced by an upward drag exerted by the fluid.*

velocity, and on the first power of the viscosity. If the ball is falling under gravity, the force is mg, and a measurement of m, g, r, μ, and v determines k_1. If the velocity increases, a term for which b is 2 evidently becomes greater in comparison with the one first found. If $b = 2$, $a = 2$, $c = 1$, and $d = 0$, or

$$F_{\mathrm{drag}} = k_2(L)^2(L/T)^2(M/L^3)$$

This is a retarding force proportional to the product of the square of the dimensions of the ball, the square of the velocity, and the density of the fluid. The ratio of these forces is, of course, dimensionless, and involves the parameters in the form:

$$(L)(L/T)(M/L^3)/(M/LT), \qquad \mathrm{or} \qquad \rho v L/\mu$$

This ratio is the Reynolds Number.

The role of compressibility in the mechanical motion of gases becomes increasingly important at higher velocities of flow, but its greatest quali- tative effect upon the phenomena of gas behavior is that it permits the propagation of compressional waves through the gas. These com- pressional waves, which are the same as those we call *sound waves*, are variations in pressure and associated variations in density that are propagated through the medium in the same way that surface waves are propagated over a liquid surface. The generic function representing a travelling wave is recalled from Chap. 6 to be a function of time and space of the form $(t \pm x/v)$, where v is the velocity of propagation of the wave disturbance. As an instance of the application of the law of conservation of energy for the derivation of useful properties of matter in bulk, it is shown in the final section of this chapter that the value of v for compressional waves in a gas—which are not of too great a magnitude—is $(\rho K)^{-1/2}$, where ρ is the gas density and K is the compressibility or the fractional change in volume with pressure. The value of the compressibility K depends somewhat upon the external conditions, for there is always some transformation of mechanical energy into energy of random motion of the gas during processes of compression and expansion. The order of magnitude of K, however, can be ascertained by assuming the perfect gas law and an approximately constant temperature:

$$PV = RT \qquad \mathrm{or} \qquad P = RTV^{-1}$$

Then the compressibility is defined as:

$$K = \frac{1}{V}\frac{dV}{dP} = -\frac{1}{V(dP/dV)} = \frac{1}{V(RTV^{-2})} = \frac{V}{RT}$$

and the velocity is, therefore:

$$v = (\rho K)^{-1/2} = \left(\frac{RT}{\rho V}\right)^{1/2} = \left(\frac{RT}{M}\right)^{1/2}$$

where M equals the mass of one mole. Or, if m is the mass of one molecule:

$$v = \left(\frac{kT}{m}\right)^{1/2}$$

The dependence of v on temperature shows that the velocity of sound is greater in hot air than in cold. This dependence also produces a distortion of the wave fronts as they pass through temperature gradients, and has a marked effect on the propagation of sound through the earth's atmosphere. If the air is cooler near the surface than at a great height, the wave travels faster as it gets higher, and tends to focus back on the earth, enhancing the sound heard (Fig. 19-8). Also, of course, winds effect sound waves, since they constitute a mass motion of the medium. Favorable velocity gradients with height, together with favorable winds, can markedly increase the detectabilities of sound sources.

It is, moreover, quite possible for the relative velocity of a gas and its boundary to exceed the velocity of sound in the gas, e.g., in supersonic flight or in the passage of a high speed bullet or projectile. Under these conditions shock waves emanate from any irregularities or discontinuities on the solid surfaces. These shocks are the envelopes of the acoustic waves emitted by sharp changes of contour. Along these envelopes the acoustic wave fronts pile up, leading to sharp variations across the

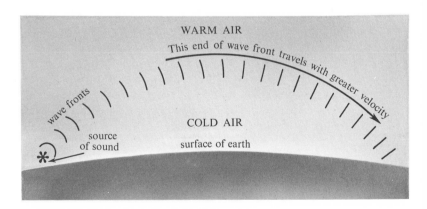

Figure 19-8   *Refraction or bending of a sound wave caused by a temperature gradient in the transmitting medium.*

shock wave front of the pressure, temperature, and density parameters. At a time t_1 the projectile can be thought of in position 1 of Fig. 19-9, emitting a wave due to the disturbance made by its nose. At a time t_2 it will have spread out in a spherical wave front of radius r, where $r/(t_2 - t_1) = v$, the velocity of the acoustic wave. If the projectile is moving with a velocity $v' = d/(t_2 - t_1)$, it will have reached position 2

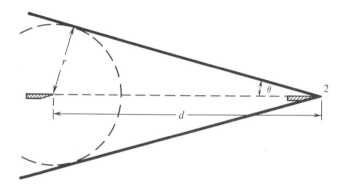

A disturbance created at position *1* travels a distance r with velocity v, while the projectile travels a distance d with velocity v'. The angle θ of the cone containing this spherical wave is given by: $\sin \theta = r/d = v/v'$.

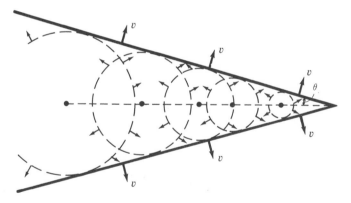

The cone angle θ depends only on the velocities v and v'. Hence the cone forms the envelope of disturbances originating from all points of the projectile's path. Waves interfere constructively only in the direction perpendicular to the cone surface which, therefore, represents a shock wave travelling outward with velocity v.

Figure 19-9   *Conical shock wave from a projectile.*

at the time t_2. The waves emitted by the nose at intermediate points will also be tangent to the cone of half angle θ, where $\sin \theta = v/v'$; this conical envelope is called the *shock wave*. The *Mach number* is the ratio of the relative rate of motion of the projectile through the gas to the velocity of sound in the gas. At Mach 1, $\sin \theta = 1$, and $\theta = 90°$. For a Mach number less than one, no shock wave is apparent.

19-3 The liquid state

The quantitative molecular theory of liquids is much less advanced than that of gases. The principal reason for this is that the details of intermolecular forces are not sufficiently well known for a quantitative treatment of them, and these forces are of much greater moment in liquid than in gaseous phenomena. However, it is evident that these forces are on the whole attractive, tending to pull the molecules of the liquid together, thus, producing the most compact configuration permitted under gravitational and other circumstances influencing the geometry. The forces between molecules, of course, become repulsive when the proximity is sufficiently close, for they do not coalesce, and tend to lose their identity in the liquid or solid state. The distance of separation between molecules when these attractive and repulsive forces determined by the particular electronic structure of the molecules balance one another accounts for the gross volume they occupy. It is rather as if the molecules were small semielastic solid bodies. The circumstances in a liquid somewhat resemble those of a large vessel subject to continuous agitation, which is filled with small elastic spheres. These are held together by gravity within the vessel, but the relative random motion is such that the individual spheres interchange neighbors constantly. There is no rigidity to this structure, although the mean distance between spheres in the vessel or between molecules in the liquid is reasonably sharply defined.

Homogeneous liquids consist of one kind of molecule only, and in the case of water it is the small triangular shaped combination of two atoms of hydrogen and one atom of oxygen, as shown in Fig. 19-10. The electron structure is largely centered on the oxygen atom. The two hydrogen-oxygen line-of-centers make an angle of about 105° with each other. Liquids in which the molecules are not all of one kind, but which are heterogeneous in the sense that the liquid contains a certain admixture of foreign molecules, are known as *solutions*. All foreign molecules are not capable of solution; i.e., dispersal on an atomic or molecular scale in an otherwise homogeneous liquid. This matter, though still imperfectly understood, is doubtless related to the particular molecular properties of the solute and solvent. Certain solutions are so intimately related to the individual molecular parameters that water molecules are found to nest neatly in relatively permanent lace-like structures around these dissolved molecules, forming what are essentially large complex—though somewhat transient—molecules called *hydrates*.

The effects of intermolecular forces in a fluid are most obvious in the form that the bounding surface of a liquid takes under various circum-

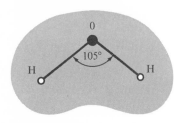

Figure 19-10 *Water molecule: the angle between the lines joining the two hydrogen nuclei to the oxygen nucleus within the electronic structure is 105° for water.*

stances. The simplest instance would be a quiescent mass of liquid under no external forces, as would be the case if it were far removed from any other gravitating masses. The gravitational forces of attraction would tend to hold the molecules of the liquid together in a spherical form. But, if the total mass is not very great, the gravitational forces are small in comparison with the intermolecular forces arising from their electron structures, and may be neglected. The electron structure forces may also be seen to conform the mass of liquid into the shape of a sphere. The attractive forces between molecules tend to cluster them as closely together as possible, and it is readily seen that surface molecules have but half the number of nearest neighbors as do interior molecules (Fig. 19-11). The equilibrium situation is then that in which there is a maximum number of molecules with as many close neighbors as possible, which is the same as saying that there is the smallest possible number of surface molecules or a minimum surface area. The sphere is the three-dimensional form having the least surface area for the volume enclosed. The result of the intermolecular attractions makes the surface of the liquid consist of a skin in tension that tends to reduce the surface to a minimum. Indeed, the effects of these intermolecular forces are commonly described in terms of the equivalent surface tensions of fluids, which may be thought of as being effective not only on free surfaces but also on surfaces of contact with other immiscible fluids or bounding surfaces of a solid in contact with a fluid.

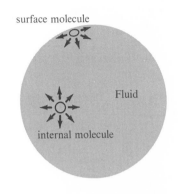

Figure 19-11 *Spherical form of a liquid under no external forces.*

When two immiscible fluids are in contact, the boundary is a single surface. A rain drop, for instance, is such a surface distorted somewhat from sphericity by the viscous forces of the air through which it falls. A water molecule at the surface of a stationary drop would be subject to the opposing long-range attractive forces of neighboring water and air molecules, and also to the opposing short-range repulsive forces of both molecular types. It is obvious from symmetry that each of the four forces must act perpendicularly to the air-water boundary (Fig. 19-12) and, neglecting gravitational effects, the four forces must balance.

A water drop on a horizontal waxed table top is deformed from the spherical shape partly by the action of gravitational forces; but in the vicinity of the water-wax interface, the intermolecular forces predominate and gravitational forces may be ignored. The water surface makes an angle θ with the surface of the table. The water molecule depicted in Fig. 19-13 near this line of contact is subject to a strong inward force of attraction F_1, and a weaker force of attraction F_2 to the wax. Again, symmetry requires that the attraction to the wax be vertically downward and that the inward force bisect the angle $\pi - \theta$ between the water surface and the table top. The resultant F of these two attractive forces must be perpendicular to the water surface, because

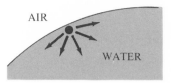

Long-range attractive forces between a surface water molecule and its neighbors within the drop.

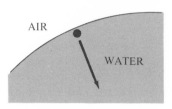

Resultant attractive force is perpendicular to the surface.

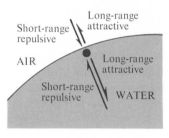

The four forces balance.

Figure 19-12   *A water molecule at the surface of a spherical drop is in equilibrium under the action of four forces.*

this is the direction of any balancing short-range forces. The construction of Fig. 19-13c shows that the three forces F_1, F_2, and F form an isosceles triangle with $F = F_2$. The sides of any triangle are proportional to the sines of the opposite angles, and hence:

$$\frac{F_2}{\sin (\theta/2)} = \frac{F_1}{\sin (\pi - \theta)} = \frac{F_1}{\sin \theta} = \frac{F_1}{2 \sin (\theta/2) \cos (\theta/2)}$$

or:
$$F_1 = 2F_2 \cos (\theta/2)$$

A drop of water placed on a non-waxed table top is observed to spread out so that the angle of contact θ between water and table top approaches $\pi/2$, or 180°. As shown in Fig. 19-14, this results from a greatly increased force of attraction F_2 between the water molecules and those of the solid surface. The water is said to *wet* the surface. A film of wax just a few molecules thick is sufficient to prevent the above

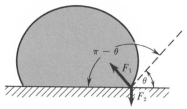

A molecule at the surface of the water and near the waxed surface is subject to two attractive molecular forces F_1 and F_2.

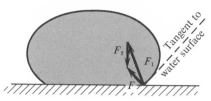

The resultant force F must be perpendicular to the surface of the water.

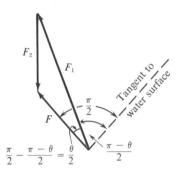

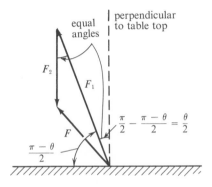

Construction showing that the forces F_1 and F_2 and their resultant F form an isosceles triangle with base angles $\theta/2$.

Figure 19-13 *A water drop makes a small angle of contact θ with a waxed table top.*

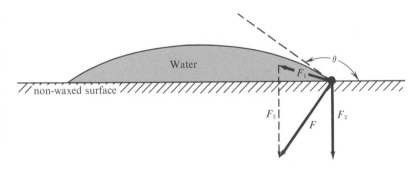

Figure 19-14 *The angle of contact between a liquid and a solid which it wets approaches 180° or $\pi/2$.*

wetting. This is an indication of the range of the so-called *long-range* intermolecular forces.

If the forces at the interface are such that the angle θ becomes 180°, then the fluid is said to completely wet the solid surface. This is the situation with good lubricants where a film of fluid spreads out on the surface as far as it can. If the supply of fluid is limited, the film tends to become only a molecule or so thick before the spreading stops. This is not the only requirement of a good lubricating fluid, for the film must be tough and self-healing when broken, and must protect the surface from contact with the opposite bearing surface. Two smooth, dry surfaces in contact will stick, just as two optical flats may be wrung together so that they may not be separated without pulling away portions of one or another of the surfaces. The lubricating film prevents the contiguity of the solid bearing surfaces and consequent sticking due to the intermolecular forces between them.

The two-dimensional films that wet a liquid or solid surface by spreading over them present many interesting and important phenomena. Certain of these films behave like two-dimensional gases in that the molecules of the film do not tend to stick together, but spread out over the surface just as a gas spreads throughout a volume. The force that the gas film exerts is very similar to the pressure exerted by a gas. By moving a barrier over the surface that enlarges or constricts the area available to the surface gas film, the product FA, where F is the force per unit length and A the area occupied by the film, can be shown to be equal to RT, analogous to the product PV for a gas. Other films are more of the nature of a liquid or a solid in that the molecules of the film do not spread beyond the area in which they may remain

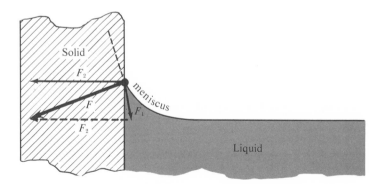

Figure 19-15   *If a liquid wets its container, the meniscus is concave up.*

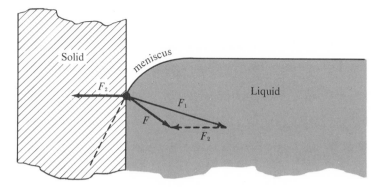

Figure 19-16 *If a liquid does not wet its container, the meniscus is concave down.*

closely in contact with one another. In general, these films are composed of molecules of which one end tends to extend downward, as if in solution in the underlying liquid, so that all of the molecules of the film are ordered in like orientation. The nature of these forces and the ordered proximity brought about in such films is doubtless related to the catalytic effect of certain surfaces. This is the ability of molecules adsorbed tightly to liquid or solid surfaces to react with one another chemically. Catalytic processes are of great importance in chemistry, and although the details of these mechanisms are not by any means completely understood, it is clear that the processes of surface adsorption are essential in the reaction mechanism.

As a further example of the forces of intermolecular attraction, consider the surface of a liquid near the walls of its container. If the liquid wets the material of the container, the liquid appears to be drawn up the sides, and again the two forces of attraction acting on a surface liquid molecule are seen in Fig. 19-15 to produce a resultant force that is perpendicular to the liquid surface. This phenomenon is observable when water is poured into a clean glass tumbler. Figure 19-16 illustrates the reverse phenomenon as observed for mercury in a glass container. The attraction between fluid molecules is much greater than that between a fluid molecule and a neighboring glass molecule. The fluid surface is then concave downward close to the container wall. If a narrow bore clean glass tube (capillary tube) is dipped into a pool of water, the water is drawn up the tube by so-called capillary action (Fig. 19-17). This may be understood as the minimizing of the total potential energy of the system. Although the gravitational potential energy is thereby increased, many of the water molecules are brought into closer proximity

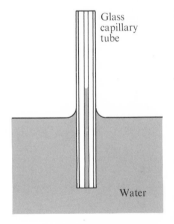

Figure 19-17 *Water in a glass capillary tube rises above the level of the surrounding water surface.*

with glass molecules for which they have a great affinity, and thus the net potential energy associated with the intermolecular forces of attraction is decreased. An analogous argument will explain why mercury is drawn down by capillary action in a glass tube (Fig. 19-18).

19-4 *Supplementary section: propagation of a wave through a compressible fluid, as in the case of a sound wave through a gas*

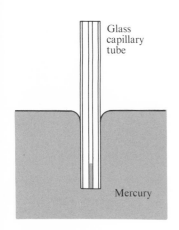

Figure 19-18 *Mercury in a glass capillary tube is depressed below the level of the surrounding mercury surface.*

Consider a long column of a compressible fluid of unit cross section into which a remote piston at the far left (Fig. 19-19) moves to the right, maintaining a constant density ρ_1 ahead of it. The region of transition from the density ρ_1 to the normal density ρ_0 is observed to travel down the column to the right. If the piston oscillates back and forth like the diaphragm of a loudspeaker, a train of periodic waves will traverse the column, and the sections 1 and 2 of Fig. 19-19 may be thought of as neighboring points of maximum and minimum density in this wave train. Midway between them lies the section 0 of normal density ρ_0.

Assume the rate at which the density wave moves to the right is c; since it retains its form, the amount of fluid within the transition region from section 1 to section 0, assumed to be moving steadily to the right with the wave velocity c, remains constant. The fluid in the region of normal density ρ_0 is stationary, but that in a region of maximum density

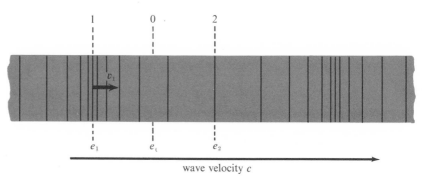

wave velocity c

Figure 19-19 *Propagation of a wave through a compressible fluid. The wave consists of a series of compressions, 1, and rarefactions, 2, all moving to the right with the wave velocity c.*

ρ_1 is moving forward with some velocity v_1, which is less than the wave velocity c. As the wave moves to the right, fluid is added to the section between 1 and 0 at a rate $\rho_0 c$ to the right of the transition region. At the left of this region, the wave moves with velocity $c - v_1$, relative to the fluid; hence fluid is lost from the transition region at the rate $\rho_1(c - v_1)$. If the mass of fluid in the region is to remain constant, then:

$$\rho_0 c = \rho_1(c - v_1)$$

As the wave section between 1 and 0 moves to the right, it continually enters a region of density ρ_0, where the net forward momentum of the fluid is zero. Behind it, it leaves a region where the momentum per unit volume is $\rho_1 v_1$. Since the wave moves at the velocity c, the rate of change of momentum in this region of the wave is $\rho_1 v_1 c$. The forces that bring about this rate of change of momentum are the pressures across the bounding lamina 1 and 0, namely P_1 in the direction of c, and P_0 in the opposite direction. Thus, equating the net force to the rate of change of momentum:

$$P_1 - P_0 = \rho_1 v_1 c$$

Eliminating $\rho_1 v_1$ between the equation of motion and that stating the condition for a constant mass of gas in the wave between lamina 1 and lamina 0:

$$c^2 = \frac{P_1 - P_0}{\rho_1 - \rho_0}$$

An equivalent argument could be applied to any two lamina of the fluid. It is obvious that at all points of the fluid the density must be proportional to the pressure at that point, assuming the temperature is constant. Thus, considering a very thin section of the wave, we may write:

$$c^2 = \frac{dP}{d\rho}$$

This is a very general expression for the square of the velocity of a wave in a fluid; it applies to waves of any magnitude from ordinary sound waves, in which the differences in pressure and density are quite small, to shock and explosive waves, where these differences can be very great. The velocity of a sound wave can be written more simply in terms of the quantity known as the compressibility, which is the fractional change in volume induced by a small change in pressure:

$$K = -\frac{1}{V}\frac{dV}{dP}$$

It is approximately constant under ordinary conditions for a particular gas if the variations in pressure and volume are not large. For a given mass of gas, a certain fractional increase in volume will result in the same fractional decrease in density, i.e.,

$$\frac{d\rho}{\rho} = -\frac{dV}{V}$$

Therefore:
$$c^2 = \frac{dP}{d\rho} = -\frac{V}{\rho}\frac{dP}{dV}$$

$$= (\rho K)^{-1}$$

or:
$$c = (\rho K)^{-1/2}$$

as stated in the text.

Further reading:

BERNAL, J. D., "The Structure of Liquids," *Scientific American*, vol. 203, No. 2, p. 124 (1960).

BUSWELL, A. M., AND RODEBUSH, W. H., "Water," *Scientific American*, vol. 194, No. 4, p. 76 (1956).

CORNISH, J. J., "The Boundary Layer," *Scientific American*, vol. 191, No. 2, p. 72 (1954).

COX, E. F., "Atomic Bomb Blast Waves," *Scientific American*, vol. 188, No. 4, p. 94 (1953).

LEVELT, J. M. H., "Some Aspects of Molecular Physics," *American Journal of Physics*, vol. 28, No. 3, p. 192 (1960).

McCHESNEY, M., "Shock Waves and High Temperatures," *Scientific American*, vol. 208, No. 2, p. 109 (1963).

REINER, M., "The Flow of Matter," *Scientific American*, vol. 201, No. 6, p. 122 (1959).

ROGERS, E. M., *Physics for the Enquiring Mind*, Princeton University Press, Chap. 6 (1960).

SMITH, C. S., "The Shape of Things," *Scientific American*, vol. 190, No. 1, p. 58 (1954).

Problems

19-1 Water flows down a river 100 m. wide at an average velocity of 0.1 m.sec.$^{-1}$. Estimate the drag force exerted on a riverside wharf whose underwater surface area flanking the river is 90 m^2. What assumption must be made in order to perform the calculation? Is the estimate likely to be too high or too low? The viscosity of water is approximately 10^{-1} kg.m.$^{-1}$sec.$^{-1}$.

19-2 Vortex motion is invariably produced in the region of a small outlet to a large container of fluid. Why?

19-3 The end of a hose is deeply immersed in a large body of water. Water is emitted slowly from the nozzle and spreads out uniformly in all directions. If the velocity of the water is 0.01 m.sec.$^{-1}$ at a distance of 0.1 m. from the nozzle, what is the velocity at a distance of 1 m.? An isolated point charge is an electrostatic analogue to the above point source of fluid. What is the electrostatic analogue to the fluid velocity?

19-4 An unmounted fan operates in the air—well clear of any deflecting surfaces such as floor, ceiling, or walls. Sketch the lines of air flow. Ignore any turbulence or rotation of air about the fan's axis. What is the electro-magnetic analogue to the fan?

19-5 Atmospheric pressure at the surface of the earth is approximately 10^5 N.m.$^{-2}$, and the air density is approximately 1 kg.m.$^{-3}$. Assuming the atmosphere to be incompressible, and hence of uniform density (which it certainly is not), obtain a minimum value for the thickness of the earth's atmosphere. What is the pressure at an ocean depth of 10 m.? Water has a density of 10^3 kg.m.$^{-3}$.

19-6 When honey is allowed to fall from a spoon onto a plate a few inches below, the rate of flow increases rapidly at first, but never becomes comparable to that of water in a similar situation. As the supply of honey in the spoon is depleted, the continuous cord of honey that links spoon to plate narrows in girth and finally breaks part way down. The "stalactite" of honey left hanging from the spoon is then observed to shrink rapidly—i.e., the honey actually rises back up to the spoon. Explain all these features of a common household phenomenon, applying your knowledge of physics.

19-7 The velocity of light in water is only $\frac{3}{4}$ its velocity c in free space. Only the latter velocity is an insurmountable barrier to any wave or particle. The electrons from high-energy particle accelerators have velocities approaching c and emit a cone of radiation known as Cerenkov radiation. What is the half-angle of this cone?

19-8 Water will not *wet* a greasy surface unless a wetting agent is added. What property should the molecules of a good wetting agent have? Wetting agents, such as soap, make good detergents; why?

19-9 Prove that the vertical rise of liquid in a capillary tube is inversely proportional to the internal radius of the tube. (Hint: if y is a function of x, then when y has a maximum or minimum value, dy/dx has the value zero.)

19-10 What is the direction of fluid flow at the point 2 in Fig. 19-19? What are the directions of flow on either side of the points 0, 1, and 2?

20 The solid state of matter

20-1 Amorphous solids

The application of our knowledge of the properties of atoms and molecules to the theory of crystalline aggregates has led to very impressive advances in our understanding of the properties of the solid state of matter, and also to practical technological advances of great importance in many fields of application. The ancient and empirical body of lore, having to do with ceramics and metallurgy has been completely transformed during the past few decades through our knowledge of the physics of the solid state. This relatively precise and quantitative body of knowledge of the properties of closely packed atoms, has enabled us to produce the wide variety of materials with specified characteristics available for today's technology. Though the quantitative details of the external force fields of the electron structures of atoms and molecules are not, in general, amenable to precise calculation, the symmetries and the qualitative nature of the outer electronic states provide information upon which the general theoretical structure can be formulated in terms of empirical parameters. The more symmetrical and highly ordered the configuration, the simpler is the structure, and the more satisfactory our present understanding of it.

Glasses, which resemble to a considerable extent the structure of a liquid in which the random motion has been sufficiently reduced by the extraction of internal energy to limit the mobility of the molecules, present the least symmetrical of solid structures. The internal energy is of the vibratory and, to some extent, the rotational type. While the mean distance to nearest neighbors is just about the same for all molecules, these do not define a regular spatial lattice, but rather represent a more chaotic and random distribution throughout the solid. They are said to be amorphous, in being without any simple and readily characterized form.

There is also a category of substances, lying between amorphous supercooled liquids or glasses and typical crystals with regular lattice structures, which—because of the great extent of their individual molecules—exhibit quite highly-ordered arrangements over volumes that are limited, but large compared to that occupied by a single atom. These are the gels, glues, rubbers, fibers, semi-glassy materials, and the constituents of animal and vegetable tissue. The study of these substances was a most intractable one until very recently. But current advances in chemical and biochemical theory and technique have led to a phenomenal gain in knowledge about these materials, which promises to be as stimulating and revolutionary as any of the great scientific achievements of the past. One class of these substances consists of molecules in the form of chains of very great but indefinite lengths of which the links are identical regularly recurring molecular groups. These are called *polymers*—meaning of many parts—and the chain-like structures may be of a simple linear form or may display branching or solid crossings (see Fig. 20-1). The molecular links may be very simple or quite complex spatial structures that may be highly ordered in an alternating pattern or in a spiral structure about the axis of the chain. Alternatively, they may be distributed at angles about this axis in a random fashion. Another class of these substances is the materials peculiar to biochemistry, which resemble the simpler polymers in being chains of which the links are characteristic molecular groups. But in proteins and nucleic acids the links are characteristically much more complex molecules, they appear to be of more determinate length, and are generally associated together in parallel or helically intertwined structures. The cells of living tissue consist of complexes of gigantic molecules of this ordered type. Great strides are being made toward understanding life processes through the study of the chemical reactions in which they participate.

An account of this fascinating field of enormously complex but highly-ordered atomic aggregates is beyond the scope of our account of the properties of solids. However, the nature of the chain structure of simple polymers may be quite briefly related to certain of the physical properties that bulk material exhibits. If the chains contain many branchings and crossings, there is little precise resemblance among the chains, and they tend to form a loosely associated web-like structure that is rubbery, gluey, or viscous over a range of internal thermal energy or temperature. However, as the order among these chains increases, with similar orientation of the links along the axis and few if any branches, they can assume closely parallel configurations, with

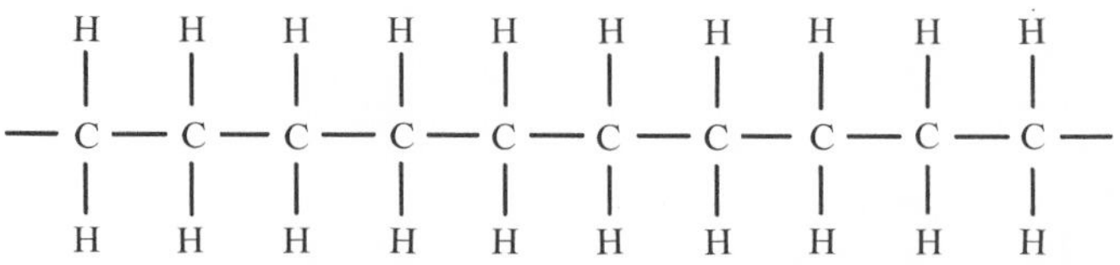

The purely linear form of links (H—C—H) in the polymer chain

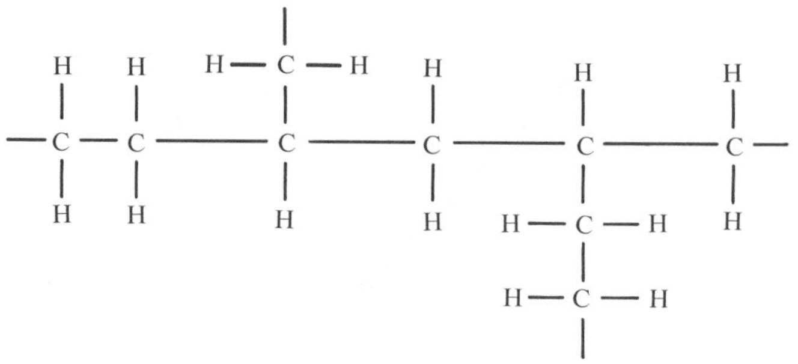

Branches

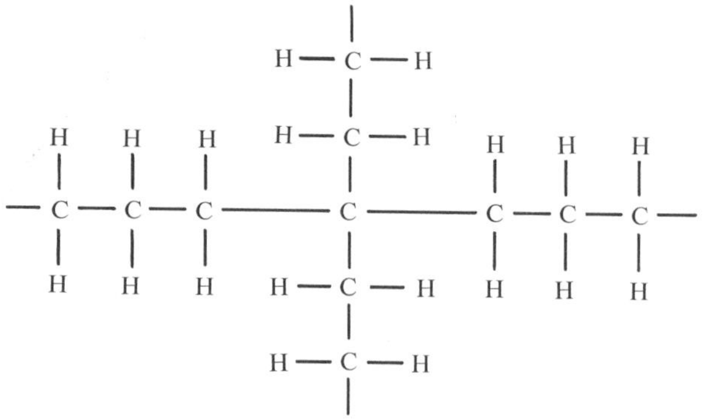

Crossing

Figure 20-1 *The simplest polymer (polyethylene). The H's are hydrogen and the C's carbon atoms. The dashes represent electron bonds.*

significant registry of the individual links between neighboring chains. In such circumstances, at low temperatures, the structure is quite rigid and there is a narrow transition temperature range above which the energy of molecular motion separates the neighboring chains sufficiently for them to slide past one another quite easily, exhibiting the properties of fluid flow. For a further account of these substances, their method of preparation, and their properties, the references at the end of this chapter should be consulted.

The simplest types of solids are the crystals that are ideally characterized by a high degree of symmetry and structural regularity. Evidence
for this was presented in Chap. 12, in which the diffraction of electromagnetic waves by spatial lattices was described. The nature of the
observed diffraction patterns implies the regularity of the lattice structure, and also reflects the particular types of symmetries that are present; in addition they furnish a device for the measurement of wave
length, which was the matter of particular interest in that context.
The atoms or molecules comprising the lattice are arranged in the form
of a unit pattern that reproduces itself periodically through the crystal
lattice in the direction of any one of the crystal axes. A displacement
of the crystal as a whole by any multiple of the distance corresponding
to a dimension of the unit cell returns each atom of the crystal into
precise spatial registry with a neighboring counterpart. The translational and other symmetries play an essential role in the physical properties of real crystals, though these are neither indefinite in extent nor
completely perfect in their lattice structures.

EXAMPLE. One may in his imagination, pass many different systems
of parallel planes through a crystal, which will pass through or include
all the atoms in the crystal. In a cubic crystal, one may choose the
planes separated by the interatomic distances perpendicular to any
of the three principal axes. Or, in general, one may choose the series
of planes parallel to the one passing through any arbitrary choice of
three atoms. In Fig. 20-2, for simplicity, only those atoms lying along
the axes near the origin are shown. Any such set of planes will pass
through all the atoms in a crystal, even one of very great extent. Hence
the number of atoms to be found per unit area of any one plane belonging to such a family must be proportional to the separation between
the planes of that family, for the ratio of atoms per unit area of a
plane to the separation of the planes is the ratio of the total number of
atoms to the total volume, which is the density of atoms in the crystal.
The Fig. 20-2 indicates with dashed and dotted lines the intersections
of certain crystal planes with the coordinate planes xy, yz, and zx.
The plane passing through the first atom above the origin parallel to
the xy plane evidently contains the same number of atoms per unit
area as the xy plane, namely $1/d^2$; the ratio of this to d is $1/d^3$. The
plane passing through the first atom from the origin along the x and
z axes and parallel to the y axis has $1/\sqrt{2}d^2$ atoms per unit area; the
separation of parallel planes of this family is $\sqrt{2}d/2$, and the ratio is
again $1/d^3$. Similarly, it may be shown that the density of atoms in the

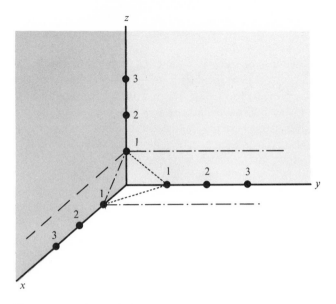

Figure 20-2 *Crystal planes: the intersections with the fiducial planes of a plane belonging to each of the three families passing through the point z = 1 and (a) parallel to the (x, y) plane, (b) passing through the point x = 1 and parallel to the y axis, and (c) passing through the point x = 1 and y = 1.*

plane passing through the first atom out along each axis from the origin is $1/\sqrt{3}d^2$; the separation of the parallel planes of this family is $d/\sqrt{3}$, leading to the same ratio.

The imperfections of real crystals play an important part in determining their mechanical properties. Nearly perfect crystals are, for instance, much more readily sheared along crystal planes of major population than are imperfect crystals. Imperfections such as vacant lattice sites, displaced atoms, or impurities act as keys or wedges that tend to prevent the slippage of one plane over another that takes place quite readily in a pure, perfect crystal. Actual crystals are more frequently than not agglomerations of small crystal blocks randomly oriented, cemented together by a rubble of molecules and crystal fragments. As these aggregates as a whole present a much less perfect and symmetrical structure, they are also much more resistant to shearing or the sliding of one plane of atoms over another, since regular planes do not extend for any great distance till they meet the boundary of another small crystallite oriented at a somewhat different angle from the first. The cold working of metals brings about this crushing and reorienting of subcrystal units and, hence, in general, strengthens the crystal aggregate and reduces its likelihood of deforming under an external force. Pure single crystals of zinc, for instance, will not support their own weight if they are several centimeters in extent, but after being bent back and forth a few times the long lattice planes are broken up and the crystal becomes tough and brittle.

Molecular crystals   20-3

Crystals may be divided into a number of different categories on the basis of their physical properties. The type that exhibits the least typical crystalline properties are called molecular crystals. These are rather loosely bound aggregates of atoms with closed electron shells like the ones in the rare gases, or molecules characterized by a strong internal binding of their atoms that have little interaction between one molecule and its neighbors. Properties of molecular crystals are determined by the atomic or molecular structures of their constituents rather than by the crystal forces holding these sub-units unstably together. Solids that require little thermal energy to change their forms to liquids or gases are generally of this type. In addition, the rare gases and the permanent gases of our atmosphere, such as hydrogen, oxygen, and nitrogen when cooled, form crystals of this type, and the crystals of elements such as phosphorus, sulfur, selenium, tellurium, and iodine are of this nature.

One form of crystalline carbon, known as graphite, also exhibits very limited crystalline properties. It is composed of thin lamina, often only one atom thick, not too many atoms in area, consisting of hexagonal reticula of carbon atoms (Fig. 20-3). These plates have little tendency to stick together and slide easily over one another. They even provide a useful lubricant between metal surfaces. They are essentially large two-dimensional molecules of indefinite molecular weight, intermediate between large molecules and small crystals. Another form of crystalline carbon, the diamond, is of an entirely different character. It crystallizes in large highly-ordered volumes of great mechanical strength and rigidity, and exhibits the same type of symmetry that characterizes silicon, which will be described later in the section on valence crystals.

Figure 20-3   *Two-dimensional graphite lattice.*

20-4 *Polar crystals*

A typical class of crystals that are capable of developing under carefully controlled conditions into very large single crystals with a minimum of imperfections are the polar crystals of which common salt, NaCl, is an example. The x-ray interference patterns show that the arrangement of these atoms is one of cubic symmetry with closely packed alternating atoms of sodium and chlorine designated by dots and circles in Fig. 20-4. The bonds are of the electron-sharing type, but as Na has one $3s$ electron and Cl lacks a $3p$ electron, the excess electron of Na tends to enter the Cl structure, leaving the Na atom positively charged and the Cl atom negatively charged. The principal attractive forces between nearest neighbors are thus of a straightforward electrostatic nature, though the repulsive forces that keep the atoms apart at the lattice distance are of the interelectronic type. The polar crystals of which NaCl is an example are simple, highly-ordered crystals with no free electrons, but with all electrons well placed and closely bound to the lattice centers. Though the detailed characteristics of the electronic structure resulting from these closely packed atoms are not well enough known to permit the precise calculation of all of the mechanical properties, both qualitatively and quantitatively there is good agreement between theory and experiment for crystals of this type. The nature of the imperfections, such as vacant lattice sites and misplaced interstitial atoms, are also reasonably predictable, and the existence of such areas of imperfection are observable experimentally. Defects in precise local registry between lines or planes of atoms can be brought about by mechanical distortion; this phenomenon is observed, and has been well-studied. The surfaces of these crystals, though reasonably planar and regular, also display imperfections generally in the form of cracks and fissures. These weaken the crystals mechanically in much the same way as does a tear in paper or a nick in a glass rod or plate. Such surface defects are predominantly responsible for the smaller values of the maximum stress that will be supported before failure than would be expected from the reasonably well-known values of the crystal energies.

EXAMPLE. In the case of a polar crystal like sodium chloride the total energy of an aggregate of these atoms may, with little error, be taken as the energy liberated by permitting the several ions or charged atoms to assemble themselves from a great distance. The electrostatic energy between two atomic centers, each of charge e and separated by the distance d, is

$$U = K \frac{e^2}{d}$$

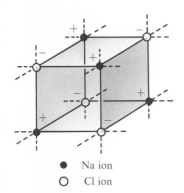

● Na ion
○ Cl ion

Figure 20-4 *NaCl crystal unit cell.*

The potential energy of the central atom of Fig. 20-5 due to the presence of its six nearest neighbors A of opposite charge is

$$U = -6K\frac{e^2}{d}$$

For the next nearest neghbors B at the edges of the cube, of which there are 12, at distance $\sqrt{2}d$:

$$U_2 = 12K\frac{e^2}{\sqrt{2}d} = 8.48K\frac{e^2}{d}$$

For the charges C at the close cube corners, of which there are 8, at distance $\sqrt{3}d$:

$$U_3 = -8K\frac{e^2}{\sqrt{3}d} = -4.62K\frac{e^2}{d}$$

Thus the energy of the central atom due to the closest cube of atoms is $U' = n'Ke^2/d$, where $n' = -2.14$. The calculation for the next enclosing cube follows the same lines yielding $U'' = n''Ke^2/d$, where $n'' = 0.62$. If this process is continued, the total energy of a central ion in such a

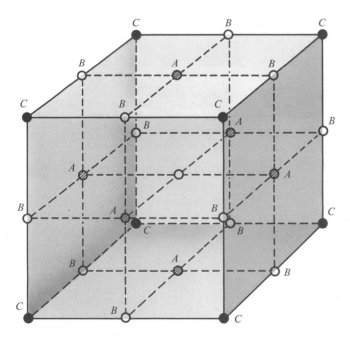

Figure 20-5 *All atoms designated by the same letter in the above cubic crystal lattice are equidistant from the central atom.*

lattice approaches $U = nKe^2/d$, where $n = -1.75$. The total energy of a large crystal of this type, where the contribution of volume atoms greatly exceeds that of surface atoms is the above quantity times the number of atoms in the volume, divided by two, since otherwise the binding energy between each ion pair is counted twice.

The above type of calculation may be carried out in the same way for an ion on a surface rather than one imbedded in a volume, choosing a surface normal to a principle axis. This yields an energy for an individual surface ion of about $1.23Ke^2/d$. If a large crystal is given a sharp tap at a point on its surface it will tend to separate, or cleave, along a plane surface known as a cleavage plane. Crystals like sodium chloride tend to cleave along planes normal to one of the principal axes, agreeing with the results of calculations such as those preceding, which indicate that the energy necessary to produce a new crystal area is less for such planes than for others of the families of planes in the crystal.

However, the force per unit area that must be applied normal to a principal plane to pull the crystal in two is generally considerably less than these calculations would indicate. If two surfaces of unit area are to be produced, the amount of energy theoretically required is given by the preceding calculations as $(1.75 - 1.23)N'Ke^2/d$, where N' is the number of atoms per unit area of the crystal surface. If this is to be provided by a force acting through some small multiple of d, say $5d$, which removes the ions largely from the field of attraction of one another, the force F per unit area averaged over this distance must be given approximately by

$$F \times 5d = 0.52 \frac{Ke^2N'}{d}$$

or:

$$F = 0.1 \frac{Ke^2}{d^2} N$$

where N is the number of atoms per unit volume of the crystal. This is about 100 times the forces per unit area that are necessary to pull such a crystal apart. Most actual crystals contain imperfections and surface fissures that greatly weaken the crystal, which accounts for this discrepancy. But by careful preparation of very slender crystals, values of the breaking tension can be produced that approach the order of magnitude of that derived theoretically.

A crystal that has interesting electrical properties but is less symmetrical than sodium chloride is quartz, SiO_2. It too can be grown in large transparent crystals of even greater strength than sodium chloride. In the form being considered here, the silicon atoms lie in any one layer in the manner of closely packed balls upon a table top, each with six regularly spaced nearest neighbors. Above and below each silicon atom are two oxygen atoms in a tetrahedral structure with the silicon atoms at the center. The next lower layer of the crystal is again a closely packed plane of silicon atoms sharing the lower oxygen atoms of the layer above it; but instead of being registered neatly beneath the spheres or vacant spaces above it, this layer is slightly displaced. The displacement is such that when reproduced by the next lower layer, the atoms in every third layer are found to lie vertically below one another. The effect of this produces either a left- or right-handed helical axis down through the layers, which may be seen in Fig. 20-6, showing for simplicity only the silicon atoms. Such crystals exhibit the interesting and useful property of rotating the sense of polarized light propagated along these axes in the direction in which they spiral in the particular quartz sample. They also have the property of displaying charges on opposite faces

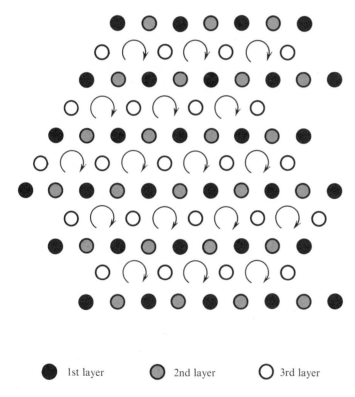

● 1st layer　　◉ 2nd layer　　○ 3rd layer

Figure 20-6 *Successive hexagonal-layer patterns of silicon atoms looking down from above into a quartz crystal.*

when they are elongated or compressed in a direction perpendicular to these helical axes.

EXAMPLE. The method utilized in an earlier example, dealing with the dependence of viscous fluid motion on the pertinent physical parameters, can also be used for determining the dependence of the velocity of propagation of waves through a fluid or a solid. In the case of a fluid there is a restoring force generated by compressing it, but none in the case of shearing it between two surfaces moving differentially parallel to one another. In the case of a solid, which by definition resists shear, there would be restoring forces brought into play for either compression or shear. Thus there would be one kind of a wave, namely a compressional one, in the case of a liquid and two kinds, namely compressional and shearing, in the case of a solid. The dimensional argument includes all of these, for the elastic constant of the material either solid or fluid may be defined as the force per unit area divided by the displacement per unit length that it causes. Writing K for this constant, it is evidently of the dimensions $(F/L^2)/(L/L) = M/LT^2$. The velocity of propagation v may also depend on the density ρ of the medium, which is of dimensions M/L^3, and possibly also on the wave length λ, or frequency of the wave. Thus the equation for the velocity of dimensions L/T would be

$$v = kK^a\rho^b\lambda^c$$

The dimensional equation would be:

$$\left(\frac{L}{T}\right) = \left(\frac{M}{LT^2}\right)^a \left(\frac{M}{L^3}\right)^b (L)^c$$

and: $a + b = 0$, $-a - 3b + c = 1$, $-2a = -1$

yielding: $a = \tfrac{1}{2}$, $b = -\tfrac{1}{2}$, $c = 0$

Thus the velocity of propagation of such a wave is given by:

$$v = k\left(\frac{K}{\rho}\right)^{1/2}$$

where k is a dimensionless constant.

Of course, K will generally not only differ depending on whether the motion is compressional or shearing for a given solid, but will also differ from one solid or liquid to another. The same argument may be employed to calculate the velocity of propagation of an electromagnetic wave, such as light, through a transparent crystal. In this case the shearing force exerted by the electric field of the light wave on the electrons and ions of the crystal, which is perpendicular to the direction of propagation of the wave, is in general dependent on the direction of the electric field with respect to the crystal axes. Unless the crystal structure is so symmetrical that the displacement of the electrons surrounding the nuclei at the lattice points under the influence of the electric field of the light wave is the same for any orientation of this field about the direction of propagation, the velocity of propagation of the light wave through the crystal will vary with this orientation.

Valence crystals   20-5

Another type of tightly bonded, highly regular crystal is the valence crystal, in which like atoms form essentially molecular bonds with one another extending indefinitely throughout the body of the crystal. Carbon in the form of diamond and silicon and germanium, all tetravalent atoms, form this type of crystal. If centers each with 4 arms extending from them at equal angles are assembled together so that each arm connects a center to a neighbor, it is found that these tetrahedra assemble in a lattice with cubic symmetry, since the arms of the tetrahedral distribution extend out to four of the corners of a cube if the atom is placed centrally within it, as seen in Fig. 20-7. Thus the four electron-sharing bonds with opposite spins connect receptive neighboring atoms in such a structure; a highly symmetrical and very strong and stable configuration results. It should be noted, however, that the rotational symmetries of this structure are not the same as those of the cube indicated in Chap. 1. A rotation about one of the four-fold axes must be accompanied by a displacement parallel to the axis of rotation, i.e. a screw type of motion, to bring all atoms into coincidence again. These crystals tend to be mechanically rigid and perfect, and there are no free electrons except near imperfections. This description closely corresponds to the experimental observations of these crystals. The electrical properties of such crystals are very sensitive indeed to impurities, and very high degrees of purity must be maintained if the normally insulating properties of such crystals are to be observed. The effect of a few foreign atoms—one in 10^8 or 10^9—is to introduce locally an electron above the normal complement, or to cause a local dearth of electrons, either of which results in a large proportional increase in conductivity.

However, if the temperature even of an impurity-free crystal of this type is raised considerably, some small fraction of the bonding electrons are liberated by their thermal energy from their cementing role between

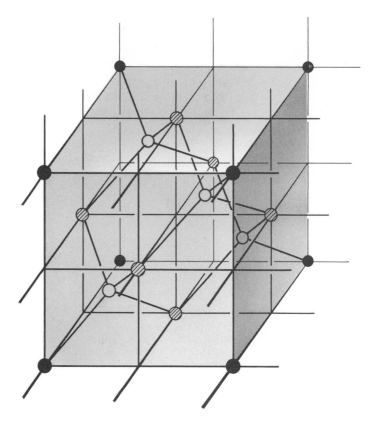

Figure 20-7 *Tetragonal crystal lattice;* ● *atoms at the corners of the large cube,* ⊘ *atoms at the faces of the large cube, and* ○ *atoms at the centers of four of the eight small constituent cubes.*

two atoms; they become free to traverse the crystal under the influence of an applied electric field. Thus the electrical conductivity increases with temperature, though it remains small in comparison with typical metallic conductors that will be mentioned later. Such valence crystals are called *semiconductors*, since they are intermediate in electrical conductivity between insulators, such as pure polar lattices, and metallic conductors. They are specifically called *intrinsic semiconductors* to distinguish them from valence crystals that have a higher conductivity due specifically to the presence of impurity atoms. If an electron is freed from a bond by thermal energy, it leaves behind it an electron vacancy called a *hole*; sequential occupancy by electrons from up-field causes the hole to travel in the opposite direction from the free electron under the influence of an electric field. Hence the hole behaves like a positive carrier of electricity, and adds to the electrical conductivity.

Impurities imbedded in a silicon or germanium crystal may also supply excess electrons or holes locally, which are then free to move through the crystal and add to the conductivity. Such crystals with a small proportion of foreign atoms are called *extrinsic semiconductors*. If a pentavalent atom from the next column to the right in the periodic table, such as arsenic or phosphorus, is the impurity, then an extra electron is provided, and the semiconductor is known as a negative, or *n-type* semiconductor. If a trivalent atom from the column to the left in the periodic table, such as indium or gallium, constitutes the impurity then there is a lack of one electron at the site, and a hole appears, constituting a positive or *p-type* semiconductor. Substances with traces of various types of impurities are of great practical importance in electronic circuits, for combinations of these and the interfaces where they meet can be induced to perform the functions of amplification, rectification, switching, and control, and can, in general, discharge the specialized functions that had heretofore required the use of complex electrical devices. They perform these functions with a much smaller expenditure of power and with greater efficiency, permanence, reliability, and adaptability than vacuum tubes or gas discharges; hence they present great practical advantages.

EXAMPLE. The way in which extrinsic semiconductors in various combinations function in electric circuits is readily understood from the point of view of the difference in electric potential or the potential energy per unit charge that develops between *p*-type and *n*-type materials on either side of a junction between them. The *n*-type has an excess density of electrons and the *p*-type a paucity; so when they are in intimate electrical contact, some electrons that are free to move flow from the *n*-type to the *p*-type, until an equilibrium is established. If a unit positive charge is moved from the *p*-type, it essentially moves from a region of negative charge density into one of positive charge density, and, as this is evidently in opposition to the electrical force upon it, the unit charge must be given an amount of energy necessary to effect its movement if it is to cross the boundary. The solid curve of the left-hand diagram in Fig. 20-8 indicates the energy increase required to effect the transit of a unit positive charge across the $p-n$ junction under these conditions. If a battery is connected in the sense indicated in the center diagram, the *n*-type potential is decreased and the *p*-type potential is increased, reducing the potential difference across the junction. If the battery is connected in the opposite sense, as on the right in the diagram, the potential difference across the junction is increased. In the first

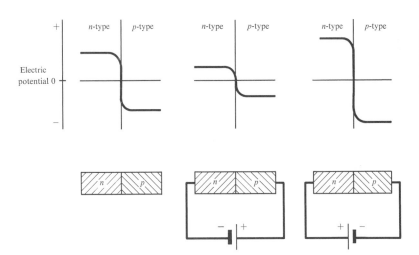

Figure 20-8 *Electric potential across a p-n junction for different externally applied potentials.*

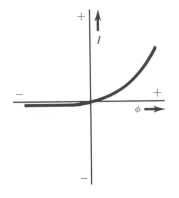

Figure 20-9 *Characteristic curve for a p-n junction, showing the relationship between current and potential difference across the junction.*

case the energy difference to be overcome by the transit of a charge through the junction is less; in the second case greater, and hence the electrical resistance is less in the former case than in the latter. The current for a given battery potential is dependent upon its sense of connection to the junction, and the relation between current and potential difference applied to the junction will resemble that of Fig. 20-9.

If two *p-n* junctions are placed in series with, say, the *n*-type material sandwiched between two *p*-type blocks, it is readily seen how varying the potential difference between the *n*-type material and one of its *p*-type neighbors can effectively act as the opening or closing of an electrical switch controlling the flow of a current through the two junctions. Such a device is known as a transistor. The *p-n* junctions can be constructed with very minute dimensions and with great ease and reliability; it is upon the base of this solid-state electronics that the current developments in computer technology rest.

Semiconductors are useful in other capacities than electrical circuit elements because of the dependence of their electrical conductivity upon temperature and upon illumination. The large positive temperature coefficient of conductivity renders them useful thermometers and thermal control elements. The dependence of conductivity on illumination comes about in the following way: normally *n*-type germanium, containing say a trace of arsenic, has deposited on one of its surfaces a thin film of gallium, which on diffusing in a few atomic diameters

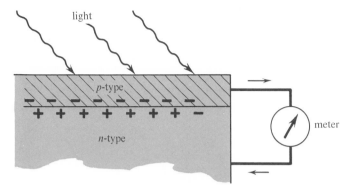

Figure 20-10 *Photosensitive p-n junction.*

provides a layer of *p*-type germanium. The free electrons tend to diffuse over into the *p*-type, carrying, of course, a negative charge, so that the outer gallium layer becomes negative and the underlying material positive, as shown in Fig. 20-10. When light is incident upon the surface, photons are absorbed by the electrons giving them more than enough energy to disturb the thermal energy balance maintained by diffusion of electrons and the electrostatic forces at the boundary. The electronic current thus set up can be used to operate a current meter, such as a photographic light meter, or to operate low-power-level electrical devices, such as the solar battery.

Metals 20-6

The remaining class of crystals to be discussed is that consisting of the metallic crystals or metals. Such crystals are those formed by copper, zinc, iron, gold, silver, etc., which present large scale properties of toughness, great tensile strength, and high electrical conductivity. The mechanical properties are very largely the results of polycrystalline structures and impurities, for pure single crystals of these elements are quite soft and deformable along those crystal planes where the sliding of one layer of atoms over another readily takes place. However, high electrical conductivity is a unique and inherent property of metals.

The great majority of metallic crystal lattices are those representing the closest possible packing together of spheres. These lattices can be illustrated by placing marbles or ping pong balls in a flat tray with a low retaining rim and noting the ordered arrangement that crowding

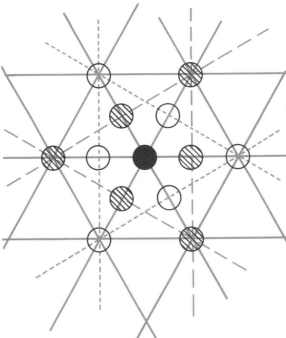

Figure 20-11 *Looking down the cubic diagonal of a cell of a face-centered cubic lattice. The black dot* ● *represents the nearest and farthest corner atom in line. The hatched dots* ◒ *are the next nearest atoms along the line of sight, and the open dots* ○ *are the farthest along the line of sight. Solid lines are the cubic axes. Dashed and dotted lines are the hexagonal axes parallel to the plane of the figure.*

brings about. Also, the nature of these lattices and, in particular, the types of imperfections to which they are subject can be seen by building up an assembly of small uniformly sized soap bubbles. It is seen by either method that the first layer of closely packed spheres has hexagonal symmetry. Each sphere is surrounded by six contiguous neighbors. When the next layer is added, the spheres rest in half of the depressions in the contour of the first layer, adding three more neighbors to each sphere in that layer. The next layer lies similarly above the second, but it will be seen that the spheres in it can either lie immediately above those in the first layer, or they have the alternative of lying over spaces in both the lower layers. The former case retains the hexagonal symmetry about the vertical and the latter does not. Looked at from an angle, the latter configuration is seen to be equally well described as an assembly of cubes with atoms at the centers of the faces as well as at the corners (Fig. 20-11). Thus it possesses complete cubic symmetry, which the lattices of diamond and silicon do not. There is little difference in energy between these two possible configurations; in each case the spheres have 12 nearest neighbors, and together they represent the crystalline form of almost all metallic lattices. The ease with which one layer may slide over another, as in the shearing of a lattice, is quite evident, and the role of impurities or imperfections in registry is also easily envisaged.

The metals are characterized by atoms that, when arranged in these closely-packed lattices, have one or two loosely bound outer electrons. The packing is so close and the binding of these electrons to individual atoms so slight that these electrons are essentially shared as a group by all of the constituent atoms of the crystal. They are comparatively free to move about within the lattice under the influence of externally applied electric fields. Their motion is not rapid, but is rather of the nature of a drift velocity through the lattice of a few centimeters a second; the large number of these electrons available enables high current densities to be produced. The lattice centers interfere with the wave pattern of motion of these electrons: irregularities, impurities, imperfections, and the magnitude of thermal oscillation of the atoms all tend to impede the freedom of motion of the conduction electrons. The last factor explains why the electrical resistance of a metal increases with temperature; or, alternatively stated, the temperature coefficient of electrical conduction is observed to be negative in metals. At very low temperatures, certain metals show the phenomenon of superconductivity, in which an electric current once started will persist with little diminution for long periods of time.

In general, the exclusion principle insures that on the average the electron spins and magnetic moments are oppositely oriented and there is no permanent net magnetic moment in a crystal. However, in the case of certain metals, notably iron, cobalt, and nickel, the internal electron structure of each atom has a single electron within its inner shells, the spin of which is not counterbalanced; hence these electrons are free to contribute to a considerable net magnetic moment if all of them are aligned. The forces operative in the close packing of the lattice are the electrostatic and electron-sharing forces. For certain critical values of the separation of atomic centers, these tend to orient the internal electron spins, and consequently the moments of these magnetic atoms. The forces may be such that they are aligned alternately in opposite directions, in which case they effectively cancel the magnetic effects of each other. Alternatively, for certain crystal forms with a favorable spacing between neighboring atoms, the forces give rise to uniformity in the direction of the electron spins over small

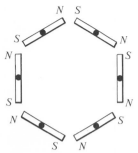

Stable configuration of a circle of compass needles.

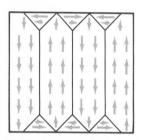

Neighboring magnetized domains in an iron crystal assuming the directions of magnetization indicated by the arrows that tend to provide closed loops of the magnetic force vector within the material.

Figure 20-12

crystal blocks or domains. The magnetic forces between these domains induce the direction of magnetization in neighboring domains, which will provide closed paths of the vector of the magnetic force, much as a circle of compass needles tends to take up north-to-south pole configurations (Fig. 20-12). However, by the application of strong external magnetic fields, these forces may be overcome over large volumes of the material, and the like-oriented domains then give rise to a strong external magnetic field (Fig. 20-13). Once so oriented, the rigidity of a lattice that has been given great strength by impurities or imperfections is such that the magnetic moments of the domains retain their orientations against the internal magnetic forces. Thus even after the removal of the magnetic field, which induced the ordered orientation of the magnetic moments of the domains, these magnetic moments may remain all oriented in the same direction, and a "permanent magnet" results.

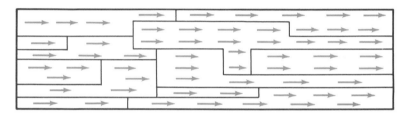

Figure 20-13 *Schematic alignment of domains in a hard magnetic material that resists the reorienting effect and hence produces a permanent external magnetic field.*

Further reading:

BARDEEN, J., "Research Leading to Point-contact Transistors," *Science*, vol. 126, No. 3264, p. 105 (1957).

BOZORTH, R. M., "Magnetic Materials," *Scientific American*, vol. 192, No. 1, p. 68 (1955).

BRIDGMAN, P. W., "Synthetic Diamonds," *Scientific American*, vol. 193, No. 5, p. 42 (1955).

CRICK, F. H. C., "Nucleic Acids," *Scientific American*, vol. 197, No. 3, p. 188 (1957).

CUFF, F. B., JR. AND SCHETKY, L. McD., "Dislocations in Metals," *Scientific American*, vol. 193, No. 1, p. 80 (1955).

DASH, W. C. AND TWEET, A. G., "Observing Dislocations in Crystals," *Scientific American*, vol. 205, No. 4, p. 107 (1961).

DEBYE, P. J. W., "How Giant Molecules are Measured," *Scientific American*, vol. 197, No. 3, p. 90 (1957).

DOTY, P., "Proteins," *Scientific American*, vol. 197, No. 3, p. 173 (1957).

LESSING, L. P., "Pure Metals," *Scientific American*, vol. 191, No. 1, p. 36 (1954).

LUDWIG, G. W., "Electron Spin Resonance," *Science*, vol. 135, No. 3507, p. 899 (1962).

MARK, H. F., "Giant Molecules," *Scientific American*, vol. 197, No. 3, p. 80 (1957).

MATTHIAS, B. T., "Superconductivity," *Scientific American*, vol. 197, No. 5, p. 92 (1957).

MOOSER, E., "Semiconducting Compounds," *Science*, vol. 132, No. 3436, p. 285 (1960).

MULLER, E. W., "Atoms Visualized," *Scientific American*, vol. 196, No. 6, p. 113 (1957).

NATTA, G., "How Giant Molecules are Made," *Scientific American*, vol. 197, No. 3, p. 98 (1957).

PIETENPOL, W. J., "Transistor Designs: the First Decade," *Bell Laboratories Research*, vol. 36, p. 202 (1958).

PRENER, J. S. AND SALLENGER, D. B., "Phosphors," *Scientific American*, vol. 191, No. 4, p. 62 (1954).

RAISBECK, G., "The Solar Battery," *Scientific American*, vol. 193, No. 6, p. 102 (1955).

SMART, J. S., "Neel Theory of Ferrimagnetism," *American Journal of Physics*, vol. 23, No. 6, p. 356 (1955).

SPROULL, R. L., "Conduction of Heat in Solids," *Scientific American*, vol. 207, No. 6, p. 92 (1962).

STEELE, E. L., "Descriptive Theory of Semiconductors," *American Journal of Physics*, vol. 25, No. 3, p. 174 (1957).

Problems

20-1 Calculate the average potential energy per ion in a large crystal of common salt (NaCl) for which the atomic spacing is 2.8×10^{-12} m.

20-2 The ionization potential of neutral sodium atoms is 5.1 V. The binding energy of the extra electron in a negative chlorine ion is 3.8 e.V. Using the result of the previous problem, calculate the energy released when sodium and chlorine atoms combine to produce a kilogram of common salt crystals.

20-3 A crystal is shattered into small fragments. How can these be distinguished from fragments of glass?

20-4 What type of semiconducting material results when silicon is doped with aluminum?

20-5 When a solid is subjected to an electric field of intensity E, the free electrons drift with a velocity $v = \mu E$, where μ is defined as the *mobility*. Calculate the current I produced in a conductor of cross section A by a potential drop ϕ along its length l, assuming there are n free electrons per unit volume, carrying a charge e, and having a mobility μ. Hence show that the mobility $\mu = e/n\rho$, where ρ is the resistivity of the conducting material.

20-6 Sketch the potential energy surface experienced by an electron in the vicinity of an isolated positive ion. Sketch the potential energy surface along a line of atoms extending in from the surface of a metal. Show the potential energy surface outside as well as inside the metal. Indicate the approximate total energy of the *free* electrons in the metal relative to this surface. Indicate the work function of the particular metal. Sketch a third diagram for a pure semiconducting material and indicate the total energy of its highest energy electrons relative to the potential energy surface.

20-7 The rate of electron emission by a heated metallic filament is proportional to $a\epsilon^{-b/T}$, where T is the absolute temperature and b is a constant; a is a function of T, but may be treated as a constant compared with the rapidly varying exponential factor. Justify the above expression and show that the constant b is simply the ratio of the metal's work function to Boltzmann's constant.

20-8 Insulators are generally transparent to visible light, whereas metals and semiconductors are opaque. Why? To what region of the near visible electromagnetic spectrum might insulators be opaque? What region of the near visible spectrum might semiconductors transmit?

20-9 Copper is one of the best electrical conductors, and also one of the best thermal conductors. Glass on the other hand is both a good electrical and thermal insulator. Is this relationship of electrical and thermal conductivities common? Why?

20-10 What effect would hammering have on a permanent magnet? What effect would heating to a high temperature have? Explain.

Techniques of atomic measurement

Measurements of atomic parameters   21-1

Physics is preeminently the area of science in which accuracy of measurement plays the greatest role. Measurements require great imagination, insight, patience, and skill. Success in solving the technical problems presented in fashioning precision instruments out of available materials has marked the great observers and experimental scientists from the earliest days of the observation of planetary motions to the present explorations of atomic nuclei. The conception of significant experiments, the recognition of unexpected but significant phenomena encountered in the course of them, and the interpretation of their broadly ramifying implications has evoked all the capability of genius. A high degree of accuracy has always been a hallmark of both the immediate and future value of experimental results. Without the precise measurements of the motion of the planets against the background of the fixed stars, the heliocentric theory would not have been established; without the precision measurements of the velocity of light, the concept of relativity would not have been cogent; and without accurate measurements of the atomic constants, our present understanding of the basic constituents of matter could not have been achieved.

The number of experimentally significant figures to which the values of the important quantities referred to in earlier chapters are known is a very real measure of our knowledge about them and the phenomena to which they relate. The fact that we know the value of the gravitational constant G to only about one part in a thousand, and the velocity of light in vacuum c to one part in a million very possibly conceals our present ignorance of significant relationships that the former may have to the latter. The accurate measurement of atomic constants in terms of the standards of length and time (see Sec. 2-2 and 2-3), such as atomic spacing in crystals and the determination of the rate of circulation and precession of charged and spinning atomic particles in magnetic fields, is accomplished by the precise comparison of wave lengths and frequencies of electromagnetic radiation. The precision in such measurements ranges from the order of a few parts in 10^7 to a few parts in 10^5. Accurate atomic measurements that involve an extension of the standard of mass—the kilogram—present greater difficulties; such direct measurements are usually less precise as, are also the measurements of atomic charges and e/m ratios that reflect the larger errors involved in measurement of velocity-dependent forces between electric charges. Comparisons of atomic masses can be made much more precisely than can absolute measurements of them in terms of the kilogram. The overall accuracies to which the atomic constants are known tend to be equalized by the plurality of theoretical relationships between them.

As pointed out in the early chapters, the ultimate data observed and recorded in any measurement are the relative positions of objects or markings, such as pointers and scales, or images on photographic plates. The wave-like aspect of matter suggests that a limitation to spatial delineation of an object being observed would be its DeBroglie wave length. This is indeed an ultimate limitation; but in the cases of objects large enough to be observed directly or under the magnification of high power microscopes, this wave length is so small that it does not blur the objects. Hence it may be ignored as a cause of observational error in location, but it must be taken into account in the design and interpretation of experiments involving the interaction of elementary particles with each other, or with atomic and molecular complexes. Another, and in this case important limitation on direct experimental observations of the location of objects is related to the Brownian motion mentioned in Chap. 12, which is an instance of the average energy of motion shared among all of the participants in an assembly in thermal equilibrium, described in Chap. 18. Visible objects are found to be in appreciable oscillatory, translational, or rotational motion at ordinary temperatures. It is this fact that places the practical limit on the precision of measurement of position. This limitation is evidently proportionally greater if the energy changes being measured are comparable to the average thermal energy shared by the measuring devices than it would be if the energy changes are large compared with this average thermal energy. The following discussion will, in consequence, be separated into two parts: the first relating to relatively low energy events; the second to high energy events.

It has been seen that the phenomena of the association of atoms in small and large molecules, and in the aggregated forms of matter called liquids and solids, involve energies of contiguity of the order of from 0.1 to 10 e.V. The upper limit arises because the outer electrons of atomic structures that form the bonds between atoms are themselves attached to their parent structures, with energies of this magnitude. The lower limit is largely determined by the temperature at which we make our observations or perform our experiments. The lower the temperature, i.e., the less the thermal energy of agitation, the greater the opportunity for substances with weaker bonding tendencies to form atomic and molecular clusters in liquids or crystals. The most intransigent of the gases, helium, which has the least energy of atomic association, and hence the least tendency to form molecules and crystals, liquifies and crystallizes at a few degrees absolute. In the temperature region congenial to human life, which is about 17°C. or $T = 290°K.$, the average thermal energy associated, say, with the translational motion of an atom of a gas is $\frac{3}{2}kT$, or 7.5×10^{-21} J. This is equal to 0.047 e.V. As this measures the average energy shared in an assembly obeying the distribution law, we wouldn't commonly expect to observe permanent atomic aggregates with binding energies as low as this.

The fluctuating sea of energy exchange or thermal agitation among the entities whose average state is described by the distribution law is referred to by communication engineers as *thermal noise*. It imposes the practical limit in most instances on the amplitude of a meaningful signal that can be recognized or detected with satisfying assurance. As an electromagnetic wave spreads out from a source, the inverse square law attenuates it, and the amplitude decreases rapidly with distance. Similarly, waves sent along wires decrease in amplitude due to the resistance and other dissipative circumstances associated with the materials that they encounter. When the energy carried by such waves falls well below the order of magnitude of the thermal fluctuation, the information they contain is irrecoverably lost. Amplifying systems are spaced along communication lines in a way that ensures that these signals are never lost in the noise background. In the older type of thermionic amplifiers, the background was characterized by the temperature of the cathode at, say, 600°K., whereas, within a transistor amplifier at room temperature, the value of T is about half as great, and the mean noise energy is less by this factor. Hence weaker signals may be reclaimed from the background; or, alternatively, fewer amplifiers are required per unit length of line with cool solid-state circuit elements.

Cosmological information comes to us from outer space in the form of electromagnetic waves, bringing us clues as to the structure of our galaxy, the other galaxies that make up the visible universe, and the vast stretches of intervening space. The information that lies in the visible region of the spectrum comes from luminous bodies either directly or by reflection. As these bodies are already hot, the inherent noise level is high, and little is gained by using low-temperature amplifiers. On the other hand, radio telescopes concentrate the long-wave length radiation from cold outer space, such as the 0.21 m. radiation from hydrogen, mentioned in Chap. 15. Here the background noise is low, and meaningful signals can most advantageously be recovered by special crystal amplifiers operating at the very low temperatures produced by surrounding them with baths of liquid helium.

The mechanical and electrical measurements, even up to measurement of the highest frequency of microwaves used in electrical engineering, are clearly of the cumulative average type, in which the sum of the effects of many quanta of energy furnish the data of the experiment. This is also generally true for most measurements in optics and atomic physics. The spectrometer records the reception of many photons of identical energy in the production of colored slit images on the photographic plate; the photoelectric cell responds to many photons of visible radiation in its usual applications; and in the mass spectrograph, or mass spectrometer, the darkening of the photographic plate or the current carried by ions to the collecting electrode is a result of the reception of many successive ions of like mass following the same path. However, in pressing all these measurements to their ultimate sensitivity to detect small effects caused by a few photons or material particles, we find that the noise background proves to be the limiting factor.

The fluctuations that occur in small samples of this ambient sea of noise can themselves be studied. They provide significant information regarding atomic assemblages. The very existence of these fluctuations in a statistically describable way confirms the correctness of atomic theory and its statistical formulation. In the neighborhood of the conditions of temperature and pressure at which the gas and liquid phases of a particular substance merge, the magnitude of density fluctuation is particularly large; observations of these fluctuations furnishes one of the methods of determining the magnitude of Boltzmann's constant k. Also, the fluctuations in the thermionic current of electrons from a heated surface, under conditions of such low electric gradients that the thermal equilibrium of the electrons is little affected, provide a method of determining the charge an electron carries, e. Other low energy phenomena exhibited by groups of coordinated atoms, as in the case of the change in direction of magnetization of small regions in ferromagnetic crystals, can also be observed.

However, it is generally necessary to get well up out of the noise band of energy if individual atomic events are to be easily and unambiguously identified, and used for obtaining precise and quantitative information. It is very difficult to detect and identify single low-energy events against this sea of background energy flux in all of its kinetic, potential, and radiant forms. With a few possible exceptions, photons, with wave lengths considerably longer than 10^{-6} m., corresponding to about 1 e.V. of energy, cannot be separately isolated and amplified.

It will be recalled from Chap. 18 that the law of energy distribution among the constituents in a large aggregate of physical entities in thermal equilibrium with one another is predominantly of the exponential form. Though there is a weighting factor represented by g_j, which is dependent upon the density of energy levels of different types, it is of secondary importance, particularly in the high energy region, since the exponential function changes so rapidly with its argument that it largely obscures the effect of minor factors. Thus, for photons, electrons, atoms, or still larger systems, the probability of observing a participant in the energy reservoir with an energy u_j large compared with kT is determined predominantly by the function $\epsilon^{-u_j/kT}$. Thus the ratio of the number of components of the assembly with, say, 100 times the energy $kT/2$ to the number possessing this particular energy is ϵ^{-50} or about 3×10^{-22}. Among the 6×10^{23} molecules in a mole of gas, only about 200 would stand out by deviating to the extent of 100 times from the mean energy associated with translation in a given direction, or to the extent of 10 times the mean velocity along an axis.

The photoelectric cell depends for its action upon the release of electrons from a surface, as a consequence of the absorption of a photon with an energy in excess of a critical energy of the order of one electron volt. The production of ions in a gas, upon which electrical conduction through it depends, is again the consequence of the absorption of energy from a photon or an electron with an energy in excess of a critical amount of the order of ten electron volts by a gas molecule. The statistical thermal equilibrium at room temperature provides enough sufficiently energetic electrons and photons to lead to easily measurable electron currents from the surfaces of common photocells and through gases at medium pressures. If one is trying to measure small effects in a laboratory against this confusing background, one may, if possible, conduct the experiment at lower temperatures, thus decreasing the denominator in the exponent u_j/kT. This expedient can be very effective, for a gain of a factor of 10 in the exponent of ϵ reduces the incidence of unwanted effects by a factor of the order of 30,000. An alternative expedient is to take advantage of the absence of any correlation between noise fluctuations occurring in independent instruments, or in the one instrument at different times.

EXAMPLE. *Coincidence technique.* Frequently, atomic events to be studied are recorded by a pulse in some detector of known efficiency, say ε, where ε is the probability of an atomic particle entering the detector and producing a sufficiently large pulse to be recorded. If the number of atomic events occurring per second is n, then the number of true pulses recorded per second is $n\varepsilon$. The detector will also record a number, say N, of noise pulses per second, and these mask the true pulses if $n\varepsilon/N$—the so-called "signal-to-noise" ratio—is much less than 1.

However, when an event to be studied is accompanied by the emission of two detectable particles, or when the one emitted particle has sufficient energy to pass through and be detected almost simultaneously by

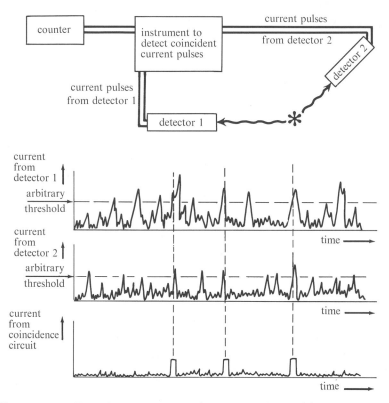

Figure 21-1 *Two detectors arranged to count in coincidence. Current pulses exceeding an arbitrarily selected threshold from each detector are counted. The lower the threshold is, the greater the number of "noise" pulses counted. "True" pulses corresponding to the passage of an atomic particle through a detector are indicated above by vertical arrows. Vertical dashed lines indicate coincidence events which are predominantly "true" events because only these are correlated in time for the two detectors.*

two detectors, then the signal-to-noise ratio may be increased by accepting only those events that give pulses from both detectors, which are coincident in time. Thus, if the second detector of Fig. 21-1 also has an efficiency ε independent of the first, then the probability of a true pulse in the first detector being accompanied by a related true pulse in the second detector is just the efficiency ε of the second detector. Therefore, the true coincident count per second is $(n\varepsilon)\varepsilon$, or $n\varepsilon^2$. On the other hand, the coincidence of two noise pulses is a purely random process. If the second detector has similar noise characteristics to the first, and the counting system is only able to differentiate in time between two pulses separated by t seconds (the so-called "resolving time" of the counting system), then the probability that a noise pulse in the first detector will be followed by a noise pulse in the second detector within a time t is simply the number of noise pulses in the second detector in that time, i.e., Nt. Therefore, the noise coincidence count per second is $N(Nt)$, or N^2t, and the signal-to-noise coincidence ratio is $n\varepsilon^2/N^2t$. Typical figures might be: $n = 10^4$, $N = 10^3$, $\varepsilon = 10^{-2}$, and $t = 10^{-9}$. Thus the "signal-to-noise" ratio in a single detector would be $n\varepsilon/N$, or 10^{-1}, and the true pulses would be obscured by ten times the number of noise pulses. However, the coincidence ratio would be $n\varepsilon^2/N^2t$, or 1000. The improvement factor achieved by such a coincidence technique is evidently $(n\varepsilon^2/N^2t)/(n\varepsilon/N)$ or ε/Nt. It is seen that the coincidence count rate due to noise pulses is an even more sensitive function of temperature than the noise count rate in a single detector, depending as it does on the second power of the single's rate N.

Measurement of single high-energy atomic events 21-3

The measurement of single atomic events becomes more easily accomplished as the energy rises. Techniques are well-developed for detecting the presence of individual photons, electrons, or ions with energies in excess of 100 e.V. When the energy is in the range well above 1000 e.V., quantitative measurements of the energy and the direction of the momentum can both be made quite readily in the instances involving single atoms or quanta.

The techniques for measurements involving a charged particle depend upon the gradual dissipation of the energy of the particle due to the electric forces between it and the components of the atomic systems through or near which it passes. Its passage, which is equivalent to a sudden pulse of electric field, transfers energy from the particle to the atomic system by exciting the electronic system to higher energy states, or by removing one or more of the electrons from the loosely or tightly bound atomic states. The radiation produced by the return of these atoms to their normal states and by their eventual recapture of electrons may be absorbed and reemitted by more distant atoms as the radiation spreads outward. Thus the energy of the particle is gradually dissipated in the form of the disruption of the atomic systems near its path until, after a long series of individual encounters, its initial energy, being steadily degraded through primary and secondary processes, is completely expended. In the case of stopping in a crystalline solid, energy is also dissipated in the disruption of the orderly lattice structure of the constituent atoms. When charged particles of high velocity pass through the electric field of an atom they may lose energy by the direct emission of photons.

One generic type of equipment measures the energy loss of a high-speed particle traversing a region containing gaseous, liquid, or crystalline material by recording either the electric charge separated in the course of the event, or the intensity of the nearly simultaneously-emitted quanta of radiation that accompany it. On the average it is found that one ion pair is produced in air for the loss of about 35 e.V. of energy by the particle. Hence the stopping of a 35,000 e.V. particle results in the production of about 1000 free electrons. The distance required to stop such a particle clearly depends upon the atomic density of the material that is traversed. It also depends on the velocity of the particle; for equally energetic particles of different mass, the lighter has the higher velocity and goes farther, leaving a less dense path of ionization behind it. Furthermore, the larger the charge carried by a particle, the stronger is the electric field it produces, and the denser is the resulting excitation and ionization in its path. Either technique—the electrical measurement of the separated charge or the measurement of the intensity of the pulse of radiation emitted—involves an empirical calibration, because sufficiently precise calculations of the roles of all the complicated individual processes that take place in the disruption and reassembly of the atomic systems are beyond our ability. The number of ions, for instance, formed by the complete stoppage of a particle of a given kind, such as an electron or photon, accelerated to a known energy when passing through a particular gas, say nitrogen, is measured over a sufficiently wide variation of conditions to provide the graphic or tabular data which then enables one—by measuring the ionization produced by a particle of known type but unknown energy—to deduce the value of the energy.

The experimental apparatus employed falls into two general types. The first consists of a chamber containing a gas or mixture of gases and two electrodes that support a sufficient potential difference, and are so disposed as to draw out rapidly all the ions produced by the passage of an energetic particle through the chamber. For instance, in Fig. 21-2, ions and electrons produced within the volume defined by the cylindrical electrode are drawn to it and the central wire, and cause a flow of current through the resistance R. The potential difference across the ends of the resistance as a result of the current pulse may be measured directly, or may be amplified by a known amount and then displayed on an oscilloscope screen and measured. The details of devices of this type, known as *ionization chambers* or *gas counters*, are subject to wide variation, but under the proper conditions they not only record the passage of an ionizing particle through the sensitive volume with a reliable and reasonably high efficiency, but they also, by recording the magnitude of the current pulse, yield a measure of the energy the particle dissipates within the sensitive volume from which the ions are collected.

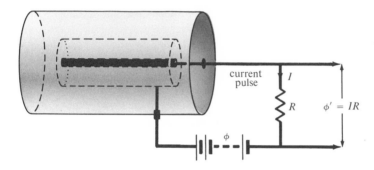

Figure 21-2   *Gas type of particle counter.*

A second type of particle counter, which also permits energy measurements, is that in which the active region usually consists of a liquid or crystal rather than a gas. As there are more atoms per unit volume in a liquid or solid than in a gas, an ionizing particle of a given energy is stopped in a shorter distance. Hence, for the same energy of the particle, the counter can be physically smaller. This provides better geometry for measurement; or, for the same size counter, higher-energy particles can be measured. Crystals such as silver chloride, zinc sulfide, or diamond yield pulses of electric current between electrodes on their faces when a particle traverses them, as in the case of the gas counter (Fig. 21-3). Also, certain organic and inorganic crystals, and organic liquids, such as anthracene, naphthalene, cadmium tungstate, and terphenyl

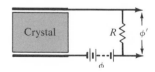

Figure 21-3   *Crystal counter.*

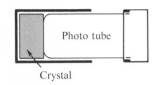

Figure 21-4 *Counter and photo tube combination.*

emit pulses of fluorescent radiation in the blue to ultraviolet region of the spectrum when they are traversed by a charged particle. These scintillating materials may also be used to detect photons which, in traversing matter, liberate high-energy electrons, thus dissipating their energy in the form of excitation and ionization by this secondary process. In the case of such a counter, the burst of fluorescent energy, which is a measure of the energy loss of the primary particle in the crystal, is detected and measured by the electrons it liberates from the cathode of a photoelectric tube, which is disposed in such a way as to receive the pulse of radiation and in turn to give rise to a pulse of electric current (Fig. 21-4).

It is evident from the preceding discussion of typical devices that if the entire length of the ionizing path lies within the sensitive region of the counter, the measurement provides a value for the energy of the particle recorded. In such a situation, it is equally clear that no information is furnished as to the direction of the momentum vector, for a crossing in any direction of the sensitive region of the counter liberates the same charge from its ionized molecular systems, or generates the same intensity of light pulse from the rearrangement of their electronic structures. If, on the other hand, the energy loss in a counter is much less than the energy of the particle, only a small fraction of the latter is recorded; the event is noted, but a value for the energy is not obtained. In such a case, however, it is evidently possible to place a number of counters in line and, by means of an electrical recording system that is activated by practically simultaneous events in all the counters, it

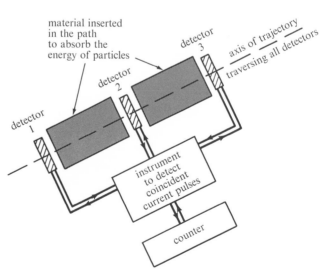

Figure 21-5 *Configuration of particle detectors to determine the energy of recorded events and the axis of the particles' trajectory.*

may be determined that the particle's trajectory lay along the line joining the counters. A measure of the energy may be achieved by placing material of high stopping power between the counters until coincidences are no longer recorded (Fig. 21-5). Such experimental techniques, either alone or in conjunction with the chamber techniques that will be mentioned later, provided much of the early exploratory evidence in the field of high energy physics.

There is a second class of high-energy particle detection devices that provide information about the direction of the momentum as well as about the energy, in a very direct and simple way. In these devices, the actual trajectory of the particle, as well as the trajectories of the secondary ionizing particles to which it gives rise, are rendered visible and measurable. As in the case of the energy-measuring counters, the volumes involved may be gaseous, liquid, or solid. The first devices of this type to be used extensively were of the gaseous type, and called *cloud chambers* (Fig. 21-6). Droplets of water tend to form in a supersaturated atmosphere when there are nuclei, in the form of dust, or electrically charged particles present to act as centers of condensation. Thus, if the condition of supersaturation is induced in water-vapor-laden air just before or after the passage of an ionizing particle through it, the condensation of minute droplets of water will take place upon the ions

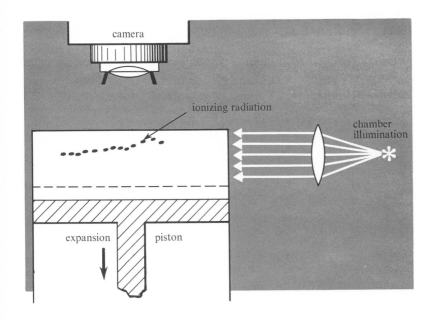

Figure 21-6   *Cloud chamber.*

that are left behind by the passages of the particle, and, of course, upon any other ions that may have been produced by secondary or tertiary processes. In the cloud chamber, a glass-enclosed region of saturated air or other gas has its temperature suddenly lowered by an expansion induced by a slight withdrawal of a piston. The conditions of super-saturation are thus brought about. If the chamber is strongly illuminated, the tracks of droplets appear as brilliant light-scattering centers against a dark background, and may be photographed by a simple or a stereo-scopic camera. In the latter case, the pictures may be reprojected and the tracks reproduced in space for detailed study and measurement.

An important recent variation of this technique is the bubble chamber, which works in an inverse way. Liquid in a chamber—generally liquid hydrogen—is expanded slightly by the motion of a piston; along the track of an ionizing particle, bubbles of vapor are formed. These may be photographed in the same way as the droplets in a cloud chamber. The primary advantage of the bubble chamber is the greater density and hence greater stopping power of the liquid. Evidently a magnetic field may be produced in the chamber by winding a current-carrying coil about it. The paths of the particles then assume a curvature, and from the radius r the magnitude of the momentum may be deduced by the relation $r = mv/eH$. Thirdly, the tracks of a high-energy particle through a solid may be made visible if the particle can cause the silver halide grains in a photographic emulsion to be developable. Special emulsions particularly adapted to this purpose are available; exposure to the particle flux, and subsequent photographic development provides a permanent record in the form of tracks of developed photographic grains along the path traversed by ionizing particles.

The great advantages of the techniques that provide information on the direction of the momentum of particles as well as on the energy of particles are two: 1) the additional data on momentum; and 2) the great additional clarity that comes from a visual portrayal. Such a presentation is imaginatively very stimulating and gives the illusion of seeing the basic phenomena that are taking place. Visual representation has undoubtedly very greatly accelerated the rate of acquisition of knowledge and insight in matters of high-energy particle physics. A representative process is indicated schematically in the Fig. 21-7. A track leading from a source of particles is observed to branch at a certain point. The density of the tracks, which represents the number of ions formed per unit length, provides a measure of the rate of energy loss, the total energy, and the nature of the particle. The angles provide the momentum vectors. Thus the above figure could represent the collision between a high-speed doubly-charged helium nucleus (α particle) with the nucleus of a hydrogen atom (proton) that is projected

Figure 21-7   *Schematic por-trayal of particle paths.*

off at the angle ϕ. By the application of a magnetic field to the region under study, the paths become curves that, to the extent that the loss of energy may be neglected, are arcs of circles. The curvature provides a measure of the momentum as well.

Thus a great deal of information can be derived from such observations and these techniques have been responsible for the major advances in our understanding of high energy atomic and nuclear processes which have marked the past half century.

Further reading:

COLLINS, G. B., "Scintillation Counters," *Scientific American*, vol. 189, No. 5, p. 36 (1953).

DEBENEDETTI, S., "The Mossbauer Effect," *Scientific American*, vol. 202, No. 4, p. 72 (1960).

GLASER, D. A., "The Bubble Chamber," *Scientific American*, vol. 192, No. 2, p. 46 (1955).

MARSHAK, R. E., "The Nuclear Force," *Scientific American*, vol. 202, No. 3, p. 98 (1960).

O'NEILL, G. K., "The Spark Chamber," *Scientific American*, vol. 207, No. 2, p. 36 (1962).

TAMM, I. E., "Radiation of Particles with Speeds Greater Than That of Light," *American Scientist*, vol. 47, No. 2, p. 169 (1959).

YAGODA, H., "The Tracks of Nuclear Particles," *Scientific American*, vol. 194, No. 5, p. 40 (1956).

Problems

21-1 If the second detector of the coincidence experiment described in the text had an effective efficiency of 100 per cent (for example, it might be placed immediately behind the first detector and be long enough to guarantee detection of any particle traversing the first detector), then what would be the improvement factor for the signal-to-noise ratio obtained by the use of the coincidence technique?

21-2 (a) Very small steady currents may be measured with a galvanometer having the motion of its coil heavily damped, a long time then being required for the system to attain its equilibrium deflection because of the slow response. Why could this be an advantage?
(b) It is possible to detect a signal fluctuation whose strength is comparable to that of the noise, if the fluctuation has a constant rate of repetition. The signal received at the detector is recorded as a function of time over a time

interval equal to the period of repetition. This recording process is repeated continuously, with the records for all subsequent time intervals being added to the first, to build up a composite record. Explain the advantage of this method.

21-3   When a heavy, charged particle of high energy moves past an electron, the perpendicular distance b from the electron to the path of the heavy particle does not have time to change appreciably during the encounter. The small amount of momentum given to the electron is therefore dependent only upon the electrostatic force between the charges, the velocity v of the particle, and b, the so-called *impact parameter*. Use the method of dimensional analysis, applied in the previous two chapters, to deduce the exact nature of the dependence on these quantities; hence show that the energy gained by the electron is proportional to $Z^2e^4/b^2v^2m_0$, where m_0 is the mass of the electron.

21-4   Use the formula from the previous problem to deduce the energies of an alpha particle and a deuteron that are found to lose energy at the same rate as a 10 M.e.V. proton. By rate, here, is meant the energy loss per unit distance travelled through the medium.

21-5   A thin detector of uniform thickness is often used to measure the rate of energy loss dU/dx by a charged particle which loses most of its energy U in a thick detector placed immediately behind the first. Use the formula of Problem 21-3 to show that the two measurements may be combined to yield information about the mass and charge of the particle as well as its energy.

21-6   Why is lead a good absorber of gamma radiation? Is it also ideal for slowing down high-energy neutrons? Will protons travel further through lead or water? Why?

21-7   Thicknesses of materials used for slowing down charged particles are often measured in units of g.cm.$^{-2}$. Why is this a suitable unit? How many centimeters thick is 0.1 g.cm.$^{-2}$ of aluminum? The density of aluminum is 2.7 g.cm.$^{-3}$.

21-8   A charged particle of energy 5 M.e.V. loses all its energy by ionization of air in a chamber. If the free electrons so formed are all collected and passed at a uniform rate through a resistance of 10^8 Ohms in a period of 10^{-3} sec., what is the magnitude of the potential drop thus produced across the resistance?

21-9   A gamma ray of energy 2 M.e.V. enters a large crystal of sodium iodide and dissipates its energy by the processes of Compton collisions and the photoelectric effect. The free electrons so produced are ultimately stopped in the crystal, which emits blue light of wave length 4×10^{-7} m. If the total energy dissipated appeared in the form of this fluorescent radiation, how many photons would be emitted? In what other form might some of the energy appear?

21-10   A proton of energy 10 M.e.V. creates 7×10^4 ion pairs per g.cm.$^{-2}$ of air traversed. Approximately how much energy does it lose in traversing a cloud chamber of diameter 0.2 m. containing air of density 10^{-3} g.cm.$^{-3}$?

Radioactivity 22

Introduction 22-1

The cumulative effects of relatively low-energy atomic processes concerned with the motion of atoms and molecules, their combination and dissociation, and their emission of visible radiation, are the phenomena immediately appreciable and commonly encountered. But as was pointed out in the preceding chapter, the scientific apparatus initially devised for studying cumulative atomic processes has been adapted to the observation of single high-energy events. This has greatly enlarged our view of the physical phenomena that take place around us. It will be seen that the basic concepts derived from our observations of matter on a large scale, refined and extended to the descriptions of atoms and their interaction—such as mass, momentum, angular momentum, energy, charge, and magnetic moment—can also be employed in formulating a theory or description of the higher-energy processes that involve atomic nuclei. In constructing the theory of atomic events certain concepts were extended and took on new features; for instance, the periodic or wave description of particles, and the intrinsic spin feature of angular momentum. Similarly, it will also be necessary to accept the existence of still more novel phenomena, such as the appearance of new kinds of interactions between particles and the creation and disappearance of particles other than photons, if the high-energy events associated with atomic nuclei are to be adequately encompassed within the conceptual framework of our universe, its symmetries, and its conservation laws.

Early observations of radioactivity 22-2

The first observations that led to the opening up of this area of investigation, which in recent years has developed a technology of such great importance, were made by Henri Becquerel in Paris in 1896. He was stimulated by the discovery of x-rays by Conrad Roentgen to investigate the fluorescence—or emission of visible light—by various crystalline substances that exhibited this phenomenon when exposed to x-rays. He found that uranium salts that had not been previously exposed to either x-rays or visible light continuously and spontaneously emitted some type of radiation that was capable of affecting a photographic emulsion, even through several layers of material opaque to ordinary light. He also observed that the presence of these salts produced ionization in air, i.e., rendered it electrically conducting so that electricity could flow through it and charged bodies in the neighborhood of the salt would lose their charge. G. C. Schmidt and Mme. M. Curie found that salts of thorium possessed similar properties; Pierre and Marie Curie proceeded to perform a chemical separation of the elements in

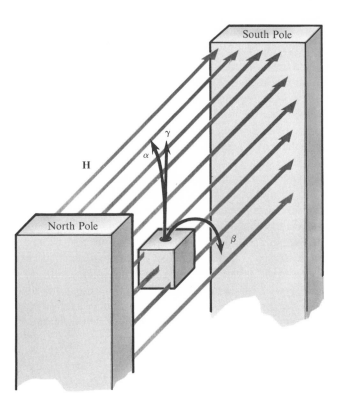

Figure 22-1   *A source of α, β, and γ rays is placed at the bottom of a hole drilled in a lead block. The block is placed in a magnetic field H. As the three types of rays emerge, they are deflected in different directions by the field.*

the uranium ore, Pitchblend, and isolated a substance, radium, that was relatively more active than the uranium studied previously.

The chemical and physical techniques available at that time would be considered very crude and rudimentary today, so that it is not surprising that many years of careful and painstaking work by able investigators in France, Germany, and England were required before the various chemical elements of high atomic weight in the uranium and thorium ores were identified and isolated, and their chemical and physical properties were studied and analyzed. Our particular interest lies not so much in the chemical nature of these elements lying between lead, of atomic number 82, and uranium of atomic number 92, as in the phenomena they exhibit of emitting ionizing radiations and the physical nature of these radiations. F. O. Giesel, and also S. Meyer and E. von Schweidler, showed that at least some part of these radiations could be deflected from a straight path by the application of a strong magnetic field, and hence carried electric charge. The more easily deflected radiation was bent in the sense that corresponded to the carrying of a negative charge, and was given the identification of beta (β) radiation. The less easily deflected radiation was shown by Ernest Rutherford to be positively charged, and was called alpha (α) radiation. R. Strutt found there was a component that was completely undeflected, and hence was presumably uncharged, which was called gamma (γ) radiation. These observations are illustrated in Fig. 22-1.

Radiations from radioactive substances   22-3

As these radiations were investigated further, the ratios of charge-to-mass for alpha and beta rays were determined by simultaneous measurements of momentum and energy. It was found that the ratio for beta rays corresponded to that for ordinary electrons, if due allowance was made for the relativistic increase in mass to be expected for electrons travelling at the high velocity observed for this radiation. Hence the beta particles were quite unambiguously identified as electrons emitted by some high-energy process from the radioactive atoms. In the case of the alpha rays, the charge-to-mass ratio corresponded to that for doubly-charged helium atoms. In a historic experiment performed by Rutherford, a thin-walled vessel containing a source of alpha rays was placed inside a thick-walled vessel. The alpha rays were able to penetrate the thin wall, to be stopped and collected in the outer vessel, whereupon they lost their charge by picking up electrons from surrounding material. When an electrical discharge was later induced in the outer vessel, the characteristic emission spectrum of helium was observed. This was a clear indication that the alpha rays are, in fact, doubly charged helium atoms; since helium atoms have but two electrons, the alpha rays must be helium atomic nuclei. When gamma rays traversed a cloud chamber, the tracks of many high-speed electrons were produced. When these were studied in terms of their momentum and energy, it was found that they consisted of two groups called photoelectrons and Compton electrons. The former were distributed in energy and angle, as would be anticipated if they had been initially tightly bound in the inner orbits of atomic structures and had gained from an incident photon sufficient energy to escape with considerable excess kinetic energy. The latter were distributed in energy and momentum, as predicted by the Compton scattering process described in Chap. 14. Thus these corresponded to initially loosely bound electrons in the outer orbits of atomic systems, which, in comparison with a high-energy incident photon, would behave as essentially free electrons at rest. Thus gamma radiation from radioactive substances was identified as consisting of photons.

All of these radiations, alpha, beta, and gamma, were found to be predominantly of high energy, i.e., in the range of 10^6 e.V. As more detailed studies proceeded during the first quarter of the century, it became evident that each of the twenty natural radioactive elements that had been isolated emitted its particular pattern of radiation. Some emitted primarily beta radiations, though the high speed electrons were accompanied by secondary photons or gamma radiation, due to the conversion of beta ray energy into photons in the emitting atom, or to the stopping of the electrons and consequent emission of photons by other atoms. The energy spectrum of the beta rays was found to be continuous, with an upper limit at some characteristic value, and with a maximum number at about one quarter the maximum energy value. The form of the curve (illustrated in Fig. 22-2), giving the numerical distribution of beta rays with energy, was found to be much the same for all beta emitters, except that often the curve appeared to be the superposition of two or more curves of the same general form but having different maximum energies.

In counter distinction to this continuous energy distribution of beta rays it was found that the alpha rays were emitted in monoenergetic groups, analogous to the sharply delineated line spectra of photons emitted by the electron structure of atoms. Most of the radioactive nuclei that emit alpha rays emit a plurality of distinct groups; the energies of the two groups from the francium isotope, for instance, of mass number 221, being 6.33 and 6.12 in units of 10^6 e.V., as illustrated in Fig. 22-3. As more refined experimental methods are applied to the study of these radiations, additional groups of energies are being discovered.

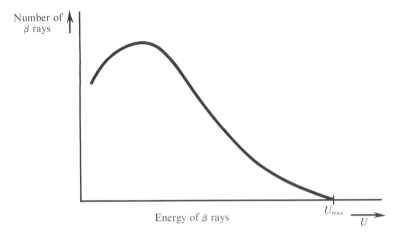

Figure 22-2 *Characteristic distribution of energies (energy spectrum) of β rays from a radioactive source.*

The gamma rays emitted by radioactive substances have both a continuous spectrum and a line spectrum. The study of these leads to the conclusion that the continuous spectrum is of secondary origin, arising from the conversion of beta ray and secondary electron energy into the form of photons, just as x-rays and other electromagnetic radiations are generated. The line spectrum of gamma rays, however, appears to be associated with primary nuclear processes, for its patterns of lines are identifiable with particular radioactive elements and can be related in terms of energy to the alpha ray spectra, as if specific nuclear transitions took place in part by the emission of an alpha ray and in part by the emission of a gamma ray. Thus the sum of the energy of a particular alpha ray and a particular gamma ray is often the same as the sum for a

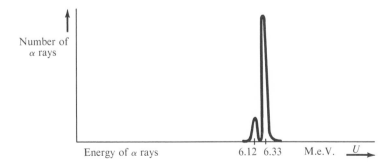

Figure 22-3 *Energy spectrum of α rays from the radioactive isotope Francium 221.*

second gamma ray and a second alpha ray, as would be expected if these were accompanying or sequential processes representing alternative methods available to the nucleus of the element for accomplishing the change from one well-defined energy state to another. This is illustrated in Fig. 22-4. A similar relationship holds between the characteristic maximum energies of beta ray groups and the energies of gamma rays that may accompany their emission; however, the relationship is less obvious because of the continuous nature of the beta spectrum.

From the above discussion, the characteristics of the emanations or rays emitted by radioactive substances may be summarized as follows:

1. A characteristic spectrum of monoenergetic groups of helium nuclei (alpha rays), uniquely related to the particular radioactive element.

2. A continuous energy spectrum of electrons (beta rays) with a characteristic energy maximum and numerical distribution, or the superposition of several beta groups having different maximum energies also characteristic of the particular radioactive element.

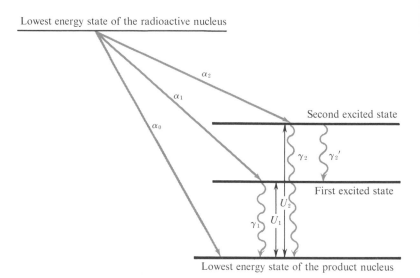

Figure 22-4 *The radioactive nucleus at the left emits alpha rays to form the nucleus at the right. The alpha rays α_0, which leave the product nucleus unexcited, have the maximum energy. Those leaving the product nucleus excited to an energy state U_1 have correspondingly less energy. The energy difference reappears in the form of a gamma ray γ_1, as the nucleus de-excites. A lower energy alpha ray such as α_2 might be accompanied by a single gamma ray γ_2, or by a chain of gamma rays $\gamma_2' + \gamma_1$. In all cases the total energy of the alpha rays plus any associated gamma rays is the same.*

3. A line spectrum of photons (gamma rays) frequently associated with respect to energy, with the characteristic alpha particle groups, or the characteristic maximum energies of the beta ray groups.

4. Secondary products arising from the stopping and absorption of the primary alpha, beta and gamma radiation; these secondary products being photo- and Compton-electrons and photons.

The fourth of the above groups of emanations is accounted for by the process of photon emission incident to the rearrangement of the electron structure surrounding an atomic nucleus, as discussed earlier in Chaps. 15 and 16. The other three categories present novel aspects peculiar to nuclear processes. The emission of helium nuclei suggests that they are particularly stable configurations of the constituents of nuclei that tend to adhere in a nuclear disintegration. The association of photons with radioactive disintegrations is concordant with the existence of electromagnetic interactions between the charged components of nuclei. The second group, namely the beta rays, presents a phenomenon that is more difficult to understand in terms of the concepts that have so far been introduced. Its discussion will be postponed until Chap. 25.

Laws of radioactive decay   22-4

Early in the study of radioactivity, as soon, in fact, as the different radioactive substances were separated from their common ores, the striking fact became evident that any one of these elements did not continue indefinitely to emit its radiations at a constant rate, but that its activity decreased with time. This was demonstrated by E. Rutherford and F. Soddy in 1903, by precipitating various radioactive elements from solutions of uranium and thorium ores. Possibly the simplest instance to demonstrate this is to collect the gas radon, which is slowly liberated from a solution of a uranium salt, and on removing a sample of it, to observe its alpha ray activity over a period of time. It is found to decrease regularly and to have almost disappeared in a period of about a month. If sealed in a small glass tube, the residual helium gas from the alpha particles emitted may be observed spectroscopically, as previously noted. Chemical analysis shows that lead is also a residue. In the meantime, the uranium solution continues to generate more radon gas as before. This strongly suggests the hypothesis, which has been confirmed by many other observations, that in the process of emitting the radiations previously described, one chemical element is transmuted into another.

In fact, a detailed analysis of the known radioactive substances shows that there are several series of radioactive families or sequences that occur in nature, the heaviest member of which decays into a so-called "daughter" product, which in turn itself decays. Through succeeding generations, eventually the end product, which is a stable element, is reached. Each of the members of a series has its own characteristic rate of decay or transformation that is regular and invariable, whether the

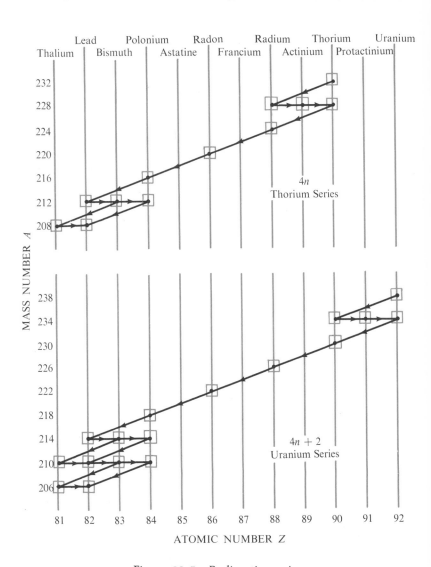

Figure 22-5 *Radioactive series.*

decay is accompanied by the emission of an alpha or a beta ray. The situation may be most conveniently portrayed in the form of the accompanying chart (Fig. 22-5) in which the individual radioactive isotopes are arranged in terms of their atomic number Z, which is the nuclear charge or number of electrons in the atomic structure, and the mass number A, which is the integer nearest to the atomic weight. The transition processes are indicated for the emission of an alpha particle by two steps down and to the left, corresponding to a decrease in the

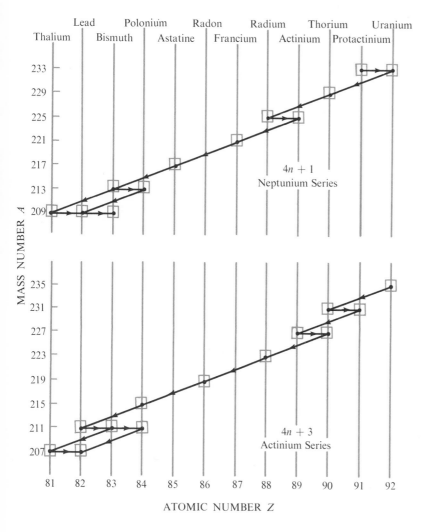

Figure 22-5 *(Continued)*.

mass number by 4, which is the mass number of helium, and a decrease in the atomic number by 2, which is the atomic number of helium. The transition process for the emission of a beta particle, or an electron, is indicated by the increase in the atomic number by 1, since the charge on the electron is -1. There is no change in the mass number since the electron mass is only about $1/1836$ that of the hydrogen atom of mass number 1.

Since the mass number must change by a step of four units or none at all in such a series, there can be four series before the atomic species of the same charge and mass is duplicated. Three of these series were known to the early investigators. Modern research concerning the nuclear reactions in which these heavy atoms participate has disclosed the fourth series. It has also extended our knowledge of the unstable atoms of greater charge and mass than uranium that have probably disappeared with time from the earth's crust. And it has disclosed certain alternate decay reactions in radioactive series that occur with small probabilities. The accompanying diagrams are simplified and intended primarily to be illustrative. The initial elements found in nature at which these series begin are the uranium isotopes of mass number 235, $(4n + 3)$ series, 238, $(4n + 2)$ series, and thorium of mass number 232, $(4n)$ series. The terminal stable element is lead, the isotopes being of mass number 207, 206, and 208 respectively. Each of the isotopes on the chart, except for those of bismuth, are shown as having only one method of transformation. In the case of the bismuth isotopes, however, alternative possibilities exist. A fraction of the isotopes disintegrate with alpha emission, and a fraction with beta emission. The subsequent transformation involves the opposite type of emission, so that the end product of each is lead. The reasons underlying the basic instability of most of the elements lying above lead in the periodic table cannot be given here. In Chap. 23, they will be shown to depend on the repulsive Coulomb forces within the atomic nucleus.

22-5   *The rate of radioactive decay*

The rate at which a radioactive process takes place can be measured by the rate of particle emission, or the amount of ionization produced, number of cloud chamber tracks, or number of scintillations observed per second. Since every event in a radioactive process represents the death of a parent atom and the birth of a daughter atom, the activity expressed as particles emitted per second represents the rate of decay of the parent. Thus if n is the number of parent atoms present, the rate of increase of this number will be dn/dt, which will obviously be negative; hence the activity may be written as $-dn/dt$, or the rate of decrease of n.

If several pure samples of the one radioactive element are examined, it is found that the activity is proportional to the mass of the parent element present, and, therefore, proportional to the number n of parent atoms present. Thus we may write:

$$-\frac{dn}{dt} = \lambda n$$

where λ is a constant known as the *decay constant*. It is characteristic of the particular radioactive decay process. If it is large, the substance decays rapidly; if it is small, the substance decays slowly.

This is the type of decay law one would anticipate, if the process were a random one with a character such that a radioactive nucleus possesses within itself an instability so that on the average a certain constant characteristic fraction of that type of nucleus decays within a given time interval. The behavior of any one nucleus cannot be predicted; but statistically, when dealing with large numbers of nuclei, one can be assured that the decay or death rate will describe the average rate at which transformations occur.

The decay law may be written:

$$\frac{dn}{-\lambda dt} = n$$

Since the change $d(-\lambda t)$ may be written as $-\lambda\, dt$, λ being a constant, the decay law may alternatively be written:

$$\frac{dn}{d(-\lambda t)} = n$$

This is of the form $dn/dx = n$, which is the characteristic of an exponential relationship $n = \epsilon^x$, or more generally $n = n_0\epsilon^x$, where n_0 is a constant. In this case:

$$n = n_0\epsilon^{-\lambda t}$$

where n_0 is the number of parent atoms present initially when $t = 0$. The quantity actually measured in observing radioactive decay is the *activity* $-dn/dt$. The activity is usually represented by the letter a. Since dn/dt is proportional to n, the dependence of a on time is of the same exponential form as n. Hence:

$$a = a_0\epsilon^{-\lambda t}$$

The exponential character of the curves for a and n is shown in Fig. 22-6.

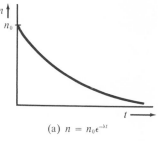

(a) $n = n_0\epsilon^{-\lambda t}$

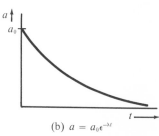

(b) $a = a_0\epsilon^{-\lambda t}$

Figure 22-6 *The number of atoms n and the activity a of a radioactive sample both decrease exponentially with time.*

The equilibrium concentrations of the members of a radioactive family, as would be found, for instance, after a very long time in a sample originally containing uranium 238, can readily be determined by noting that the steady state is the one in which the rate of addition to each atomic species is the same as the rate it decays. Thus $dn_1/dt = dn_2/dt = dn_3/dt$, etc., or $n_1\lambda_1 = n_2\lambda_2 = n_3\lambda_3$, etc.; the number of each species present is inversely proportional to that species' decay constant. The length of time that elapses before the number of atoms of a certain species is reduced to half its initial value is called the *half life T*. This is evidently given by:

$$\frac{n_0}{2} = n_0\epsilon^{-\lambda T}$$

where T is the half life. Therefore:

$$\frac{1}{2} = \epsilon^{-\lambda T} = \frac{1}{\epsilon^{\lambda T}}$$

and:

$$2 = \epsilon^{\lambda T}$$

Then:

$$\ln 2 = \ln \epsilon^{\lambda T} = \lambda T$$

Hence:

$$T = \frac{\ln 2}{\lambda} = \frac{0.693}{\lambda}$$

The half life is found to vary widely from such large values as 4.5×10^9 years for uranium 238 to very short values, such as 3×10^{-7} sec. for polonium 212. The techniques employed to measure such a wide spread of life times, of course, differ greatly, but the general principle of exponential decay is the common law for all radioactive processes.

22-6 *Use of radioactive materials in dating; the establishment of calendars*

Naturally occuring radioactive isotopes have proven very valuable as clocks or calendars for the dating of geological events. As an instance, if one is able to determine the fraction of the uranium in a sample of a rock or a meteorite that has changed through a radioactive process into one of the isotopes of lead, one may use the preceding equations to determine the time that has elapsed since the uranium was laid down or has crystalized in the particular sample. Thus the uranium isotope of mass number $238(U^{238})$, which decays to the lead isotope of mass number 206(Pb^{206}), has a half life of 4.50×10^9 years; the other products between uranium and lead have so much shorter lives that they may be neglected, and the lead may be thought of as appearing directly from the uranium decay. If n_0 is the number of uranium atoms initially present, the number at the end of a time t will be:

$$n_U = n_0 \epsilon^{-\lambda t}$$

where $\lambda = 0.693/(4.5 \times 10^9) = 1.54 \times 10^{-10}$/year. The ratio of the number of lead atoms produced to the number of uranium atoms remaining is:

$$\frac{n_{Pb}}{n_U} = \frac{n_0 - n_U}{n_U} = \epsilon^{\lambda t} - 1$$

and solving this equation for the time, t is given by:

$$t = \frac{1}{\lambda} \ln \frac{n_{Pb} + n_U}{n_U}$$

If all the Pb^{206} is not due to the decay of the uranium associated with it, but has been in some part laid down at the same time as the uranium, one may be misled. It is only recently that C. Paterson and R. Hayden, through the analysis of the lead in meteorites that contain uranium and in those which do not, have provided a reliable value for the content of Pb^{206} that is to be expected normally, and that is independent of any uranium that may be present. It is the ratio of Pb^{206} to the Pb^{204}, which is not a radioactive product, that is actually measured. Using this information as a basic datum, the time since the formation of the earth's crust and the birth of meteorites emerges from the previously given expression to be about 4×10^9 years.

As will be seen in the course of later chapters, there are isotopes of the lighter elements also whose nuclei are unstable and decay into other atomic species. These are produced by naturally occurring or artificially induced nuclear reactions analogous to chemical reactions, as will be discussed in the following chapter. One of these that is particularly useful in establishing the dates of formation of materials containing carbon up to a span of 50,000 years or so is a radioactive isotope of carbon having a mass of 14 units rather than the customary 12 units characteristic of ordinary carbon. It may be made artificially in ways that will be seen later, and is also produced in the earth's atmosphere by particles called *neutrons*, which will be discussed more fully in the next chapter, that reach us from the sun. The nature of the reaction between a neutron and a nitrogen nucleus in our atmosphere will be described in the following chapter, but for our present purpose it is sufficient to know that the neutrons that leave the sun, which are themselves unstable and decay with time, are emitted with such high velocities that about 2.6 of them reach one square centimeter of our atmosphere per second from the sun. Most of these encounter nitrogen nuclei to produce an equal number of carbon 14 atoms in this area per second. Thus, in the atmospheric equilibrium, this is also the number of carbon 14 atoms per square centimeter of surface that decay per second. The half life of carbon 14 is about 5750 years. The nature of its decay is the beta process in which an electron is emitted, resulting in the nucleus of next higher atomic number, namely nitrogen 14. The mixing of the carbon by air and sea currents, and its passage through the various chemical processes in the formation of CO_2, carbonates, and organic materials is rapid in comparison with the half life of radio carbon, so the carbon 14 is well-mixed with all forms of ordinary carbon C^{12} in mobile molecules. The number of disintegrations per second per gram of material is known as the *specific activity*. The specific activity of carbon due to the decay of C^{14} should be equal to the rate of formation per unit area divided by the mass of carbon found per unit area of the earth's surface. The latter figure is about 8.25 gm./cm.^{2} Hence a sample of ordinary carbon with C^{12} and C^{14} in equilibrium should exhibit about 0.3 disintegrations per second per gram. It is found experimentally that a gram of natural carbon does exhibit 0.23 ± 0.02 decays/sec. This result is in good agreement with the above figure.

The experimental equipment for measuring such low rates of decay is necessarily elaborate and difficult to operate because of the necessity to exclude the effect of extraneous disturbances to the greatest extent possible. However, with careful measurements, and assuming that the rate of neutron reception from the sun has remained constant over many thousands of years, it is possible to date ancient carboniferous objects. When these grew or crystalized they were in equilibrium with the reservoir of C^{12} and C^{14} at its standard specific activity; after solidification, the decay of its C^{14} with a half life of about 5750 years gradually reduced the specific activity of the particular sample. The specific activity at the end of a time t would then be $a = a_0 \epsilon^{-\lambda t}$, where a_0 is 0.23 per second, and λ is about $0.693/5750 = 1.21 \times 10^{-4}$/year. The age of the sample in years would then be given by:

$$ t = \frac{1}{\lambda} \ln \frac{a_0}{a} $$

The error in the determination of the interval since the solidification of the carbon sample increases rapidly with the increase in age and in consequent decrease in the actual counting rate observed. But the method is a useful one, up to intervals of the order of ten half lives. The results agree with results obtained from alternative methods of dating such carbon-containing objects, such as by their historical or archeological context, or by tree-ring dating. By extension, the method is proving to be one of the most useful available for determining the age of organic or carboniferous materials less than 25 or 30 thousand years old. The problem is further complicated by the significant amounts of carbon 14 that are created at the explosion of atomic bombs. W. F. Libby has given the figure of 8 kg. of radio carbon as the amount produced by the explosion of a one-megaton hydrogen bomb. A short calculation shows that 8 kg. is equivalent to the production of C^{14} by solar neutrons in the earth's atmosphere in several hundred years. By 1963, the carbon 14 content of the earth's atmosphere had risen by 100 per cent as a result of such bomb tests. Fortunately the figure has since decreased.

Further reading:

ALDRICH, L. T. AND WETHERILL, G. W., "Chronology of Radioactive Decay," *Annual Review of Nuclear Science*, vol. 8, p. 257 (1958).

ANDERSON, E. C., "Production and Distribution of Natural Radiocarbon," *Annual Review of Nuclear Science*, vol. 2, p. 63 (1953).

BROWN, H., "The Age of the Solar System," *Scientific American*, vol. 196, No. 4, p. 80 (1957).

FERGUSSON, G. J., "Radiocarbon Dating System," *Nucleonics*, vol. 13, p. 18 (1955).

KOHMAN, T. P. AND SAITO, N., "Radioactivity in Geology and Cosmology," *Annual Review of Nuclear Science*, vol. 4, p. 401 (1954).

KULP, J. L., "Geologic Time Scale," *Science*, vol. 133, No. 3459, p. 1105 (1961).

LIBBY, W. F., "Accuracy of Radiocarbon Dates," *Science*, vol. 140, No. 3564, p. 278 (1963).

SEABORG, G. T. AND FRITSCH, A. R., "The Synthetic Elements," *Scientific American*, vol. 208, No. 4, p. 68 (1963).

SPENCER, S. M., "They're Revealing the World's Oldest Secrets," *Saturday Evening Post*, vol. 225, No. 37, p. 36 (1953).

WETHERILL, G. W., "Radioactivity of Potassium and Geologic Time," *Science*, vol. 126, No. 3273, p. 545 (1957).

Problems

22-1 The figure shows the trajectories of an α particle and a β particle, which start from the same point and move in a uniform magnetic field perpendicular to the paper. Find the ratio D_α/D_β if

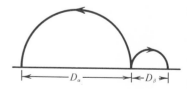

(a) each starts with the same velocity.
(b) each starts with the same momentum.
(c) each starts with the same energy.

22-2   An element *A* decays to another element *B* by emission of *α*-particles. The observed spectrum is shown below.

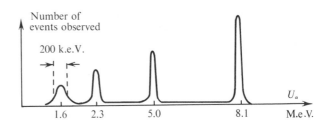

(a) Predict some of the energy levels of element *B*.
(b) Predict the *γ*-spectrum that will be emitted.
(c) It is suggested that the 5.0 M.e.V. *α*-group is due to some impurity, and is unrelated to elements *A* and *B*. How can this hypothesis be checked?

22-3   A radioactive isotope emits alpha particles of energies 10.62, 5.49, 2.06, and 0.58 M.e.V. As far as possible, predict what energy gamma rays might be found in coincidence with each of these alpha "rays." Also predict some energies of excitation that the residual nucleus can have.

22-4   (a) In Problem 22-2 the lowest energy *α*-group has a "width" of 200 k.e.V. What does this indicate? Give a quantitative answer if possible.
(b) Would you expect the lowest energy *α*-group to have the greatest "width"? Why?
(c) Considering the "width" of the 1.6 M.e.V. *α*-group, what effect would you expect to see in the *γ*-spectrum?

22-5   As shown in the following chapter, it is possible to produce radioactive isotopes of the lighter elements. The alpha-decay of the chlorine isotope of mass 32 to the phosphorus isotope of mass 28 may be written: $Cl^{32} \rightarrow P^{28}$. Complete the circled gaps in the following sequences:

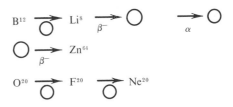

22-6   A radioactive isotope emits both β and γ radiation (but no α radiation). The γ radiation is of energy 1.06 M.e.V. The β rays have a maximum energy of 2.57 M.e.V., but the β spectrum does not appear to have the customary shape, being somewhat skewed more than usual towards the lower energies. Suggest a possible explanation and a way of testing this explanation with the available data. If you can, suggest also an experimental test that could be conducted.

22-7   In 24 years, a radioactive isotope decreases in mass from 64 kg. to 2 kg. What is its half-life?

22-8   The stable isotopes of the first ten elements of the periodic table are:

$_1H^1$ $_2He^3$ $_3Li^6$ $_4Be^9$ $_5B^{10}$ $_6C^{12}$ $_7N^{14}$ $_8O^{16}$ $_9F^{19}$ $_{10}Ne^{20}$
$_1H^2$ $_2He^4$ $_3Li^7$ $_5B^{11}$ $_6C^{13}$ $_7N^{15}$ $_8O^{17}$ $_{10}Ne^{21}$
                                                              $_8O^{18}$ $_{10}Ne^{22}$

How would you expect the following isotopes to decay:

$$Be^{10}, \quad B^{12}, \quad C^{14}, \quad N^{16}, \quad Be^8?$$

22-9   0.008 kg. of a radioisotope is observed to decay for a period of 90 days, leaving only 0.001 kg. of the original isotope. What is the half-life of the isotope?

22-10   A radioactive isotope A decays with half-life T_A into a second radio-isotope B of half-life T_B, which in turn decays into a third radioisotope of half-life T_C. If the isotopes are all in radioactive equilibrium, what are the ratios of the number of atoms present of each? If their atomic masses are A_A, A_B, and A_C, what are the ratios of their masses present?

22-11   If 10 per cent of a radioactive element decays away in 1 day, how much of the original amount will remain after 10 days?

22-12 $_6C^{11}$ has a half-life of 20 min., and $_7N^{13}$ has a half-life of 10 min. Starting with 50 g. of C^{11} and 800 g. of N^{13}, how long will it be before the masses of each radioactive isotope are equal, and what will these masses be then?

22-13   Two radioisotopes have decay constants in the ratio $\lambda_1/\lambda_2 = 5$. What is the ratio of their half-lives T_1/T_2?

22-14 U^{238} has a half-life of 4.50×10^9 years. If 1 kg. of U^{238} were present $4\frac{1}{2}$ billion years ago, how much is now present? The final product of decay is Pb^{206}. How much of this will have been formed?

23 *Atomic nuclei and their constituents*

23-1   *Artificially induced nuclear reactions*

The work of Rutherford and his co-workers on the scattering of alpha particles, which led to the concept of the nuclear atom, was described in Chap. 15. When targets of low atomic number and therefore small Coulomb repulsion were used by these workers, it was found that at certain close encounters of alpha particles and nuclei the original alpha particle path terminated at a pronounced fork, readily distinguishable from the paths in an elastic nuclear collision. The two subsequent prongs consisted of a long-range particle, which presented a lighter ionization per unit path corresponding to a proton, and a recoiling heavier nucleus, which produced a short dense path of ions. The cloud chamber photographs of such events in air showed that these forked tracks could be adequately accounted for in terms of a reaction taking place between the helium nucleus and the nucleus of a struck nitrogen atom, from which emerged a high-speed proton and a recoiling oxygen nucleus. The appearance of such a forked track is indicated schematically in the accompanying Fig. 23-1.

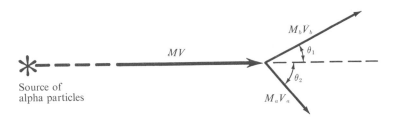

Figure 23-1   *Representation of the paths of particles participating in an induced nuclear disintegration.*

From a knowledge of the track length of the alpha particle from its source to the collision point, and a knowledge of the energy of the particle emitted by the source, the momentum of the alpha particle at the collision point can be determined. From a measurement of the angles θ_1 and θ_2, the momenta $M_a V_a$ and $M_b V_b$ can be found, since

$$MV = M_b V_b \cos \theta_1 + M_a V_a \cos \theta_2$$

$$0 = M_b V_b \sin \theta_1 - M_a V_a \sin \theta_2$$

hence:

$$M_a V_a = MV \sin \theta_1 / \sin (\theta_1 + \theta_2)$$

$$M_b V_b = MV \sin \theta_2 / \sin (\theta_1 + \theta_2)$$

The lengths and characters of the tracks from the fork are found to be consistent with these equations. Thus, the event may be described appropriately as a nuclear reaction, and written in a way analogous to a chemical reaction:

$$_2\text{He}^4 + {_7}\text{N}^{14} \rightarrow {_9}\text{F}^{18} \rightarrow {_8}\text{O}^{17} + {_1}\text{H}^1$$

where the superscripts are the mass numbers and the subscripts the atomic numbers of the atomic nuclei involved. The difference between the initial energy ($\frac{1}{2} MV^2$) and the final energy ($\frac{1}{2} M_b V_b{}^2 + \frac{1}{2} M_a V_a{}^2$), is found from Rutherford's and P.M.S. Blackett's measurements to be about 1.2 million e.V. This is the amount of energy that disappears from the kinetic form in the reaction. The measurement of the atomic masses of the participants in this reaction in atomic mass units (a.m.u.) is found from mass spectrometer measurements to be:

$$M_{\text{He}^4} = 4.002603 \qquad M_{\text{O}^{17}} = 16.999133$$
$$M_{\text{N}^{14}} = 14.003074 \qquad M_{\text{H}^1} = 1.007825$$
$$\text{Sum} = 18.005677 \qquad \text{Sum} = 18.006958$$

The mass difference is seen to be 1.281×10^{-3} a.m.u., and since 1 a.m.u. is equivalent to 9.31×10^8 e.V., the energy required to account for the mass increase of the reacting atoms is 1.19×10^6 e.V., in excellent agreement with the observations of the disintegration process as given above. Reactions of this type were the first artificial nuclear disintegrations or reactions to be observed. In addition to the nuclei of nitrogen, the nuclei of aluminum, magnesium, and fluorine were observed to exhibit examples of proton emission when struck by alpha particles.

The emission of protons by nuclei of atoms of various species in nuclear reactions of this type lent experimental support to the hypothesis, first advanced by an English physician named William Prout in 1815, that all atoms are composed of hydrogen. When isotopes were discovered a century later, the approximately integral mass numbers associated with them again suggested that nuclei were composed of hydrogen nuclei or protons, excepting, of course, that the mass number was not equal to the atomic number, but was always greater than the latter, except in the case of the proton itself. The possibility was considered that electrons were another constituent of nuclei and were present in such a number that $(A - Z)$ of them neutralized the charge of this number of protons yielding the mass number A, and atomic number, or charge Z. Electrons indeed appeared in beta decay processes, but it was very difficult to conceive of them as constituents of a nucleus because of their small mass, as discussed in Sect. 15-3.

23-2   *The discovery of the neutron*

One of the most helpful steps in the experimental establishment of a theory of the atomic nucleus was the identification of a particle that has a mass slightly greater than that of the proton and no electric charge. This particle was given the name *neutron* by James Chadwick, its discoverer. The story of its experimental identification is a particularly interesting one. In 1930, W. Bothe and H. Becker in Germany observed that when either beryllium or boron was exposed to alpha particles, the protons emitted were accompanied by a very penetrating radiation capable of passing through several millimeters of brass. As the only radiation known at the time capable of such penetration was electromagnetic radiation (photons) Bothe and Becker concluded that they were observing short wave length radiation of this type, namely, gamma radiation. I. Curie and F. Joliot then proceeded to measure the absorption of the radiation by sheets of lead. From a knowledge of the absorption coefficients of x-rays and gamma rays of relatively low and known energy, extrapolated by the aid of the theory of the photoelectric and Compton processes, they concluded that the energy of the gamma rays from boron was about 11 million election volts (M.e.V.), and that of the gamma rays from beryllium was in the range from 15 to 20 M.e.V. We now know that their ignorance of another process by which gamma radiation is converted into charged particles, which will be described in the following chapter, invalidated their conclusions, but another independent observation also called these conclusions into question.

It was found that when the hydrocarbon paraffin was used as an absorber for this radiation from beryllium, long-range protons came from the paraffin; if these were projected by a Compton-type of collision between a gamma ray and a proton, the energy of the gamma ray deduced from the proton energies would have to be of the order of 55

M.e.V., instead of the order of 10 to 20 M.e.V. as given above. This unsatisfactory state of affairs was resolved by James Chadwick, who studied the distribution of the protons projected from paraffin and also the distribution of nitrogen atoms in a cloud chamber, which were likewise projected by this radiation. The maximum energy that a quantum of energy $h\nu$ can give to a particle of rest mass m_0 is, by the Compton equation of Chap. 14

$$h\nu - h\nu' = h\nu \left[1 + (m_0 c^2 / 2 h\nu)\right]^{-1}$$

The maximum energy of the projected protons was found to be about 5.7 M.e.V., corresponding to an $h\nu$ of about 55 M.e.V. Using this value for $h\nu$ and the mass of a nitrogen nucleus, the latter should acquire a maximum energy of 0.45 M.e.V. at a collision, whereas nitrogen atoms with energies up to 1.3 M.e.V. were actually observed. This is obviously very unsatisfactory. However, if it is postulated that the "penetrating radiation," previously thought to be gamma radiation, is actually a neutral particle of mass M_n, then the maximum velocity transferred at a head-on collision with a nuclear mass M at which the total energy is conserved would, in accordance with the conclusions of Chap. 4, be given by

$$v = 2 \frac{M_n}{M_n + M} v_0$$

where v_0 is the initial velocity of M_n. The maximum energy that would be transmitted to a mass M at such an elastic collision would thus be

$$U = \frac{1}{2} M v^2 = 2 \ M \left(1 + \frac{M}{M_n}\right)^{-2} v_0^2$$

Hence the ratio of the maximum energies that would be observed for two masses of projected nuclei, namely, M_1 for hydrogen and $14 M_1$ for nitrogen, would be:

$$(U_{\text{proton}} / U_{\text{nitrogen}}) = \frac{1}{14} \left(\frac{1 + 14x}{1 + x}\right)^2$$

where x is the ratio of the mass of the proton or hydrogen nucleus to the mass of the impinging particle. If the maxima of the energies of the projected particles are taken as 5.6 and 1.3 M.e.V. respectively for the protons and the nitrogen nuclei, the value of x is found to be slightly over unity. Thus these collision observations are consistent with the assumption that the nuclei are projected as a result of an impact by an atomic particle with a mass approximately equal to that of a proton.

The explanation of the "radiation" emitted by beryllium or boron, when alpha particles impinge on these nuclei, as being of the nature of a neutral particle of mass approximately that of the proton accounts particularly well for the additional experimental observation that material containing hydrogen is an extremely effective absorber for this "radiation." This is evident from the fact noted in connection with collision phenomena that the maximum energy interchange between colliding masses can take place when these masses are equal. Also, since the postulated particle is without any electric charge, and hence does not interact electrically with the constituent electrons of the atomic systems near which it passes, its penetration of matter could well be as great as that observed by Curie and Joliot. A description consistent with all these observations is thus provided. Since the maximum projected energy of the proton is found to be 5.6 M.e.V., and the proton and neutron masses are approximately equal, this is also the kinetic energy of the neutrons produced when beryllium is bombarded with alpha particles. The reaction at which they are formed would then be written:

$$_2He^4 + _4Be^9 \rightarrow _6C^{13} \rightarrow _6C^{12} + _0n^1$$

The conclusion of Chadwick that he was dealing with a neutral particle of approximately the proton's mass has been confirmed by many other experiments since 1932, and the existence of the neutron is now well established. The proton and the neutron provide the two most convenient building blocks in the description of the structure of atomic nuclei. The most precise mass value for the neutron is derived from the photodisintegration of the deuteron, which is the hydrogen atomic nucleus of mass 2, consisting of one proton and one neutron. The masses of the hydrogen isotopes of mass numbers 1 and 2 can be determined precisely with the mass spectrograph, and are found to be 1.007825 and 2.014102 a.m.u. respectively. It is found that high energy x-rays, or gamma rays, on passing through deuterium (heavy hydrogen gas) produce protons by photodisintegration of the deuterium nucleus, if their energy exceeds the threshold value of about 2.224 M.e.V. This energy corresponds to 0.002388 a.m.u.; hence the conservation of energy applied to the photoelectric disintegration equation yields:

$$_1H^2 + h\nu_0 \rightarrow _1H^1 + _0n^1$$

$2.014102 = {}_1H^2$ mass energy	$2.016490 =$ energy input
$0.002388 = h\nu_0$ photon energy	$- 1.007825 = {}_1H^1$ mass energy
$2.016490 =$ energy input	$1.008665 = {}_0n^1$ mass energy

or the neutron mass is 1.008665 a.m.u. The results of other nuclear experiments with light atoms agree with this value of the neutron mass.

Many reactions have now been studied, and the energies required to initiate the reactions under the influence of photons, protons, neutrons, or alpha particles (2 protons + 2 neutrons) and the energies that are liberated when reactions take place yield a self-consistent table of atomic masses which, within the limits of error of the mass spectrographic measurements, agree with these results as well. Representative values are given in Table 23-1. The accuracy is of the order of 1 unit in

Table 23-1 *Atomic mass values of the lighter isotopes*[1]

Z	A	M (a.m.u.)	$(M - A)/A$
0(n)	1	1.008665	.008665
1(H)	1	1.007825	.007825
1	2	2.014102	.007051
1	3	3.016050	.005350
2(He)	3	3.016030	.005343
2	4	4.002603	.000651
3(Li)	6	6.015125	.002521
3	7	7.016004	.002286
4(Be)	9	9.012186	.001354
5(B)	10	10.012939	.001294
5	11	11.009305	.000846
6(C)	12	12.000000	—0—
7(N)	14	14.003074	+.000220
8(O)	16	15.994915	−.000318
9(F)	19	18.998405	−.000840
10(Ne)	20	19.992440	−.000378

[1] Data abbreviated from 1964 Atomic Mass Table. J. H. E. Mattauch, W. Thiele, and A. H. Wapstra, *Nuclear Physics*, vol. 67, p. 1 (1965).

the last place. It may be noted here that one reaction induced by neutrons is that by means of which C^{14} referred to in the preceding chapter is produced. In that reaction, a proton is emitted and additional energy to the extent of 6.2×10^5 e.V. is available for the kinetic energy of the resultant particles. The reaction would be written:

$$_7N^{14} + {_0n^1} \rightarrow {_7N^{15}} \rightarrow {_6C^{14}} + {_1H^1} + (0.62 \times 10^6 \text{ e.V.})$$

If the table of precise masses is continued on through the heavier elements, it is found that the quantity $(M - A)/A$ reaches an approximately constant value of about -10^{-3} for the elements in the neighborhood of chromium and zinc, and then slowly increases again to about zero for the heavy elements in the neighborhood of mercury and thalium. This quantity is known as the *packing fraction*, and is clearly a measure of the binding energy per nucleon for a particular atomic species, where *nucleon* is the generic name for a proton or neutron. Thus it represents the energy per nucleon in the form of mass that disappears due to the binding together of the constituent nucleons forming the isotope in question.

The mass values given in the accompanying table are atomic mass values. Precise nuclear mass values are obtained by subtracting the total mass of all the atomic electrons less their binding energies. Thus the mass of the proton or hydrogen nucleus of mass number one is 1.007825 a.m.u. less 0.000549 a.m.u., (the mass of the single atomic electron) plus the ionization energy. The ionization potential of hydrogen is 13.6 V., i.e., 13.6 e.V. or 1.46×10^{-8} a.m.u. is the ionization energy. This latter figure is negligible compared with the accuracy of the atomic and electronic masses above and may, therefore, be disregarded. Thus the proton mass is found to be:

$$M_p = M_H - m_0 = 1.007825 - 0.000549 = 1.007276 \text{ a.m.u.}$$

The neutron has a greater mass than the proton by 0.001389 a.m.u., or 1.293 M.e.V. Thus energy to the amount of this value could appear upon the conversion of a neutron to a proton, which could take place if it lost a unit of negative charge and changed from the charge zero to the charge $+e$. If this occurred by the appearance of an electron, the energy represented by the mass of an electron ($m_0 = 5.49 \times 10^{-4}$ a.m.u. $= 0.511$ M.e.V.) would have to be subtracted from the above figure. Hence the energy of 0.782 M.e.V. would be available as kinetic energy for the electron and proton at the end of the transformation of the neutron in accordance with the equation:

$$_0n^1 \rightarrow {}_1p^1 + {}_{-1}e^0 + 0.782 \quad \text{M.e.V.}$$

Free neutrons actually undergo this beta-decay process, with a maximum energy of the beta spectrum corresponding to the above value to within about 2 per cent. The electron, being much lighter than the proton, receives practically all of the kinetic energy because of the conservation of momentum. Though free neutrons decay in this way with a half-life of about 1100 sec., or 18.5 min., they do not do so as constituents of a stable atom. In these aggregates, the neutrons, if they exist specifically as such, are constrained by the configuration of the other nucleons to remain neutrons. Alternatively stated, there is an equilibrium between neutrons and protons, the details of which we do not completely understand, but which gives rise to the stable elements we know.

Structure of atomic nuclei   23-3

The evidence regarding the constitution of atomic nuclei thus leads us to the conclusion that they consist of aggregates of neutrons and protons bound together by forces such that they occupy small volumes with linear dimensions of the order of 10^{-15} m. The effective number of protons is the atomic number Z, and the effective number of neutrons is $(A - Z)$, where A is the total mass number. There are atoms with different values of A over a small range, but the same Z, which, of course, represent isotopes. There are also atoms with the same A, but with Z differing by one or two units, i.e., the same number of nucleons but a different distribution between protons and neutrons. These are known as *isobars*. A consideration of the general nature of the binding energy of nuclei yields some suggestive information relative to the forces or energies of interaction between nucleons. The solid curve of the accompanying figure (Fig. 23-2), giving binding energy as a function of mass number, represents the trend of the binding energy for the known mass numbers up to about 190 on the assumption that the components of the nuclei are protons and neutrons. The binding energy B may be

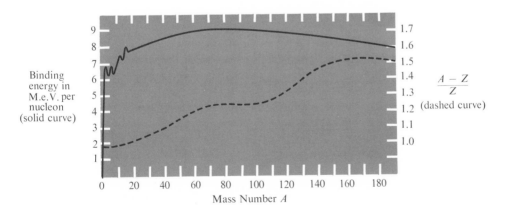

Figure 23-2   *Binding energies of naturally occurring atomic species.*

written as the difference between the sum of the masses of the constituents and the mass of the aggregate:

$$B = ZM_p + (A - Z)M_n - M$$

and dividing by A to obtain the binding energy per nucleon:

$$\frac{B}{A} = M_n - \frac{Z}{A}(M_n - M_p) - \frac{M}{A}$$

$$= (M_n - 1) - \frac{Z}{A}(M_n - M_p) - P$$

where P is the packing fraction $(M - A)/A$. The curve rises rapidly and oscillates a bit for low mass numbers, indicating a rapid variation of energy per nucleon and a dependence upon the particular structural configuration in the range where there are few nucleons per nucleus. The irregularity in the curve is primarily associated with the exceptionally large binding energy apparently possessed by aggregates of four nucleons, which consist of two protons and two neutrons. The helium nucleus (alpha particle) stands out, as does that of beryllium 8, carbon 12, and oxygen 16, which may be considered as 1, 2, 3, and 4 of these units respectively.

Above $A = 20$ the curve rises slowly and smoothly to a maximum in the neighborhood of $A = 60$, and then decreases slowly with greater mass numbers. In the same figure is drawn a dashed curve of the average neutron-proton ratio $(A - Z)/Z$ from which it is seen that this ratio rises somewhat step-wise with a value of about 1.2 over much of the middle range. Thus, Z/A may be taken for approximate purposes as about 0.5, and P is close to -10^{-3}. Therefore:

$$\frac{B}{A} = 0.008665 - 0.5\,(0.00139) + 0.001$$

$$= 0.009 \text{ a.m.u.} \approx 8 \text{ M.e.V.}$$

Hence the binding energy per nucleon for elements near the center of the periodic table is of the order of 8 M.e.V.

Thus the binding energies are very large for the constituents of nuclei, and, for a wide mass number range, they are approximately constant. This indicates that the interaction between nucleons must be predominantly of what is called a *saturated* type. This means that the interaction is almost entirely between nearest neighbors in the nucleus; there is little interaction between nucleons relatively distant from one another. This is similar to the situation of mutual attraction between the molecules of a fluid as described in Chap. 19. It is in contrast to a law such as that of Coulomb for electrostatic attraction, where the energy of interaction varies gradually as $1/r$. If each nucleon interacts only with its nearest neighbors, the energy would be proportional to the number of nucleons, which it is approximately. Whereas if each nucleon equally attracted approximately all the rest, the energy would be proportional to the number of pairs of nucleons, i.e., $A(A - 1)/2$, or it would vary approximately as A^2, which is not found to be the case.

Alpha particle scattering experiments provided our first crude information on nuclear sizes. More recently precise scattering experiments employing particles from accelerators with energies up to about 5×10^8 e.V. have provided more detailed information. Robert Hofstadter, of Stanford University, has shown that the effective nuclear radius can be written as $(1.07 \pm 0.02) \times 10^{-15} A^{1/3}$ m. The fact that this is proportional to $A^{1/3}$ indicates compatibility with the assumption that a nucleus is composed of a number A of relatively incompressible similar units, since this would then lead to a radius proportional to the cube root of the volume of the aggregate of the constituent units. The boundary of the nucleus is not sharp, but effectively grades off through a layer about $2.4 \pm 0.7 \times 10^{-15}$ m. thick. Assuming then a nucleus of rather tightly packed protons and neutrons, held together by a nearest-neighbor type of force, further details of the energy curve receive a qualitative explanation. The ratio of the surface to the volume of a sphere varies inversely as the $\frac{2}{3}$ power of the radius, and, assuming the nucleons to be grouped together as relatively incompressible volumes, the fraction of them at the surface of the nucleus would decrease with increasing numbers of nucleons as $A^{-1/3}$. These surface nucleons would make a less-than-average contribution to the energy, having fewer neighbors; hence the energy curve should rise from low mass numbers as observed. The electrostatic repulsion of the protons is also discernable both in the tendency for stable nuclei to have more neutrons than protons for large A's, and also in the tendency for the energy per nucleon to fall in the latter half of the range. The electrostatic energy, not deriving from a saturation type of force, should vary with Z^2 and also inversely with the nuclear radius R. Thus, taking Z as about $A/2$ and R as proportional to $A^{1/3}$, the binding energy per nucleon should decrease for larger nuclei at the rate $A^{5/3}$, due to electrostatic effects. This accounts for the decrease in binding energy per nucleon for large mass numbers.

The forces that hold nucleons together in a liquid drop type of structure clearly must derive from an interaction between these particles unlike anything that we have previously encountered. Since there is a net positive charge on the structure, the interaction cannot be of the electrostatic type. However, it is evident from the preceding paragraph that the effect of the electrostatic interaction is not negligible in comparison with the inter-nucleon interaction. Indeed, if the order of magnitude of the electrostatic energy is calculated from the expression KZ^2e^2/R, where R is taken as the nuclear dimension 10^{-15} m., it is found that this energy is of the order of half a million e.V., which is a factor of only ten or twenty less than the binding energy per nucleon. The gravitational interaction can clearly not be influential, since it is a factor of 10^{-36} less than the electrostatic one. In Chap. 25 a weak interaction between protons and electrons will be discussed, but this is again too small to account for nuclear forces.

In consequence, if the energy of interaction between nucleons is to be accounted for, a new type of fundamental mode of interaction must be invoked. This has been done, following the suggestion of the Japanese physicist Hideki Yukawa. He suggested that nucleons interact with one another through the mutual absorption and emission of a particle called a *meson*. This is closely analogous to the interaction between electrons or other charged particles through the mutual absorption and emission of photons. The observed short-range nature of nucleon interactions follows naturally if the meson, in distinction to the photon, has a finite rest mass several hundred times that of the electron.

Extensive experimental evidence, which will be referred to in later chapters, confirmed the existence of mesons some years after they were postulated by Yukawa for furnishing the binding energy between nucleons. Indeed, two different kinds of particles with masses intermediate between nucleons and electrons were found. The one involved here will be referred to as a *pion* to distinguish it from another meson that will be mentioned later.

In the pion theory, protons and neutrons may be considered as different aspects of the same particle. The exchange of a charged pion converts one into the other, and the energy associated with the pion exchange process is the binding energy. Protons may be held to protons, and neutrons to neutrons, by the exchange of neutral or uncharged pions. The proton-proton, neutron-neutron, and proton-neutron forces are all of about the same value.

This can be seen quite readily from the atomic masses of $_1\text{H}^3$ and $_2\text{He}^3$ given in the earlier table. The $_1\text{H}^3$ nucleus consists of two neutrons and one proton, so there are two pion bonds between a neutron and a proton: $2(n \leftrightarrow p)$; and one between the two neutrons: $1(n \leftrightarrow n)$. The $_2\text{He}^3$ nucleus consists of one neutron and two protons so the pion bonds are: $2(n \leftrightarrow p)$; and: $1(p \leftrightarrow p)$. Subtracting one electron mass from the atomic mass of $_1\text{H}^3$ yields the nuclear mass 3.015501 a.m.u.; subtracting two electron masses from the mass of $_2\text{He}^3$ yields the nuclear mass 3.014930 a.m.u. The difference between these is 0.000571 a.m.u. or 0.532 M.e.V. The electrostatic energy between two electronic charges a distance γ apart is $(1.44 \times 10^{-15}/\gamma)$ M.e.V. Hence the energy difference between the nuclei of $_1H^3$ and $_2He^3$ of 0.532 M.e.V. is quite adequately accounted for by the electrostatic energy of the two protons in the $_2He^3$ nucleus of dimensions of the order of 3×10^{-15} m.

Thus it would appear that the pion bonds holding two protons together in a nucleus are much the same energetically as those holding two neutrons together. If one calculates the difference between the mass of the nucleus $_1H^3$ and the sum of the masses of two neutrons and one proton, it is found to be 0.009105 a.m.u. Similarly the binding energy of $_2He^3$ is found to be 0.008287 a.m.u. Thus if the pion $(n \leftrightarrow n)$, $(p \leftrightarrow p)$, and $(n \leftrightarrow p)$ bonds all represented about the same energy of binding, this energy would be of the order of 3 M.e.V. However, these three types of nuclear forces are not identical, and their small differences probably account for the fact that the nuclear neutrons do not decay into protons and electrons and that there is a tendency toward the pairing of both neutrons and protons in stable nuclei.

Further reading:

BOHR, A., "On the Structure of Atomic Nuclei," *American Journal of Physics*, vol. 25, No. 8, p. 547 (1957).

GAMOW, G., *The Atom and its Nucleus*, Prentice-Hall (1961).

HOFSTADTER, R., "Structure of Nuclei and Nucleons," *Science*, vol. 136, No. 3521, p. 1013 (1962).

HOFSTADTER, R., "The Atomic Nucleus," *Scientific American*, vol. 195, No. 1, p. 55 (1956).

MAYER, M. G., "The Shell Model," *Science*, vol. 145, No. 3636, p. 999 (1964).

ROSEN, L., "Interaction of Medium-Energy Nucleons with Complex Nuclei," *Physics Today*, vol. 16, No. 11, p. 21 (1963).

DE SHALIT, A., "Remarks on Nuclear Structure," *Science*, vol. 153, No. 3740, p. 1063 (1966).

VAN WAGENINGEN, R., "Nuclear Models," *American Journal of Physics*, vol. 28, No. 5, p. 425 (1960).

WEISSKOPF, V. F. AND ROSENBAUM, E. P. ,"A Model of the Nucleus," *Scientific American*, vol. 193, No. 6, p. 84 (1955).

WIGNER, E. P., "On the Development of the Compound Nucleus Model," *American Journal of Physics*, vol. 23, p. 371 (1955).

WILETS, LAWRENCE, "Shape of the Nucleus," *Science*, vol. 129, No. 3346, p. 361 (Feb., 1959).

Problems

23-1 A particle of mass M strikes a second particle, and energy Q is evolved in the subsequent reaction. The reaction products of mass M_b and M_a are then projected at respective angles of θ_1 and θ_2 on either side of the direction of incidence. Adopting the symbols U for kinetic energy, and p for momentum, take the special situation of $\theta_1 = 60°$ and $\theta_2 = 30°$, and show that $p_a/p_b = \sqrt{3}$. Hence show that $U_a/U_b = 3M_b/M_a$. Show that $p = zp_b$ and $U_b/U = M/(4M_b)$. Finally show that $Q = (M/4M_b + 3M/4M_a - 1)U$.

23-2 Complete the following reactions:

$$_{11}Na^{23} + {}_1H^1 \rightarrow \qquad \rightarrow {}_{10}Ne^{20} +$$
$$_{19}K^{39} + \qquad \rightarrow {}_{21}Sc^{42} \rightarrow \qquad + {}_1H^2$$
$$+ {}_0n^1 \rightarrow {}_5B^{12} \rightarrow {}_6C^{12} +$$
$$+ {}_1H^2 \rightarrow {}_8O^{16} \rightarrow {}_8O^{15} +$$
$$_6C^{13} + {}_1H^1 \rightarrow \qquad \rightarrow \qquad + {}_2He^4$$

23-3 Find the Q value for each of the following reactions:

$$_4Be^9 + {}_2He^4 \rightarrow {}_6C^{12} + {}_0n^1 + Q$$
$$_9F^{19} + {}_1H^1 \rightarrow {}_{10}Ne^{20} + Q$$

23-4 Show whether or not tritium or $_1H^3$ can energetically decay by β emission, and find the Q *value* for this reaction.

23-5 A target of oxygen gas (mostly $_8O^{16}$) is bombarded with a beam of $_2He^3$ ions of energy 12.00 M.e.V. Neutrons are emitted, and the unstable nucleus $_{10}Ne^{18}$ is temporarily formed. If the total energy of both reaction products is 8.81 M.e.V., find the mass of the $_{10}Ne^{18}$ atom.

23-6 A neutron of energy 10 M.e.V. makes a head-on collision with a stationary proton; what is the energy of each particle and their directions of motion after the collision?

23-7 In a diffraction experiment, neutrons from a nuclear reactor are shown to have the same wave length as the electrons produced by an electron gun. The velocity of the neutrons is v. What is the velocity of the electrons?

23-8 What is the composition of a fluorine nucleus? If, in making up a fluorine nucleus from its constituents, the last nucleon to be added is a proton, then what is the binding energy of this last proton (in M.e.V.)? What is the total binding energy of a fluorine nucleus (in M.e.V.)?

23-9 The neutral pion has a mass of 264 electron masses. How many M.e.V. of energy are needed to create a neutral pion?

23-10 Certain nuclei, such as $_8O^{16}$, $_{20}Ca^{40}$, and $_{82}Pb^{208}$, appear to be associated with greater symmetries and somewhat greater stabilities than their neighbors in the table of isotopes. These effects cannot be attributed solely to the clustering of alpha particles. Suggest a plausible explanation.

The generation and annihilation of particles

Discovery of the positive electron   24-1

The discussion of electrons and photons in Chap. 14 described the inter-action of these two types of particles, including the emission of photons and their scattering and partial or total absorption by electrons. The discussion was concerned primarily with the low-energy range of atomic rather than nuclear phenomena. The existence of beta rays and the interaction of nuclear particles with photons and electrons clearly requires that the theory or description of the phenomena involving these two types of particles must be adequate up through the relativistic range where the total energy mc^2 is well in excess of the rest mass energy m_0c^2 of the electron. This requires framing the statement of the conserva-tion of energy from which the specific behavior of the electron can be derived in the general terms that were set forth in Chap. 8, namely:

$$\left(\frac{U}{c}\right)^2 = (mv)^2 + (m_0c)^2$$

It was noted by P.A.M. Dirac that, owing to the quadratic form of this equation, either positive or negative values of U would provide satisfactory solutions. This was originally considered a defect of the theory, a spurious group of negative energy values being provided that had no physical meaning. It was recognized that such solutions might be associated with particles of negative mass, if such were known to exist, but of course they were not. A particle with negative rest mass

m_0 would also have a negative effective mass m and, consequently, a negative momentum mv, i.e., its momentum would be oppositely directed to its velocity. According to relativistic theory, a particle of positive mass m and total energy mc^2 can have a minimum energy m_0c^2 corresponding to its rest mass m_0. Positive energies less than this minimum value are forbidden because the particle would cease to exist. Dirac's theory would allow an equivalent set of negative energy states with a maximum negative energy of $-m_0c^2$, as depicted in Fig. 24-1. Electrons could then have energies between $-$infinity and $+$infinity, with an energy gap of depth $2m_0c^2$ around zero energy. Dirac explained the apparent absence in nature of negative-energy electrons by assuming that such states, being lowest in energy, were normally completely occupied according to the Pauli exclusion principle. It must then be assumed that electrons in such filled negative-energy states are unobservable. The only way in which we could observe an electron from this region would be to give it sufficient energy to raise it into the positive-energy region. This would require a photon of energy equal to $2m_0c^2$ or more.

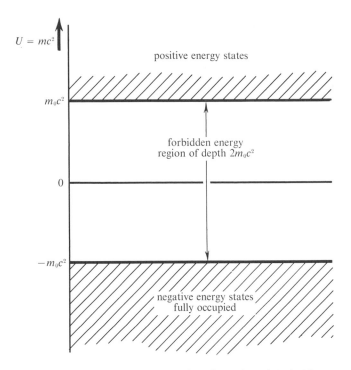

Figure 24-1 *Schematic depiction of the allowed and forbidden energy states of an electron according to Dirac.*

On being raised to the positive-energy region, the electron would become observable as a normal electron. At the same time, the hole that is left behind, representing the absence of a negative-energy electron of negative mass and negative charge, would be indistinguishable from the presence of a positive-energy electron of positive mass and positive charge. Thus it is postulated that a photon of energy $2m_0c^2$ (about 1.014 M.e.V.), or greater, can disappear with the simultaneous appearance of a pair of electrons carrying opposite charges. This is illustrated in Fig. 24-2. As a pictorial analogy, consider a closed glass vessel filled with water. As long as the vessel is full and no air-water interface is visible, it is difficult to tell whether or not the vessel contains water; but if a drop of water is removed, then not only is this drop observable outside the vessel, but the bubble within the vessel is also observable. However, this bubble, representing the absence of water, has opposite properties; for while water tends to fall, the bubble tends to rise. The analogy is not a perfect one and must not be carried beyond this point.

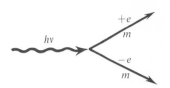

Figure 24-2 *Pair production.*

The only elementary particle with positive charge known at the time of Dirac's suggestion was the proton. This, however, does not bear a close resemblance to the electron; its mass is about 1,836 times the mass of an electron, and its magnetic moment is about 0.00152 times as great as that of the electron. Hence Dirac's theory or description of the electron energy predicted too much. However, in 1932, in the course of taking cloud chamber photographs in a magnetic field of the particles reaching the earth from outer space and their products in our atmosphere, Carl D. Anderson of the California Institute of Technology observed clear evidence of a particle that, by virtue of its sense of curvature, carried a positive charge but had a mass of the order of magnitude of that of the electron. The mass can, of course, be inferred from the equation stated in the preceding paragraph, since the ionization along the track is proportional to U and the radius of curvature is proportional to mv. Since the only particle previously known with a positive charge was the proton, it was important to be quite sure that it was not a proton that was being observed. The track passed through a thin lead plate in the cloud chamber; on entering the plate the product of the magnetic field and its radius of curvature was 0.21 in our units, and on leaving the plate after being slowed down somewhat this product was 0.05 (Fig. 24-3). From the discussion in Chap. 11, this product Hr is equal to mv/e for the particle, so the momentum had decreased to about $\frac{1}{4}$ of its original value on passing through the lead plate. If the proton mass is used for m, the kinetic energy may be calculated; it is then found that the length of the track above the plate is much greater than could be produced by a proton of that energy. On the other hand, if a mass of the order of that of the electron is used, the energy

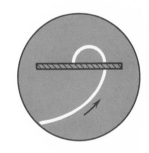

Figure 24-3 *Schematic illustration of a positron passing through a lead plate in a cloud chamber in a magnetic field. The radius of curvature on emerging from the plate is less than that on entering it.*

implied by the momentum or curvature is much larger. The kinetic energy is given in terms of the momentum p by:

$$mc^2 - m_0c^2 = \frac{(p)^2}{m} + \frac{(m_0c)^2}{m} - m_0c^2$$

and, since m is much smaller for the electron than for the proton, the curvature and path length are reconcilable.

Subsequently, many more photographs of such particles by Anderson and other experimenters have been taken, and, indeed, events are commonly photographed indicating the production of pairs of particles, one an electron of the ordinary sort and the other an electron with a positive charge but the same magnitude of e/m. The positive particle was given the name *positron* by Anderson. Its position in the description of atomic phenomena is most readily and naturally interpreted as being the particle corresponding to a vacancy in the normally filled negative energy states of electrons predicted by Dirac from the relativistic form of the expression for the conservation of energy. The electron and the positron, together with certain other more recently discovered particles considerably less massive than nucleons, which will be mentioned later, are known as *leptons*—from the Greek root meaning fine or delicate— for these elementary particles have a number of attributes in common, and are the lightest class of particles we know.

24-2 *Production and annihilation of electrons and positrons*

The process of the formation of a pair of positive and negative electrons by a photon is one of the most important processes of photon absorption or disappearance in the energy range above $2m_0c^2$, or 1.014 M.e.V., which is clearly the threshold beneath which the energy of the photon is inadequate to bring about the process. Above this threshold, the likelihood of the process increases rapidly; for energies greater than three or four million electron Volts, pair production is the dominant process of photon energy dissipation. The excess of photon energy above this amount goes primarily into the kinetic energy of the particles. Following the Compton effect argument of Chap. 14, it can be seen that the formation of two particles of the same mass by a photon in free space is not compatible with both the conservation of momentum and energy; hence the process is limited to taking place in the neighborhood of atoms or atomic nuclei that can then take up the requisite energy and momentum differences. The inverse process, namely, that of the recombination of an electron and positron, also takes place as illustrated in Fig. 24-4. This is evidenced by the sharp line in the energy spectrum of photons corresponding to the value m_0c^2 or 0.507 M.e.V., which is observed to be emitted from a region where positrons have been produced or are present. The reason that the photon energy is equal to m_0c^2 rather than $2m_0c^2$ is that the most probable method of positron disappearance is at a process where two photons, rather than one, are emitted. If one photon is emitted, there must again be some neighboring atomic system to absorb the considerable excess momentum. But if two photons are produced, they may be oppositely directed, and in carrying away the energy of the electron and positron $m_0c^2 + m_0c^2$, assumed for simplicity to be at rest, they may also preserve the total momentum. If the kinetic energies of the combining material particles are not very large, one would anticipate precisely equal frequencies and opposite directions of propagation for the photons. The less likely one-photon processes are also observed, as are those occasional processes in which the energy is radiated as three photons.

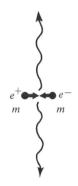

Figure 24-4 *Mutual annihilation of a positron-electron pair to produce two photons.*

The probability of the process of recombination depends inversely upon the excess energy and momentum that must be disposed of to a neighboring atomic system. Thus the probability of being absorbed per unit path length through matter is less for high-energy positrons, and increases as the positron is slowed down by the energy dissipation accompanying its passage through atomic systems. It is most likely to disappear by combining with an electron near the natural end of its path when it is moving relatively slowly. For this reason, the spectrum of photons associated with a source of positrons is always observed to have a maximum of intensity near the value m_0c^2.

The most remarkable and significant fact about this electron-positron relationship is that it exists at all; it is like nothing that has been encountered previously. The ephemeral nature of photons has long been recognized and accepted. These appear and disappear in processes of emission and absorption, and having no rest mass, they travel between the emission and absorption processes with the constant velocity c. In the case of the electron, however, the finite rest mass has long been associated with permanent existence, and the acknowledgement that it too can disappear presents quite a new phenomenon. Admittedly, we do not know the interpretation of the electron rest mass, but it may well be associated with the photons that have their genesis in the changes of the energy state of an electron. If there is no interaction between electrons other than the exchange of photons, which is associated with the electromagnetic interaction, this would indicate that the mass of the electron is entirely associated with its charge. This is in contrast to the nucleons, where energy and therefore mass may be associated with the exchange of mesons, as discussed in the previous chapter.

As was seen in the description of atomic systems in Chap. 15, electrons do not combine with nucleons such as the proton, for reasons that are unclear to us. But there appears to be a law of nature that states that leptons and nucleons are quite separate, noncombining types of entities. We may postulate that each type of entity may separately be created or destroyed in pairs. For every particle there is a so-called anti-particle; an anti-electron is a positron and an anti-proton is a negative proton, such as has recently been produced in high-energy experiments. But there is an incompatibility between leptons and nucleons, which prevents their merging and mutually annihilating one another: leptons rather form stable associations, with the nucleons clustered closely together as the central core of an atomic system; the electrons arrange themselves about it in a circumambient structure determining the chemical properties of the atom thus formed. Were it not for this incompatibility between these two types of particles, preventing their too-close association and mutual annihilation, our stable universe would not be possible.

The positron is an entity sharing this new physical property of compatibility with the electron through which the two are enabled to coalesce and annihilate one another, the energy being radiated as photons, and the various fundamental properties of the particles being jointly conserved. The charge is conserved as such; equal and opposite amounts disappear in the annihilation process or appear in the process of pair production. Energy is conserved in the recombination process, or in that of pair production by a high-energy photon. Momentum is conserved in the pair production process and in the annihilation process. In instances of the occurrence of processes in the neighborhood of an atomic nucleus, this nucleus may participate and absorb any excess energy. The angular momentum is likewise conserved. The spins of the electron and positron being each $\frac{1}{2}$ in units of $h/2\pi$ may result in a net zero angular momentum, if they come together with oppositely directed angular momenta; the two emergent photons with opposite polarizations carry away $+1$ and -1 units of $h/2\pi$, and maintain the angular momentum balance. The angular momentum may also be conserved if the electron and positron combine with spins of like orientation, i.e., a net of $h/2\pi$ of angular momentum by the emission of an odd number of quanta of energy or photons. In the Dirac picture, this apparent generation and destruction in pairs may be thought of as a conservation of the total number of members of the lepton family counting anti-particles as negative members. The elevation of an electron from a negative- to a positive-energy state results in the physical appearance of a negative electron, together with its anti-particle or positron. Thus, with the acceptance of this new property of particles, which we have called compatibility for joint production or mutual annihilation, the previous set of conservation laws is supplemented by the new ones of conservation of leptons and nucleons separately.

Positronium   24-3

It is interesting to consider briefly what would take place if a positron and electron approach one another, not along their line of centers, but in such a way that they have a few units of orbital angular momentum. If the excess kinetic energy of approach is radiated away or transferred to other nearby systems, one might expect that the two particles of equal mass and opposite charge would circulate about their common center of gravity in much the manner of two gravitating masses. The system would formally resemble a hydrogen atom, except that the positron replaces the proton; the ephemeral element thus formed has been named *positronium*. The center of gravity being half way between the two particles, instead of essentially at the proton as in the case of hydrogen, the radii of the orbits of a positronium are twice those of the hydrogen atom; the energies, being proportional to $1/r$, are half as great. The visible radiation to be expected, by analogy with the hydrogen spectrum, is too weak to have been observed, but detailed experiments on annihilation as a function of gas pressure, magnetic field, and angles of photon emission confirm the general type of behavior that would be predicted. These observations confirm the equality of the electron and positron masses to an accuracy of about 1 part in 10^4.

Positron beta-emission processes   24-4

With the discovery of the positron, one is naturally led (by considerations of symmetry) to look for beta-emission processes in which a positron is emitted instead of an electron, and also to see if a negative particle compatible with the proton does not exist as well. One is also tempted to speculate on the possibility that there may be a particle with the mass of an electron, but without any charge at all. In the matter of positive beta-emission, this phenomenon was observed and properly identified very shortly after Anderson's discovery of the positron. While it does not take place in the natural radioactive series, it does take place as a result of nuclear reactions or artificial disintegrations in which unstable nuclei are temporarily formed. As a result of nuclear reactions brought about by the bombardment of stable nuclei with alpha particles, protons, neutrons, photons, etc., nuclei may result which are unstable in the sense of the naturally occurring radioactive nuclei. They have half lives that vary between wide limits, and in changing to stable forms, may do so by the beta-type of emission process in which a broad energy spectrum of either electrons or positrons is emitted.

If the artificial radioactive isotope that is formed initially is greater in mass than the stable isotopes of the element, the tendency in such processes is to emit a negative beta particle. Alternatively, if the radioactive isotope is less in mass than the stable isotope of the element, a positive beta particle, or positron, is generally emitted.

As an example, the region in the neighborhood of carbon and nitrogen in the atomic sequence is shown in Fig. 24-5. The stable elements are indicated by solid dots. If artificially formed isotopes lying above or below the diagonal trend of stability are formed, the beta-decay process is of such a nature as to emit a lepton the sign of which will produce the nearest stable isotope. Thus the following representative beta-type decays are observed with these light elements:

	Half-life T	Maximum energy of β spectrum
$_6C^{11} \rightarrow \, _5B^{11} + \, _1e^0$	20.5 min.	0.98×10^6 e.V.
$_6C^{14} \rightarrow \, _7N^{14} + \, _{-1}e^0$	5750 yr.	0.156×10^6 e.V.
$_7N^{13} \rightarrow \, _6C^{13} + \, _1e^0$	9.93 min.	1.21×10^6 e.V.
$_7N^{16} \rightarrow \, _8O^{16} + \, _{-1}e^0$	7.35 sec.	10.3×10^6 e.V.
$_8O^{15} \rightarrow \, _7N^{15} + \, _1e^0$	126 sec.	1.7×10^6 e.V.
$_8O^{19} \rightarrow \, _9F^{19} + \, _{-1}e^0$	27 sec.	4.5×10^6 e.V.

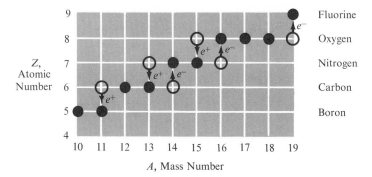

Figure 24-5 *Representative lepton emission processes in the light elements.*

As another instance, copper 64 emits both positive and negative beta particles with the same half life and very little difference in maximum energy. The positron energy maximum exceeds that of the electron energy distribution by about 80,000 e.V., which is of the order of magnitude that could be accounted for by the opposite electric forces exerted on these charged particles by the copper nucleus after emission.

No particle is known with the electron mass and zero charge. It would be unreasonable to expect that such a particle should exist, if the electron mass is intimately bound up with its charge and consequent photon-radiating potentiality. However, another light, uncharged particle, which is intimately associated with an electron, does exist. It was called the *neutrino*, or "little neutron," by the Italian physicist Enrico Fermi. Like the photon, it is an extreme relativistic particle with no rest mass and the velocity of light, but unlike the photon its interaction with matter is not associated with charge. It is, however, a close relative of electrons, and participates in the generative processes that will be described in connection with the discussion of radioactive beta-emission processes in the following chapter.

Compatible heavy particles—antimatter   24-5

The discovery of the positron as a compatible particle for annihilatory combination with the electron is evidence of a previously unknown symmetry in nature. Proceeding on this principle of symmetry, which has always been one of the most intuitive guidelines for research, one is immediately led to inquire whether there does not exist a negative proton. This would be a particle with a mass equal to that of the proton, a similar angular momentum or spin and accompanying magnetic moment, but with a negative charge equal in magnitude to the positive charge of the proton. It would also have the property of compatibility with the proton, and by combining with it, could bring about pairs of other compatible particles or photons of electromagnetic radiation or both, within the energetic and momentum possibilities of the particular event.

The existence of negative protons was established by the group of University of California scientists using the very high-energy particles accelerated by the 6,200 M.e.V. proton synchrotron at Berkeley. For this achievement, Emilio Segre and Owen Chamberlain were awarded the Nobel prize in physics for 1959. These particles, which were found to emerge from the target struck by the high-energy beam of ions, were identified as having a unit negative charge and the mass of a proton, by measurements of the momentum and energy, and of the sense of deflection in a magnetic field. They are negative protons, or *anti-protons*, in the sense that upon encountering an ordinary positively charged proton, the two combine together just as do positive and negative electrons, except that the energy liberated is 1,836 times as great; thus in the two-photon process, the energy of each is 938 M.e.V. Our world and universe is apparently composed of positive protons and negative electrons, but one similar could be produced using the opposite or anti-particles of these two entities.

EXAMPLE. Consider the creation of a proton-anti-proton pair in the bombardment of a stationary proton by a proton of high energy, according to the reaction:

$$P + P \rightarrow P + P + P + \bar{P}$$

The minimum projectile energy required to produce this reaction may be calculated by assuming that the final particles adhere and move together with a common velocity V. If v is the velocity of the projectile and m_p the proton rest mass, the energy equation is

$$\frac{m_p c^2}{\sqrt{1 - v^2/c^2}} + m_p c^2 = \frac{4 m_p c}{\sqrt{1 - V^2/c^2}}$$

Also, equating the momentum of the incident proton and that of the four product protons

$$\frac{m_p v}{\sqrt{1 - v^2/c^2}} = \frac{4 m_p V}{\sqrt{1 - V^2/c^2}}$$

These two equations may be solved by the use of simple algebra to yield a projectile energy of:

$$\frac{m_p c^2}{\sqrt{1 - v^2/c^2}} = 7 m_p c^2$$

i.e., the incident proton must be projected with an energy equal to seven times its rest energy.

Finally, one is led to speculate about the position of the neutron in the natural scheme of symmetry among the elementary particles of which our universe appears to be composed. The neutron is related to the proton, the latter being a particle that results from radioactive decay of a neutron as a result of a beta-decay process. The neutron mass is somewhat different from that of the proton and, though its intrinsic angular momentum or spin is the same, its magnetic moment is also somewhat different. If there is an anti-proton, should there not also be an *anti-neutron*, which could be formed in a high-energy process and which, being compatible with a neutron, could coalesce with one in an annihilation process? It would also presumably have the property of decaying into an anti-proton as a result of a positron beta-decay process. This particle has actually been observed experimentally by the Berkeley group in the course of their experiments, establishing the existence of the anti-proton. A high-energy anti-proton seems to disappear in absorbing material, presumably by combining with a proton, producing a neutron and an anti-neutron. The latter is detected a short distance away by its combination with an ordinary neutron in an atomic nucleus and the liberation of the mass energy of the pair, which gives rise to a disruption of the nucleus of which the neutron formed a part. The energy and momentum balance can be verified from the bubble chamber record of the event; the correctness of the description is thus attested.

Thus it is now established that the elementary particles such as electrons, protons, and neutrons we have discussed so far have compatible anti-particles. If a particle is charged, then its anti-particle differs in sign of charge; if it is uncharged, then both are neutral. They exhibit the property of coincident generation and also mutual annihilation when brought into close proximity. The nucleons (protons and neutrons) and their anti-particles are found to be members of a larger family group known as *baryons*. We then have two groups of elementary particles, namely baryons and leptons, each of which exhibits the property of conservation of number. All members of both groups have an intrinsic spin of $\frac{1}{2}(h/2\pi)$. However, pions and the photon, which have intrinsic spins of zero or of an integral multiple of $h/2\pi$, do not have this property. We have already seen that the π-meson or pion and the photon are the particles associated with forces between the members of the conserved families.

The conservation laws so far encountered, which together summarize most of our knowledge and understanding of the physical world, are expressed in Table 24-1.

Table 24-1   *Certain basic conservation laws*

1. Conservation of Energy.
2. Conservation of Momentum.
3. Conservation of Angular Momentum.
4. Conservation of Electric Charge.
5. Conservation of Baryon Family Members.
6. Conservation of Lepton Family Members.

It will be recalled that in Sect. 1-3 the various types of symmetry were discussed briefly, and were said to be of great usefulness in describing and understanding the types of basic physical phenomena with which we are concerned. Rotational and reflection symmetries were seen to be particularly useful in describing the various types of ordered crystaline structures that are formed by aggregates of atoms (Chap. 20). In a way, the fact that we can treat time as uniform and continuous, and that space appears to be quite uniform from place to place and isotropic for any angular rotation, which enables us to choose axes arbitrarily, is evidence of a kind of symmetry in our universe. Dynamic processes, when observed in a mirror, which has the effect of reversing the sign of one coordinate, also appear to follow Newton's laws of motion. A reversal of the time axis under which an observed series of events would be retraced in the opposite order is also concordant with individual atomic processes as we know them. But, of course, the systematic reversal of all of the complicated processes in large aggregates of atoms making up matter in bulk is such an unlikely event that our imagination boggles at it, and the reversal of a moving picture of a growth process, for instance, appears quite ludicrous.

The specific relations between symmetries and the conservation laws is particularly interesting, but their derivation requires a knowledge of the laws of quantum mechanics, which is beyond the scope of this treatment. The fact that the laws are symmetrical for translation in time is equivalent to the conservation of energy. The fact that these laws are symmetrical for spatial displacements implies the conservation of momentum. Their invariance under rotation of the axes through a finite angle implies the conservation of angular momentum. Another symmetry property of the laws of quantum mechanics, which has no classical analog, implies the conservation of charge.

Since electric charges as such are not visible either directly or in mirrors, it would appear that the concept of mirror symmetry is quite irrelevant to the law of the conservation of electric charge. The assignment of positive and negative signs to the two types of electric charge is quite arbitrary, the only essential observation being that there are indeed two kinds of electric charge. Like kinds repel and unlike kinds attract one another. However, since the discovery of the existence of particle and anti-particle pairs, such as the electron and positron, or the proton and negatively charged anti-proton, which are able to annihilate one another, the more natural extension of the concept of mirror symmetry is to consider the appropriate mirror image of a particle as its anti-particle, implying a change in the sign of electric charge upon reflexion. The strongest arguments for this alternative come from our inability to formulate a rigorous theory of elementary particles consistent with the theory of relativity without adopting this convention, but the details of this argument lie beyond our competence to present them in an elementary way.

There is, however, some added realism to this idea, which comes from the simple observation that an electrically charged particle placed before a plane metallic conductor—which is indeed an optical mirror—is found to be attracted toward it with precisely the same force as if the mirror were absent and a charge of equal magnitude but opposite sign were present at a distance behind the mirror equal to the distance of the charged particle in front of it.

EXAMPLE. It may be shown that the force with which a point charge e would be attracted to an infinite conducting plane or mirror surface at a distance d is the same as if the mirror were absent and a charge of like magnitude but opposite sign were located at the mirror image of the charge, i.e., at a distance $2d$ along an axis perpendicular to the mirror surface.

The presence of the charge $+e$ produces electrical forces on the charges in the conducting plane or mirror before it such that these charges move through the conductor until the only force, if any, that each of these mobile charges experiences is normal to the conducting surface. For if there were a component of the force along the conducting

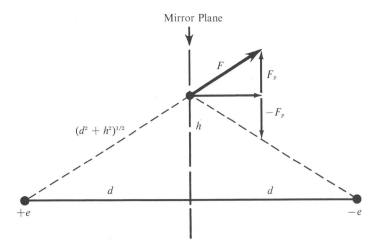

Figure 24-6 *Illustration of the equivalence of the electrical force upon the charge e brought about either by a conducting mirror surface at a distance d or by a negative charge at a distance 2d along the perpendicular from the charge to the mirror.*

surface, the mobile charges would be free to move in response to it. The charge $+e$ would then experience the forces upon it caused by the distribution of charges on the surface of the conductor that would ensue. It may be shown that if the conducting surface is removed and a charge $-e$ is placed at a distance $2d$ along the axis normal to the surface which had been there, this charge together with the charge $+e$ produces a resultant electric field that is normal to the plane previously occupied by the conducting surface. Hence the effective force on the charge $+e$ is the same in both instances. This may be seen by referring to Fig. 24-6. The force that would be exerted by $+e$ on a unit charge in the plane of the mirror is: $F = Ke/(d^2 + h^2)$. The component of this parallel to the surface is this quantity times $h/(d^2 + h^2)^{1/2}$, or $F_p = Keh/(d^2 + h^2)^{3/2}$. The force parallel to the surface exerted at the same point on a unit charge by the charge $-e$ would be the same in magnitude but opposite in sign. Thus a plane bisecting perpendicularly the line joining $+e$ and $-e$ is the one fulfilling the condition that there is no electrical force along it at any point; the effect upon the charge $+e$ is the same as if a distribution of charges on the plane brought this situation about, or if the conducting plane were absent and the charge $-e$ were present.

Further reading:

DeBenedetti, S., and Corben, H. C., "Positronium," *Annual Review of Nuclear Science*, vol. 4, p. 191 (1954).

Good, R. H., Jr., "Massless Particles," *American Journal of Physics*, vol. 28, No. 7, p. 659 (1960).

Peierls, R. E., "The Atomic Nucleus," *Scientific American*, vol. 200, No. 1, p. 75 (1959).

Reines and Cowan, C. L., Jr., "Neutrino Physics," *Physics Today*, vol. 10, No. 8, p. 12 (1957).

Segrè, E., "Anti-Nucleons," *Annual Review of Nuclear Science*, vol. 8, p. 127 (1958).

Segrè, E., "Anti-Nucleons," *American Journal of Physics*, vol. 25, No. 6, p. 363 (1957).

Segrè, E. and Wiegand, C. E., "The Anti-Proton," *Scientific American*, vol. 194, No. 6, p. 37 (1956).

Problems

24-1 What is the frequency of the two γ-rays produced on the annihilation of an electron-positron pair at rest?

24-2 An electron-positron pair with opposite spins is annihilated when both members of the pair are virtually stationary. What can be said about the energies of the two photons produced, and about their directions and their helicities, i.e., their directions of spin (right-handed or left-handed)? Can anything be said about the directions of emission of three photons? Give reasons for each answer.

24-3 What is the wave length of the two γ-rays produced on the annihilation of a proton-antiproton pair at rest?

24-4 Sketch the energy spectra to be expected for an α source, a β^- source, and a β^+ source. Assume each decays to a single well-defined final state. If possible, predict the effect that the nuclear charge would have on the shapes of the β spectra.

24-5 Predict the mode of decay for each of the following radioactive isotopes: He^6, Be^{10}, B^{12}, C^{10}, and C^{15}.

24-6 In β^+ decay, a nuclear proton is converted to a neutron. In β^- decay, the opposite transformation occurs. Could each of these processes take place outside the nucleus in free space?

24-7 Calculate the momentum of each of the 2 photons produced when a neutron and antineutron at rest are annihilated.

24-8 Describe the above event in terms of Dirac's *negative energy states* and *forbidden energy region*. Why are 2 photons rather than 1 normally produced?

24-9 1 kg. of antimatter is combined with 1 kg. of matter. Compute the energy evolved in M.e.V. and in Joules. Compute the wave length of the two photons produced by the mutual annihilation of a proton-antiproton pair.

24-10 Why would you not expect the following to mutually annihilate: (a) a neutron and an antiproton (b) a proton and an electron (c) 2 electrons (d) a neutron and a photon?

25 Neutrinos and the interactions between leptons and nucleons

25-1 Summary of the interactions between elementary particles that have been discussed in preceding chapters

The interaction between massive particles that was the first encountered historically was that of gravitation. It might well be called the Newtonian interaction, since Newton was the first to recognize its universality. It is one of the only two long-range interactions that we know, the other being the electrical or electromagnetic one. It is intimately related to our concept of mass. The universal law of gravitation in the form stated by Newton determines the motion of large uncharged masses, such as those of the solar system. This simple statement sums up our entire knowledge of the important interaction between material bodies; the lack of precision with which we know the constant G appearing in the statement of the interaction suggests our area of ignorance. Since the gravitational and electrostatic laws of force are of the same form, one may not unreasonably compare the magnitudes of these interactions by considering the ratio of the gravitational attraction between two of the elemental baryons, such as two protons, with the electrostatic repulsion between them that arises from the electric charges they carry. If one examines the ratio $(Gm^2/r^2)/(Ke^2/r^2)$, one finds it to be of the order of 10^{-36}, which indicates the relatively negligible effect of gravity in comparison with the electrostatic interaction. Thus the Newtonian interaction of particles through their gravitational effect is so small that it is negligible in terms of any experimental observations we can make, and we need not include it in the balance of effects that bring about the atomic phenomena we observe on the surface of the earth.

The description of the interaction between electric charges, whether they are relatively at rest or in motion, can be supplemented very helpfully—as has been seen in preceding chapters—by the introduction of the concept of the photon as the intermediary through which energy is emitted by one charge and absorbed by another. The photon is an extreme relativistic particle that has no rest mass and travels with the velocity of light. Its energy is $h\nu$, its momentum $h\nu/c$, and the angular momentum oriented forward or backward along its trajectory is $h/2\pi$. The process of the interaction between electrons through the intermediary of a photon is called a *Dirac process* (Fig. 25-1), in recognition of the development of the quantum theory of electrical interactions by P. A. M. Dirac, which provided a very complete and detailed account of phenomena of this sort.

The interaction between nucleons, such as protons and neutrons, is through an intermediary called a pion, which is not a massless relativistic particle at all, but one with a mass of about 270 times the rest mass of the electron. The pion can also carry a charge equal to or opposite to that of the electron, or it can be uncharged. Unlike the photon, it has no spin or intrinsic angular momentum. With the rest mass is associated an energy mc^2 of about 2.2×10^{-11} J. If in the exchange of pions between baryons such as protons and neutrons this energy is involved, the uncertainty principle states that a time given by $\delta U \delta t \approx h$ is required. The value of δt is thus about 3×10^{-23} sec. As the greatest speed with which an interaction between two baryons could be propagated is the velocity of light c, the separation of two such interacting baryons cannot be greater than about 10^{-14} m. This is seen to be about the size of baryon aggregates in nuclei. The process of the exchange of pions is called the *Yukawa process* (Fig. 25-1). It was initially postulated by the Japanese physicist H. Yukawa in order to account for nuclear binding energies. Finally, it should be noted that though the pion may carry a charge, it has no intrinsic angular momentum or spin, and hence it has no magnetic moment, which makes it analogous to the photon rather than the electron.

A comparison of the relative strengths of the Yukawa and Dirac interactions is difficult and somewhat arbitrary, because the spatial

Energetic electron undergoing its transformation to a less energetic electron emitting a gamma ray.

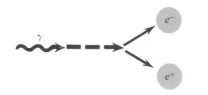

Gamma ray conversion into a positive and negative electron.

Illustrations of electromagnetic or Dirac types of processes. Neighboring particles are required to satisfy the condition of conservation of momentum.

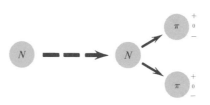

An energetic nucleon emitting one or more pions either charged or uncharged.

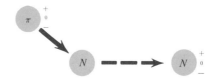

A nucleon absorbing a pion and producing a different and more energetic nucleon.

Illustration of a Yukawa type of process. Neighboring particles are required to satisfy the condition of conservation of momentum.

Figure 25-1 *The dashed arrows indicate possible or virtual processes that are inherent in the nature of the entities involved, and which actually take place if sufficient energy is available.*

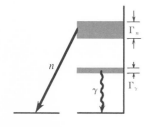

Figure 25-2 *The "width" or energy spread of a nuclear state is inversely proportional to its half-life. It is greater for a state that can decay rapidly via a strong interaction.*

dependence of their associated forces and energies are very different. Perhaps the most meaningful simple comparison is obtained from studies of atomic nuclei that may undergo a transformation of either type. Two of the permitted states of excitation of one such nucleus are depicted in Fig. 25-2. It will be noted that these energy levels, or states of excitation, are shown as broad lines, the upper one exceedingly broad, as though there were some uncertainty δU in their energies. Such is actually the case, and the spectra observed for nuclear reactions that pass through these states exhibit line widths corresponding to these uncertainties. The uncertainties in energy δU are related to uncertainties δt in the lifetime of these states. The latter are represented by the half lives T of the states. The relationship is that of the uncertainty principle:

$$\delta U \delta t \approx h \quad \text{or} \quad \delta t \approx h/\delta U$$

Since the halflife T is obviously inversely proportional to the strength of the interaction through which the state decays, δU is apparently a measure of this strength. It is commonly denoted by the symbol Γ and represents the probability of occurence of the reaction. The relation between halflife T and reaction strength Γ is then of the form:

$$\Gamma T \approx h$$

Of course this treatment has ignored the dynamics of the problem, which may have a profound influence upon the time scale for any given reaction. The upper excited state of Fig. 25-2 is depicted as decaying via nucleon emission (a Yukawa process) to some other nucleus. It has a "width" Γ_n. The lower of the two excited states is below the threshold energy for particle emission, and hence decays to the ground or unexcited state of the same nucleus by emission of a gamma ray of several MeV (a Dirac process). It has a width $\Gamma\gamma$. Experimentally, it is observed that Γ_n is typically of the order of 0.1 M.e.V., whereas $\Gamma\gamma$ is only about 100 e.V. Thus the relative strengths of the Dirac and Yukawa processes is of the order of:

$$\frac{\Gamma\gamma}{\Gamma_n} \approx 10^{-3}$$

The interaction process between leptons and nucleons   25-2

The previous discussion of the interactions between elementary particles has assumed that the only interaction between electrons and nucleons is the one deriving from electric and electromagnetic forces. However, this is inadequate by itself to account for a process such as the observed beta-type of radioactive decay in which an electron is emitted from the transforming nucleus. In this instance, the electron family numbers appear at first sight not to be conserved. Also the beta-decay process was recognized as a rather peculiar one, from the time of its discovery, because of the continuous spectrum of electron energies, which would imply a continuous spectrum of energy levels in the atomic nuclei involved. Simply interpreted, this would represent quite a unique situation, unparalleled among all the other phenomena of atomic and nuclear physics. As experimental evidence accumulated, the basic conservation laws of momentum and angular momentum also appeared to be violated by the simple interpretation of the observation of beta-decay as being the unaccompanied emission of an electron by a nucleus or nucleon.

Shortly after the discovery of the neutron, Enrico Fermi, then at the University of Rome, proposed a novel theory of beta-decay that agreed with the facts as they were then known, and maintained the concept of discrete energy levels in atomic nuclei, and hence discrete isotopic masses. It also maintained all the conservation laws listed in the preceding section and is in accord with all experimental evidence to date. The theory involves the introduction of an additional elementary particle, or particle-pair, called the *neutrino*, or "little neutron," and its mirror image or anti-particle (Fig. 25-3). Neutrinos are like photons in being extreme relativistic particles of no rest mass travelling with the velocity of light. They are, of course, capable of transmitting energy and momentum and, as in the case of the photon or any particle for

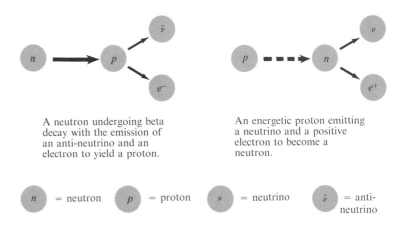

A neutron undergoing beta decay with the emission of an anti-neutrino and an electron to yield a proton.

An energetic proton emitting a neutrino and a positive electron to become a neutron.

n = neutron p = proton ν = neutrino $\bar{\nu}$ = anti-neutrino

Figure 25-3   *Illustrations of the Fermi process representing lower energies or weaker interactions than the Dirac or Yukawa processes. The dashed arrow indicates a possible or virtual process inherent in the nature of the entities involved, and which actually take place when the energy is available. The inverse processes are equally possible.*

which the rest mass m_0 vanishes, the energy U and the momentum p are related by $U/c = p$. Again, like right- and left-circularly polarized photons, the neutrinos are assumed to have an intrinsic angular momentum directed in either a right or left circular sense about the direction of propagation; the sense of the rotation of the neutrino being that of an advancing left-hand screw or helix, and that of the anti-neutrino being that of an advancing right-hand helix. Here the photon analogy ends, and there are two marked differences between neutrinos and photons: (1) the angular momentum carried by a neutrino is $\frac{1}{2}(h/2\pi)$ and that carried by a photon is $h/2\pi$ or twice as great; and (2) the neutrino is not associated with the property of electric charge possessed by electrons or protons, i.e., its interaction with these particles is not of an electromagnetic nature. The absence of rest mass and of any electromagnetic interaction with charged particles would appear to render this particle well nigh undetectable, and indeed it almost does; but not quite, and the evidence for existence is now complete and convincing.

Evidence for the existence of the neutrino   25-3

The first reason for introducing the neutrino, which is very convincing even if it is indirect, is that without it there is a discrepancy between the quantized energy pattern of nature and the continuous nature of the energy spectrum of beta particles. If the nucleus and the electron are the only two participating particles, the energy from the parent nuclear mass appearing as kinetic energy in the process must be divided between them; since the electron is much the lighter particle, the momentum conservation argument of Sect. 4-4 shows that practically all of the energy is carried away by the electron.

The nucleus in most cases must then be left with varying amounts of energy, namely, the amount corresponding to the differences between $U_{\max}$ and U_1, for the case in which the beta particle is observed with the energy U_1 (Fig. 25-4). In the case of light nuclei such as the proton and neutron, for which the masses can be measured with high precision, a spread of mass values corresponding to the range $m = U_{\max}/c^2$ should be observed. But this is not the case. Hence the energy difference $(U_{\max} - U_1)$ must be carried away at the process by some entity other than the electron. A third particle must be postulated to provide the energy balance, and as photons or other known particles are frequently not observed, the introduction of the neutrino is essential.

The second somewhat similar line of argument relates to the conservation of angular momentum. The angular momenta of both the mother

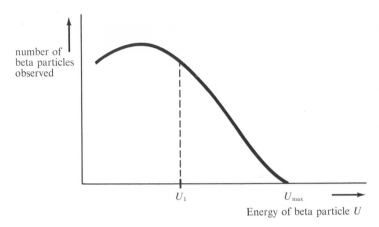

Figure 25-4 *Nature of observed beta-particle energy spectrum.*

and daughter nuclei are known in many cases from spectroscopic evidence. It appears that in a beta-decay process the spin or intrinsic angular momentum either does not change at all or, if there is a change, it is by a unit of $h/2\pi$. The electron has an intrinsic spin of half this value; the only way in which the observations could be reconciled is that there is another participant in the beta-decay process besides the nucleus and the beta particle, i.e., a particle that also has an intrinsic spin of $\frac{1}{2}(h/2\pi)$ in order to conserve angular momentum and account for the initial and final values of the angular momentum that are observed. The neutrino must have the spin of $\frac{1}{2}(h/2\pi)$ to fulfill this requirement. Recent experiments have shown that the neutrino is essentially a particle of a left-hand screw nature with its angular momentum directed along its trajectory, whereas an anti-neutrino is a right-hand screw type of particle with angular momentum in the opposite sense directed along its trajectory (Fig. 25-5).

The third line of argument relates to the conservation of linear momentum. With the postulation of the existence of a neutrino, three particles result from a beta-decay process. But as the recoiling nucleus travels only a very short distance, it is difficult to say whether the electron and nuclear paths are colinear, as would be the case for two particles, or as would not be expected for three. Nevertheless, a considerable number of experimenters found in ionization and cloud chamber observations that there was evidence for an imbalance in the momentum of the nucleus and beta particle that could be accounted for by a neutrino. Possibly the most unambiguous and convincing observations were those of J. Allen upon the beta-decay of beryllium

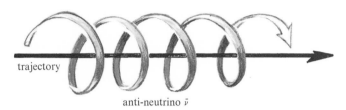

Figure 25-5 *Relative senses of angular momentum or screw motion associated with the direction of motion of neutrinos.*

of mass number seven. This nucleus would be expected to emit a positron changing to lithium seven according to the considerations of Chap. 24, but an alternative to this is that one of the orbital electrons be absorbed by the nucleus and a neutrino emitted for energy, momentum and angular momentum balance. Thus

$$_4\text{Be}^7 + {}_{-1}e^0 \rightarrow {}_3\text{Li}^7 + {}_0\nu^0$$

In accordance with the conservation of momentum, the momenta of the neutrino and of the lithium atom are equal in magnitude and oppositely directed. Thus

$$\frac{U_\nu}{c} = M_{\text{Li}}v_{\text{Li}}$$

where U_ν/c is written for the neutrino's momentum rather than mv because, like the photon, the neutrino has no rest mass and is propagated with the velocity of light. Also, the total energy available is the change in mass that takes place, multiplied by c^2, or:

$$U_{\text{total}} = (\delta M)c^2 = \tfrac{1}{2}M_{\text{Li}}v_{\text{Li}}^2 + U_\nu$$

Eliminating U_ν, it is found that the velocity of the lithium atom is approximately $(\delta M)c/M_{\text{Li}}$, and the kinetic energy of the lithium atom is

$$U_{\text{Li}} = \frac{1}{2} M_{\text{Li}}v_{\text{Li}}^2 = \frac{(\delta M)^2 c^2}{2M_{\text{Li}}}$$

where $(\delta M) = M_{\text{Be}} + m_e - M_{\text{Li}}$. From the known values of the masses of the particles, the energy represented by $(\delta M)c^2$ is found to be about 1.36 M.e.V., and the kinetic energy of the lithium atom is found to be of the order of 100 e.V. This is a very small energy to measure, but by the aid of a specially designed electron multiplier tube, the electrons liberated when these lithium atoms struck the plate were detected and the anticipated result obtained.

The fourth and final line of argument for the existence of the neutrino and anti-neutrino comes from the direct observation of the nuclear reactions which they induce. Having no charge, the neutrino produces no ions in the course of its passage through matter; also projected electrons at elastic collisions analogous to protons projected by neutrons would be very difficult to observe. Furthermore, the theoretical likelihood of observing neutrino-induced nuclear reactions is very small, making the detection of such effects difficult as well. However, the very large neutrino emission by nuclear reactors provides an opportunity to perform an experiment to detect such reactions. F. Reines and C. L. Cowan, Jr. have done so successfully using an experimental arrangement illustrated schematically in Fig. 25-6.

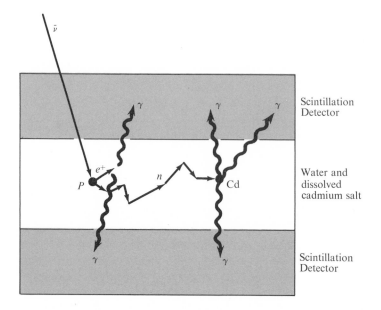

Figure 25-6 *Identification of an anti-neutrino reaction. The gamma rays γ from the positron annihilation are simultaneous and have an energy of 0.5 M.e.V.; those from the neutron capture by cadmium total about 9 M.e.V.*

The beta processes involving the proton and neutron are the following:

$$_0n^1 \rightarrow {_1p^1} + {_{-1}e^0} + {_0\bar\nu^0} \quad \text{or} \quad {_0\nu^0} + {_0n^1} \rightarrow {_1p^1} + {_{-1}e^0}$$

$$_1p^1 \rightarrow {_0n^1} + {_1e^0} + {_0\nu^0} \quad \text{or} \quad {_0\bar\nu^0} + {_1p^1} \rightarrow {_0n^1} + {_1e^0}$$

where the bar over the ν indicates the anti-neutrino. One might then anticipate that the anti-neutrinos liberated in great numbers from the neutrons decaying in the flux from a nuclear reactor (described in the following chapter) would combine with protons to yield neutrons and positrons. The equation consistent with this would be the fourth one of those above, any requisite additional energy being supplied by the anti-neutrino. Upon exposing large volumes of water with small amounts of a cadmium salt dissolved in them to the flux of neutrinos from a large reactor, the two related events to be expected were observed. The first of these is the simultaneous emission of the photons produced by the annihilation of the positron; the second, following in a few millionths of a second, is the emission of photons when the neutron that is produced encounters a cadmium nucleus and is absorbed by it. Cadmium has a very large probability of absorbing a slowly moving neutron, which is the reason for its use in this experiment. The observation of this reaction, difficult as it was, not only gave final confirmation of the existence of the neutrino, but it also differentiated between the neutrino and anti-neutrino. Similar types of experiments, such as the absorption of a neutrino by a chlorine atom of atomic number 17 with the production of an atom of argon of atomic number 18 and a negative electron, have been tried unsuccessfully. These experiments evidently require the change of a neutron to a proton in the nucleus, and by our previous argument would require a neutrino rather than an anti-neutrino. Since the neutron decay process in the nuclear reactor provides anti-neutrinos rather than neutrinos, one would not expect the chlorine-to-argon reaction to take place; thus the general correctness of the above description appears to be confirmed.

The smallness of the effects associated with neutrinos and the experimental difficulties encountered in verifying their existence and determining their properties, indicate the very weak nature of the *Fermi interactions* (Fig. 25-3) in which they are involved. The strength of these reactions may be estimated in relation to other interactions by comparing the intervals of time that are associated with the beta decay and the other radiations of a nucleus discussed in Sect. 25-1. There the electromagnetic interaction was seen to be associated with a time $T\gamma = h/\Gamma\gamma$, which is of the order of 10^{-16} sec. Half-lives for nuclear states that decay only by beta emission are distributed over several orders of magnitude, with 10^{-2} sec. as a fairly typical value. The ratio of these lifetimes is 10^{14}, implying that the Dirac interaction is stronger than the Fermi interaction by about this factor. As a consequence, although photons are absorbed in a few atomic layers of a substance, neutrinos penetrate many kilometers through solid materials.

25-4 *Asymmetry associated with neutrino processes*

In the course of investigating processes in which neutrinos take part, physicists were surprised to find that they are somewhat less symmetrical than are the more familiar processes that involve photons or pions. An experiment performed at the National Bureau of Standards, by C. S. Wu and her associates at the suggestion of C. N. Yang and T. D. Lee, was the first that clearly brought this feature to light (Fig. 25-7). In this experiment, the isotope of cobalt of atomic weight 60, the nucleus of which possesses a finite magnetic moment, was placed in the magnetic field of a current-carrying solenoid. At the low temperature that was brought about, which was of the order of $0.01\,°K$, the magnetic moments of the nuclei align themselves almost completely with the field pointing in the direction that represents the orientation of lowest energy.

Cobalt 60 ($_{27}\mathrm{Co}^{60}$) decays during a long period of about five years by the beta process, in the course of which one may think of one of the neutrons in the nucleus changing to a proton in accordance with the equation:

$$_1n^0 \rightarrow {_1p^1} + {_{-1}e^0} + {_0\bar{\nu}^0}$$

resulting in nickel of atomic weight 60 ($_{28}\mathrm{Ni}^{60}$). Gamma rays are also emitted subsequently in the course of rearrangement of the nucleons in the nickel 60 nucleus. The surprising observation was that the electrons were not found to be emitted equally abundantly—or alternatively stated, with equal probability—both in the direction of the magnetic field and oppositely to it, as is always found to be the case for the emission of electromagnetic radiation or photons. On the contrary, the electron or beta ray intensity was much greater in the direction antiparallel to the magnetic field than parallel to it. As in the case of photons, the electron emission was found to be symmetrical in azimuth about the axis of the field.

This was a surprising result because all previous experience with strong interactions, such as the Dirac and Yukawa processes, had indicated that physical phenomena were invariant when the directions of one or more of the coordinate axes were reversed; e.g., as the direction

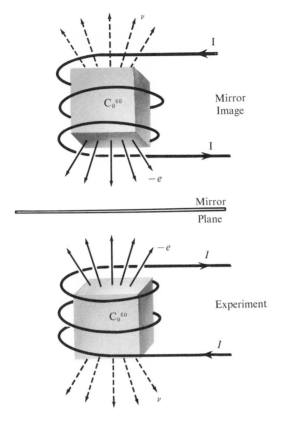

Figure 25-7 *The mirror image of the above experiment, obtained by inversion of one of the spatial coordinates, corresponds to a nonphysical situation.*

of the axis normal to a mirror is reversed by reflection in it. The photons following the beta decay are emitted equally in the direction of the lined up spins of the cobalt nuclei and in the opposite direction. The photons emitted by the electron structure of an atom when it changes from one energetic configuration to another in a magnetic field have always been found to emerge as numerously along the field axis in one direction as in the other. A helicity, i.e., an association of an axis of rotation with a direction of translation, has of course long been associated with a photon; it is known that the rate of propagation of photons with the two different senses of helicity—left and right handed—was different along the helical axis of quartz or through large molecules having a helical configuration of their component atoms. Indeed, right-

or left-circularly polarized light can be produced in this way. But photons are their own anti-particles, and are emitted equally in all electromagnetic or Dirac processes with both helicities. No asymmetry, such as the asymmetry seen in the emission of electrons by the lined up cobalt nuclei had ever been observed.

However, in the weak interaction between neutrinos and electrons, it is evident that the magnetic field cannot be considered as simply an axis of symmetry, but that it must be recognized as a vector determined by the sense of circulation of the electric charges in the coil producing it. If in the mirror image of Fig. 25-8, reflection is taken as reversing the sign of the electric charges as well as the axis perpendicular to the

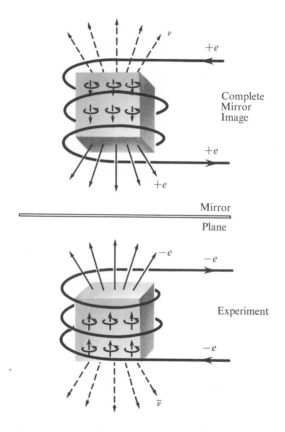

Figure 25-8   *The true mirror image of an experiment shows an inversion of all spatial coordinates and any charges involved. The small vertical arrows on the nuclei represent the magnetic moments of the spinning nuclei.*

mirror, the predictions are then in accord with experiment. Of course, in the mirror image the cobalt nuclei emit positrons instead of electrons, and neutrinos instead of anti-neutrinos. The neutrino has a left-handed helicity and the anti-neutrino a right-handed one.

In concluding, it is interesting to note that the postulate stating that the neutrino and its anti-particle are extreme relativistic particles, which —like photons—always travel with the velocity of light, is verified by the consistency of the observations that associate a specific helicity with each. This fact—that their velocity is always c—enables us to picture their vector angular momentum as being unambiguously lined up either in the direction of their velocity or in the opposite direction. This cannot be done in the case of a particle of finite rest mass. Since such a particle cannot achieve the velocity of light, it would be possible for another particle or an observer to be moving more or less rapidly with respect to it. It would appear to be approaching one and receding from the other as the direction of the relative velocity vector would be reversed and that of the angular momentum vector would remain the same. Hence it would appear to have one sense of helicity to a particle moving more slowly than it, and the opposite sense of helicity to one moving more rapidly.

Further reading:

BURKHARDT, H., "Elementary Particle Physics," *American Journal of Physics*, vol. 28, No. 3, p. 202 (1960).

FEINBERG, G. AND GOLDHABER, M., "The Conservation Laws of Physics," *Scientific American*, vol. 209, No. 4, p. 36 (1963).

GELL-MANN, M. AND ROSENBAUM, E. P., "Elementary Particles," *Scientific American*, vol. 197, No. 1, p. 72 (1957).

LEE, T. D., "Weak Interactions and Non-Conservation of Parity," *Science*, vol. 127, No. 3298, p. 569 (1958).

MARSHAK, R. E., "Elementary Particles of Modern Physics," *Science*, vol. 132, No. 3422, p. 269 (1960).

MORRISON, P., "Approximate Nature of Physical Symmetries," *American Journal of Physics*, vol. 26, No. 5, p. 358 (1958).

MORRISON, P., "Neutrino Astronomy," *Scientific American*, vol. 207, No. 2, p. 90 (1962).

MORRISON, P., "The Neutrino," *Scientific American*, vol. 194, No. 1, p. 58 (1956).

REINER, F. AND SELLSCHOP, J. P. F., "Neutrinos from the Atmosphere and Beyond," *Scientific American*, vol. 214, No. 2, p. 40 (1966).

WIGNER, E. P., "Violations of Symmetry in Physics," *Scientific American*, vol. 213, No. 6, p. 28 (1965).

WU, TA-YOU, "Laws of Conservation of Parity and Time Reversal," *American Journal of Physics*, vol. 26, No. 6, p. 568 (1958).

YANG, C. N., "Law of Parity Conservation and Symmetry Laws," *Science*, vol. 127, No. 3298, p. 565 (1958).

Problems

25-1 If the atomic number and the precise atomic mass of a new neutron-rich isotope are known, how may it be predicted whether decay will occur via neutron emission or via β^+ emission?

25-2 Sketch the energy spectrum to be expected for neutrinos emitted during a β-decay process.

25-3 Which, if any, of the following reactions can occur, and what forbids each of the others:
$$p + \bar{p} \rightarrow n + \bar{n}$$
$$n \rightarrow p + e + \nu$$
$$p + p \rightarrow p + \bar{p} + n + n$$
$$e + e \rightarrow \bar{p} + \bar{p}$$

25-4 Which, if any, of the following reactions can occur, and what forbids each of the others:
$$p + \bar{p} \rightarrow n + n$$
$$n \rightarrow p + e$$
$$\bar{p} + \nu \rightarrow \bar{n} + e$$
$$e + \bar{\nu} \rightarrow \gamma$$

25-5 Predict the mode of decay of an antineutron.

25-6 As an alternative mode of decay to β^+ emission, nuclei sometimes capture an electron from the innermost shell of electrons—so-called *K-capture*. Write down the appropriate nuclear reaction equation.

25-7 Neutrons emitted in nuclear reactions have ranges of the order of 10^{-1} m. in solid materials. What range might therefore be expected for the neutrinos from nuclear reactions?

25-8 Ne^{19} has a half-life of 17.7 sec. for the emission of β^+ radiation, and Ne^{23} has a half-life of 40.2 sec. for the emission of β^- radiation. If a large volume of sodium fluoride (NaFl) is subjected to an extremely intense burst of neutrinos produced near a nuclear reactor, then which half-life, if any, might, in theory be detected by a beta counter? Would this experiment be a practical one?

25-9 Is it possible to define *left* and *right* by means of electromagnetic phenomena alone? i.e., without assuming a knowledge of north or south poles, clockwise or anticlockwise motion, etc., or anything that is arbitrary or associated with some chance quirk of nature?

25-10 Draw a *right-handed* clock, the hand of which is rotated by a drum on which is wound a rope supporting a heavy weight. Beside it draw a *left-handed* clock of similar type. Will both clocks measure time equally well? What type of symmetry is this?

26 The fission of atomic nuclei and nuclear reactors

26-1 Nuclear fission

In the course of an experimental investigation of neutron-induced reactions in some of the heaviest elements, Enrico Fermi, in 1934, observed certain puzzling phenomena that were not correctly recognized and understood until 1938 by two other investigators, O. Hahn and F. Strassmann. Fermi and his collaborators found that on exposing uranium to neutrons, artificial radioactive substances were produced, with periods of decay that did not correspond to those of any of the natural radioactive substances, and hence were interpreted by them as being due to elements heavier than uranium—or "trans-uranic" elements—containing additional neutrons and protons. I. Curie and Savitch found that one of the artificial radioactive elements so produced, having a 3.5 hour half-life, appeared to be chemically similar to lanthanum. Hahn and Strassmann showed that certain of the activities observed were actually due to the elements barium, lanthanum, cerium, and krypton. Thus these latter experimenters reached the conclusion that the absorption of a neutron by uranium caused the atomic nucleus of that element to separate into at least two heavy nuclear fragments rather than to emit a single nucleon or alpha particle in accordance with the types of processes that had previously been observed. This was our first recognition of the phenomenon of nuclear fission, which in an amazingly short time, under the impetus of military pressure, was to assume trascendent significance as a weapon of unprecedented power, and which was later to become a source of thermal energy, competitive with the known chemical fuels, and to provide unparalleled stimulus to a wide area of research in the physical and biological sciences.

Having established the novel nature of this phenomenon, analogous to the splitting up of a drop of liquid when set into violent oscillation by some source of energy, its details were intensively investigated and the processes taking place were soon understood. It was found that fission could be brought about in all of the heavy elements by bombardment with photons, neutrons, or protons, and that it even occurred spontaneously—though very rarely—in the case of uranium. Though the nucleus of a heavy element may split into as many as three or four major fragments, the most probable process is that it splits into two parts of slightly unequal mass. Thus, if one plots the fractional yield of the fragment elements resulting from the fission of a heavy element as a function of the mass number, it is found that the curve, as shown in Fig. 26-1, is symmetrical about the value of half the mass number of the original element.

In the case of the absorption of a neutron by uranium (235), the elements produced in an amount greater than one per cent lie between

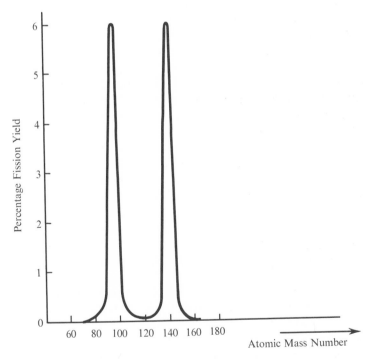

Figure 26-1 U^{235} fission yield.

mass numbers 86 and 106, and between mass numbers 130 and 150, as shown in Fig. 26-1; the sum of the median values 96 and 140 yields the initial mass number 236.

In addition to the major fractions, other nuclear fragments appear during the fission process. A small fraction of fission protons or alpha particles appear, and also 2 or 3 per cent of the available energy is radiated in the form of photons of about 2 M.e.V. The most important of the minor fragments, however, are the neutrons. About 7 per cent of the energy is carried away by so-called "prompt" neutrons which are emitted with an average energy of about 2 M.e.V. apiece, along with the fission process. In addition to these, there are certain "delayed" neutrons—less than one per cent of the prompt neutrons—which are emitted later by the decay of the artificially created radioactive major fragments of the fission process. On the average, about 2.3 neutrons are emitted at each fission; these will be seen to be particularly important from the point of view of the possibility of a self-sustaining, or chain reaction. The small number of delayed neutrons are also important because they facilitate the control of such a chain reaction.

When a nucleus such as uranium 236 undergoes fission, it may be thought of as splitting into two major fragments, which together instantaneously possess 144 neutrons and 92 protons. If these neutrons and protons were divided in just the ratio of 144 to 92, the fragments would lie somewhere on the solid line of Fig. 26-2, joining the point representing uranium 236 with the origin; and, if the ratio differed somewhat between the two fragments, one would lie a little above and the other a little below this line. The dashed line of this figure is drawn through the center of gravity of the observed stable isotopes; so it is seen that the fragments have too few protons for stability, or alternatively are "neutron-rich," compared to stable nuclear configurations. It would be quite reasonable for them to boil off or reject neutrons during the fragmentation process in order to approach the normal, stable ratio. The emission of electrons as beta particles would accomplish the same thing—moving to the right rather than downward in the diagram—and the region of the stable ratio would be approached. However, as we saw in the preceding chapter, electron emission is a much slower process and does not compete effectively with neutron emission. The average number of neutrons emitted per fission is less than would be indicated by the distance between the dashed and solid lines of Fig. 26-2, for there are reasonably stable neutron-rich isotopes that are artificially radioactive above the dashed curve, and any of these resulting from the fission process decay slowly to stable isotopes.

The energy liberated per fission event is very large. The mass of uranium 235 is 235.116 a.m.u., and the mass of the triggering neutron is

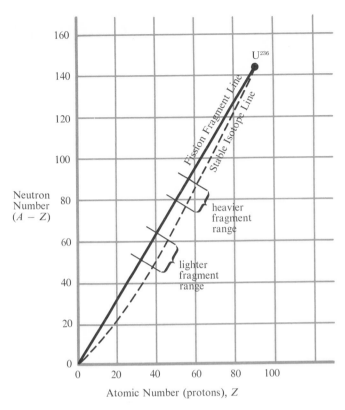

Figure 26-2 *Fission fragment decay toward stable isotope proton-neutron proportion.*

1.009 a.m.u. Assume, e.g., that the immediate products of the fission process are elements with mass numbers in the neighborhood of 96 and 140. The stable elements in this portion of the atomic sequence have masses less than the mass number by about 0.058 a.m.u. Hence the amount of energy in the form of mass eventually disappearing per fission event is the mass excess of the uranium nucleus and neutron plus the mass deficiency of each product nucleus, or $0.116 + 0.009 + 0.116 = 0.241$ a.m.u., or about 220 M.e.V. When the kinetic energies of the immediate major fission fragments are measured directly, it is found that there are two groups of fragments, the lighter with an average energy of about 93.1 M.e.V. and the heavier with an energy of about 61.4 M.e.V., or an average total of 154.5 M.e.V. This is in reasonable agreement with the foregoing figure, when it is recalled that much of the energy goes off in other forms. Measurements of the total energy converted into heat in the uranium sample itself per fission process lead to a value of 177 M.e.V. To this must be added 25 M.e.V. of energy, which is not to be absorbed in the uranium, but is lost by escaping gamma radiation, neutrons and neutrinos., Hence the average total energy liberated per fission event is experimentally found to be approximately equal to that deduced from the measured atomic mass values. This is a very large figure indeed in comparison with other nuclear processes, and corresponds to about 0.1 per cent decrease in the mass of the reacting nuclei.

The triggering of the fission process in heavy nuclei of atomic numbers 90 and above can apparently be induced by the addition of between 5 and 6 M.e.V. of energy, brought to it by an incident particle. The binding energy per nucleon in the neighborhood of atomic numbers 90 and above is found to be about 5.5 M.e.V., so that if an incident nucleon possesses a few additional M.e.V. of kinetic energy, the fission process can always be brought about. As the balance is very close between the fission triggering energy and the simple binding energy, the process might be expected to occur in some instances even when the incident nucleon is moving very slowly. There is a slight tendency to a pairing of nucleons in a nucleus; in a nucleus such as that of uranium ($Z = 92$), or thorium ($Z = 90$), in which there are already even numbers of protons, there is a greater binding energy for a neutron when the mass number A is odd; i.e., when there is initially an odd number of nucleons and an additional one will make an integral number of pairs, than when A is even and there is initially an integral number of pairs. This difference is of the order of 0.5 M.e.V.; hence it would be more likely for U^{235} to undergo fission on the absorption of a slow neutron than it would be for U^{238}. It is found experimentally that the 235 isotope does undergo fission with slow neutrons and that 238 does not.

U^{235} is the only naturally occurring heavy element that fulfills the conditions for fission with slow neutrons. But there are two other isotopes that can be produced artificially by neutron bombardment that have similar properties. The first of these is produced when thorium 232 captures a neutron. The resulting Th^{233} undergoes two successive beta disintegrations, yielding U^{233} as follows:

$$_{90}Th^{232} + {_0}n^1 \rightarrow {_{90}}Th^{233} \rightarrow {_{91}}Pa^{233} + {_{-1}}e^0 + {_0}\bar{\nu}^0$$
$$\searrow {_{92}}U^{233} + {_{-1}}e^0 + {_0}\bar{\nu}^0$$
$$(T = 23 \text{ min.}) \quad (T = 27.4 \text{ days})$$

This resulting isotope of Uranium, having an odd mass number, might be expected to undergo slow neutron fission, and it does. The second is produced when uranium 238 captures a slow neutron, which may be accomplished without producing fission. The resulting U^{239} decays, again with two successive beta emissions, resulting in trans-uranic nuclei that have been given the names neptunium and plutonium for the other planets.

$$_{92}U^{238} + _{0}n^{1} \rightarrow _{92}U^{239} \rightarrow _{93}Np^{239} + _{-1}e^{0} + _{0}\bar{\nu}^{0}$$
$$_{94}Pu^{239} + _{-1}e^{0} + _{0}\bar{\nu}^{0}$$

$(T = 23.5 \text{ min.})$ $(T = 23 \text{ days})$

Again, plutonium (239) might be expected to undergo slow-neutron fission because of the odd number of neutrons in its nucleus; it does also.

Nuclear reactors   26-2

The capacity for fission with slow neutrons is very important because of its bearing upon the possibility of initiating a controllable nuclear chain reaction as a result of which large quantities of energy become available and may be converted into heat, in a practical manner, on a utilitarian scale. In the first place, the likelihood of absorption of a slow neutron subsequent to which fission may take place is found to be proportional to the time spent by a moving neutron in the neighborhood of the nucleus. Thus the absorption probability is inversely proportional to the velocity of the neutron and, if slow neutrons will bring about fission at all, the slower they go, the more effectively this takes place. They can be slowed down by elastic collisions with other nuclei and, since the fractional energy transferred is greater when the colliding masses are nearly equal, light nuclei are preferable to heavy nuclei for this function. This kind of regulation is called *moderating* the neutrons. In the second place, neutrons must be conserved for collisions with fissionable nuclei, and presented with the least opportunity of either passing out of the region occupied by such nuclei or of colliding with nuclei with which they would combine and consequently become unavailable for producing further fissions. Hence favorable conditions are presented by large physical dimensions and compact geometrical arrangements representing large volumes per unit peripheral area through which the neutrons can escape. The structural and moderating materials must also be such that there is minimum likelihood of neutron-induced nuclear reactions with their nuclei. The light elements hydrogen, deuterium, helium, carbon, and oxygen are good moderators; aluminum or stainless steel are suitable as structural materials. Control elements for absorbing excess neutrons when this is desired must have the opposite property, namely, that of reacting with a high probability with slow neutrons; here cadmium is particularly suitable.

Since more energy is released per fission than is necessary to produce a second fission, a chain reaction, wherein each nuclear event on the average sets off one or more succeeding events and the number of reactions per unit time increases exponentially, is possible. On the average, more than one neutron must be generated per fission event and react with another fissionable nucleus in order to bring about an increasing rate of reaction essential to initiate a self-sustaining operation. This condition is known as the *critical threshold*. Any excess of available neutrons must then be controllable so that when the desired rate of reaction, or power level, is reached, it may be maintained by suitable control rod adjustment. The number of neutrons emerging from a U^{235} fission, which is about 2.3, is adequate to permit the construction of power reactors in sizes that are readily achievable. The first such reactor was constructed and operated by the Metallurgical Laboratory of the Manhattan Project in Chicago on December 2, 1942. It was in the form of a cubic stack of graphite blocks, regularly interpenetrated with horizontal natural uranium rods (99.28 per cent U^{238}, 0.72 per cent U^{235}), as illustrated schematically in Fig. 26-3. The structure was

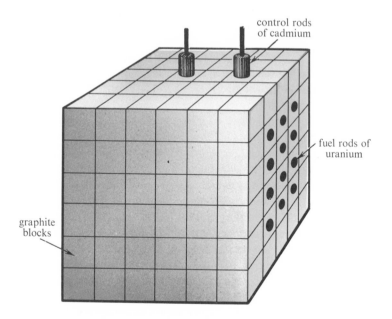

Figure 26-3   *Schematic nuclear reactor.*

some yards on an edge, and a few vertical pipes permitted monitoring and checking the rate of activity. By keeping the reactor "sub-critical" for prompt neutrons alone, the relatively slow buildup of delayed neutrons helped control the reaction. The beginning of the chain reaction was observed by thermocouples throughout the reactor, which registered a rise in temperature when the self-sustaining reaction had been achieved. Reactors of essentially similar pattern with forced ventilation to transfer the heat generated in them have since been used in both experimental and practical power reactors in the United States and in other countries.

Since the first success in 1942, reactors of many different kinds and for many different purposes have been constructed. There are homogeneous reactors in which a uranium salt is dissolved in water and the solution provides the reacting material, the moderator, and also the heat-exchange mechanism. There are heterogeneous reactors in which the nuclear fuel slugs, or rods, and the solid or liquid moderator are arranged in a rigid interpenetrating lattice. Each type employs some method of circulating the homogeneous reactant or a separate cooling fluid for the transfer of the heat generated, either for the purpose of controlling the temperature of the reactor, or for utilizing the heat for the performance of external work.

Reactors may be classified in various ways: (1) in terms of the fuel, which may be natural uranium or uranium enriched in U^{235} by isotope separation; (2) in terms of the moderator, which may, for instance, be graphite, or light or heavy water; (3) in terms of the coolant, which may be a gas such as helium, or a liquid such as water, or a liquid metal; (4) in terms of the power level; (5) in terms of the average range of neutron energies producing fission; etc. They may also be considered in terms of function. One type is the *research reactor* for the study of physical phenomena and the production of artificially radioactive isotopes to be used in research and elsewhere. These are generally made as flexible as possible, with reasonably high neutron fluxes—10^{12} to 10^{14} neutrons per square centimeter per second—over an adequate, but usually small volume and good access arrangements for experimental manipulation. Another type is the *breeder reactor*, which is designed in such a way that the largest possible number of excess neutrons are absorbed by suitably disposed potential fuel units, such as U^{238}, or Th^{232}, so that Pu^{239} or U^{233} may be formed as a by-product for subsequent use as reactor fuel or other purposes. These reactors are large, and it is necessary to supply quantities of cooling water, e.g., from an adjacent river, in order to carry away the enormous amounts of heat that are generated. The third type is the *power reactor*, which is built for efficiency as a heat engine; the rise in temperature is as great as the fuel, coolant, and materials of construction will permit. Such reactors have been constructed for electric power generation and submarine propulsion, with power levels ranging from those characteristic of standard public service steam generating stations down to small marine propulsion plants. It is possible that a combination of power and breeder reactor can be built, which, by suitable disposition of potential fuel as part of the shielding material, may be able both to breed fuel and to generate power economically.

The power nuclear reactor is important for two reasons: the first is that it permits the tapping of a new energy source—namely, that of the nuclei of uranium and thorium—to supplement the present sources of chemical energy from fossil fuels such as coal, oil, and gas, which are subject to depletion in the foreseeable future; the second is the provision of fuel with a very high ratio of energy to mass. Each fission event releases about 200 M.e.V., which is equivalent to 3.20×10^{-11} J. per fissioning atom. A kilogram of U^{235} represents $1/235$ kilomoles and, therefore, contains $N_0/235$, or 2.56×10^{24} atoms, where N_0 is Avogadro's number of 6.025×10^{26} atoms per kilomole. Complete fission of a kilogram of U^{235} would thus liberate 8.37×10^{13} J. Fuel oil when burned provides about 45 J. per gram, so that an equivalent weight of fuel oil would be about 2×10^9 kg. Actually, this is not quite a fair comparison, for not more than about 1 per cent of the uranium would be used up before the fuel would have to be chemically treated, but it is easily seen that there is a factor of the order of 10^7 in the power-to-weight ratio for nuclear fuels in comparison with chemical fuels. Hence, in those locations where the cost of fuel transportation is high, nuclear fuels may offer considerable economic advantage.

There is an additional rather specialized advantage enjoyed by nuclear fuel over chemical fuel, namely, that it generates heat or "burns" without access to atmospheric oxygen. Thus nuclear power plants are relatively more self-contained; in special applications, such as that of submarine propulsion, this can be a distinct advantage. In a submarine the supply of oxygen is limited during submergence and, as military objectives may require very extended periods of submergence, the fact that the nuclear power plant is independent of the ambient oxygen atmosphere is a crucial consideration in its employment.

The power reactor, however, has many technical disadvantages. In the course of the nuclear reaction that takes place, there is an intense emission of neutrons and gamma rays, and screening walls many feet thick of steel and concrete must be erected to protect personnel from the radiation from the reactor. The neutrons, in passing through the structural material of the reactor, displace by collision many of the atoms composing the regular crystalline structure, which is essential to the mechanical properties of these materials. Hence these materials may become brittle, swell, and disintegrate and, because of the complete mechanical failure that eventually may ensue, cease to be able to perform their structural functions. Many of the decay products, or the "ash" of the nuclear reaction, are strong neutron absorbers; by robbing the reactor of neutrons, they eventually reduce the attainable power level. The fuel elements must then be removed and subjected to chemical purification to remove these inhibiting residues and the uranium then recast in suitable form for reincorporation in the reactor. These lengthy and difficult processes must be carried out by remote control behind elaborate shields, because the fission products are intensely radioactive and as dangerous as the operating reactor itself. The half-life of many of the fission products is quite long—varying from several days to several years—and empirically it is found that the activity of the conglomerate decays at a rate that can be represented as depending on the time to the -1.2 power in the interval from about 10 sec. to 10^7 sec., or 100 days. Since the activity of the fission products is very intense, these products constitute a health hazard not only at the time of immediate disposal but for many years afterwards. The problem of waste disposal is one of the most serious problems faced by nuclear engineers in the operation of power reactors.

The fission reactor that has been discussed up to this point is the type that depends upon fission by slow neutrons, in which the rate of release of nuclear energy can be readily controlled by the disposition of slow-neutron absorbing materials in the reactor. Since fission can be brought about in all heavy nuclei, particularly uranium 238, by fast neutrons, it is possible to bring about very fast chain reaction fission processes by the employment of fast neutrons. Though the reactors presently employed for power purposes are of the "slow reactor" type—so called because they employ slow neutrons—"fast reactors"—employing the fast or unmoderated neutrons—are being extensively studied and investigated. It would be necessary to resort to these more hazardous devices for airplane or rocket propulsion because they present certain important advantages in efficiency.

Because the process is such a rapid one, and is more hazardous in common employment, fast neutron fission reactions have so far been primarily used for producing atomic weapons rather than power production. However, as a powerful explosive, it surpasses chemical explosives to about the same degree that uranium 235 exceeds chemical fuels in its power-to-weight ratio. The principal problem in the employment of U^{235} and U^{238} as an explosive is that of maintaining the constituents in a close dense mass for a sufficient time interval to permit the reaction to proceed far enough to produce fission in any considerable fraction of the reactants. For as the reaction proceeds and energy is generated, the temperature and pressure rise with a consequent tendency for the mass to fly apart and destroy the close geometry upon which the fission process depends. The two halves of the mass may be propelled together and may be surrounded by massive tampers of uranium. Other mechanical devices may be employed to maximize the consumption of uranium before the explosive movement proceeds too far. This is the basis of the early fission bombs used in World War II.

26-3 *Applications of reactor technology research*

Undoubtedly one of the most important consequences of the development of nuclear reactors is the impetus that has been given to scientific research. Reactors provide the essential facilities for the study of neutron behavior and neutron induced nuclear reactions. Also, in them may be produced the radioactive isotopes of the medium weight elements that are such valuable tools in a wide range of research enterprises in the physical and biological sciences. Very intense fluxes of neutrons traverse the center of reactors; the study of the physical and biological effects of these have provided very important advances in our knowledge of materials and of living cells. Neutrons may be piped out of the reactor shield, and narrow ranges of velocities may be isolated by mechanical devices similar to the toothed wheel technique for measuring the velocity of light described in Chap. 7. Neutrons with a velocity characteristic of thermal energies at room temperature have appropriate wave lengths for the investigation of crystal structures by diffraction techniques and, as they are scattered by the nuclei rather than by the electron structures as are photons, they contribute important complementary information about solids and liquids.

From the fission products of power reactors, several hundred radioactive isotopes can be separated and made available in many useful ways. These are not all primary products, but the isotopes immediately formed generally decay with beta and gamma emission, successively more slowly, through chains of intermediate products until stable isotopes are reached. This is a movement to the right from the solid line to the region of stability in the earlier figure (Fig. 26-2). Table 26-1 lists certain of the long-lived fission products of high yield. The element technetium

Table 26-1

fission product	yield	half-life	beta energy	gamma energy
$_{38}Sr^{89}$	4.6%	53 d.	1.5 M.e.V.	
$_{38}Sr^{90}$	5.0%	25 y.	0.60	
$_{39}Y^{91}$	5.9%	57 d.	1.53, 0.33	1.2
$_{40}Zr^{95}$	6.4%	65 d.	1.1, 0.90, 0.40 0.36, 0.25	0.75, 0.72
$_{43}Tc^{99}$	6.2%	2.1×10^5 y.	0.3	
$_{54}Xe^{133}$	6.0%	5.3 d.	0.35	0.08
$_{55}Cs^{137}$	6.0%	30 y.	1.2, 0.5	0.7
$_{56}Ba^{140}$	6.1%	13 d.	1.0, 0.4	0.5, 0.3, 0.16
$_{58}Ce^{141}$	6.0%	33 d.	0.58, 0.44	0.03
$_{59}Pr^{143}$	6.0%	14 d.	0.9	0.14

($Z = 43$) listed is one that, for all practical purposes, can be said to have no stable isotope. It was first discovered in 1937 by C. Perrer and E. Segre, in the course of nuclear experiments.

Artificial radioactive isotopes are employed in either of two ways. The radioactivity may itself be the quality desired, as in the case of intense sources that are prepared for industrial, therapeutic, or research purposes. For instance, the stable isotope of the element Cobalt ($_{27}Co^{59}$) may be irradiated by reactor neutrons and the isotope $_{27}Co^{60}$ may be produced. This has a half-life of 5.3 yr. and emits gamma rays of 1.1 and 1.3 M.e.V., as well as beta rays of lower energy. Very intense sources can be produced and can provide a relatively inexpensive substitute for radium in cancer therapy. It has several hundred times the activity per unit weight of radium and the tissue dosage per disintegration is about twice as great. Large sources of Co^{60} can be used to replace high voltage x-ray tubes for both therapy and for the radiography of fabricated metal parts for detecting faults. Small sources in thin metallic tubes or needles may be inserted in living tissue for local therapy.

Certain elements tend to localize in specific parts of the body, as for instance, iodine in the thyroid gland and strontium and calcium in the bones. Radioactive iodine ($_{53}I^{131}$), having a half-life of 8 days, can be given to a patient whose thyroid gland requires radiation treatment and, being specifically localized in the organ, prevents incidental and undesired radiation of other tissues while providing maximum local radiation dosage. A related technique is that which makes use of the magnetic forces that tend to draw certain molecules such as those containing iron into regions of strong magnetic fields. Radioactive iron suspended in some appropriate form in the blood can be concentrated in certain body areas by producing strong fields by the use of current-carrying coils of wire, or by the placement of permanent or electromagnets. Thus the immediately adjacent areas may be exposed to much more intense radiation effects than are other parts of the body.

The other way in which radioactive isotopes are used is one in which the ease of detectability is the primary consideration. The presence of a small sample in the neighborhood of a counter of disintegration events is all that is required to provide a quantitative determination of the amount of the isotopes present. Since very great dilution factors are technically feasible, such isotopes can be used as tracers that are carried along by samples of matter through a variety of chemical reactions or physical processes, and the fraction of the initial atoms entering the process that appear at successive stages or places can be determined. Thus ocean currents or winds in the atmosphere can be studied with respect to both speed and direction by "salting" a particular location with tracer isotopes and observing when and where they later appear. The rate of flow of fluids in pipes and the circulation of the blood can be recorded in the same way. An important application of this nature is the study of wear in metal parts. If some radioactive material is added to the metal of a piston ring, the wear against the cylinder walls results in the rubbing off of the tracer isotopes with the metal itself. Measurements of the radioactive content of the lubricating oil provide the data from which the rate of wear of the piston ring can be determined.

The chemical specificity of tracer isotopes makes them particularly important in the study of chemical and biological processes. If traces of radioactive isotopes are included with the stable isotopes of elements used in the synthesis of chemical compounds, much useful information can be obtained on molecular structure and the particular location in a complex molecule that is occupied by an atom or molecule that is added. Carbon 14 and hydrogen 3 (tritium) are particularly useful in organic chemistry. These tools present the most promising possibility for technical advance in the complex field of biochemistry that has ever been placed in the hands of scientists. The rate of metabolism of calcium and phosphorus can be studied by means of their radioactive isotopes; the functions of such metallic isotopes as iron in the blood can also be studied by this technique.

Radioactive isotopes can be used in such small quantities that they present no danger to health, but the hazard that is presented to plant, animal, and human life by the large scale manufacture of bombs and reactors and by the production and employment of high-level radioactive wastes is very great. Elaborate and painstaking measures are necessary to insure a minimum of danger to life. The details of the biological processes that result from exposure to high-energy photons, electrons, protons, alpha particles, or to neutrons are but very imperfectly understood, though this is a field that is currently the subject of intense study and investigation. It would appear that the basic processes are of two types—the first being the disturbance of the electron structure of atoms and molecules, as in the case of the excitation and ionization produced by the passage of photons and electrons and other charged particles; the second being the displacement or alteration of nuclei produced by proton, alpha particle, neutron, or other heavy particle collisions. It is evident that both types of processes can profoundly alter the complex molecular aggregates upon which the processes of life and growth depend.

A simple, but possibly too crude, measure of the effectiveness of radiations on biological processes is the number of free electrons or positive ions that is produced by their passage through matter. Biological exposure to radiation and the damage thus caused is commonly measured by the *roentgen* for photons, or the *rep* (roentgen equivalent, physical) for any other type of radiation. This is the amount of radiation that on absorption by tissue liberates about 0.01 J. of energy per kilogram. On the average, the energy expended per unit ionizing event in matter is about 32.5 e.V., or 5.2×10^{-18} J. Hence one rep corresponds to the formation of about 2×10^{15} ion pairs per kilogram of tissue, or about 2 ion pairs per cubic micron.

It is not entirely clear to us whether all radiation damage is cumulative or not. Cells undoubtedly have some recuperative powers, and if the damage does not involve the chromosomes or other critical growth mechanisms, the impairment of function may be transient and recovery of the cell complete. Even in the case of particularly sensitive cell mechanisms, such as the genes in the chromosomes, there may be some very low-level threshold below which the damage is self-reparable, though this is by no means sure. It does appear, however, that dense ionization or nuclear impacts are more damaging per rep than is the relatively more sparse ionization per unit path length associate with the passage of photons and electrons. Thus the relative biological effectiveness (*R.B.E.*) of different radiations is currently thought to be given by the following numbers:

Relative Biological Effectiveness (*R.B.E.*)

x or gamma photons or beta particles 1	Fast neutrons or protons 10
Neutrons (slow) 5	Alpha particles 20

From this table it is seen that for the same total ionization the biological damage caused by a fast neutron is thought to be 10 times as great, and hence the permissable dosage in reps is one-tenth as great as for a photon. Hence the measure of radiation from the point of view of damage to life, in particular to man, is the *rem*, (roentgen equivalent, man) where the rem = 1 rep $\times$ R.B.E.

Any radiation is biologically damaging, and to be avoided, but there is a certain background of radiation that is of necessity accepted. The common exposure due to cosmic rays (Chap. 27) and natural radioactivity is about 0.1 rem/year, but inhabitants of high altitude areas, such as the Andes or the Himalayas receive at least 10 times this dose, and dwellers on the radioactive monozite sands of Travancore in India receive as much as 50 times this dose. There is a small inhabited island off the coast of New Zealand where even this radiation level may be exceeded. The frequency of genetic defects among these populations does not seem to be in proportion to the gonadal rem dosage. This supports the hypothesis that such defects are not determined entirely by the level of ionizing radiation. Indeed we know that there are other circumstances that influence genetic mutations, such as chemical environment and temperature, and we must learn much more about the conditions determining normal or abnormal cell growth before we are in a position to assess the particular role of radiation with assurance. The probable gonadal dose due to diagnostic and therapeutic x-ray exposure of the average person during his life is of the order of 5 rem. As indicated above, the safe quantity of radiation from the point of view of genetics, where the effects of successive generations are cumulative, is not known. However, this is currently taken as about 10 rem for the general population, and from 50 to 100 rem for people who must work with radiation.

Workers in the neighborhood of reactors are currently considered to be safe if their weekly dosage is less than 0.3 rem, and the accepted safety standards in force for such workers and the general population are probably conservative as far as individual health is concerned, though there is some question about their propriety in the matter of an ultimate genetic effect. The tendency for certain isotopes to be concentrated in biological processes necessitates special consideration; thus the radioactive strontium from fission bomb fall-out concentrates in animal bony structure, and is one of the chief hazards from this source. Quite large therapeutic doses of x-radiation can be tolerated locally, but the potential damage must always be weighed in considering radiation therapy. An overall body dose of 500 rem at one time results in a 50 per cent fatality in man.

Further reading:

Articles on Ionizing Radiation, *Scientific American*, vol. 201, No. 3 (1959).

GHIORSO, A. AND SEABORG, G. T., "The Newest Synthetic Elements," *Scientific American*, vol. 195, No. 6, p. 66 (1956).

HUGHES, D. J., "The Reactor as a Research Instrument," *Scientific American*, vol. 189, No. 2, p. 82 (1953).

LIBBY, W. F., "Tritium in Nature," *Scientific American*, vol. 190, No. 4, p. 38 (1954).

ROCHLIN, R. S., "Radioisotopes Take on a Bigger Role in Industry," *General Electric Review*, vol. 60, p. 39 (Nov., 1957).

SEABORG, G. T., "The Man-Made Chemical Elements Beyond Uranium," *Physics Today*, vol. 15, No. 8, p. 19 (1962).

WEINBERG, A. M., "Breeder Reactors," *Scientific American*, vol. 202, No. 1, p. 82 (1960).

WEINBERG, A. M., "Energy as an Ultimate Raw Material," *Physics Today*, vol. 12, No. 11, p. 18 (1959).

WEINBERG, A. M., "Power Reactors," *Scientific American*, vol. 191, No. 6, p. 33 (1954).

Problems

26-1 The fission yield curve of Fig. 26-1 is symmetrical about the median atomic mass number. Is this to be expected? Why?

26-2 The stable isotopes for atomic numbers 15 through 21 are: $_{15}P^{31}$, $_{16}S^{32}$, $_{16}S^{33}$, $_{16}S^{34}$, $_{16}S^{36}$, $_{17}Cl^{35}$, $_{17}Cl^{37}$, $_{18}A^{36}$, $_{18}A^{38}$, $_{18}A^{40}$, $_{19}K^{39}$, $_{19}K^{41}$, $_{20}Ca^{40}$, $_{20}Ca^{42}$, $_{20}Ca^{43}$, $_{20}Ca^{44}$, $_{20}Ca^{46}$, $_{20}Ca^{48}$, $_{21}Sc^{45}$. What is most remarkable about this series, and what is the explanation?

26-3 The amount by which an isotope's atomic mass M exceeds its mass number A is known as its *mass excess* (M-A). The mass excesses for U^{235}, U^{236}, U^{238}, U^{239}, and the neutron are 110.71, 111.70, 115.42, 118.26, and

8.37 M.e.V. respectively. Calculate the binding energy of the last neutron in U^{236} and U^{239}, and show that the difference is 1.85 M.e.V.

26-4 What fraction of its energy is lost by a neutron in a head-on collision with a carbon atom?

26-5 If 177 M.e.V. of energy is obtained from the fission of one uranium atom of mass 233.03 mass units, how much energy may be obtained from the fission of 10 per cent of a 1 kg. lump of uranium 233?

26-6 If 10 per cent of the neutrons escape from a cubic reactor 1 m. on a side, how many will escape from a similar reactor 2 m. on a side?

26-7 Deuterium is heavier and more expensive than hydrogen. What possible advantage could it have as a moderating material? What is the ratio of energy losses by a neutron in a head-on collision with a deuterium atom and with a hydrogen atom?

26-8 Where is most of the heat generated in a reactor of the type depicted in the text?

26-9 If the neutron gain per fission event is 0.1 after allowing for all modes of loss in a reactor, how many generations are needed to double the number of free neutrons?

26-10 Assume the background exposure to radiation from cosmic rays and natural radioactivity is about 0.1 rem/year, that the average value of the R.B.E. for this radiation is 5, and that the human body weighs approximately 100 kg. How many Joules of energy are absorbed by the body over a period of 50 years exposure to this radiation? How many ion pairs are created. A concentrated dose of 500 rem results in a 50 per cent fatality rate. How many Joules does this represent on the same assumptions? Compare this to the energy dissipated (mostly in the form of heat) by the filament of a 100 Watt light bulb, which burns for 1 sec.

Nuclear fusion reactions and cosmic rays

27

Energetics of chemical or nuclear fusion reactions
27-1

It was seen in the preceding chapter that fission reactions release energy by the production of nuclei near the center of the mass number range, at the expense of heavy nuclei that are more massive per nucleon. However, Fig. 23-2 shows that reactions in which the lighter elements, in particular hydrogen, may be combined together to produce medium-weight nuclei would be exothermic and liberate energy as well. The fission reaction in certain heavy elements of odd mass number may be triggered by a slow neutron analogous to the triggering of a chemical explosive by a slight shock or jar. The reactions between light nuclei on the other hand are analogous to ordinary chemical reactions in which a certain minimum kinetic energy of the participants is frequently necessary to overcome an energy barrier that prevents the reaction from taking place at an ordinary low-speed encounter. When the reacting particles, however, possess this minimum energy, they may adhere or combine and more energy may be released in the kinetic form as a result of this combination than was present initially (Fig. 27-1). In such cases there is a close analogy with the burning of chemical fuels. The energy liberated by the first few particles reacting is partially converted by collision interactions into kinetic energy of other particles in their neighborhood, thus imparting to them the enhanced ability to

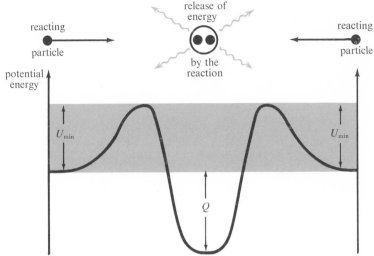

Participants must have a minimum kinetic energy U_{min} in order to surmount the barrier and produce a reaction. Extra energy Q is released as a result of the reaction.

Figure 27-1 *Schematic potential energy curve as a function of distance of approach for a chemical or fusion reaction.*

react in turn. The process thus continues in a self-sustaining manner and at a rate determined by the energy balance, which is the ratio of the amount of energy that remains among the reactants raising the temperature and pressure to the amount lost to the reactants in the form of energy radiated away or used to perform external work.

27-2   *Nuclear fusion reactions*

Thus, if appropriate conditions can be brought about, it is possible for light nuclei to combine in a continuing, self-perpetuating reaction capable of transforming mass energy into other forms such as radiation, and even to generate electric power directly, as in the case of the chemical reactions taking place in electric cells. Such nuclear reactions are referred to as *fusion reactions*.

At the present time scientists are investigating techniques for harnessing and controlling these fusion reactions. If they are successful we will have available a limitless source of power for the production of electricity.

The energy liberated per unit mass of light nuclear fuel is very large in comparison with chemical reactions, just as it is in the case of heavy nuclear fuel or fission reactions. Also the energy barrier that must be overcome by the reactants before they adhere or combine is much larger than for chemical reactants. Because of this, the velocities of the particles must be very high, corresponding to relatively enormous temperatures. This increases the importance of the efficient communication of energy from the reaction products to the fuel particles to bring them up to reacting velocities. It imposes much higher temperature and pressure conditions for the reaction equilibrium and the containment of the reaction for the controlled generation of electric power. These conditions have not yet been met.

Techniques for the controlled employment of fusion reactions for the generation of electric power are currently under active investigation in many laboratories and countries. In contrast to temperatures of a few hundred or a few thousand degrees absolute, necessary to maintain chemical reactions, temperatures of many millions of degrees absolute appear to be required for sustaining nuclear fusion reactions. This is because the entire energy scale for nuclear reactions is of the order of a million times the chemical reaction energy scale. Clearly no ordinary solid materials can contain reactants at such temperatures as these, for any known material would instantly vaporize. It appears that an intense magnetic field is the most promising arena for containing high energy particles reacting together. Particles moving among others at such energies are largely stripped of their electrons, and hence, being electrically charged, they describe helices about the direction of a magnetic field (Sect. 11-3). It may readily be shown that positive and negative charges moving in a cylindrical volume in which the intensity of the magnetic field increases toward the boundaries tend to be confined to the neighborhood of the axis. Similarly, increasing intensities of the magnetic field near the ends of such a region can also tend to confine the ions to the central portion, as if they were in a magnetic cage or bottle (Fig. 27-2).

High enough energies to initiate the fission reaction can be imparted by electromagnetic means to the ions of the reactant substances. Some of the kinetic energy will, of course, be lost by radiation during the resulting acceleration. If we are able to devise suitable configurations of restraining magnetic fields to maintain them in sufficiently close proximity and at sufficiently high energies, the nuclear fusion reactions should be induced. It is also possible that some of the kinetic energy produced by the reaction may, by suitable geometrical dispositions, be converted directly into electromagnetic energy, removing the limitations that would be imposed by requiring a separate heat engine. As

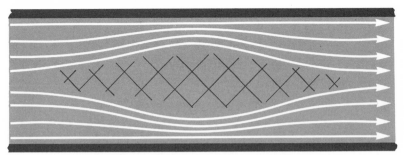

Arrows represent the direction of the magnetic field.

Central region $\times\times\times$ represents the confined ion plasma.

Figure 27-2 *Strong magnetic fields may be designed that tend to confine ions in a spatial region.*

yet, however, a self-sustaining reaction of this type has not been achieved, because the electrodynamic problems inherent in constraining large numbers of rapidly moving charged particles with their associated electromagnetic fields have not yet been solved. Thus, though fusion energy or the "burning of water" is theoretically possible, much experimental effort lies ahead before controlled power will be available from this source.

Nuclear explosions involving hydrogen and possibly other light elements can be brought about if they are triggered by a fission reaction. Such devices utilize the containment furnished by the inertia of a tamping envelope and the mass of the reactants themselves, i.e., since the reaction takes place very rapidly, a transient equilibrium of temperature and pressure can be brought about during the time in which the reactants are held in proximity by the inertia of the containing masses, which permits a considerable fraction of the light element fuel to participate in the nuclear reaction. If the principal constituent is deuterium ($_1H^2$), the reactions can be written as follows:

$$_1H^2 + {}_1H^2 \rightarrow {}_1H^3 + {}_1H^1 + 4 \text{ M.e.V.}$$

and

$$_1H^2 + {}_1H^3 \rightarrow {}_2He^4 + {}_0n^1 + 17.6 \text{ M.e.V.}$$

or

$$_1H^2 + {}_1H^2 \rightarrow {}_2He^3 + {}_0n^1 + 3.25 \text{ M.e.V.}$$

and

$$_1H^2 + {}_2He^3 \rightarrow {}_2He^4 + {}_1H^1 + 18.3 \text{ M.e.V.}$$

Each of these possibilities yields an energy of about 21.6 M.e.V., and each is about equally probable. The energy in Joules per unit mass of deuterium consumed is found by multiplying this quantity by the electronic charge, e, and Avogadro's number, N, and dividing by the mass of the number of kilomoles of molecular deuterium participating, which is 6 kg. This quantity is then: $(21.6 \times 10^6)(Ne)/(3 \times 2) = 34.6 \times 10^{13}$ J. per kg., which is about four times the energy per unit mass obtainable from the fission of uranium. Thus, though there may be greater difficulty in holding the reactants together to bring about as great a fraction of fuel consumption, as in the case of a fission explosion, the energy inherently available is somewhat greater, and it has been demonstrated that the requisite conditions are achievable. It is important to note that the reaction products, $_1He^4$, $_1H^1$, and $_0n^1$ differ in character from the products of fission explosions. The neutrons react quickly with common elements, producing less subsequent radioactivity than in the case of fission. The other products are permanent, so the health hazards accompanying the products of fusion are very much less. Also the primary reactants, being hydrogen rather than uranium, are naturally more abundant, readily available, and cheaper.

Fusion as the source of stellar energy   27-3

On the scale of astral events, the small but always attractive force of gravity provides a gravitational bottle to contain fusion reactions, though on the smaller terrestrial scale, we are unable to use this force for that purpose. The greater part of the energy radiated away into space by intensely hot stars such as our sun is derived from the fusion processes taking place in them. About 90 per cent of the material of our universe is hydrogen; the hydrogen line spectrum is most prominent in all stellar spectra, and interstellar space contains a few atoms of hydrogen per cubic centimeter, as shown by the absorption of the 21 cm. radio wave length mentioned in Sect. 15-5. The next most abundant element cosmically is helium, which is present to about 9 per cent. The balance, of the order of 1 per cent, consists of all the other chemical elements, metals, non-metals, and gases, such as oxygen, nitrogen, neon, etc. The elements found on the surface of the earth are not representative of the universe, because the earth's gravitational field is inadequate to hold light gases such as hydrogen and helium in its atmosphere. At the high temperatures that were characteristic of our planet at the time when it separated from the sun, the thermal velocities of these light gases far exceeded the velocity of escape from the earth, as explained in Sect. 18-4. In consequence, the materials constituting the earth are representative of the heavier elements making up the 1 per cent of the cosmic distribution, namely, iron and its associated elements, which form the dense molten core of the earth, and the lighter elements such as silicon, oxygen, calcium, and magnesium, which predominate in the solid crust that is somewhat less than half the earth's radius in thickness.

It would appear that a star such as our sun is formed when there is a local condensation of interstellar matter, which, as it shrinks together, gains kinetic energy at the expense of gravitational energy. The addition of a thin shell of matter of mass dm to a sphere of mass m and radius r, from such a remote distance that the reciprocal of r is negligible, liberates an amount of gravitational energy equal to $Gm\,dm/r$. The ultimate sphere built up in this way would not be of uniform density, because of the variation of the internal forces; but to a first approximation, a uniform density can be assumed, and if this is written ρ, the mass of the sphere is given by $m = \frac{4}{3}\pi\rho r^3$, and the mass of the spherical shell by $dm = 4\pi\rho r^2\,dr$ (Fig. 27-3). Expressing the gravitational energy liberated by the accretion of the shell dm in terms of r rather than m, the change in energy becomes:

$$\frac{16\pi^2}{3}\,G\rho^2 r^4\,dr$$

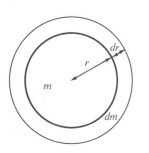

Figure 27-3 *Illustrative diagram of a shrinking gravitating mass.*

The coefficient of dr is the rate of addition of energy with r, and hence by the formula for the sum of the rates given in Sect. 2-5, the total energy represented by the agglomeration of previously widely dispersed particles into the sphere is $\frac{16}{15}\pi^2 G\rho^2 r^5$, or $\frac{3}{5}Gm^2/r$. Thus, as a sphere shrinks, retaining a constant amount of matter, the energy increases as r decreases and the temperature, which is a measure of the gravitational potential energy converted to the kinetic form, rises. The average velocity of the atomic nuclei reaches a point where the barrier to nuclear reactions is surmounted by the fastest particles, and nuclear energy of fusion is generated in the mass. The equilibrium of temperature, pressure, and size is determined by the rate of energy loss from the surface, the rates of generation of energy by gravitational contraction, and the occurrence of the nuclear reactions. The time scale of the process is a very long one, and the masses involved are, of course, very large. But the rate of generation of energy per unit volume is not great by our terrestrial standards, and the gravitational forces hold the reacting mass together against the kinetic and radiation pressures generated within.

The reactions taking place are principally those that build medium-weight atoms out of hydrogen and helium. Deuterium is formed from hydrogen by the reaction

$$_1H^1 + {}_1H^1 \rightarrow {}_1H^2 + {}_1e^0 + {}_0\nu^0 + 2.2 \text{ M.e.V.}$$

The neutrino escapes, in general, from the star; the deuterium combines in accordance with the fusion processes described earlier, leading to a net equation for the formation of helium from hydrogen of the following form:

$$4_1H^1 \rightarrow {}_2He^4 + 2_1e^0 + 2_0\nu^0 + 26.7 \text{ M.e.V.}$$

About 0.5 M.e.V. is carried away by the neutrinos, and the rest, including that from the recombination of positrons and extra-nuclear electrons, contributes to the energy balance. As seen from the masses in Table 23-1 the helium nuclei consisting of paired protons and neutrons have particularly large binding energies and are very stable. These form the building blocks for heavier elements; two combine to give Be^8 which, though it is unstable, stays together on the average long enough to combine with another helium nucleus to form C^{12}, which in turn can be attacked by another helium nucleus to form O^{16}, etc.

Certain of these elements, such as C^{12}, Ne^{20}, Mg^{24}, and Si^{28} can in turn undergo cyclic processes upon impact by protons, which, in total, yield again the production of helium from hydrogen. As an example:

$${}_6C^{12} + {}_1H^1 \rightarrow {}_7N^{13} \rightarrow {}_6C^{13} + {}_1e^0 + {}_0\nu^0$$
$$\downarrow$$
$$\text{photon}$$

$${}_6C^{13} + {}_1H^1 \rightarrow {}_7N^{14}$$
$$\downarrow$$
$$\text{photon}$$

$${}_7N^{14} + {}_1H^1 \rightarrow {}_8O^{15} \rightarrow {}_7N^{15} + {}_1e^0 + {}_0\nu^0$$
$$\downarrow$$
$$\text{photon}$$

$${}_7N^{15} + {}_1H^1 \rightarrow {}_8O^{16} \text{ either} \rightarrow {}_8O^{16} + \text{photon}$$
$$\text{or} \rightarrow {}_6C^{12} + {}_2He^4$$

In each case, the photon emission accompanies the decay of a nucleus to its unexcited state. In general, as for N^{13} and O^{15}, this will precede beta decay because the Dirac or electromagnetic interaction is stronger than the Fermi or "weak" interaction. N^{14} is stable. O^{16} is also stable when unexcited, but it is formed with sufficient energy to emit an alpha particle. Since the internucleon force is a "strong" interaction, it takes precedence over the electromagnetic interaction, and alpha particle emission is the more probable one. In this case, carbon is present at the beginning and the end, and acts essentially as a catalyst for the reaction previously stated in which four hydrogen atoms combine to form one atom of helium. In consequence, the total energy liberated is the same amount as that given earlier, about 5.5 M.e.V. appearing largely in association with the beta and gamma radiation. In the first alternative, which is the less likely one, an oxygen atom is formed from a carbon atom and four hydrogen atoms; as can be seen by referring to the mass values, about 7 M.e.V. more energy is released. About 12.2 M.e.V. is associated largely with the accompanying beta and gamma radiation. Cyclic processes, such as that first described, build up atoms whose nuclei are integral multiples of the neutron-proton constitution of the helium nucleus, and hence may be thought of as "helium-burning" processes. A variety of less probable processes involving the emission and absorption of neutrons and protons build up the other stable isotopes of these elements as well as the nuclei of the intervening elements in the atomic sequence.

The ultimate fate of the star depends upon many factors, one of which is the extent to which the stellar material is well-mixed, and the reactions proceed in a continuous fashion to their ultimate conclusion. More frequently than not, the mixing is apparently incomplete, and large local concentrations of hydrogen and helium lead to conditions in which the mass explodes or expands rapidly against gravitational forces, leading to cooling and greater mixing, after which the mass again contracts and the reactions are induced as before. Much of the hydrogen is apparently consumed by the time this phase of violent fluctuation in volume is reached. During the second stage of contraction, the principal reactions taking place are of the helium-burning type, such as:

$$C^{12} + He^4 \rightarrow O^{16} + \text{photons} \quad \text{and} \quad O^{16} + He^4 \rightarrow Ne^{20} + \text{photons}$$

27-4 *Cosmic rays*

In view of the foregoing account of the processes taking place in our sun and the stars, it is not surprising that the products of combustion from these celestial furnaces in the form of nucleons, pions, electrons, and photons should impinge in some quantity upon our atmosphere and the surface of the earth. Photons in and near the visible range have, of course, always been known to come from both the sun and the stars, but the presence of high-energy particles was not appreciated until the techniques of photography, ionization chambers, and particle counters were evolved and employed in the early studies of radioactivity. Early continental experimenters during the second decade of this century, such as A. Gockel, V. F. Hess and W. Kolhorster, sent ionization chambers up in balloons to heights of several miles and found the intensity of ambient ionization to be many times that at the surface of the earth. R. A. Millikan and I. S. Bowen performed similar experiments in the United States, and also measured the intensity of ionization deep in mountain lakes, finding that the particles producing this ionization were capable of traversing many meters of water. Ever since these early observations, the study of *cosmic rays*, as they are called, has attracted the talents of some of the ablest physicists. Their work has contributed significantly to the growing body of knowledge of high-energy processes.

Except for this radiation, identifiable as coming from the sun, cosmic rays were found to impinge upon the earth's atmosphere with approximately equal intensities from all directions. In total magnitude of energy flow, they approximate the photon intensity of starlight. It was found that the intensity of this radiation as observed near the surface of the earth varied not only with the amount of absorbing material above the recording apparatus, but also with latitude, or more precisely with magnetic latitude relative to the direction of the major axis of the earth's magnetic field. The radiation was found to be more intense at the earth's magnetic poles, as would be the case if at least some of the radiation was in the form of incoming charged particles that would suffer little deflection when moving parallel to the earth's magnetic field, but would be bent into tortuous helix-like trajectories if approaching across the earth's magnetic field. Some of these curves followed by the more energetic particles have such large radii of curvature that they meet the earth's surface in spite of their deflection, but others with less momentum pursue spiraling paths high in the atmosphere and are never recorded at the surface. Thus one component of cosmic radiation has been identified with charged particles and measures of their momenta have been provided. Such studies have helped us determine that the radiation reaching us from outer space has, in addition to a neutral component of photons and neutrons, a charged component of electrons and atomic nuclei. These types of nuclei are representative of the elemental composition of the universe, namely, about 90 per cent protons, about 9 per cent helium or alpha particles, and about 1 per cent of all of the heavier elements. Their energies range from about 10^{10} to 10^{20} e.V.

This at first sight appears to be a surprisingly high energy range, for it exceeds that which could be derived from a nuclear reaction. The mass energy of a unit of atomic weight, or approximately the mass energy of a proton or a neutron, is 9.31×10^8 e.V., and the total conversion of the mass of a uranium atom into kinetic energy would yield only 238 times this quantity, or 2.21×10^{11} e.V., which is about the lower limit of cosmic ray energies. We know of only two forms of interaction to supplement this energy source that are effective over large distances. These are the gravitational and electromagnetic ones. The first is quite inadequate, but the second offers reasonable possibilities. The motion of great cosmic clouds of ionized atoms, equivalent to cosmic electric currents powered by nuclear and gravitational energy, produce changing magnetic fields and magnetic potentials A. As was seen in Sect. 11-3, electromotive forces equal to dA/dt, which can accelerate ions, appear when A changes with the time, and the average value of A and the related magnetic field produces curved or tortuous paths that can tend to confine the particles at least to within our galaxy, or the "milky way."

The relatively low intensity of cosmic radiation was a handicap in presenting a sufficient number of instances of typical high-energy phenomena to expand our understanding of them at any considerable rate; it was not until devices were built that could produce high-energy events in considerable quantity, and also until the theory of the interactions between elementary particles had made some progress, that our understanding advanced more rapidly.

However, certain types of processes were first observed and appreciated in the course of cosmic ray investigations. These presented many novel forms of great interest. The principal form of energy loss is through the electromagnetic interaction between the charged particles and the electrons of the atoms of the earth's atmosphere which they first encounter. At these extreme relativistic energies, the effective mass or inertia of an electron is very great, and it can receive in an elastic collision a large fraction of the energy of the incoming particle. It then, on being projected forward, radiates photons—again largely in the forward direction, because of the great momentum involved—and these successive electrons and photons multiply by radiation and pair production in a cascading process called an *avalanche* or *shower*. The cosmic-ray particles thus dissipate their 10^{10} to 10^{20} e.V. of energy in billions of subsidiary particles largely in the forward direction, in accordance with the conservation of momentum (Fig. 27-4). These spectacular events can be observed with counters and cloud chambers, and from the magnitude of the shower, the initial energy of the cosmic-ray particle can be inferred. The number of ion pairs produced per unit volume per unit time near the surface of the earth due to such processes is of the order of 1 cm.$^{-3}$ sec.$^{-1}$. This number increases by a large factor at great heights, since most showers dissipate their energy before reaching the surface. Of course at still greater heights near the top of the atmosphere, the number of ions per unit volume decreases due to the smaller number of atoms or molecules that are present.

Cosmic-ray particles can also lose their energy in direct nuclear impacts. The collision of such a particle with a heavy nucleus is a very spectacular event, for the nucleus flies apart in scores of particles; the process is observed as a many-spined star in photographic emulsions. A typical example of such an event is shown in Plate 2. In addition

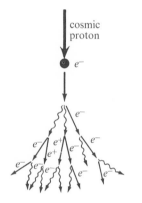

Figure 27-4 *Schematic cosmic ray shower.*

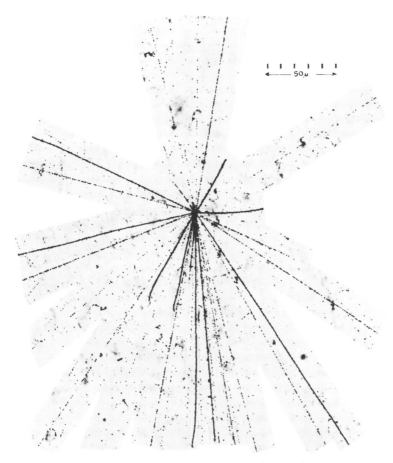

Plate 2 *Cosmic ray star: disintegration of a silver or bromine atom in a nuclear emulsion by an incoming proton of energy 3×10^{10} e.V. shown entering at the top of the photograph. The tracks radiating from the center where the nuclear disintegration took place are shower particles, mostly pions. (From The Study of Elementary Particles by the Photographic Method by C. F. Powell, P. H. Fowler, and D. H. Perkins. Pergamon Press, London, 1959.)*

to these events, the cosmic-ray particles and their high-energy secondaries were found to produce a large family of hitherto unknown particles on their way to the final depletion of their energy in the form of photons, which are ultimately absorbed in ordinary atomic excitation and ionization. The characteristics of certain of these particles were determined by measuring their momenta and energies and noting the type of processes in which they participate.

It was in the study of cosmic rays that the pions, which account for nuclear binding energies, were first encountered. These particles with zero spin come, as we have seen, in three varieties; the positive and negative ones have masses of 273.2 electron masses, and the neutral ones have a mass equal to 264.2 times the electron rest mass. In the course of these studies it was first found that charged pions decay with a half-life of about 2×10^{-8} sec. into other lighter particles with the pion's charge and masses of 206.7 times the electron's rest mass. These particles have been called *muons*. They are closely related to electrons in having spins of $h/4\pi$, and they are accompanied by their own neutrinos, which are distinct from the electron neutrinos. The process is of the Fermi type, with a conservation law of leptons just as in the case of beta decay. Infrequently, the charged pion may decay directly into an electron and electron-neutrino without passing through the intermediate muon stage. The muons decay into electrons with their characteristic neutrinos by the Fermi process with a half-life of about 2.2×10^{-6} sec. The neutral pion, which is lighter than the charged pions, decays into two gamma ray photons, somewhat analogous to the positron-electron decay. The half-life for this process is about 2×10^{-16} sec. It was in the study of the highest energy cosmic ray events that still other heavier particles were observed, but our present understanding of these events has been so much more rapidly expanded through the use of devices for accelerating charged particles to great energies that a systematic account of them will be reserved until the following chapter.

Further reading:

BURBIDGE, G., "The Origin of Cosmic Rays," *Scientific American*, vol. 215, No. 2, p. 32 (1966).

GAMOW, G., "Modern Cosmology," *Scientific American*, vol. 190, No. 3, p. 54 (1954).

ROBERTS, W. C., "Corpuscles From the Sun," *Scientific American*, vol. 192, No. 2, p. 40 (1955).

SANELAGE, A., "The Birth and Death of a Star," *American Journal of Physics*, vol. 25, No. 8, p. 525 (1957).

LILLEY, A. E., "The Absorption of Radio Waves in Space," *Scientific American*, vol. 197, No. 1, p. 48 (1957).

KORF, S. A., "The Origin and Implications of the Cosmic Radiation," *American Scientist*, vol. 45, No. 4, p. 281 (1957).

MARSHAK, R. E., "Pions," *Scientific American*, vol. 196, No. 1, p. 84 (1957).

Park, D., "Recent Advances in Physics," *American Journal of Physics*, vol. 26, No. 3, p. 210 (1958).

Burbidge, G. and M., "Formation of Elements in the Stars," *Science*, vol. 128, No. 3321, p. 387 (1958).

Spitzer, L., Jr., "The Stellarator," *Scientific American*, vol. 199, No. 4, p. 28 (1958).

Rossi, B., "High Energy Cosmic Rays," *Scientific American*, vol. 201, No. 5, p. 134 (1959).

Van Allen, J. A., "Radiation Belts Around the Earth," *Scientific American*, vol. 200, No. 3, p. 39 (1959).

Huang, S., "Life Outside the Solar System," *Scientific American*, vol. 202, No. 4, p. 55 (1960).

Thomson, G. P., "Thermonuclear Reactions," *American Journal of Physics*, vol. 28, No. 3, p. 221 (1960).

Scarsi, L., "Cosmic Radiation," *American Journal of Physics*, vol. 28, p. 213 (1960).

Greenstein, J. L., "Stellar Evolution and the Origin of the Chemical Elements." *American Scientist*, vol. 49, No. 4, p. 449 (1961).

Chiu, H. Y., "Gravitational Collapse," *Physics Today*, vol. 17, No. 5, p. 21, (1964).

Fowler, W. A., "Nuclear Clues to the Early History of the Solar System," *Science*, vol. 135, No. 3508, p. 1037 (1962).

Hafner, E. M., "Cosmic Electromagnetic Radiation," *Science*, vol. 145, No. 3638, p. 1263 (1964).

Hughes, V. W., "The Muonium Atom," *Scientific American*, vol. 214, No. 4, p. 93 (1966).

Lederman, L. M., "The Two Neutrino Experiment," *Scientific American*, vol. 208, No. 3, p. 60 (1963).

Penman, S., "The Muon," *Scientific American*, vol. 205, No. 1, p. 46 (1961).

Problems

27-1 How many M.e.V. are released in the fusion of 3 atoms of He^4 to form 1 atom of C^{12}?

27-2 Obtain a rough estimate of the temperature needed to excite the fusion reaction by assuming that the charged constituents of the two reacting deuterons have to approach within a distance d of one another, where d is the diameter of a helium nucleus. Assume that each deuteron has the average kinetic energy of its surroundings and use the formula from Chap. 23 to calculate the radius of the helium nucleus.

27-3   How many neutrinos are produced by the fusion of 1 kg. of hydrogen to form deuterium?

27-4   How many Joules are released by the fusion of 1 kg. of H^1 to form He^4? The sun radiates 4×10^{26} J. per sec. What is the rate of hydrogen consumption if the above process is the main source of energy?

27-5   How many solar neutrinos are emitted per second, and how much radiation do they carry off, if the total rate of energy output by the sun is 4×10^{26} J. per sec., produced mainly in the formation of He^4 from H^1?

27-6   What kinetic energy would a neutron have after being attracted to the earth from a great distance by the earth's gravitational field? To what temperature would this correspond?

27-7   From the data given in Problem 27-5, calculate the total solar power incident on the earth. How many solar neutrinos strike the earth every second?

27-8   Why is there a critical mass for fission but not for fusion?

27-9   What is the velocity of a proton of energy 10^{20} e.V.? How long would such a proton take to orbit around the circumference of our galaxy of diameter 60,000 *light years*? Approximately how long would it take for a proton of twice the above energy? A light year is the distance travelled by light in the period of a year.

27-10   How strong a magnetic field would be required to contain each of the above protons in such a limiting orbit?

High-energy particle events

28

Particle accelerators   28-1

During the first third of the present century, cosmic rays and radioactive phenomena provided physicists with their only opportunity to study particles possessing energies in the range of millions of electron Volts. One of the difficulties encountered during this period was the weakness of the available sources of such particles. It is difficult to isolate natural radioactive sources that emit large amounts of alpha, beta, or gamma rays, and cosmic ray events provided only a relatively sparse source of data to early observational methods. Another impediment to rapid progress was the complete novelty of most of the aspects of the phenomena encountered. This necessitated a break in traditional patterns of thought, the evolution of new concepts, and the discovery of new laws governing the reactions observed. All of these required thorough reevaluation before new and fruitful methods of experimentation could be designed. It was evident from the outset, however, that a rapid advance in this fascinating and puzzling frontier of knowledge would require two types of technical progress. The first would be greater flexibility and precision in methods of measuring the structure and behavior of high-energy particles, such as those described in Chap. 21. The second would be the evolution of devices that could provide greater sources of high-energy particles, preferably of a type that would furnish these particles in narrowly defined energy intervals to facilitate the interpretation of the events observed.

The electrical interaction clearly offers the greatest promise for the generation of high-energy particles, for gravitation is important in achieving this purpose only on a cosmic scale, and the strong interaction between nucleons is characterized by being of only a few million electron Volts (M.e.V.) per particle. Confining our attention thus to electrical methods, it will be recalled that the energy gained by a particle of charge e upon moving from a point where the electrical potential is ϕ_1 to another, where the potential is ϕ_2, is $e(\phi_1 - \phi_2)$. In order that this product be large, it would be advantageous if e were large, but on a per-particle basis, it has been seen that nature provides us with only one magnitude of charge. It is thus necessary to devise methods whereby the effective potential difference as seen by the particles may be increased from their point of origin to their point of impact upon other particles with which they can interact. This can be done in various obvious ways, and in others that are less straightforward and more ingenious. These all depend upon the energies of interaction between charges at rest or in relative motion, in accordance with principles set forth in Chaps. 9 and 10.

Figure 28-1 *Schematic section through one form of Van de Graaff generator.*

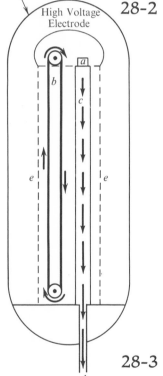

Pressure Container

High Voltage Electrode

a

b

c

e e

d

a — Ion source
b — Charging belt
c — Accelerating tube
d — Target
e — Insulating column

28-2   *Electrostatic and electromagnetic machines*

Among the more standard methods that had long been in use in laboratories for the study of electrical discharges in gases and in the generation of x-radiation are electrostatic machines and high voltage transformers. The later technique, in the hands of J. D. Cockcroft and E. T. S. Walton, produced the first device for the acceleration of ions to an energy whereby they could effect a nuclear disintegration. This was achieved in 1932 at 600,000 V. This is a lower potential than that now employed in some electric power transmission lines. Shortly before that time, R. J. Van de Graaff devised an electrostatic machine using a moving belt principle, which maintained an electrostatic potential difference of 1.5×10^6 V. between an electrode and the ground. But the problems of lightning-like breakdown prevented its use for nuclear investigations for some years. The Van de Graaff technique, using special ambient gases at high pressures for insulation, has now been extended to the range above 10^7 V. This type of generator constitutes one of the most important sources of particles now available for investigating nuclear phenomena within its energy range (Fig. 28-1).

28-3   *Linear cyclic accelerators*

The achievement of very much higher particle energies, however, had to await the development of methods of acceleration that employ high-frequency electrical oscillations of moderate voltage amplitude so disposed and phased as to present to the charged particles continuously accelerating potentials at a series of gaps between electrodes as the particles traverse a predetermined path between the gaps. Such accelerators have now been developed in a wide variety of forms, one of which was first demonstrated by R. Wederoe in 1928. In one form of such devices shown in the accompanying figure, the ions follow a rectilinear path from source to target; in consequence, such devices are given the generic name of *liniacs*. This device can, of course, be used to accelerate either positive protons or negative electrons. In Fig. 28-2, positive ions are depicted schematically between odd-numbered

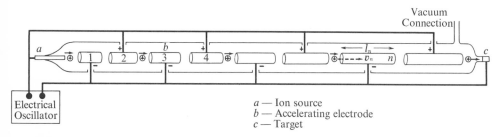

a — Ion source
b — Accelerating electrode
c — Target

Figure 28-2   *Schematic view of a linear accelerator with the instantaneous charge distribution appropriate for accelerating positively charged ions at the alternate gaps.*

gaps at the favorable voltage phase for acceleration. Evidently negative ions would encounter a favoring accelerating potential at even-numbered gaps at the same time. The long cylindrical chamber enclosing the ion source, electrodes, and target, is evacuated of all gas by a pumping system.

The ions are injected from the discharge tube source; the lengths of the accelerating electrodes and the period of electrical oscillation producing the potential difference between them are such that as ions traverse the structure they receive an increment of energy equal to $e\phi_0$, where ϕ_0 is the peak of the alternating potential at each gap. Thus bunches of ions travel successively down the tube to the target. If the velocity of the ion leaving the n'th gap is v_n, and the length of the following electrode is l_n, the time of transit of the electrode is l_n/v_n. If this transit time is equal to half the period T of electrical oscillation, then, on reaching the following gap, the opposite phase of the voltage from that shown in Fig. 28-2 will be encountered and the ion may again be accelerated. Thus, for a constant frequency ν of electrical oscillation, the lengths of the electrodes must steadily increase, such that the n'th electrode will have a length

$$l_n = v_n \frac{T}{2} = \frac{v_n}{2\nu}$$

Present machines of this particular type do not accelerate protons to energies where the effective mass exceeds the rest mass very greatly, and consequently the nonrelativistic expression for the added energy may be employed. Thus at the n'th gap, the energy may be written as $\frac{1}{2}mv_n{}^2$, which is evidently also equal to $ne\phi_0$ by the time the n'th gap is passed. In consequence, this value of the velocity may be used to determine the appropriate length of the following electrode:

$$l_n = \frac{1}{\nu} \left(\frac{ne\phi_0}{2m} \right)^{1/2}$$

The lengths of the electrodes are thus seen to be proportional to the square roots of the succeeding integers n. The final U_N is equal to $Ne\phi_0$, where N is the total number of gaps traversed and accelerations experienced.

A large number of linear accelerators employing variants of the technique just described have been constructed in recent years and employed for the acceleration of protons and heavier ions. At energies of about 7.5 M.e.V., ion currents as large as $\frac{1}{10}$ amp. have been attained. At higher energies the limitation on the number of ions accelerated per second are much greater, but for brief periods of time currents of several thousandths of an Ampere can be obtained at ion energies of 50 M.e.V. or greater. These machines may be used directly for high-energy nuclear experimentation; they are also used to inject ions into the still higher energy accelerators that will be described later. Machines following this technique for the acceleration of electrons are unworkable, because of the great lengths required to match the velocities closely approaching that of light, which the electrons attain at energies of a few M.e.V. Another variant is the propagation of electromagnetic waves down the accelerating tube upon the crests of which successive bunches of electrons may ride, much as a surf rider rides on the slope of an incoming ocean wave. Machines using this technique have been built, offering certain marked advantages over the circular accelerators later to be described, since loss of energy by the radiation of photons when charged particles are accelerated in a circular path is avoided.

The very great lengths that would be involved in constructing machines to produce energies a hundred or a thousand times those that have been attained by the devices so far described lead inevitably to the technique of bending the ion beam in an approximately circular path by the use of a magnetic field and the repeated traversal of such a path with successive accelerations up to higher and higher energies. The first embodiment of this principle was due to E. O. Lawrence and M. S. Livingston about 1930. Their machine was called a *cyclotron*. In this machine, the accelerating electrodes between which an alternating electrical potential was applied were placed in a large disc-shaped uniform magnetic field. In such a field as was seen in Sect. 11-3, a particle of charge e and mass m tends in equilibrium to move in a circular path which is in a plane normal to the magnetic field H with an angular velocity ω, where ω is given by:

$$\omega = \frac{e}{m} H$$

Thus it may be periodically accelerated by an oscillating electric field with frequency $\omega/2\pi$ and the circulation of the particle will remain in phase with the alternating accelerating potential throughout successive cycles.

As Figs. 28-3 and 28-4 indicate, in the first machines of this type the uniform magnetic field is produced by the electric current flowing in turns of wire about a large magnet, the poles of which form the upper and lower circular surfaces between which the vacuum chamber is placed. In this chamber, and largely filling it, are two copper electrodes in the form of two shallow hemi-cylinders face-to-face within which ions are free to traverse approximately circular paths passing through the gap between the electrodes, called D's from their shape. Ions are generated in a small discharge near the center, and as these are drawn alternately to the D's, they gain energy twice a cycle. Spiralling outward until reaching the outer perimeter, they can be drawn still further beyond the confines of the magnetic field by the application of an electrical potential to an extracting electrode and thereafter proceed to strike a target. Alternatively, the target may be placed within the vacuum chamber near the periphery of the field, where it is struck by the ions as they reach the peripheral radius.

The expression for the angular velocity of rotation of the ion in the magnetic field directly gives the relation between the momentum of the ion and its radius of curvature. Since $\omega = v/r$, then $mv = reH$, and the

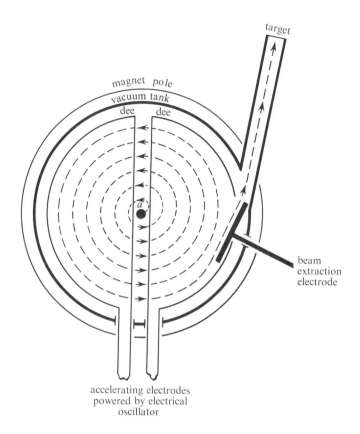

target

magnet pole
vacuum tank
dee   dee

a

beam
extraction
electrode

accelerating electrodes
powered by electrical
oscillator

Figure 28-3 *Principle of operation of the cyclotron, showing beam of
ions from central ion source spiralling out through hollow dees. Radius of
curvature in magnetic field increases as energy of ion increases.*

momentum is seen to be directly proportional to the radius of the
circular path traversed by the ion. From the relativistic expression for
the relation between the momentum and the energy, $(U/c)^2 = (mv)^2 + (m_0c)^2$, the energy can also be expressed in terms of the radius of
the path:

$$(U/c)^2 = (reH)^2 + (m_0c)^2$$

Thus the parameters of the ion being accelerated, namely, e and m_0,
together with the strength of the magnetic field and the radius of the
largest possible path determine the energy that can be obtained. From
this expression, it would appear that the magnitude of the alternating
potential difference between the D's is irrelevant. This is not strictly so,
for if it is too small, the spiral path becomes inordinately long. More

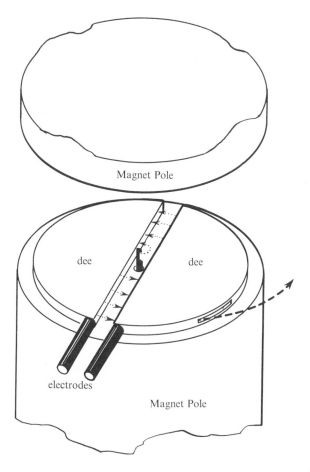

Figure 28-4 *View of cyclotron with upper magnet pole raised and vacuum tank removed to show hollow dees and central ion source with slot for exit of ions. Dashed line represents a circulating ion beam that leaves the machine through a slot shown in the side of one dee. The extraction electrode (not shown) is positioned at this slot.*

important, however, is the fact that the increasing mass requires a decreasing frequency to maintain precise synchronism, and troublesome oscillatory effects and the straying of the beam from the median plane tend to limit the maximum energy that can be achieved, even with large magnets and high magnetic fields. Although the use of a nonuniform magnetic field can maintain a focussed beam, the mass of the magnet required for a machine of this type is the greatest obstacle to achieving the highest energies desired. A cyclotron at the University of California in Berkeley has a four thousand ton magnet and decreases frequency of the electrical alternations to ensure synchronism, and as a result, produces ions of 730 M.e.V.

The limitation on energy imposed by this magnet design can be overcome by going to the ring-shaped conformation illustrated in Fig. 28-5. In this embodiment, groups of ions injected into the ring-shaped vacuum chamber with relatively high initial energies are induced to follow the same geometrical path during the entire period of acceleration by varying the frequency of the electrical accelerating potential and also the strength of the retaining magnetic field. The ions are periodically injected by a Van de Graaff or linear accelerator, with energies of a few M.e.V.; while constrained to follow a race-course-like path by a series of relatively small magnets along its periphery, they receive an electrical impulse when passing through an electrical accelerating electrode.

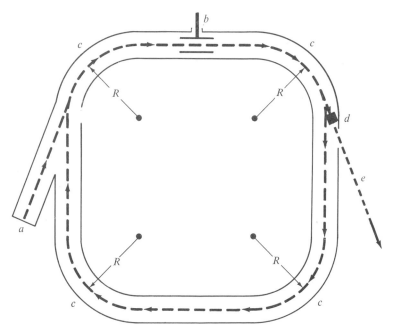

a — Ion source and injector.
b — Accelerating electrode.
c — Magnet sectors of radius R.
d — Internal target
e — Beam of secondary particles projected forward from the target.

Figure 28-5   *Schematic sketch of a synchrotron.*

These devices, called *synchrotrons*, are even larger, more technically complex, and more costly than the large cyclotrons. Their power requirements are high, the shielding required to protect the operating personnel from the generated radiation is massive, and the technical and supporting staffs required are both numerous. But the energy of the particles produced is in the range of thousands of M.e.V., which begins to approach the cosmic ray range. The experience gained in devising accelerating machines has added to our insight on the likely processes of generating cosmic rays. Given the accelerating electric fields and confining magnetic fields the dimensions of our galaxy are such that it is not unreasonable to expect the production of cosmic ions with energies up to 10^{16} or even 10^{20} e.V. A number of large synchrotrons are in operation, or are under construction, at research centers around the world. At Dubna, U.S.S.R. and at the Argonne National Laboratories, Lamont, Illinois are machines with maximum energies of about 10^4 M.e.V.; at Geneva, Switzerland, a consortium of European nations have built one with an energy maximum of 2.8×10^4 M.e.V.; at the Brookhaven National Laboratory, Upton, Long Island, New York, the Associated Universities operate one capable of 3.3×10^4 M.e.V. The largest synchroton at present under construction is at Serpakov, U.S.S.R., with a maximum energy that may exceed 5×10^4 M.e.V.

Known types of elementary particles and their relations to one another 28-5

The growth of some dozens of multimillion-dollar laboratories, with staffs of hundreds of people to explore the basic structure of the physical world, is a phenomenon of the last two decades. Of a magnitude only possible with government support, accorded because the military uses of atomic energy established the validity of Bacon's aphorism that "Knowledge itself is power," and guided in its technical program by the competence available in the regenerative body of university scientists, rapid progress is being made in our knowledge of the patterns and properties of elemental physical events. The recent increase in the number of high-energy particles produced by accelerators and the greater refinement in the methods of detection, discrimination, and measurement that has been achieved have led to such an abundance of data that computer techniques are required for their analysis. Great ingenuity and imagination are also required to evolve the theoretical

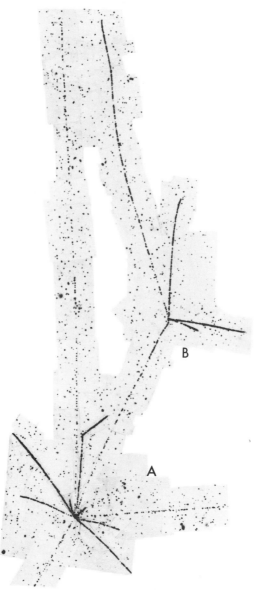

Plate 3 *One of the first two observations of the creation of a pion. The pion leaves the disintegration "A" and reaches the end of its range at "B" where it is captured by a light element, resulting in a nuclear disintegration. (From C. M. G. Powell. Nature 160, 486 (1947); reproduced in The Study of Elementary Particles by the Photographic Method by C. F. Powell, P. H. Fowler, and D. H. Perkins, Pergamon Press, London, 1959.)*

fabric needed to put the results in order and to render them comprehensible.

Though accelerators cannot as yet furnish particles in the higher cosmic-ray range, they can produce bounteously particles in the energy range of 10^{10} to 10^{11} e.V. All of this energy, however, is not available for the production of nuclear reactions, because the conservation of momentum requires that when a high-energy proton solidly encounters one relatively at rest the pair should move instantaneously forward with the momentum of the initial particle; and hence energy of translation is locked in. The energy available for appearance in other forms in the center-of-mass system is thus considerably reduced. Indeed, at the highest energies presently available, only about a fifth of that of the impinging particle is available to induce nuclear reactions. However, recalling that the energy equivalent to the electron rest mass is about 0.5 M.e.V., and that represented by the proton rest mass is about two thousand times this, or 10^3 M.e.V., the 5×10^4 M.e.V. from the largest synchrotron can energetically generate 10^4 electron pairs or 5 proton-antiproton pairs. It is thus in this range of masses up to possibly five times that of the proton that our present methods of experimental exploration are adequate.

The generalization that appears valid today is that any possible process within known conservation laws takes place and is observed. The laws known to us before the highest reaches of the energy scale were available for study were listed in Chap. 24. These have now been expanded, in some cases quite assuredly and in others rather tentatively, for it is evident that on this new frontier our ignorance is still considerable, and hypotheses are only interim guides to a final and well established theory. In the energy range of particles less massive than the protons, the picture is taking on some clarity. High-energy experiments have disclosed no additional novelties in the characteristics of the electron family since the discovery of the neutrino companion in processes of generation and recombination described in Chap. 25. But the next lightest particle we know, namely the muon, which has been briefly referred to, was poorly understood until Columbia University scientists working with the Brookhaven accelerator established its close analogy with the electron and its quite separate conservation law in 1962. Thus the conservation laws listed in Chap. 24 must be supplemented by another law analogous to number six, namely, number 7: Conservation of Muon Family Members.

The experiment establishing that the muon, like the electron, is associated in its transformation with a neutrino, but that this muon-neutrino is quite separate and distinct from the electron-neutrino will be briefly described as illustrative of the techniques and problems of high-energy experiments. Generically, the muon closely resembles the electron in possessing one unit of charge, either positive or negative, μ^+ and μ^-, and in possessing a half unit of intrinsic angular momentum or spin, namely $h/4\pi$. Its mass, however, is 206.77 times the mass of the electron. This provides the most obvious experimental method of distinguishing between the electron and the muon, since heavier particles produce denser trails of ions during their passage through matter. Muons, like electrons, have precisely measured magnetic moments, and again, interacting as do electrons chiefly through electromagnetic forces, their magnetic moment calculated on this premise agrees well with the measured value. They are not permanent constituents of our world, since they decay into the lighter electron with an average lifetime of 2.212×10^{-6} sec., the excess of mass appearing as the energy of the electron and neutrinos accompanying the event.

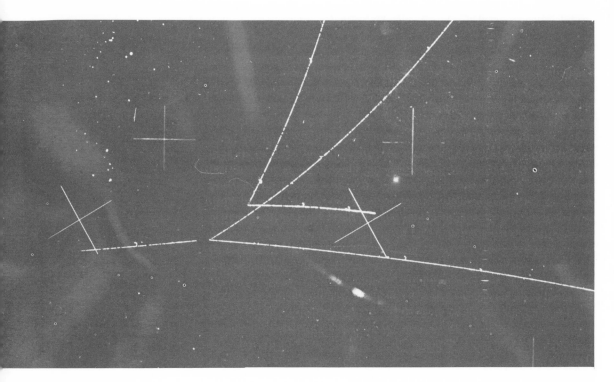

Plate 4   *A negative pion of momentum 1.8 B.e.V./c. collides with a proton in a bubble chamber. Of the three neutral particles from the reaction $\pi^- + p \to K^\circ + \Lambda + \pi^\circ$, the neutral pion (with a very short lifetime of the order of 10^{-16} sec.) decays into two γ-rays which are not observed. The two "strange" neutral particles K° and Λ have a lifetime of the order of 10^{-10} sec. They undergo the decay modes $K^\circ \to \pi^+ + \pi^-$ and $\Lambda \to p + \pi^-$. A magnetic field is applied to the bubble chamber which gives the negatively charged particles an upward curvature. The large crosses are not tracks of particles but fiducial markings for measurement purposes. (By courtesy of W. Selove and the Brookhaven National Laboratory.)*

The objective of the Brookhaven experiment was to observe muon-neutrino capture reactions analogous to those that established the existence of the electron-neutrino, namely:

$$_0\bar{\nu}_\mu^0 + {}_1p^1 \rightarrow {}_0n^1 + {}_1\mu \quad \text{and} \quad {}_0\nu_\mu^0 + {}_0n^1 \rightarrow {}_1p^0 + {}_{-1}\mu$$

These, of course, require higher neutrino energies than in the case of the electron-neutrino capture process, since the rest mass energy of the muon exceeds that of the electron by a factor of about 200, but at the high initial energy of the accelerator the 10^8 M.e.V. needed is no problem. The neutrinos required are produced as a result of a cascade of processes occurring when the accelerated protons impinge on the target of the synchrotron. A copious supply of pions, the binding particles of nuclei, are formed; almost all of these are transformed or

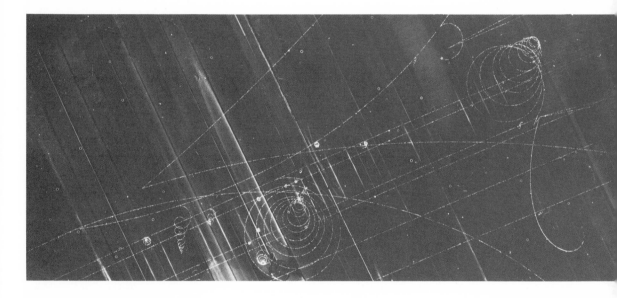

Plate 5 *In this bubble chamber picture at a higher momentum (8 B.e.V./c.) of the incoming negative pion a more complex reaction takes place: $\pi^- + p \rightarrow K^\circ + K^\circ + \pi^+ + \pi^- + n$. The neutron (lifetime of 10^9 sec.) leaves the chamber and is not observed. The two K° particles decay into two pions $K^\circ \rightarrow \pi^+ \pi^-$. The spirals in this picture are electrons bent into circular orbits by the magnetic field. Because of radiation losses the radius of the circles changes and gives rise to the spirals. The spiral at the right-hand side of the picture is related to a pion reaction in which a μ meson was created. The μ meson decayed into an electron and two neutrinos $\mu^- \rightarrow e^- + \nu + \bar{\nu}$. (By courtesy of W. Selove and the Brookhaven National Laboratory.)*

decay in about 2.55×10^{-8} sec. into muons and their neutrinos in accordance with the processes:

$$\pi^+ \rightarrow \mu^+ + \nu_\mu \quad \text{and} \quad \pi^- \rightarrow \mu^- + \bar{\nu}_\mu$$

Only about one in ten thousand decay in the only alternate way, into electrons and their associated neutrinos. Thus all of the debris from the nuclear disintegrations at the target, namely heavy particles, pions, muons, electrons, neutrinos and photons, are projected forward in a narrow-angle cone about the beam direction because of the high initial momentum in that direction that is conserved in the course of all processes. The erection of a rampart of forty-four feet of iron in this path stops almost all charged particles and photons through strong nuclear and electromagnetic interactions, and only the neutrinos emerge (Fig. 28-6).

Behind this great iron shield was placed a spark chamber in the form of 90 closely spaced four-foot square aluminum sheets with a sufficiently high potential between each successive sheet to cause a spark to jump between them along the path of an ionizing particle through the intervening air. The difference in ionization per unit length of path between an electron and a muon enabled the spark chamber to distinguish between them. With the accelerator in operation, great numbers of neutrinos traverse the spark chamber, each with a chance of about 1 in 10^8 of reacting with a nucleus and producing a charged muon or electron that the chamber would record. During some 300 hours of operation, which represented the acceleration of 10^{17} to 10^{18} protons in the synchrotron, about 30 spark tracks were photographed. All of these corresponded to muon tracks. The conclusion was clear that the great preponderance of neutrinos traversing the chamber, pro-

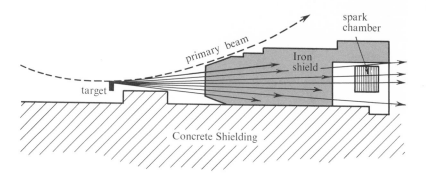

Figure 28-6 *Sketch of the geometrical disposition of the components of equipment in the muon neutrino experiment.*

duced when pions decayed to muons near the target, were capable of regenerating muons at nuclear encounters, but were incapable of producing electrons. Thus neutrinos do come in two family types, one associated with the appearance and disappearance of electrons, and the other with the appearance and disappearance of muons. To the best of our present knowledge, the two kinds of neutrinos are the same in every other way, being massless, relativistic, uncharged particles and anti-particles with spins of $h/4\pi$ to match the spins of electrons and muons. The one observable difference between the two families of neutrinos is that one is compatible to participate in reactions involving muons and the other in reactions involving electrons.

A summary of our knowledge of those particles having masses less than that of the proton is given in Table 28-1. The customary units are used, and the general picture this table gives agrees with the experimental results so far obtained. There are certain more or less well-defined families of particles that are related by the events of birth and

Table 28-1   *Summary of properties of known particles with masses less than that of the proton*

general name	particle name and symbol		mass in units of the electron mass m_0	charge in units of the proton charge e	magnetic moment in units of ($eh/4\pi m_0$)	anti-particle	life time in seconds	spontaneous decay mode
electro-magnetic particle	photon, γ		0	0	0	γ	indefinite	none
electron family	electron, e^-		1	-1	1.001596	e^+	permanent	none
	electron-neutrino ν_e		0	0	0	$\bar{\nu}_e$	indefinite	none
muon family	muon, μ^-		206.77	-1	1.001162	μ^+	2.12×10^{-6}	$\mu^- \to e^- + \bar{\nu}_e + \nu_\mu$
	muon-neutrino, ν_μ		0	0	0	$\bar{\nu}_\mu$	indefinite	none
mesons	pions	π^+	273.2	$+1$	0	π^-	2.55×10^{-8}	$\pi^+ \to \mu^+ + \nu_\mu$
		π°	264.2	0	0	π°	1.9×10^{-16}	$\pi^\circ \to \gamma + \gamma$
		π^-	273.2	-1	0	π^+	2.55×10^{-8}	$\pi^- \to \mu^- + \bar{\nu}_\mu$
	kaon	K^+	966.6	$+1$	0	K^-	1.22×10^{-8}	$K^+ \to \pi^+ + \pi^\circ$
		K°	974	0	0	$\bar{K}^\circ$	6×10^{-8} and 10^{-10}	$K^\circ \to \pi^+ + \pi^-$

death. A massless particle travels at the constant velocity of light in order to convey energy and momentum and to be detectable under the requirements of the theory of relativity. A particle that has both charge and spin, in general, has a magnetic moment as well. And relatively heavy particles have the mass energy to permit them to decay into lighter particles, conserving the fundamental parameters and conforming to the family or generic relationships indicated by the table. Neglecting the gravitational interaction, not included in the tables, all these particles except the photon appear to share the weak type of interaction with one another. This is the only interaction affecting the neutrinos, for instance, and for this reason their reactions are few and far between, and their paths are long even through the densest of matter. Photons and charged particles are subject to the electromagnetic reaction that is vastly greater as we have seen; their reactions occur much more rapidly, and their unimpeded paths through matter are very short. The pions and kaons, which—like muons—are named after letters of the Greek or Roman alphabets, also participate in the strong interaction between nucleons; indeed pions are the binding agent between these more massive building elements in the nuclei of matter, according to our current view. This interaction is not tremendously greater than the electromagnetic one, though it is significantly greater, as was seen in Chap. 25. The kaon, of which no account has been given here, is a more recent addition to the elementary particle family than any but the neutrinos, and is less well understood than most, though its relationship in spin and modes of decay appears to associate it firmly with pions in the meson family.

In the energy range of the proton's mass and above, a new and more complex set of phenomena appear, which are as yet very imperfectly understood, and which taken together represent the frontier of experimentation and of our knowledge of high-energy events. This is the very high-energy range as set by present day facilities; and, though the variety of effects observed becomes greater than at lower energies, it does not become as enormously complex as it might were it not that additional limiting laws of conservation or restriction appear in such events that limit the variety of interaction patterns that are observed. In this account, our description must be very limited and tentative as the next few years of observation will hopefully clarify and simplify the rather chaotic state of our present understanding of what takes place.

At sufficiently high energies, particles, some of which have rest masses very considerably exceeding that of the proton, are produced for relatively brief times. The first excursion into this uncharted area was made by G. Rochester and C. C. Butler of Manchester University who observed in a chamber a track of a negative pion that encountered a proton and after several gaps, apparently traversed by uncharged particles, was followed by two v-shaped tracks as indicated in Fig. 28-7. A measurement of the momenta of visible tracks from their curvature in the magnetic field led to the conclusion that at the point 1, two neutral particles were produced which, on being projected forward, produced at points 2 and 3 pairs of oppositely charged particles that followed the ion tracks that were photographed. The energies and momenta were consistent with assigning at point 2 the genesis of a positive and negative pion by a kaon and at point 3 a negative pion and a proton as a result of a particle with a rest mass of 2182.8 electron masses, which exceeds that of the proton. Such a neutral particle has been christened a Λ (lambda) particle. It belongs to the baryon genus. The reactions in which these particles participate would be written:

$$K^\circ \to \pi^+ + \pi^- \quad \text{and} \quad \Lambda^\circ \to p^+ + \pi^-$$

Subsequent observations indicated that many such events occur in bubble chamber photographs, and it was found that in addition to the Λ particles, still heavier ones, christened Σ (sigma) and Ξ (xi), are generated and live for times of the order of 10^{-10} sec. before decaying into pions and baryons. The Σ and Ξ particles have masses of about 2330 and 2570 times the electron mass; each occurs in both charged and neutral

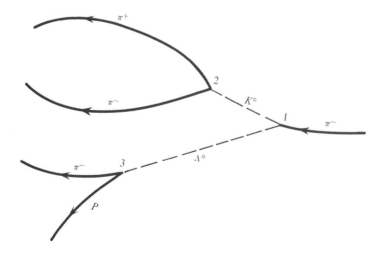

Figure 28-7 *Illustration of an event following a π impingement on a proton producing two neutral particles, one of which is a meson K° and one a Λ° particle, heavier than a proton, which in turn decay into ionizing pairs of particles as indicated.*

forms. Particles of still higher masses and of still shorter lifetimes were also inferred from types of reactions produced by the impact of high energy anti-protons upon nuclear protons from which a plurality of pions emerged, in groups such as:

$$\bar{p} + p \rightarrow (\pi^+ + \pi^-) + (\pi^+ + \pi^- + \pi^\circ)$$

implying from the conservation laws obeyed by each group that a very transitory particle, equivalent in mass to a group of either two or three pions, exists between the generation of the particles in the first bracket and those in the second.

The observational story must conclude here as being on the frontier of present experience. Now some sixty to seventy heavy entities have been identified as being participants in very high-energy events, and those which are more massive than the protons and exist for more than the briefest instant of time have been grouped with nucleons under the generic name of baryons. The almost instantaneously vanishing entities evidenced only by the groupings of resultant decay products such as the $(\pi^+ + \pi^-)$ and $(\pi^+ + \pi^- + \pi^\circ)$ instanced in the last paragraph are believed to represent a somewhat different type of energy agglomeration, and in our present ignorance are called "resonances." The name follows from the strongly enhanced probability of their generation observed when the total energy available is equal to their mass energy, as illustrated in Fig. 28-8. These new particles present intriguing symmetries occurring in pairs, triads, and larger patterns with a certain order in their charges, spins, and masses that is leading to imaginative excursions of many interesting forms in an endeavor to reduce the complex phenomena to comprehensibility. The law of conservation of baryons given in Chap. 24 on the basis of the only two baryons introduced up to that point—the nucleons proton and neutron—can be extended to include these new heavier baryons as well, since they are found to be produced or disappear in pairs as particle and anti-particle, and the net number of particles of this type remains the same before and after an event. An example of the application of this law would be the generation of a proton in the decay of a lambda particle as previously noted. This is one of the laws that limits the variety of possible happenings at a very high-energy encounter. Other laws governing these events are being identified and formulated; they are considerably more recondite and somewhat more tentative at our present state of knowledge. The rapidity of advance and, necessarily, the somewhat speculative nature of interim conclusions obscures this van of progress, but one can be quite certain that the next decade will see a deepening of our understanding of the nature of matter from atomic nuclei to stellar interiors.

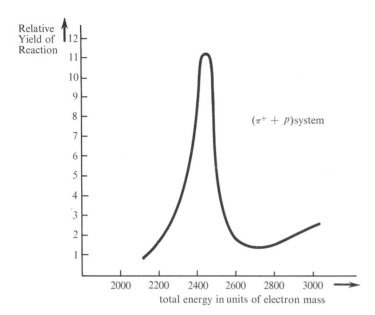

Figure 28-8 *A resonance in the yield of positive pions scattered by a hydrogen target was observed by Fermi and collaborators to occur at a bombarding energy such that the total energy (mass plus kinetic energy) of the system was 2420 m$_0$. This was named Δ (delta), the first of many resonance particles.*

Further reading:

BETH, R. A. AND LASKY, C., "The Brookhaven Alternating Gradient Synchrotron," *Science*, vol. 128, p. 1393 (1958).

BROWN, L. M., "Quarkways to Particle Symmetry," *Physics Today*, vol. 19, No. 2, p. 44 (1966).

CHEW, G. F., GELL-MANN, M., AND ROSENFELD, A. H., "Strongly Interacting Particles," *Scientific American*, vol. 210, p. 74 (1964), and vol. 211, No. 1, p. 44 (1964).

FORD, K. W., *The World of Elementary Particles*, Blaisdell Publishing Co. (1963).

FOWLER, W. B. AND SAMIOS, N. P., "The Omega-Minus Experiment," *Scientific American*, vol. 211, No. 4, p. 36 (1964).

LEDERMAN, L. M., "The Two Neutrino Experiment," *Scientific American*, vol. 208, No. 3, p. 60 (Mar., 1963).

LIVINGOOD, J. J., *Principles of Cyclic Particle Accelerators*, D. Van Nostrand and Co. (1961).

LIVINGSTON, M. S. AND MCMILLAN, E. M., "History of the Cyclotron," *Physics Today*, vol. 12, No. 10, p. 18 and 24 (1959).

PANOFSKY, W., "The Linear Accelerator," *Scientific American*, vol. 191, No. 4, p. 40 (1954).

WEISSKOPF, V. F., "The Place of Elementary Particle Research," *Physics Today*, vol. 16, No. 6, p. 26 (1963).

WILSON, R. R., "Particle Accelerators," *Scientific American*, vol. 198, No. 3, p. 64 (1958).

YANG, C.N., "Elementary Particles," Princeton University Press (1962).

Problems

28-1　A particle accelerator produces a 10^{-3} amp. beam of protons of energy 10 M.e.V. What is the minimum power consumption of such a machine?

28-2 ⋅ How long does an α-particle take to travel down an accelerating tube under the influence of a uniform electric field if its final energy is 8 M.e.V. and the tube is 7 m. long?

28-3　How many electrons per second arrive in a beam of 10^{-6} amp.?

28-4　A cyclotron has a peak potential difference of 100 k.V. between the dees. How many revolutions are required to accelerate protons to an energy of 10 M.e.V., assuming that all accelerations take place at peak potential difference?

28-5　What energy α-particle can be accelerated in a cyclotron of diameter 1 m. and frequency 2×10^7 sec.$^{-1}$?

28-6　Do the protons in a cyclotron circulate in the same sense as the electrons in its magnet coils or in the opposite sense?

28-7　A resonance for emission in a nuclear experiment corresponds to an energy of the nuclear system of 747 M.e.V. What would be the mass of a related *resonance particle*?

28-8　If the width of the above resonance is 100 M.e.V., what would be the approximate lifetime of the resonance particle?

References

GENERAL

Bridgman, P. W., *The Nature of Physical Theory*. Princeton University Press, Princeton, N. J., (Dover Reprint), 1936.

Bridgman, P. W., *The Logic of Modern Physics*. Macmillan, New York, 1927.

Clifford, W. K., *The Common Sense of the Exact Sciences*. (Dover Reprint), New York, 1955.

Einstein, A., and Infeld, L., *The Evolution of Physics*. Simon and Schuster, 1938; (Essandess paperback), New York, 1961.

Jeans, J., *The Universe Around Us*. Cambridge University Press, Cambridge, England, 1929; Macmillan, New York, 1944.

Peierls, R. E., *The Laws of Nature*. Scribners, New York, 1956.

HISTORICAL

Cajori, F., *A History of Physics*. Macmillan, New York, 1929.

Crew, H., *The Rise of Modern Physics*. Williams and Wilkins, Baltimore, Md., 1928.

Magie, W. F., *A Source Book of Physics*. McGraw-Hill, New York, 1935.

Sarton, G., *A History of Science*. Harvard University Press, Cambridge, Mass., 1952.

Singer, C., *A Short History of Scientific Ideas*. Clarendon Press, Fairlawn, N. J., 1959.

PHILOSOPHICAL

Gardner, M., *The Ambidextrous Universe*. Basic Books, New York, 1965.

Popper, K. R., *Logic of Scientific Discovery*. Basic Books, New York, 1959.

Schroedinger, E., *What is Life and Other Scientific Essays*. Doubleday, New York, 1956.

Weyl, H., *Philosophy of Mathematics and Natural Science*. Princeton University Press, Princeton, N. J., 1949.

Weyl, H., *Symmetry*. Princeton University Press, Princeton, N. J., 1952.

Whitehead, A. N., *Science and the Modern World*. Macmillan, New York, 1926.

Whitehead, A. N., *The Principles of Natural Knowledge*. Cambridge University Press, Cambridge, England, 1925.

Yang, C. N., *Elementary Particles*. Princeton University Press, Princeton, N. J., 1961.

A considerable number of the references following the chapters in this text are to semipopular scientific journals which are generally available in academic libraries; they warrant browsing from the point of view of general scientific interest. These journals are: *Science, The Scientific American, Physics Today,* and *The American Journal of Physics.*

Answers to problems

CHAPTER 1

1-1 6, 8
1-3 Equal purity
1-5 6
1-7 $N = N_0(0.9)^t$; No
1-9 $x^7 + 7x^6\Delta x$

CHAPTER 2

2-1 East 5,000 m.; North 8,700 m
2-3 $-\mathbf{j}$
2-5 $2\mathbf{i}, 2\mathbf{j}, 2\mathbf{k}, 2\mathbf{i} + 2\mathbf{j}, 2\mathbf{j} + 2\mathbf{k}; 2\mathbf{k} + 2\mathbf{i}, 2\mathbf{i} + 2\mathbf{j} + 2\mathbf{k}$
2-7 (2.8, 2.8, 6.9)
2-9 500 m.; $\tan \theta = \frac{4}{3}$
2-11 2 rad.; 200 m
2-15 $84x^{11} + 63x^6 + 5x^4 - 12x^2; \frac{7}{13}x^{13} + \frac{9}{8}x^8 + \frac{1}{5}x^5 - x^4 + 8x + $ a constant

CHAPTER 3

3-1 $S_2 = S_3 = 1$ kg.; $S_4 = 2$ kg.; $S_5 = 1$ kg.; $S_6 = 2$ kg.; $S_7 = 1$ kg.; $S_8 = 1$ kg.; $S_9 = \sqrt{3}$ kg.; $S_{10} = 2$ kg.
3-3 160 N.
3-5 2000 N.
3-7 9.6 sec.
3-11 4.9 m.; 4.9 m.; 4.9 m.
3-13 0.5
3-17 $\tan \theta = v^2/gr$
3-19 Second, third, first; 120 N.; 1.2 rad. sec.$^{-2}$

CHAPTER 4

4-5 v increases by factor 10; no effect
4-7 Constant interchange of energy between kinetic and potential forms; $\frac{1}{2}mv_0^2 + 2mgr = \frac{1}{2}mv^2$; no work
4-11 Conservation of angular momentum
4-15 1%; 0.001 m. in forward direction

CHAPTER 5

5-3 -2.5×10^{-9} J.

5-5		left	center	right
	force	$GM(4m + M)/4d^2$ to right	0	$GM(4m + M)/4d^2$ to left
	field	$G(4m + M)/4d^2$ to right	0	$G(4m + M)/4d^2$ to left
	potential	$G(2m + M)/2d$	$2GM/d$	$G(2m + M)/2d$

Total potential energy of system is $GM(4m + M)/d$.

5-7 $v^2 = GM/r$

5-11 $-v^2$

5-13 $\frac{1}{2}\sqrt[3]{2}$

5-15 $g_e/g_m = 5$; $v_e/v_m = \sqrt{20}$

CHAPTER 6

6-1 No; force not proportional to displacement

6-3 1 m.

6-7 36.7 ft. 0.44 inches

6-9 275 sec.$^{-1}$

CHAPTER 7

7-1 v_0; $v_0(1 + (\omega r/c)\sin \omega t)^{-1}$; v_0

7-3 $v_g = v_a + v_w$

7-5 6×10^7 m. sec.$^{-1}$

7-7 2×10^{14} sec.$^{-1}$; 1.5×10^{-6} m.; 3×10^8 m. sec.$^{-1}$

7-9 98% of c.

7-11 Circular; unaltered

CHAPTER 8

8-1 11.39×10^{-31} kg.; 9.11×10^{-31} kg.

8-3 $V = (4/v^2 - 3/c^2)^{-1/2}$

8-5 1.64×10^{-13} J.; 2.73×10^{-13} J.

8-9 Decreases by factor of 1.1; unaffected

CHAPTER 9

9-1 8.6×10^{-11} C.

9-3 4.3×10^{10} N.; 8.6×10^9 N. C.$^{-1}$; 3×10^{10} V. Force and field at each charge are directed symmetrically outward.

9-5 $\dfrac{1}{2\pi}\sqrt{\dfrac{2Ee}{ml}}$

9-7 If there were a field, the charges would move under its influence; there is no field inside a hollow conductor; the potential is constant.

9-9 18×10^4 C.; 5 hours

9-11 ϕ; ϕ/R_1; ϕ; ϕ/R_2; $R_1R_2/(R_1 + R_2)$

CHAPTER 10

10-1   4 Amp upward
10-3 9×10^{14} m.sec.$^{-2}$ toward wire
10-5 c^2A^2/K
10-9 $6L_0$; n_1/n_2

CHAPTER 11

11-7 1.28×10^{-11} J.
11-9 $2\pi^2md/nIlT^2$

CHAPTER 12

12-1   NaCl; MgCl$_2$
12-3   0.0021 kg.
12-5 6.0225×10^{26}; 1.3×10^{-29} m.^{3}; 3×10^{-10} m.
12-7 3.32×10^{-26} kg.
12-9 7.2×10^{49}; 2.5×10^{-10} m.

CHAPTER 13

13-1 $E \sqrt{m/2e\phi}$
13-3 0.96×10^7 C. kg.$^{-1}$
13-5   Negative; 0.20 kg.
13-7 3.17×10^{-26} kg.; 1.44×10^{-18} C.
13-9 5.1×10^{-9}

CHAPTER 14

14-1 7.9×10^{-14} J.; 0.49 M.e.V.; 8.7×10^{-31} kg.; 1
14-9   0.60 M.e.V.

CHAPTER 15

15-1   27:32:5
15-3 2.1×10^{-24} kg. m.sec.$^{-1}$
15-7   13.6 e.V.; 0

CHAPTER 16

16-1 $\delta m_l = \pm 1$ or 0
16-3   32; $2n^2$
16-5 $h/4\pi$
16-7 $1s^2, 2s^2, 2p^6, 3s^2, 3p^6, 3d^2, 4s^2$; $1s^2, 2s^2, 2p^6, 3s^2, 3p^6, 3d^{10}, 4s^2, 4p^6, 4d^{10}, 4f^3, 5s^2, 5p^6, 6s^2$

CHAPTER 17

17-1   1/64; 1/64; 5/16; 15/64
17-3   1/216; 1/36
17-5   0.2; 4.2×10^{-3}
17-9   Area equals total number of particles N; independent of total energy of system.

CHAPTER 18

18-1 7.6×10^9 °A.
18-3 6.3×10^{-21} J.; 4.9×10^2 m.sec.$^{-1}$; 5.2×10^2 m.sec.$^{-1}$
18-5 2.1×10^{-6} rad.
18-7 9×10^4 m.
18-9 136

CHAPTER 19

19-1 3.6×10^{-8} N.; uniform velocity gradient from midstream to bank; too low
19-3 10^{-4} m.sec.$^{-1}$; field strength E
19-5 10^4 m.; 10^6 N. m.$^{-2}$
19-7 $\sin \theta = \frac{3}{4}$ and $\theta = 49°$

CHAPTER 20

20-1 900 e.V.

CHAPTER 21

21-1 $1/Nt$
21-7 0.037 cm.
21-9 6.4×10^5

CHAPTER 22

22-1 3680; 0.5; 43
22-3

energy of α-ray, M.e.V.	energy of associated level, M.e.V.	possible coincidence with γ-ray of energy, M.e.V.
10.62	0	None
5.49	5.13	5.13
2.06	8.56	8.56 or (3.43 and 5.13)
0.58	10.04	10.04 or (4.91 and 5.13) or (1.48 and 8.56) or (1.48 and 3.43 and 5.13)

22-5 α, Be^8, He^4; Cu^{64}; β^-, β^-
22-7 4.8 years
22-9 30 days
22-11 35 per cent
22-13 $\frac{1}{5}$

CHAPTER 23

23-3 5.7 M.e.V.; 12.8 M.e.V.
23-5 18.00571 a.m.u.
23-7 1840 v.
23-9 135 M.e.V.

CHAPTER 24

24-1 1.2×10^{20} sec.$^{-1}$

24-3 1.4×10^{-15} m.

24-5 β^-; β^-; β^-; β^+; β^-

24-7 5.0×10^{-19} kg.m.sec.$^{-1}$

24-9 1.8×10^{17} J.; 1.1×10^{30} M.e.V.

CHAPTER 25

25-1   Neutron emission prevails unless energetically forbidden.

25-3   Permitted; nonconservation of leptons; nonconservation of charge; nonconservation of leptons and baryons

25-5   Antiproton plus positron plus neutrino

25-7 10^{16} m.

25-9   No

CHAPTER 26

26-1   Yes; conservation of mass, assuming mostly two-body breakup

26-5 4.5×10^{25} M.e.V.

26-7   Less neutron capture; $\frac{8}{9}$

26-9   70

CHAPTER 27

27-1   7.3

27-3 3×10^{26}

27-5 1.3×10^{15}; 7.5×10^{24} J. sec.$^{-1}$

27-7 1.8×10^7 J. sec.$^{-1}$; 3.4×10^5

27-9   200,000 years; 200,000 years

CHAPTER 28

28-1 10^4 W.

28-3 6×10^{12}

28-5   80 M.e.V.

28-7 1.33×10^{-27} kg. or 0.8 a.m.u.

Appendix

SYMBOLS AND THEIR PRINCIPAL USAGE

a	Acceleration; activity; general number, variable, coefficient, or constant.
A	Area; amplitude; magnetic potential; mass number; a constant.
b	Breadth; general number, variable, coefficient, or constant.
B	Binding energy.
c	Velocity of light in vacuum; wave velocity.
C	A constant.
d	Distance; length; displacement; electronic orbit with $l = 2$.
e	Charge; electronic charge; an electron.
E	Electric field strength.
f	Function; torque per unit angular displacement; electronic orbit with $l = 3$.
F	Force; tension.
g	Gravitational acceleration.
g_j	Weighting factor for the j'th level.
G	Gravitational constant.
h	Height; Planck's constant.
H	Magnetic field strength.
$\mathbf{i}$	Unit vector in X direction.
I	Moment of inertia; electric current.
$\mathbf{j}$	Unit vector in Y direction.
k	Force per unit displacement; Boltzmann's constant; a constant.
$\mathbf{k}$	Unit vector in Z direction.
K	Electrostatic constant; compressibility; a kaon.
l	Length; orbital quantum number.
L	Angular momentum; coefficient of mutual inductance; length.
m	Mass; a number.
m_l	Magnetic quantum number.
m_0	Rest mass, in particular that of the electron.
m_s	Spin quantum number.
M	Molecular weight; mass.
M_H	Mass of hydrogen atom.
M_n	Neutron rest mass.
M_p	Proton rest mass.
M_1	Atomic mass unit.
n	A number; an integer; ordinal or principal quantum number; semiconductor with excess electrons; a neutron.
N	Avogadro's number; a number.
O	Fiducial point; focus.
p	Momentum; electronic orbit with $l = 1$; semiconductor with excess holes; a proton.
P	Pressure; power; probability; packing fraction.

Q	Liberated energy or energy of reaction.
r	Radius; radial vector; distance.
R	Radius; resistance; gas constant; Rydberg constant.
s	Separation; distance; arc length; length; electronic orbit with $l = 0$.
S	Separation; distance; length; spin angular momentum.
t	Time interval; time.
T	Period; tension; temperature; half-life; time.
u	Velocity.
u_j	Energy of the j'th state or level.
U	Energy.
U_K	Kinetic energy.
U_P	Potential energy.
v	Velocity.
V	Volume; velocity.
w	Velocity.
W	Work.
x	Displacement.
X	Coordinate axis.
y	Displacement.
Y	Coordinate axis.
z	Displacement.
Z	Coordinate axis; atomic number.
α	Angular acceleration; angle; an α-particle.
α_x	Direction cosine: $\sin\theta\cos\phi$.
α_y	Direction cosine: $\sin\theta\sin\phi$.
α_z	Direction cosine: $\cos\theta$.
β	Angle; a β-particle.
γ	Angle; a γ-ray or photon.
Γ	Gravitational field strength; strength or probability of reaction.
δ	Uncertainty in; small change in.
Δ	Error or small difference in; a delta resonance particle.
ϵ	Base of natural logarithms.
θ	Angle.
λ	Wave length; decay constant.
λ_b	De Broglie wave length.
λ_c	Compton wave length.
Λ	A lambda particle.
μ	Magnetic moment; Bohr magneton; coefficient of viscosity; a muon.
ν	Frequency; a neutrino.
Ξ	A xi particle.
π	Ratio of circumference to diameter of a circle; a pion.
ρ	Density; mass per unit length; resistivity.
Σ	Sum; a sigma particle.
τ	Torque.
ϕ	Angle; phase; electric potential.
Φ	Gravitational potential.

ω Angular velocity.

Ω Angular velocity.

Many of the above symbols appear also in vector form.

A bar above a quantity symbol indicates an average.

A bar above a particle symbol indicates an antiparticle.

$=$ Equality.

$\approx$ Approximate equality.

$\sim$ Proportionality.

! Factorial.

TRIGONOMETRIC FORMULAS

1. *Angular Relationships*

angles less than 0	*angles greater than $\frac{1}{2}\pi$*	*angles less than $\frac{1}{2}\pi$*
$\sin(-A) = -\sin A$	$\sin A = \sin(\pi - A)$	$\sin A = \cos(\frac{1}{2}\pi - A)$
$\cos(-A) = \cos A$	$\cos A = -\cos(\pi - A)$	$\cos A = \sin(\frac{1}{2}\pi - A)$
$\tan(-A) = -\tan A$	$\tan A = -\tan(\pi - A)$	$\tan A = 1/\tan(\frac{1}{2}\pi - A)$

for all angles: $\sin^2 A + \cos^2 A = 1$

2. *Identities*

$$\sin(A + B) = \sin A \cos B + \sin B \cos A$$
$$\cos(A + B) = \cos A \cos B - \sin A \sin B$$

It follows from each of the above that:

$$\sin 2A = 2 \sin A \cos A$$
$$\cos 2A = \cos^2 A - \sin^2 A = 1 - 2 \sin^2 A = 2 \cos^2 A - 1$$

3. *Dimensions of a Triangle*

If a, b, and c are the lengths of the sides opposite the angles A, B, and C, respectively of any triangle, then:

$$\frac{a}{\sin A} = \frac{b}{\sin B} = \frac{c}{\sin C} \quad \text{and} \quad c^2 = a^2 + b^2 - 2ab \cos C$$

which, if C is a right angle becomes $c^2 = a^2 + b^2$

4. *Special Values of Trigonometric Functions*

$\sin 30° = \cos 60° = \frac{1}{2}$ $\tan 30° = 1/\sqrt{3} \approx 0.5773$

$\sin 45° = \cos 45° = 1/\sqrt{2} \approx 0.7071$ $\tan 45° = 1$

$\sin 60° = \cos 30° = \sqrt{\frac{3}{2}} \approx 0.8660$ $\tan 60° = \sqrt{3} \approx 1.7320$

APPROXIMATE VALUES OF SOME NUMERICAL CONSTANTS

$\pi = 3.1416$ $\epsilon = 2.7183$ $\sqrt{2} = 1.4142$ $\sqrt{3} = 1.7320$ $\sqrt{10} = 3.1623$

SOLUTIONS OF A QUADRATIC EQUATION

$$ax^2 + bx + c = 0 \text{ has solutions: } x = \frac{-b \pm \sqrt{b^2 - 4ac}}{2a}$$

BINOMIAL EXPANSION

$$(1 + x)^n = 1 + nx + \frac{n(n-1)}{1 \cdot 2} x^2 + \frac{n(n-1)(n-2)}{1 \cdot 2 \cdot 3} x^3 + \cdots + \frac{n!}{(n-m)!m!} x^m + \cdots$$

RATES OF CHANGE

The following table shows the rate of change with x of some common functions of x: $y = y(x)$.

y	$\dfrac{dy}{dx}$
x^n	nx^{n-1}
$\dfrac{x^{n+1}}{n+1}$	x^n
Constant	0
$\ln x$	x^{-1}
ϵ^x	ϵ^x
ϵ^{ax}	$a\epsilon^{ax}$
$\sin ax$	$a \cos ax$
$\cos ax$	$-a \sin ax$
$p(x) + q(x)$	$\dfrac{dp}{dx} + \dfrac{dq}{dx}$
$p(x)q(x)$	$p \dfrac{dq}{dx} + q \dfrac{dp}{dx}$
$y(z)$	$\dfrac{dy}{dz} \dfrac{dz}{dx}$

SUMMARY OF THE NUMERICAL VALUES OF THE PRINCIPAL PHYSICAL CONSTANTS THAT APPEAR IN THE TEXT[a]

quantities	symbol	value	units	estimated error limits in its last significant figures
Velocity of Light	c	$= 2.997925 \times 10^8$	m. sec.$^{-1}$	3
Avogadro's Number	N	$= 6.02252 \times 10^{26}$	molecules kilomole^{-1}	28
Atomic Mass Unit	M_1	$= 1/N = 1.66043 \times 10^{-27}$	kg.	8
Electronic Charge	e	$= 1.60210 \times 10^{-19}$	C.	7
Electron Rest Mass	m_0	$= 9.1091 \times 10^{-31}$	kg.	4
		$= 5.48597 \times 10^{-4}$	a.m.u.	9
Proton Rest Mass	m_p	$= 1.67252 \times 10^{-27}$	kg.	8
Bohr Magneton	μ	$= 9.2732 \times 10^{-24}$	Amp. m.^{2}	6
Planck's Constant	h	$= 6.6256 \times 10^{-34}$	J. sec.	5
Boltzman's Constant	k	$= 1.38054 \times 10^{-23}$	J. °K.$^{-1}$	18
Ice Point	T_0	$= 273.15$	°K.	(definition)
Gravitation Constant	G	$= 6.670 \times 10^{-11}$	N. kg.$^{-2}$ m.^{2}	15
Electrostatic Constant	K	$= 8.98755 \times 10^9$	N. C.$^{-2}$ m.^{2}	1

[a] NAS-NRC Committee, *Physics Today*, vol. 17, p. 48, (Feb. 1964).

Shell	Heavy lines denote filling of sub-shells	I	II	III	IVa	Va	VIa	VIIa	VIII	VIII	VIII	Ia	IIa	IIIa	IV	V	VI	VII	0
K	$1s$	H 1																		He 2
L	$2s, 2p$	Li 3	Be 4	B 5											C 6	N 7	O 8	F 9	Ne 10
M	$3s, 3p$	Na 11	Mg 12	Al 13											Si 14	P 15	S 16	Cl 17	A 18
N	$4s, 3d, 4p$	K 19	Ca 20	Sc 21	Ti 22	V 23	Cr 24	Mn 25	Fe 26	Co 27	Ni 28	Cu 29	Zn 30	Ga 31	Ge 32	As 33	Se 34	Br 35	Kr 36
O	$5s, 4d, 5p$	Rb 37	Sr 38	Y 39	Zr 40	Nb 41	Mo 42	Tc 43	Ru 44	Rh 45	Pd 46	Ag 47	Cd 48	In 49	Sn 50	Sb 51	Te 52	I 53	Xe 54
P	$6s, 4f, 5d, 6p$	Cs 55	Ba 56	57–71	Hf 72	Ta 73	W 74	Re 75	Os 76	Ir 77	Pt 78	Au 79	Hg 80	Tl 81	Pb 82	Bi 83	Po 84	At 85	Rn 86
Q	$7s, 5f, \ldots \ldots$	Fr 87	Ra 88	89–103															

Lanthanide Series (Rare Earths)

La 57	Ce 58	Pr 59	Nd 60	Pm 61	Sm 62	Eu 63	Gd 64	Tb 65	Dy 66	Ho 67	Er 68	Tm 69	Yb 70	Lu 71

Actinide Series

Ac 89	Th 90	Pa 91	U 92	Np 93	Pu 94	Am 95	Cm 96	Bk 97	Cf 98	Es 99	Fm 100	Md 101	No 102	Lw 103

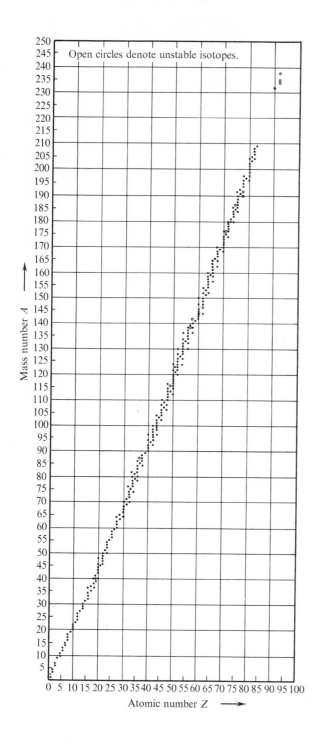